96918

HIGH POLYMERS

HIGH POLYMERS

A SERIES OF MONOGRAPHS ON THE CHEMISTRY, PHYSICS,
AND TECHNOLOGY OF HIGH POLYMERIC SUBSTANCES

Volume II

INTERSCIENCE PUBLISHERS, INC., NEW YORK
INTERSCIENCE PUBLISHERS LTD., LONDON

PHYSICAL CHEMISTRY

OF

HIGH POLYMERIC SYSTEMS

Second Completely Revised and Augmented Edition

H. MARK   and   **A. V. TOBOLSKY**

Director, Institute of Polymer Research
Polytechnic Institute of Brooklyn
Brooklyn, New York

Assistant Professor of Chemistry
Princeton University
Princeton, New Jersey

1 9 5 0

INTERSCIENCE PUBLISHERS, INC., NEW YORK
INTERSCIENCE PUBLISHERS LTD., LONDON

INTERSCIENCE PUBLISHERS, INC.
250 Fifth Avenue   New York 1, N. Y.

For Great Britain and Northern Ireland:
INTERSCIENCE PUBLISHERS LTD.
2a Southampton Row   London W. C. 1

PRINTED IN THE UNITED STATES OF AMERICA
BY MACK PRINTING CO., EASTON, PA.

PREFACE TO THE SECOND EDITION

Since publication of the first edition (1940) considerable progress has been made in most branches of polymer science, and it seemed advisable to expand and amend the text considerably. The purpose of the present volume is to present a condensed selection of the basic facts of the physical chemistry of macromolecules. In considering such fundamental methods as x-ray diffraction, infrared spectroscopy, light scattering, and so on, we felt that only brief mention should be made of the theoretical foundations and experimental methods, and that most of the space should be devoted to the presentation and discussion of the results. We have tried to present the results as much as possible in the form of tables and figures and to point out specifically the cases to which the method under discussion was successfully applied in order to elucidate the structure of macromolecules. To guide the interested reader in finding the details of the various methods, numerous references to modern comprehensive treatises and to pertinent original contributions have been inserted.

The chapters on molecular structure are followed by a treatment of our present concept of intra- and intermolecular forces. The ability to draw a clear distinction between these forces has played an important role in the establishment of the existence of long-chain molecules and macromolecular networks. Starting with the relatively simple and clear-cut cases existing in substances of low molecular weight, we have attempted to show how these results apply to the conditions prevailing in polymeric systems and to point out the way in which concepts of primary and secondary valences help to explain such basic behavior of macromolecules as crystallization, melting, solubility, etc.

The thermodynamic and kinematic behavior of polymer solutions and the mechanical properties of polymers have been intensively studied during the past ten years, and the quantitative understanding of these subjects has been substantially advanced. The same statements are true for the remarkably expanding fields of mechanism and kinetics of polymer formation and degradation. Because of the relative novelty of these developments, only a few comprehensive treatises on these subjects exist. We

v

felt, therefore, that the chapters devoted to this part of our text should present more detailed information than the earlier chapters, which deal with well-established and frequently presented scientific topics. Nevertheless, even in these chapters we attempted to present a concise summary of results and concepts and to refer to the original literature for details of mathematical derivation or experimental procedure.

In a book of this size it was impossible to mention all of the significant contributions to the field, or to name in any comprehensive or adequate way all of the workers who have developed the science and upon whose work this book is based.

During the writing of this volume, the authors have been frequently stimulated and encouraged by discussions with Drs. T. Alfrey, P. M. Doty, R. B. Mesrobian, R. D. Andrews, D. H. Johnson, and R. S. Stein, to whom they wish to express their sincerest gratitude.   Especial thanks are due to Dr. Andrews and to Dr. Johnson for help in reading proofs.

H. MARK

A. V. TOBOLSKY

June, 1950

CONTENTS

CONTENTS

I. GEOMETRY OF MOLECULES AS REVEALED BY DIFFRACTION METHODS

A. INTRODUCTION

Continued experience has shown that, in general, the smallest chemically active units of matter—atoms and ions—are not identical with the particles called molecules which we regard as the limiting units to which chemical compounds may be reduced by mechanical subdivision or other physical means and yet retain their identity. It is characteristic of molecules that they contain a definite number of constituent atoms and that they can be represented by empirical formulas such as:

$$A_x B_y C_z \ldots$$

The nature of A, B, C, as well as the relative values of x, y, z, can be determined by chemical analysis, while molecular weight determinations yield the absolute values of these subscripts. For chemical compounds of a sharply defined molecular weight, the values of x, y, z are usually small integers.

A compound like this has a definite range of stability with respect to external parameters—pressure, temperature, fields of force, etc.—within which it can be investigated. Over and above the purely numerical values of x, y, z, however, each molecule has a characteristic and definite arrangement of the constituent atoms. In small molecules, such as HCl, H_2O, and C_6H_6, the arrangement is simple and is given by the coordinates of all atoms relative to one of them chosen as origin. For example, the HCl molecule has the structure of a dumbbell, the H_2O molecule is a triangle, and the C_6H_6 molecule is a hexagon. The individual atoms of such molecules are not at rest, but vibrate about equilibrium positions. In larger organic molecules, and particularly in long-chain molecules, conditions are somewhat more complicated by such motions as internal rotations, vibrations of entire groups with respect to neighboring groups, etc., so that in many cases it is no longer possible to assign to the atoms of these molecules a definite geometric arrangement which is the same in all states of aggrega-

1

tion of the substance and under all experimental conditions. In the crystalline state, however, a definite geometrical arrangement of the individual atoms often prevails, even in the case of rather complicated molecules. We shall therefore first turn our attention to this state and describe methods for the measurement of crystal parameters which make it possible to determine the nuclear framework of even relatively complicated organic molecules.

Several methods are available for establishing the *nuclear framework* of such molecules, namely, the *interatomic distances* and the angles between connecting links—the so-called *valence angles*. In general, there is satisfactory agreement between the values obtained by different methods. Where discrepancies occur, it is usually found that the different experimental techniques do not measure identical quantities. Thus the different approaches control and supplement one another in a useful and effective way.

In presenting this review, the various methods are described briefly—with special emphasis on the range of their applicability; then, a short enumeration of the most important results is given, stressing the applications of these results in the field of polymer molecules.

It is usual—except in special cases—to work with x-rays of wave length 0.5 to about 3.0 Å., with cathode rays of 10^3 to 10^5 volts, and with neutrons of thermal velocities. The latter coincide, according to the de Broglie relation, with a range of wave length of about 0.4 to 0.04 Å. The molecules under investigation may be in the free state (gas or solution) or in the form of a homogeneous condensed phase (liquid, crystal, or mixed crystal).

The historical development of the experimental procedures began with the examination of molecules in the crystalline state, principally with the aid of x-rays. Here the early work following von Laue's[1] fundamental discovery should be cited, particularly that of W. H. and W. L. Bragg,[2] Debye-Scherrer,[3] and Hull,[4] while in subsequent years and up to the present day a great number of eminent research workers have contributed to this

[1] W. Friedrich, P. Knipping and M. von Laue, *Sitzber. bayer. Akad. Wiss.*, **5**, 303 (1912). Compare also M. v. Laue, *Roentgenstrahl Interferenzen*, Akadem. Verlagsgesellschaft, Leipzig, 1941.

[2] W. H. and W. L. Bragg, *Nature*, **90**, 410 (1912). Compare also W. H. and W. L. Bragg, *The Crystalline State*, Macmillan, New York, 1934.

[3] P. Debye and P. Scherrer, *Physik. Z.*, **17**, 277 (1916).

[4] A. W. Hull, *Phys. Rev.*, **10**, 661 (1917).

field.[5]   After the proof by Davisson and Germer[6] and by Thomson[7] of the wave nature of electrons in rapid motion, this technique was also applied to the study of molecular structure in the crystalline state.

Investigation of molecules in the gaseous state was inaugurated by Debye with x-rays and by Mark and Wierl[8] with electrons.   The latter method was greatly improved by Pauling and his collaborators and has furnished much valuable experimental data.[9]   Recently the diffraction of neutrons by crystals, liquids, and gases was reported by Shull and Wollan.[10]

B. VON LAUE METHOD

Penetration of a single stationary crystal by parallel polychromatic x-rays led to the discovery of x-ray diffraction in crystals by Friedrich, Knipping, and von Laue in 1912;   it gave the well-known symmetrical,

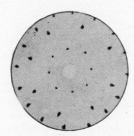

Fig. I-1.   Laue diagram, pentaerythritol.

[5] Comprehensive treatises: R. W. G. Wyckoff, *The Structure of Crystals*, Reinhold, New York, 1931, 1935; R. W. G. Wyckoff, *Crystal Structures*, Interscience, New York, 1948; P. P. Ewald, *Kristalle und Roentgenstrahlen*, Springer, Berlin, 1924; H. Mark, *Interferenz der Roentgenstrahlen*, Springer, Berlin 1924; W. P. Davey, *Crystal Structures*, McGraw-Hill, New York, 1934; F. Halla and H. Mark, *Roentgenuntersuchung von Kristallen*, Leipzig, 1937; ,G. L. Clark, *Applied X-Rays*, McGraw-Hill, New York, 1940; W. H. Zachariasen, *Theory of X-Ray Diffraction*, Wiley, New York, 1945; C. W. Bunn, *Chemical Crystallography*, Oxford Univ. Press, London, 1945.

[6] I. Davisson and L. H. Germer, *Phys. Rev.*, **30**, 772 (1927).

[7] G. P. Thomson, *Proc. Roy. Soc., London*, **A117**, 600 (1928).   Compare also G. P. Thomson and W. Cochrane, *Electronic Diffraction*, Macmillan, London, 1939, and G. I. Finch, *Ergeb. Exakt. Naturw.*, **16**, 353 (1937).

[8] P. Debye, *Ann. Physik*, **46**, 809 (1937).   H. Mark and R. Wierl, *Naturwiss.*, **18**, 205 (1930).

[9] Compare L. Pauling and collaborators in a series of more than 20 papers in the *J. Am. Chem. Soc.* from 1936 through 1948; also J. T. Randall, *Diffraction of X-Rays and Electrons*, Wiley, New York, 1934.

[10] C. G. Shull and E. O. Wollan, *Science*, **108**, 69 (1948).

TABLE I-1.   SUMMARY OF APPLICABILITY OF DIFFRACTION METHODS[a]

Desirable crystal size	Desirable crystal symmetry	No. of reflections observed	Indication	Geometric lattice parameters	Symmetry	Space group	Accuracy of intensity measured
				Property to be determined			
LAUE METHOD							
0.1 to 0.01 cm.	Any	Very large (several hundred)	Simple and certain	Impracticable	Best method	Subject to error	Inadequate; too many corrections required
ROTATING CRYSTAL METHOD OF W. H. AND W. L. BRAGG							
Photometric							
0.1 to 0.01 cm.	Any	Large; up to 200	Tedious but certain	Maximum accuracy	Not efficient	Suitable	Fairly good
Ionometric							
>0.1 cm.; natural or polished surfaces	Any; but difficult for nonorthogonal crystals	Optional; but tedious and difficult for many surfaces	Difficult but certain for many surfaces	Accurate	By intensity estimation	Reliable only with a sufficient number of planes	Standard method; extinction correction necessary
POWDER METHOD OF DEBYE, SCHERRER, AND HULL							
Photometric							
Small	Only from rhombic system upwards	Under 40	Certain only for planes of low index	Fairly accurate for a few surfaces; uncertain for higher indexed planes	Impossible	Impossible	Best photographic method
Ionometric							
Small	"	Few	"	"	"	"	Very accurate; few corrections, but of limited applicability
GONIOMETER METHOD OF WEISSENBERG, SCHIEBOLD, AND DAWSON							
0.1 to 0.01 cm.	Any	Optional; usually around 100	Absolutely reliable	Very good	Good method	Best method	Fairly good

[a] Adapted from F. Halla and H. Mark, *Röntgenographische Untersuchung von Kristallen*, Barth, Leipzig, 1937, p. 90.

sharp point diagram which certainly constitutes one of the most beautiful experimental effects in modern physics (compare Fig. I-1). However, its use for determining molecular structures in the solid state is comparatively difficult and ambiguous, for on working with "white" x-rays nearly all planes reflect simultaneously in accordance with Bragg's law (see eq. I-2). The von Laue method is therefore applicable as such only in especially simple cases (graphite, diamond, sodium chloride, calcium carbonate). Nevertheless, this method, in combination with others to be discussed, has sometimes proved particularly useful whenever the intensities of reflections from lattice planes of high indices were to be measured and reliance placed upon the precise determination of atomic coordinates. Further, it has been possible to deduce from the splitting and the broadening of the diffraction spots—the so-called asterisms—important conclusions on the occurrence of lattice distortions and mosaic crystal structure. Laue diagrams are also particularly suitable for gaining an initial insight into the symmetry of a crystal (see Table I-1).

It may be added that, with modern x-ray tubes and good fluorescent screens, the Laue spots can be observed directly on the screen without difficulty; this experiment is particularly impressive when, on the slightest movement of the irradiated crystal, bright points suddenly disappear and new spots flash up at other places. It is also possible to identify the wave length which causes the appearance of an individual spot from the relation:

$$\lambda_{min} = hc/eV \qquad (I.1)$$

by its disappearance as soon as the voltage falls below the critical value given by this relation, where V = voltage in absolute units, h = Planck's constant, c = velocity of light, and e = electrical unit charge.

C. METHOD OF W. H. AND W. L. BRAGG

If an attempt is made to reflect parallel and monochromatic x-rays from a plane surface of a single crystal, it is found that, contrary to the phenomenon of light reflection from a mirror, no appreciable intensity of reflected radiation is obtained unless the conditions expressed by Bragg's law are rigorously fulfilled. This condition is a consequence of the three-dimensional character of x-ray diffraction and states that strong reflection of the incident beam occurs only if:

$$n\lambda = 2d \sin \varphi \qquad (I.2)$$

where λ is the wave length of the x-rays used, d is the distance between subsequent lattice planes involved in the reflection, and φ is the angle between the incident beam and the reflecting planes. n is an integer, usually small, which denotes the order of the reflection; it cannot be determined from a single observation, but is usually revealed by comparing several reflections obtained at different angles, one of which will give a value of $n = 1$ or 2. Inasmuch as the ordinary law of reflection,

$$\text{angle of incidence} = \text{angle of reflection}$$

always applies in addition to Bragg's law, the angle θ between the reflected and incident beam is equal to 2φ. This angle θ is known as the *angle of deflection*; φ is called the *glancing angle*, although this designation does not have quite the same meaning ordinarily attributed to this term.

The Bragg experiment is very impressive when performed with a fluorescent screen. If a plate of crystalline sodium chloride, sugar, calcite, etc. is placed at an arbitrary angle in a parallel, monochromatic x-ray beam, no reflection is detected on a fluorescent screen placed in a position to receive a reflected beam. However, if the crystal is now rotated slowly, a bright spot of light appears on the screen as soon as the incident beam hits the surface of the crystal under such an angle φ that the λ of the x-rays, the d of the plane, and this angle φ satisfy equation (I.2) for n being a small integer.

This is due to constructive interference of the secondary waves coming from different depths of the crystal. The spot disappears just as rapidly when the crystal is rotated a little more. Reflection of the x-ray beam occurs only if the angle of incidence has the exact value given by equation (I.2). In the present case this condition is necessarily fulfilled if λ and d remain constant and φ is continually changed by rotating the crystal until it reaches the critical value required by (I.2)—the so-called reflection position.

This method permits measurements of one of the magnitudes characteristic of the given set of lattice planes—d, the distance between the planes—and has proved very useful in investigating simple crystals, particularly in the earlier stages of structure elucidation. In more complicated cases, especially in organic crystals, it is usually necessary to combine this technique with others to obtain enough evidence (see Table I-1) for the full determination of the structure.

D. METHOD OF DEBYE-SCHERRER AND HULL

Continuous variation of the angle of incidence, φ, and the corresponding satisfaction of condition (I.2) can also be attained in a different way. If, instead of a single crystal, a powder of many small crystals is placed in the path of a monochromatic parallel x-ray beam, it will happen that, because of the random orientation of the individual crystals, a lattice plane will *always* be available under the right angle in some of these crystals. The multiplicity of φ values is furnished in this case by the presence of many tiny particles which occupy all possible positions in space.

By reason of the random arrangement of the small crystals, reflection occurs at every suitably placed plane in the crystalline mass and a series of diffraction lines is obtained *simultaneously*, each belonging to a particular lattice plane. This makes it possible, as in the earlier methods, to determine experimentally the spacings of the various planes. The diffraction

Fig. I-2. Monochromatic x-ray diagram of a fine powder.

patterns appear as a number of concentric circles on a flat photographic plate and as a set of more complicated curves on the cylindrical film usually employed (as shown in Fig. I-2). Such "powder," or "Debye-Scherrer-Hull" diagrams, can also be observed directly on a fluorescent screen. They are important whenever it is impossible to grow sufficiently large single crystals of the material under investigation, *e.g.*, in metallography, colloid chemistry, and in the field of high polymers.

It may be added that the Laue diagram presents the third possibility of fulfilling Bragg's law, *i.e.*, by keeping d and φ constant, and using an x-ray beam comprising a continuous spectrum of wave lengths. Accordingly, with the aid of the variables in equation (I.2) the three methods thus far described afford a means of determining one of the characteristic parameters of a lattice plane, namely, the interplanar distance. It has been mentioned previously that this can lead to a complete elucidation of the structure of simple crystals, but in complicated cases it is necessary to know also the position in space of any lattice plane—a knowledge which can be gained by one of the following methods.

E. ROTATING CRYSTAL METHOD OF POLANYI, SCHIEBOLD, AND WEISSENBERG

This method[11] represents an extension of the Bragg procedure in so far as it intends to record photographically not only the reflections from one or more lattice planes lying parallel to the axis of rotation but also the reflections from as many other planes as possible which are oblique to this axis.

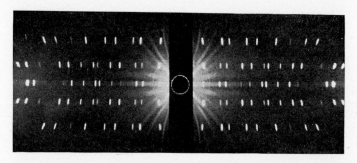

Fig. I-3.   Rotation pattern of a quartz crystal, rotated about the c axis.[11]   Radiation CuKα, $\lambda = 1.539$ kX.

This is accomplished by surrounding the specimen with a cylindrical strip of film of considerable height.   In such a way it is possible to establish a *second* parameter of the reflecting planes.   This is best achieved by using the so-called layer-line relation first derived by Polanyi,[11] which states that on such complete rotary diagrams the individual reflections arrange themselves in parallel "layer lines" and the reciprocals of the distances separating them furnish directly the period of identity along the axis of rotation.

This period of identity denotes the distance in a given direction from one lattice point to the next identical one.   The separation of the layer lines is connected with the identity period, I, by the expression:

$$I = n\lambda/\sin \mu \qquad (I.3)$$

[11] M. Polanyi, *Naturwiss.*, **9**, 337 (1921);   *Z. Physik*, **7**, 149 (1921);   H. Mark and K. Weissenberg, *Z. Physik*, **16**, 1 (1923);   **17**, 301 (1923).

[12] B. E. Warren, "X-Ray Studies of Randomness in Various Materials," in *Chemical Architecture* (Frontiers in Chemistry, Vol. V).   Interscience, New York, 1948.

where μ is the angle between the equator of the diagram and the layer line concerned (as seen from the specimen), λ the wave length, and n the number of the layer line.

The use of layer-line diagrams such as shown in Figure I-3 has fre-quently proved useful in determining more complicated structures.

With regard to reflection from planes which are not parallel to the axis of rotation, there is an important effect observable on irradiating an oriented crystal powder. If, for example, the small crystals in the irradiated spec-imen are not completely at random, but instead possess a certain orienta-tion in space, the diffraction rings mentioned above are replaced by *seg-ments* or *arcs* which throw light upon the predominant arrangement of the crystals in the sample. Since such patterns were first observed by Herzog and Jancke and Scherrer[13] in ramie fibers, they have been named fiber diagrams by Polanyi, who first explained their origin. They have played an important part in the elucidation of the structure of several high polymers and will be discussed in greater detail later.

F. X-RAY GONIOMETERS OF BOEHM, BUERGER, DAWSON, SAUTER, SCHIEBOLD, AND WEISSENBERG

Three independent parameters are required for the full characterization of a lattice plane in space (*e.g.*, the interplanar distance and two angles); therefore the need has arisen in course of time and in the face of increasingly difficult problems to obtain *three* mutually *independent* sets of experimental data for every lattice plane in order to deduce the three indices from them without making any simplifying assumptions. The so-called x-ray goni-ometers serve this purpose.[14] The desired effect is achieved by coupling the motion of the crystal and the recording film—producing diagrams as shown in Figures I-4 and I-5. The motion of the film and its relation to the reflection position of the crystal fixes just the degree of freedom lacking for the positive identification of a lattice plane. According to the nature of the problem, the choice of goniometers lies between the various instru-ments designed for this purpose by different investigators (*e.g.*, Buerger, Dawson, Boehm-Weissenberg, and Schiebold-Sauter).

---

[13] R. O. Herzog and W. Jancke, *Z. physik. Chem.*, A139, 235 (1920). P. Scherrer, *Nachr. Ges. Wiss. Gottingen*, 1918, 96.

[14] Compare M. J. Buerger, *X-Ray Crystallography*, Wiley, New York, 1942; W. E. Dawson, *Physica*, 7, 302 (1927); E. Sauter, *Z. Krist.*, 84, 156 (1933); E. Schiebold. *Z. Krist.*, 86, 377 (1933); K. Weissenberg, *Z. Physik*, 23, 229 (1924).

G. EVALUATION OF DIFFRACTION DIAGRAMS

By the use of the above-described methods, it is nearly always possible to work out experimentally a list of lattice plane spacings and reflection intensities which form the basis for the further evaluation of the diagrams. This list contains implicit data of particular interest to the chemist—such as atomic distances, valence angles, etc.—but the information is not in a directly usable form. Instead, the data must be converted by a more or less complex calculation, which is the more trustworthy the greater the

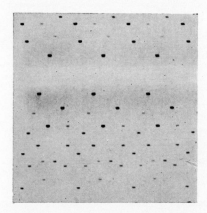

Fig. I-4. Weissenberg photograph of cyanuric triazide (courtesy I. E. Knaggs).[15]

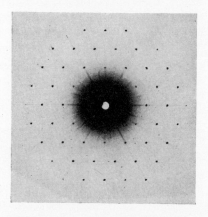

Fig. I-5. Precession goniometer photograph of a hexagonal crystal (courtesy M. J. Buerger).[16]

number of lattice planes listed and the more accurately the interplanar distances and, especially, the intensities have been measured.

It would lead too far to go into the details of such a calculation here, but it may be said that the relations involved are partly geometrical and partly physical.

In the first, geometrical, part, the *system, class, translation group,* and *space group* of the crystal under investigation are determined by systematic application of crystal structure theory in conjunction with tables. In addition the *volume* of the elementary cell, *i.e.,* the smallest unit from which

[15] K. Lonsdale, *Crystals and X-Rays.* Bell, London, 1948.

[16] M. J. Buerger, *The Photography of the Reciprocal Lattice.* American Society for X-Ray and Diffraction, August, 1944 (Murray Printing Co., Cambridge, Mass.).

the whole crystal can be built up merely by parallel displacement, is established by calculation of its *axes* and *angles*.

In the second, physical, part, the data just obtained are used in locating the centers of gravity of the constituent atoms. In this stage the intensities of the observed diffraction spots are analyzed harmonically on the basis of certain well-founded assumptions as to the scattering power of the individual atoms.

In relatively simple cases this task can be achieved by assuming a probable structure and by checking on it with the observed intensities by the use of successive approximations; obviously, by continued refinement of the calculation, a false assumption can be eliminated and a correct one built up stepwise to a high degree of accuracy (method of trial and error).

In more complicated cases, however, it becomes evident that this "synthetic" method is too arbitrary and ambiguous and that it is preferable to use the measured intensities for a real harmonic analysis of the spatial distribution of the scattering matter, *viz.*, the electronic charge clouds of the various atoms in the elementary cell. This so-called "Fourier analysis" of the x-ray patterns was first visualized by W. L. Bragg and has been improved and extended by many authors during the last ten years; it usually requires rather extensive calculations if a somewhat complicated structure is to be elucidated. In the last few years great progress was made in this field by the use of various calculating machines which permit a substantial reduction in time for the computation. The Fourier analysis of x-ray intensities can therefore be considered as the standard method of the future for the complete evaluation of x-ray diagrams.

If, finally, in one way or another, the spatial arrangement of all atoms in the elementary cell is known, the distances between the individual atoms in a molecule and the angles between the valence directions can be established.

More detailed information concerning the calculations and the special precautions to be observed may be obtained from various sources.[5] Table I-1 summarizes briefly the individual methods and their applicability.

H. DIFFRACTION STUDIES WITH MOLECULES IN THE GASEOUS STATE

The diffraction pattern of a crystal arises from a very large number of atoms or ions arranged regularly in space, and in it are mirrored the numerous distances which separate the crystallographically equivalent points in a crystal from one another. In gases, on the other hand, according to Debye and to Ehrenfest,[17] only the few *intra*molecular distances are responsible for the diffraction phenomenon because the distances *between* the separate molecules have no fixed values.   Of course, this gain in simplicity is obtained at the expense of loss in sharpness of the diagrams, because the number of individual scattering centers contributing in phase to the diffraction phenomenon is very much smaller in a gas than in a crystal.

Debye has developed a theory for evaluating diffraction patterns of gases which expresses, for a given molecular model, the intensity of the scattered radiation as a function of the angle of diffraction.   In this case, it is not generally possible to deduce a definite molecular model from the angular

Fig. I-6.   Electron diffraction diagrams of ammonium chloride (at left) and carbon tetrachloride (at right).

intensity distribution without using other auxiliary experimental data. Usually the evaluation of such diffraction patterns is based on a tentatively assumed plausible model, for which the intensity distribution is computed and then compared with the diagram actually obtained.

This type of evaluation is particularly simple and clear if there exists in the molecular model only *one* single effective distance.   For example, this is the case in CCl_4, in which according to well-founded assumptions of stereochemistry the C atom lies in the center and the Cl atoms in the corners of a regular tetrahedron.   Here and in other similar instances the intensity distribution leads to definite conclusions regarding the atomic distances and the angles between the individual valences.

[17] P. Debye, *Ann. Physik*, **46,** 809 (1915).   P. Ehrenfest, *Proc. Amst. Acad.*, **23,** 1132 (1915).   Compare also J. T. Randall, *The Diffraction of X-Rays and Electrons*, Wiley, New York, 1934.

The experimental interferometric investigation of gases with x-rays is difficult because the intensity of the scattered radiation is small, and relatively long exposures are accordingly required. This led Mark and Wierl[18] to use cathode rays of medium velocity instead of x-rays which give good diagrams in a few seconds due to the stronger scattering of electrons as compared with x-rays. Figure I-6 shows diagrams of ammonium chloride powder and CCl_4 gas. Evaluating such diagrams was originally carried out essentially in the same way as for x-rays, but was substantially improved and extended during the last fifteen years at the California Institute of Technology by Pauling and his collaborators, who measured a large number of organic molecules with great accuracy and reliability.[19]

I. SCATTERING OF NEUTRONS

A particularly interesting new method to investigate the geometry of molecules was developed recently by Shull and Wollan,[20] who used the scattering of neutrons by single crystals and crystal powders to establish the structure of the investigated systems. There are essentially three factors that make it possible to arrive at results which are difficult to obtain with x-rays or electrons.

(1) Neutrons are scattered exclusively by the nucleus which is very small and does not give rise to any intraatomic interference. As a consequence the atomic form factor for neutron scattering is independent of the angle of diffraction, whereas it shows a very strong decline at higher angles in the case of x-rays and electrons.

(2) The scattering power of hydrogen (0.16) and particularly of deuterium (0.33) is comparable with that of other heavier elements, such as oxygen (0.33) or carbon (0.38), while the scattering power of H and D for electrons or x-rays is very small. It is therefore not possible to locate hydrogen or deuterium atoms in the lattices of organic compounds with x-rays or electrons, but it is possible to do it with neutrons. Shull and Wollan have determined the structure of NaH and found that the hydrogen nuclei in this lattice are arranged in the same manner as the chlorine ions in NaCl.

(3) In certain cases neutron scattering facilitates the Fourier analysis of a given lattice because the phases of the neutrons scattered by the various nuclei in the lattice are reversed, while x-ray scattering is of the same phase.

The absence of a sharply declining atomic form factor is of special interest for the study of organic molecules in the gas phase where more dis-

[18] H. Mark and R. Wierl, *Naturwiss.*, **18**, 205 (1930); R. Wierl, *Ann. Physik*, **13**, 453 (1932).

[19] Compare, *e.g.*, L. Pauling, L. O. Brockway, et al., *J. Am. Chem. Soc.*, **61**, 927, 2693, 2922, 3173 (1939).

[20] E. O. Wollan, C. G. Shull, and M. C. Marney, *Phys. Rev.*, **73**, 527, 830 (1948); C. G. Shull and E. O. Wollan, *Science*, **108**, 69 (1948).

tinct diffraction rings should be obtainable with neutrons than with x-rays or electrons.

J. PRESENTATION AND DISCUSSION OF THE PRINCIPAL RESULTS

The results of the study of molecular structures by the various diffraction methods present themselves in different ways and can be evaluated and discussed along different lines.

The most general result is that in organic molecules there is in *first approximation* for any given *chemical bond* a *definite distance* between the atoms linked by this valence, and this is essentially true independent of other substituents carried by the two combined atoms. Today a fairly large number of such interatomic distances in organic molecules are known with remarkable accuracy. Detailed tables may be found in books and comprehensive articles of recent date.[21]

In this chapter we shall present selected numerical data for some particularly important organic linkages (Table I-2). In order to point out their reliability, values are occasionally added which have been obtained by methods other than x-ray or electron diffraction. As a whole, the agreement is fairly satisfactory.

Because of this general constancy of the primary valence bonds, rather sharp limitations are placed upon the construction and presentation of spatial molecular models. They exclude many formulas previously used for convenience in representing organic structures on paper. A famous example is the chain formula for glucose, which is still used in many textbooks as a matter of convenience, but which does not really reflect the true configuration of the molecule.*

In *second approximation*, however, we must make exceptions to the law of constant bond distances, particularly if the two united atoms carry substituents of large size or of polar character and if there are multiple bonds or aromatic rings in the system. A review of the experimental material shows that identical linkages in different molecules exhibit values, under certain conditions, which differ from one another to a degree well beyond the ex-

---

[21] Compare, *e.g.*, L. Pauling, *The Nature of the Chemical Bond*, Cornell Univ. Press, Ithaca, 1939; G. E. K. Branch and M. Calvin, *The Theory of Organic Chemistry*, Prentice-Hall, New York, 1941.

* It may be pointed out here that the modern molecular models as suggested by Stuart and by Fisher-Hirschfelder-Taylor seem to be capable of giving remarkably good illustrations of the spatial aspects of molecules. They are very useful for teaching and research, as long as their limitations are kept in mind.

TABLE I-2

DATA ON SELECTED NORMAL COVALENT BONDS[a]

Bond	Atomic distance, Å.	Dissociation energy, kcal.	Bond	Atomic distance, Å.	Dissociation energy, kcal.
			C—N nitromethane	1.46	66
H—H	0.74	103	C≡N nitriles	1.15	209
C—H methane	1.09	98	O—O peroxides	—	64
C—H ethylene	1.07	106	O=O oxygen	1.20	117
C—H acetylene	1.06	121	N—N hydrazines	1.45	37
N—H	1.01	92	N=N azo compounds	—	—
O—H	0.96	109	N≡N nitrogen	1.09	225
S—H	1.35	87	N=O nitro compounds	—	—
C—C aliphatic	1.55	80			
C—C aromatic	1.39	124	C—F	1.39	—
C=C	1.34	143	C—Cl	1.77	78
C≡C	1.20	198	C—Br	1.92	—
C—O ethers	1.42	79	C—S	1.82	—
C=O carbon monoxide	1.13	—	C—Si	1.93	—
C=O formaldehyde	1.21	173	S=S	1.92	76

[a] Compare Table 4.1 in G. W. Wheland, *The Theory of Resonance*, Wiley, New York, 1944; E. C. Bangham, *Trans. Faraday Soc.*, **44**, 845 (1948); H. A. Skinner, *J. Chem. Phys.*, **16**, 553 (1948); W. H. Beamer, *J. Am. Chem. Soc.*, **70**, 2979 (1948); K. S. Pitzer, *ibid.*, **70**, 2140 (1948).

TABLE I-3

DATA ON SINGLE BONDS IN THEIR NORMAL STATE AND AS AFFECTED BY RESONANCE

C—C bond in	Bond length, Å	State
Ethane	1.55	Normal
Propane	1.54	Normal
Polyethylene	1.54	Normal
Cyclopropane	1.53	Normal
Butadiene	1.46	Shortened
Cyanogen	1.37	Shortened
Diacetylene	1.36	Shortened

C—N bond in	Bond length, Å	State
Nitromethane	1.47	Normal
Diazomethane	1.37	Shortened
Urea	1.37	Shortened

C—O bond in	Bond length, Å	State
Dimethyl ether	1.42	Normal
Dioxane	1.46	Normal
Resorcinol	1.36	Shortened

perimental error. A few examples of such behavior are collected in Table I-3, which shows that rather large deviations from the ordinary interatomic distances are encountered as soon as a molecule contains groups or bonds that are capable of contributing resonance structures. This opens an extremely interesting way for studying experimentally the influence of substituents at a given atom on the nature and strength of a bond involving this atom, since it is a general rule—particularly in keeping with concepts of wave mechanics—that atomic distances and bond strength are closely related to one another.

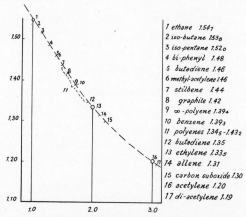

Fig. I-7. Relationship between the character of substituents and carbon-carbon bond.

Lennard-Jones, and Pauling and his co-workers, have emphasized the fact[22] that although the *single, double,* and *triple* bonds are outstanding types of the homopolar linkage, intermediate cases also exist.   In such instances the actual bond possesses characteristics intermediate between a single and a double bond, or a double and a triple bond, and the interatomic distances as well as the dissociation energies lie between those of the two pure types.   In this way one arrives at the idea of the *order of a bond* as a means of denoting its position between the single, double, and triple linkages.

In Figure I-7 the distances between two linked carbon atoms are plotted as ordinates against the order of the bond as abscissas.   One sees that the distance of 1.55 Å. is characteristic of the pure single bond, 1.35 Å. of the

[22] J. E. Lennard-Jones, *Trans. Faraday Soc.,* **25,** 668 (1929); L. Pauling, L. O. Brockway, and J. Y. Beach, *J. Am. Chem. Soc.,* **57,** 2705 (1935); **59,** 1223 (1937).

pure double bond, and 1.20 Å. of the pure triple bond. They correspond to the actual distances in ethane, ethylene, and acetylene, respectively. If *only* such bonds existed in organic molecules, the experimental data for all organic compounds would be accumulated along the ordinates erected at the points 1, 2, and 3 of the abscissas.

TABLE I-4

SEVERAL IMPORTANT VALENCE ANGLES

Type of bond	Valence angle		Compound measured	Method of measurement
Aliphatic single bond	Tetrahedron angle of about 110°		Many organic aliphatic compounds	X-ray and electron diffraction; dipole moment; band spectra
Aliphatic double bond	Nonplanar	130° 110°	Thiourea	X-ray diffraction
	Planar	120° 120°	Formaldehyde	Band spectra
	Nonplanar	125° 110°	COCl₂, COBr₂, CH₃COCl	Band spectra
Aliphatic triple bond	180°		Acetylene Hydrocyanic acid	Band spectra
Aromatic-aliphatic carbon-carbon bond	120°		Benzene derivatives	Dipole moment
\/ N |	Spatial	106–112°	NH₃	Band spectra
	Planar	120°	B₃N₃H₆	Electron diffraction
—N=	180°		Isonitriles	Dipole moment
—N⧸	Planar	130° 115°	NaNO₂	X-ray diffraction
	Spatial	120° 110°	Nitrobenzene	
\/ O		104–106°	Water	Band spectra
		128°	Ozone	Band spectra
			Diphenyl oxide	Dipole moment
		105°	OF₂	Electron diffraction
		111°	Dimethyl ether	
S /\		113°	Diphenyl sulfide	Dipole moment
		108°	S₈	X-ray diffraction

In reality, however, this is not the case. As can be seen from the figure there exist many *intermediate* distances, corresponding to intermediate types of carbon-carbon bonds, which exhibit very interesting properties with regard to degree of unsaturation and reactivity.

It may be added that the quantum mechanics of homopolar valence gives a rather detailed picture of this situation and in some cases even presents a quantitative formulation of the experimental findings.[23]

A second general and approximate rule that can be deduced from the existing material is the *constancy of the valence angles*. This, indeed, has been one of the pillars of stereochemistry and has proved sound when tested quantitatively with the aid of the newer methods. Table I-4 summarizes a few cases of general importance; Table I-5 shows nuclear distances and valence angles obtained for molecules of the type AX_2, and Table I-6 gives corresponding data for pyramidal molecules of the type AX_3.

TABLE I-5

NUCLEAR DISTANCES AND VALENCE ANGLES OF PLANE MOLECULES OF TYPE AX_2

Substance	Distance between substituents, Å.		Valence angle observed	Deformation	Normal distance between substituents, Å.
	Observed	Calcd. for 90°			
H_2O........	1.57	1.35	104° 40′	14° 40′	2.2
F_2O.........	2.22	1.98	105°	15°	3.1
Cl_2O........	2.8	2.4	111°	21°	3.7
$(CH_3)_2O$......	2.38	2.04	111°	21°	3.4–3.9
H_2S.........	1.95	1.91	92° 20′	2° 20′	2.2
S_8..........	3.37	3.0	105°	15°	3.6

TABLE I-6

NUCLEAR DISTANCES AND VALENCE ANGLES OF A FEW PYRAMIDAL MOLECULES OF TYPE AX_3

Substance	Distance X—X, Å.		Valence angle observed	Deformation	Normal distance, Å.
	Observed	Calcd. for 90°			
NH_3......	1.61	1.43	106°	16°	2.2
PCl_3......	3.13–3.18	2.83–2.9	100–104°	10–14°	3.7
$AsCl_3$.....	3.4	3.12	102°	12°	3.7

As can be seen from the data in these tables, the exact constancy of the valence angles holds only in rough approximation, and the effect of different

[23] Compare L. Pauling and E. B. Wilson, *Introduction to Quantum Mechanics*, McGraw-Hill, New York, 1935; H. Hellmann, *Einführung in die Quanten Mechanik* Wien, 1937; S. Dushman, *Elements of Quantum Mechanics*, Wiley, New York, 1938; G. E. K. Branch and M. Calvin, *Theory of Organic Chemistry*, Prentice-Hall, New York, 1941; L. Pauling in H. Gilman, Organic Chemistry, Vol. II, New York, 1938, p. 1850.

substituents can be quite appreciable. In fact, wave mechanical consider-ations of Hückel,[24] Pauling,[25] and Slater[26] indicate a value of 90° for the valence angles at the oxygen, sulfur, and nitrogen atoms because the potential energy of the system is a minimum if this angle is maintained be-tween the directions of maximum bond strength. If larger angles are found experimentally, as actually shown in Tables I-5 and I-6, we must conclude the existence of repulsive forces between the substituting atoms.

Table I-5 shows that such forces are noticeable in the water mole-cule; they increase the valence angle from 90° to 104° 40′. Actually, with a valence angle of 90°, the two hydrogen atoms would be only 1.35 Å. apart; the normal distance between two hydrogen atoms of the same molecule, but not chemically linked to one another, amounts to about 2.2 Å. The central oxygen atom would have to bring the two hydrogen atoms closer by 0.85 Å. than indicated by this critical distance if the normal valence angle of 90° were to be maintained. This compression of the charge clouds of the hydrogen atoms would require a considerable energy. The valence angle is therefore increased to establish an intermediate state that strikes a balance between the quantum-mechanical stability of the valence field of the oxygen atom on the one hand and the repulsion of the two hydrogen atoms on the other. The distance H...H is decreased from 2.2 to 1.57 and the angle of 90° increased to 104° 40′.

The validity of this interpretation is confirmed by a glance at the con-ditions in the hydrogen sulfide molecule. By reason of the greater diam-eter of the sulfur atom, the distance between the substituent hydrogen atoms is here already 1.91 Å. at the normal valence angle of 90°, so that only a small deformation of 2° 20′ is necessary for a state of equilibrium to be established in the molecule with a distance of 1.95 Å. between the two hydrogen atoms. The other data in Table I-5 are to be interpreted in a similar way and afford a rather clear and instructive picture of the inter-action between primary valence attraction and secondary valence repulsion within a molecule.

Table I-6 shows similar relations for pyramidal molecules, in which the normal valence angles can be deformed by repulsive forces between the substituent atoms up to values of 16°

Tables I-7 and I-8 contain further relevant data; in Table I-7 the dis-

[24] E. Hückel, *Z. Physik*, **60**, 423 (1930); **70**, 204 (1931); **72**, 310 (1931); **76**, 628 (1932).

[25] L. Pauling, *J. Am. Chem. Soc.*, **53**, 1367 (1931); *Phys. Rev.*, **36**, 430 (1930); **40**, 891 (1932).

[26] J. C. Slater, *Phys. Rev.*, **37**, 682 (1931); **38**, 1109 (1931).

tances between the chlorine atoms in CCl_4, $CHCl_3$, and CH_2Cl_2 are recorded. It is evident that here also a valence angle deformation has taken place with decreasing number of substituent halogen atoms, a phenomenon which has been observed by both x-ray and electron diffraction methods.

TABLE I-7

DEFORMATION OF THE TETRAHEDRON ANGLE BY SUBSTITUENTS

Molecule	Distance Cl—Cl, Å.	
	X-ray interferences	Electron interferences
CCl_4..................	2.99 ± 0.03	2.98 ± 0.03
$CHCl_3$...............	3.11 ± 0.05	3.04 ± 0.06
CH_2Cl_2..............	3.21 ± 0.11	3.16 ± 0.08

TABLE I-8

VALENCE ANGLE DEFORMATION AND HEAT OF COMBUSTION IN CYCLIC COMPOUNDS

Number of C atoms in the ring	3	4	5	6	7
Molar heat of combustion for $(CH_2)_x$ gaseous, cal...........	505.5	662.5	797	950	1103
Heat of combustion per CH_2 group, cal....................	168.5	165.5	159	158	158
Deviation from normal value, cal.........................	10.5	7.5	1	0	0
Deformation of the valence angle.......................	49° 28′	19° 28′	1° 28′	0°	0°

Table I-8 shows the relation between valence angle deformation and heat of combustion of cyclic compounds and offers a first estimate of the energy equivalent of valence angle deformation. Another approach to this equivalent is given in Table I-9. It can be seen that in deformations of the order of $10°$, energy values of the order of 1000–2000 cal. per mole are involved. On the other hand, the work required to stretch a primary valence bond *in the direction* of its greatest strength is estimated at 10^4 to 10^5 cal. per mole, for an extension of 0.1–0.2 Å. It is evident that appreciable changes in bond distances will occur in organic molecules only if the bond under consideration is surrounded by multiple bonds or by substituents of large size or strongly polar character. In contrast, variations in valence angles of the order of 10–$15°$ are frequently observed.

Table I-10 presents a few data on the *effective radii* of combined atoms in contact with like ones. The term r_0 denotes half the distance of approach of two like atoms, which are not bonded chemically, within a molecule capable of internal motion, such as the rotation of certain groups about a

TABLE I-9

VALENCE ANGLE DEFORMATION IN ENERGY UNITS

Compound	Energy for valence angle deformation, cal./mole.		Nuclear distance, 10^{-8} cm.
	By 5°	By 10°	
HCN 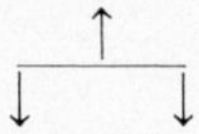	197	788	H—C = 1.08
C_2H_2 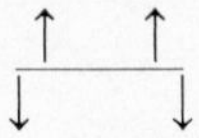	193	772	H—C = 1.08
CO_2 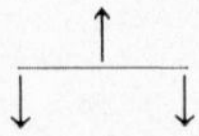	432	1730	C=O = 1.15
CS_2 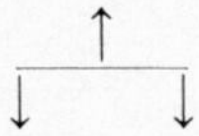	291	1160	C=S = 1.5

TABLE I-10

EFFECTIVE RADII OF LINKED PAIRS OF IDENTICAL ATOMS

Nature of atom	Effective radii, Å.	
	r_0	$r_{min.}$
Hydrogen	1.1	0.9
Nitrogen	1.6	1.3_5
Oxygen	1.5	1.2_5
Sulfur	1.8	1.5_4
Fluorine	1.5_5	1.2_5
Chlorine	1.8_5	1.5_8
Bromine	2.0_5	1.7
Iodine	2.2	1.8_2

single bond. For example, although the two hydrogen atoms in the H_2 molecule are only 0.75 Å. apart, the hydrogen atoms that are combined with carbon, oxygen, or nitrogen in an organic molecule cannot come closer to each other than about 2.2 Å. because of the repulsive forces then arising between the electronic shells of the two atoms under consideration. The column headed r_{min} in Table I-10 contains those minimum distances prevailing at room temperature in consequence of thermal agitation. They are somewhat smaller than those considered heretofore because the repulsive forces are overcome to a slight extent by the inherent kinetic energy of the separate parts of the molecule.

The results discussed until now may be summarized as follows: The parts of a large molecule attract and repel each other just as do complete molecules in a real gas, a liquid, or a crystal. Among organic substances the distance at which such forces (corresponding to van der Waals' forces) act is between 3.5 and 4.5 Å. Regarding the origin, magnitude, and importance of the attractive forces between different parts of a macromolecule, more will be said in the section on the structure of solid and liquid phases. However, when an attempt is made to force the parts of a large molecule (or even whole molecules) very close together, steadily increasing forces of repulsion have to be overcome, their ultimate effect being to limit approach to those minimum distances set forth in Table I-10. It is evident that accurate knowledge of this relation is of importance in all considerations of large molecules with internal mobility particularly in studies on the behavior of flexible chain molecules.

These data on primary *valence distances*, *valence angles*, and *effective radii* complete the evidence from which general statements about molecular geometry can be deduced from x-ray, electron, and neutron diffraction.

K. A FEW ORGANIC MOLECULES OF SPECIAL INTEREST

Before passing on to the discussion of macromolecules it may be appropriate to show with a few examples how far the diffraction methods with the modern techniques can give insight into the details of the structure of organic molecules.

First, the structure of phthalocyanine as worked out by Robertson[27] may be cited as an example of a brilliant effort in this regard. The molecule has a plane, almost square, pattern; the usual organic structural formula represented in Figure I-8a can be regarded as a fairly good approximation to the actual situation. Figure I-8b shows a contour diagram of the electronic density of nickel phthalocyanine as obtained by evaluating x-ray intensities by a complete Fourier analysis. The four benzene rings are clearly seen at the corners of the molecule and also the isoindole rings and the central nickel atom. The distance of the isoindole nitrogen from the nickel atom is 1.83 Å.; one can imagine it as being made up from the radius of the neutral nickel atom (1.24 Å.) and the radius of a double-bonded nitrogen

---

[27] J. M. Robertson and I. Woodward, *J. Chem. Soc.*, **1940**, 36.

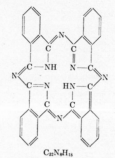

$C_{32}N_8H_{18}$

Fig. I-8a. Structural formula of
the phthalocyanine residue.

Fig. I-8b.   Distribution of electron density in nickel phthalocyanine parallel to the plane
of the molecule.   Compare this diagram with Figure I-8a.

atom (0.61 Å.).   The other dimensions of the molecule agree closely with the known normal distances of covalent bonds.   We have here a striking example of how a thorough x-ray analysis can elucidate quantitatively a complicated molecule down to its last details.   Of course, a necessary proviso is the presence of well-defined, not too small, individual crystals—a condition that can be satisfied only in exceptional cases for high polymers.

Another interesting organic molecule, the exact structure of which is not yet definitely established, is cyclooctatetraene.   It was first prepared in

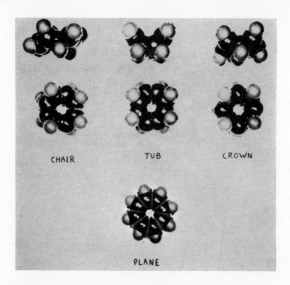

Fig. I-9.   Models showing the various possible forms of cyclooctatetraene.

1911 and 1913[28] from pseudo pelletierene, a synthesis which was successfully duplicated in 1946.[29]   In 1940 it was synthesized by direct polymerization of acetylene.[30]   It contains four double bonds and can therefore exist in a number of *cis-trans* isomers.   Three of these configurations appear to be less strained as far as the bending of valence directions and distortion of the double bonds are concerned and may therefore be presented as the probable structures of this molecule.   They are the *all cis* or "tub" form, the *all trans* or "crown" form, and the *cis-trans-cis-trans* or "chair" form.   Figure I-9 shows the various possible structures of the molecule.

[28] R. Willstätter and E. Waser, *Ber.*, **44**, 3423 (1911);   R. Willstätter and M. Heidelberger, *Ber.*, **46**, 517 (1913).

[29] A. C. Cope and C. G. Overberger, *J. Am. Chem. Soc.*, **69**, 976 (1947).

No chemical attempt has yet been made to establish to which of these forms the material, which is obtained in the above-mentioned syntheses (m.p. between −5 and −7°C.), corresponds. Recently, however, an x-ray analysis was carried out.[31]

Single crystal and powder diagrams were made and the unit cell and space group were determined. Although a straightforward Fourier analysis of this material is not yet available, the "trial and error" method has given good agreement with the observed intensities if one assumes the "tub" form and assigns 1.54 Å. to the single and 1.34 Å. to the double bonds; even small deviations from these values in the direction of making the single bonds shorter (1.49 Å.) and the double bonds longer (1.40 Å.) affect the agreement adversely.[31,32]

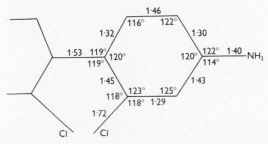

Fig. I-10. Bonds lengths and bond angles (courtesy D. L. Smare).[33]

Another interesting example for the contribution of a complete x-ray analysis to our knowledge of the details of molecular structure was given by Smare[33] in the investigation of 2,2′-dichlorobenzidine:

$$NH_2—\langle\rangle—\langle\rangle—NH_2$$
$$\overset{Cl}{}\quad\overset{Cl}{}$$

The bond lengths and bond angles can be seen in Figure I-10; each ring is essentially planar but not a regular hexagon; because of the steric influence of the two chlorine atoms, the rings are not coplanar but are rotated in

[30] W. Reppe et al., Ann., 560, 1 (1948).

[31] H. S. Kaufman, I. Fankuchen, and H. Mark, J. Chem. Phys., 15, 414 (1947); Nature, 161, 165 (1948). Cf. also recent unpublished experiments of V. Schomaker.

[32] It should be mentioned, however, that O. Hassel arrived at the crown form from electron diffraction experiments; cf. Nature, 160, 128 (1947). This form is also favored by R. Lord and E. H. Lippincott, J. A. C. S., 68, 1868 (1946), J. Chem. Phys., 16, 548 (1948).

[33] D. L. Smare, Acta Cryst., 1, 150 (1948).

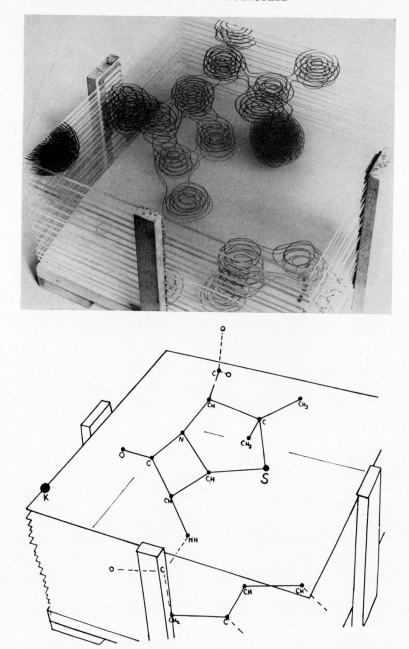

Fig. I-11.   Model of molecule of benzylpenicillin (courtesy D. Crowfoot*).

* D. Crowfoot *et al.*, in *The Chemistry of Penicillin*.   H. T. Clarke, J. R. Johnson, and Sir R. Robinson, eds., Princeton Univ. Press, Princeton, 1949, pp. 310–367.

mutually opposite directions through an angle of 36° from the *cis*-coplanar position; The C—Cl and C—N distances are normal; the distances between adjacent atoms or atomic groups of neighboring molecules are around 3.5 Å., indicating that the lattice is held together by normal van der Waals' forces.

One of the most spectacular services of x-ray analysis to organic chemistry was the assistance it gave in establishing the final structural formula of penicillin. Figure I-11 shows the model of a spatial electron density distribution of this molecule and the structural formula derived therefrom. It makes its unusual and surprising configuration clearly evident.

L. SOME SPECIAL RESULTS IN THE FIELD OF HIGH POLYMERS

X-ray and electron diffraction has contributed in *two* ways to our knowledge of large molecules: first, by helping to elucidate the *structure* of the individual molecules or parts of them, if they are constituents of a three-dimensional periodic arrangement, which, to a certain degree and with sufficient approximation, exhibits the regularity of a crystal lattice; second, by allowing a study of *texture* of high polymers in the bulk phase in which they serve many useful purposes as fibers, films, molded or extruded plastics, etc. This texture plays as important a role in the mechanical properties of organic high polymers as it does in metals and ceramics. At this point we shall enumerate only a few cases in which x-ray diffraction has contributed to our knowledge of the details of molecular structure and shall postpone the discussion of textural investigations and their relation to the mechanical behavior to Chapter X.

1. Polyhydrocarbons

One of the simplest high polymers from the point of view of chemical composition is *polyethylene*, which can be synthesized in different ways; it consists essentially of linear chains of subsequent CH_2 groups and shows a distinct tendency to "crystallize," which means to form areas with a high degree of three-dimensional order.[34] These ordered domains produce fairly good x-ray diffraction patterns, as can be seen from Figure I-12.

Comparison with the x-ray diagrams of a crystalline and amorphous

---

[34] Compare, *e.g.*, C. W. Bunn, *Trans. Faraday Soc.*, **35**, 482 (1939); R. Brill, *Z. physik. Chem.*, **B53**, 66 (1943); E. Hunter and W. G. Oakes, *Trans. Faraday Soc.*, **41**, 49 (1945); H. C. Raine, R. B. Richards, and H. Ryder, *Trans. Faraday Soc.*, **41**, 56 (1945); W. M. D. Bryant, *J. Polymer Sci.*, **2**, 547 (1947).

paraffin, as presented in Figure I-13 on p. 29, shows that the diffraction rings in the diagram of the polymer are broader than those of the crystalline material and that there is more diffuse background in the former than in the latter. This is caused essentially by the fact that the "crystallites" or domains of high geometrical order in the polymer are very small and that the sample contains a certain proportion of disordered or "amor-

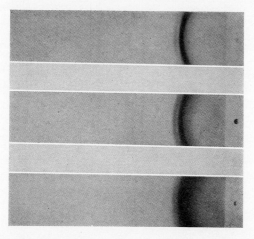

Fig. I-12.   X-ray powder photographs of three polythene samples differing widely in amorphous contents (courtesy R. B. Richards).[34a]

phous" material which is responsible for the diffuse scattering.   Investigation of polyethylene by various chemical and physical methods makes it highly probable that an individual macromolecule cannot be represented by a simple linear chain of methylene groups.   There is good reason to believe that other links, like —CO—, —CH(CH$_3$)—, —O—, and —CH:CH—, exist in the chain.   However, they are not frequent and, on the average, they amount altogether to less than one per cent of the total material. These "accidental" groups, therefore, do not noticeably affect x-ray and electron diffraction although it is proper to emphasize that they do greatly influence the chemical and physical properties of the material, such as aging in heat and light, water absorption, dielectric power losses, mechanical strength, etc.   There is also evidence to believe that the chains of polyethylene are not entirely linear, but possess a number of shorter or longer

[34a] J. L. Matthews, H. S. Peiser and R. B. Richards, *Acta Cryst.*, **2**, 82 (1949).

branches. In most samples, however, the number of branches is relatively small and does not substantially affect the capability of the chains to form areas of high three-dimensional order, which produce the type of diagram shown in Figure I-12.

It may be noted here that similar conditions, namely, accidental groups and branched chains, are not only characteristic for polyethylene but for most high polymers and have to be given consideration if one wants to understand the properties of these materials as a consequence of their structure.

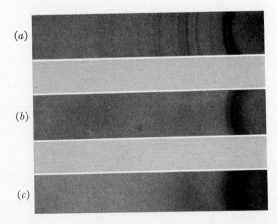

(a)

(b)

(c)

Fig. I-13. X-ray powder photographs of (a) a crystalline paraffin, (b) a polythene, and (c) an amorphous paraffin (courtesy R. B. Richards).[34a]

Evaluation of the x-ray diagrams of polyethylene by Bunn and Brill leads to a C—C distance of 1.54 Å. and a valence angle of 108°, in agreement with what one would expect from the investigation of normal paraffins. The distance between adjacent chains is 4.5 Å., which also agrees with the expected value.

Another polyhydrocarbon, which has been repeatedly and intensely studied, is hevea rubber.[35] In the relaxed state it produces—as Katz has found[36]—only a diffuse x-ray diagram (compare Fig. I-14a) but, if stretched,

[35] Compare K. H. Meyer, *Natural and Synthetic High Polymers*, Interscience, New York, 1942, p. 119.

[36] J. R. Katz, *Naturwissenschaften*, **13**, 410 (1925).

gives rise to distinct fiber patterns (compare Fig. I-14b).   Although different investigators of recent date[37] do not yet completely agree on all details

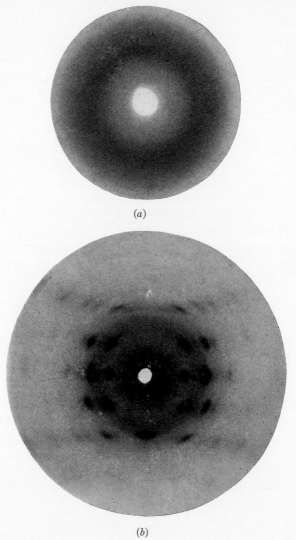

(a)

(b)

Fig. I-14.   X-ray diagrams of unstretched (a) and stretched (b) rubber.

[37] E. Hauser and H. Mark, *Kolloid-Beihefte*, **22**, 63 (1926);   H. Mark and G. v. Susich, *Kolloid-Z.*, **46**, 11 (1928);   W. Lotmar and K. H. Meyer, *Monatsh.*, **69**, 115 (1936); H. A. Morss, *J. Am. Chem. Soc.*, **60**, 2371 (1938).

of the structure, certain features of it can already be presented as reasonably well established.   One is that the individual bonds, such as C—C and C=C, appear to have their normal length and valence angles as listed in Tables I-2 and I-4, the other is that the subsequent double bonds in the individual chains are all in the *cis configuration*.   This distinguishes the hevea polymer from other polyisoprenes, such as balata and gutta percha, and is considered to be important for the typical high elasticity of rubber.[38,39]

A third polyhydrocarbon, which has been thoroughly studied with x-rays, is polyisobutylene.[40]   Again, it was found that only stretched samples give good fiber diagrams, that the normal valence distances and angles exist in the polyisobutylene molecules, and that the intermolecular separation of adjacent chains in the lattice corresponds to that encountered in normal organic substances of similar composition.   One interesting feature of this structure is that the identity period along the chain is surprisingly large, namely, 18.50 Å.   This indicates that one encounters special difficulties if one attempts to arrange parallel polyisobutylene chains in a three-dimensional lattice and, as a consequence, has to twist the backbone chain in such a manner that an identical configuration is only restored after about 18 Å.

2. Polyvinyl Derivatives

Probably the best x-ray pattern of all polyvinyl derivatives—if not of all polymers—is exhibited by polytetrafluoroethylene,[41] indicating a high degree of crystallinity and a high perfection of the individual crystalline domains; interatomic and intermolecular distances in the lattice conform with the commonly accepted figures.

Other polyvinyl derivatives, which exhibit fiber diagrams of better or poorer quality, are the chloride, the alcohol, the cyanide, and the polyvinylidene chloride.   Characteristic figures for these materials are included in Table I-11; all existing data indicate that normal valence distances and angles can be ascribed to the macromolecules of these substances.

[38] K. H. Meyer and R. Brill, *Z. Krist,* **67,** 570 (1928);   L. Misch and L. Picken, *Z. physik. Chem.,* **B36,** 398 (1937);   C. W. Bunn, *Proc. Roy. Soc., London,* **A180,** 40, 67, 82 (1942).

[39] E. Wöhlisch, *Z. Biol.,* **85,** 406 (1927);   K. H. Meyer, G. v. Susich, and E. Valkó, *Kolloid-Z.,* **59,** 208 (1932).

[40] R. Brill and F. Halla, *Naturwissenschaften,* **26,** 12 (1938);   C. S. Fuller, *Chem. Revs.,* **26,** 143 (1940).

[41] M. M. Renfrew and E. E. Lewis, *Ind. Eng. Chem.,* **38,** 870 (1946).

In the case of polyvinyl alcohol it was found by Bunn[42] that the hydroxyl groups along the chain are alternating randomly in the d and l configuration.

TABLE I-11

SOME X-RAY DATA ON POLYMERS

Material	Identity period along fiber axis or direction of stretching	Monomer units along identity period	Material	Identity period along fiber axis or direction of stretching	Monomer units along identity period
Polyethylene.............	2.53	One	β-trans-Polyisoprene....	4.7	One
Polyvinyl alcohol.........	2.52	One	cis-Polyisoprene........	8.1	Two
Polyvinyl chloride........	5.0	Two	Polyethylene sebacate...16.9		One
Polyvinylidene chloride...	4.7	Two	Polyethylene azelate....31.2		Two
Polyisobutene............	18.6	Eight	Native cellulose........	10.3	Two
Polyacrylonitrile.........	5.1	Two	Regenerated cellulose...10.3		Two
Polyethylene oxide.......	19.5	Four	Ammonia cellulose......	15.2	Three
α-trans-Polyisoprene......	8.7	Two	Cellulose trinitrate......	25.6	Five

3. Polycondensation Products

Many polyesters and polyamides have been studied with x-ray and electron diffraction[43]; most of them exhibit well-developed fiber diagrams in the drawn or stretched state. The identity periods correspond in all cases to what one would expect from the chemical structure of the materials, assuming normal valence distances and angles; the intermolecular distances between adjacent parallel chains in the lattice also appear to be normal. In the case of polyamides they offer the following interesting problem. Many facts, such as the high tenacity, the high melting point, and the difficult solubility of polyamides, suggest that there exists a considerable amount of hydrogen bonding between adjacent chains, which is probably established between neighboring CO and NH groups. It seems reasonable to assume that at these points of strongest intermolecular attraction the chains should be somewhat closer together than in between, and hence should have a slightly undulated shape.

Up to the present time, no x-ray investigation has been thorough enough to allow any (positive or negative) statement in this direction, but it seems possible that a complete Fourier analysis of particularly good nylon pat-

[42] C. W. Bunn, *Nature*, **161**, 929 (1948).

[43] Compare, *e.g.*, C. S. Fuller, *Chem. Revs.*, **26**, 143 (1940); H. Mark in R. E. Burk and O. Grummitt, *The Chemistry of Large Molecules* (*Frontiers in Chemistry*, Vol. 1), Interscience, New York, 1943.

terns might reveal something about the existence of hydrogen bonds between neighboring chains in the crystalline areas.[44]

4. Proteins

Great interest was, and still is, attached to the study of *globular* and *fibrous proteins* with x-rays and electrons. Silk fibroin[45] was early found to give fair fiber diagrams in the native state; their evaluation led to the conclusion that the molecules of silk are polypeptide chains having normal valence distances and angles.

Somewhat later a thorough study of keratin in its various states was inaugurated,[46] which led to a wealth of interesting information. It was established that the polypeptide chains can occur either in the straight state or in different states of regular folding, and that these various states

TABLE I-12

SOME X-RAY DATA ON PROTEIN MOLECULES

Material	Identity period along fiber axis	Number and state of folding of monomeric units
FIBROUS PROTEINS		
Silk fibroin	6.95	Two extended
α-Keratin	5.1	Two folded
β-Keratin	7.8	Two extended

	GLOBULAR PROTEINS			
	Elementary cell		Molecular weight	
Material	Volume, Å.³	Number of molecules	from x-ray data	from ultra-centrifuge
Ribonuclease	77,000	4	13,700	13–15,000
Insulin	298,000	6	37,400	35–40,000
Lactoglobulin	416,000	8	40,000	38–40,000
Chymotrypsin	151,000	2	54,000	40,000
Excelsin	2,670,000	6	305,800	$\simeq$300,000
Bushy stunt virus	32,000,000	2	13,000,000	7–11,000,000

[44] Compare C. S. Fuller and C. L. Erickson, *J. Am. Chem. Soc.*, **59**, 344 (1937); C. S. Fuller, W. O. Baker, C. J. Frosch, and N. R. Pape, *J. Am. Chem. Soc.*, **62**, 1905, 3275 (1940); **64**, 154 (1942).

[45] R. Brill, *Ann.*, **434**, 204 (1923); K. H. Meyer and H. Mark, *Ber.*, **61**, 1932 (1928).

[46] Compare W. T. Astbury, *Cold Spring Harbor Symposia Quant. Biol.*, **2**, 15 (1934); also *Fundamentals of Fiber Structure*, Oxford Univ. Press, London, 1933; I. Fankuchen, in *Advances in Protein Chemistry*, Vol. II, Academic Press, New York, 1945; D. Crowfoot, *Chem. Revs.*, **28**, 215 (1941).

can be reversibly transformed into each other. It seems that all chains and network structures can be accounted for with the conventional valence distances and angles, although some suggested structures appear to require an unusual amount of crowding of the substituents in certain parts of the lattice. A number of pertinent data on fibrous protein molecules can be found in Table I-12.

A thorough study of a few of the basic molecules of polypeptide chains was carried out in Pauling's laboratory by Corey and his collaborators.[47]

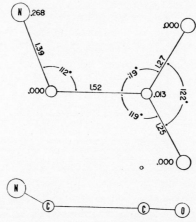

Fig. I-15. The structure of glycine viewed perpendicular (*a*) to a plane with the two O and α-C atoms and parallel (*b*) to this plane (after Albrecht and Corey[47]).

Using single crystals, these authors succeeded in measuring a large number of reflections with remarkable accuracy, and evaluated them with the aid of Fourier analysis.

Glycine was found to have a structure as shown in Figure I-15. The carboxyl group is coplanar with the α-carbon atom, while the nitrogen departs from the coplanarity by about 0.27 Å. The C=O distances, 1.25 and 1.27 Å., are in satisfactory agreement with those found in other hydrogen bonded structures, such as formic acid or oxalic acid dihydrate, and the C—C distance of 1.52 Å. is also close to the normal value for the carbon-carbon single bond. Equally normal are the valence angles found in this molecule, as shown in Figure I-15. However, the C—N distance of 1.39 Å.

[47] R. B. Corey, *J. Am. Chem. Soc.*, **60**, 1598 (1938); G. Albrecht and R. B. Corey, *J. Am. Chem. Soc.*, **61**, 1087 (1939); R. B. Corey, *Chem. Revs.*, **26**, 227 (1940); H. A. Levy and R. B. Corey, *J. Am. Chem. Soc.*, **63**, 2095 (1941).

is distinctly shorter than anticipated from other molecules, where it has
values of about 1.47 Å.* The arrangement of the molecules in the lattice
indicates the existence of hydrogen bridges parallel to the ac-planes, which
produces layers of closely packed molecules; the distances between hydro-
gen-bonded oxygen and nitrogen atoms within the same layer are between
2.76 and 2.98 Å., while the corresponding distance between adjacent layers
is between 2.93 and 3.05 Å. This is in accord with the fact that the crystals cleave readily perpendicular to the b-axis.

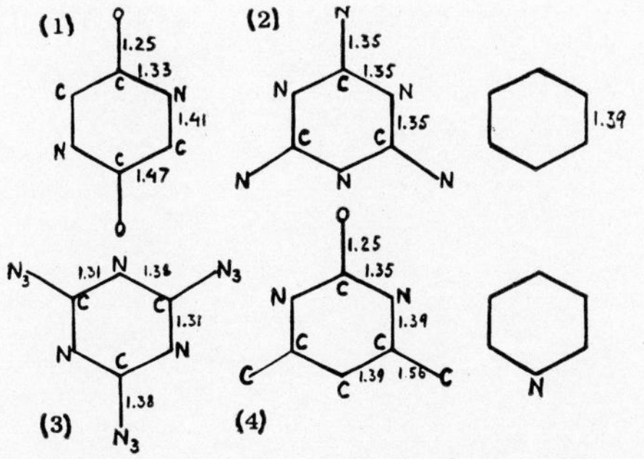

Fig. I-16. Interatomic distances for (1) diketopiperazine, (2) melamine, (3)
cyanuric triazide, and (4) 4,6-dimethyl-2-hydroxypyrimidine.

Diketopiperazine was found to be a planar ring as shown in Figure I-16.
The C=O and C=N distances of 1.25 and 1.33 Å. indicate the presence of
resonance between these bonds and are in agreement with other cases of
the same type such as urea and thiourea. The carbon-carbon bond is distinctly shortened (1.47 against 1.54) and so is the CH_2—N bond (1.41
against 1.47). Corey suggests that this is due partly to electric charge and
partly to a new type of resonance.

The individual molecules are held together in the lattice by hydrogen
bonds to form long, parallel chains throughout the crystal. The distances
between oxygen and hydrogen atoms of different molecules in the same
layer are 2.57 Å., which is slightly below the normal value for this kind of
hydrogen bond.

Recently, considerable progress was made in the investigation of *globular
proteins* by diffraction methods. It was found that these materials give

---

* It appears that more recent investigations in Pauling's laboratory in Pasadena have
established that the C—N distance in glycine is essentially normal.

excellent patterns with many sharp spots if the diagrams are taken with samples in equilibrium with water (Fig. I-17). In some cases the unit cell of the lattice could be determined and even an approximate location of the individual molecules in the cell could be considered. There also exists at present a thorough analysis of hemoglobin by Perutz,[48,49] who applied the Fourier analysis to this globular protein.

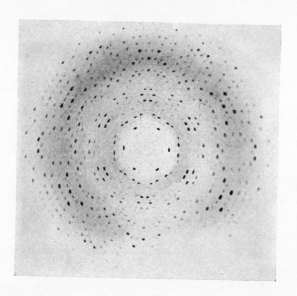

Fig. I-17.   Diffraction photograph of a single wet pepsin crystal; stationary crystal; filtered Cu radiation (courtesy M. F. Perutz).[49]

Before leaving the field of proteins it should be mentioned that x-ray diffraction has helped to establish interesting facts about solutions of certain proteins, such as tobacco mosaic virus. It was found by Bernal and Fankuchen[50] that dilute (1–2%) solutions of this material exhibit a sharp x-ray diffraction phenomenon at small angles, which indicates a highly regular arrangement of these rod-shaped molecules even at such low concentrations.

[48] M. Perutz, *Proc. Roy. Soc. London*, **A191**, 83 (1947); **A194**, 375 (1948).
[49] M. Perutz, *Research*, **2**, 52 (1949).
[50] J. D. Bernal and I. Fankuchen, *J. Gen. Physiol.*, **25**, 111 (1941); I. Fankuchen, *Ann. N. Y. Acad. Sci.*, **41**, 157 (1941).

5. Cellulose and Derivatives

The first organic high polymer which was subjected to a thorough x-ray diffraction analysis was cellulose.[51]   In its various forms of natural appearance and in different regenerated states it exhibits diagrams which range from poor to excellent, and which have helped considerably to develop the experimental technique of fiber diagrams and their theoretical evaluation.

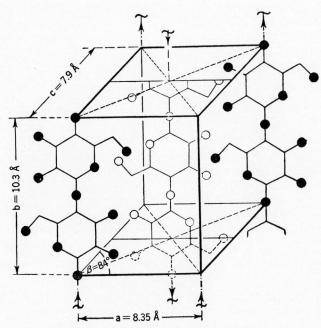

Fig. I-18.   Unit cell of native cellulose (Meyer[51]).

The structure of native cellulose has been studied by many authors and, although a straightforward Fourier analysis of the diagrams is still lacking, a highly probable structure can now be proposed, as shown in Figure I-18; it appears to represent at least a reasonably good location of the four glucose rings in the unit cell.   There is still some argument as to the exact position and mutual relationship of the hydroxyl groups between which there is obviously a considerable degree of hydrogen bonding, which would readily

[51] Compare, *e.g.*, H. Mark, *Physik und Chemie der Zellulose*, Springer, Berlin, 1932; K. H. Meyer, *Natural and Synthetic High Polymers*, Interscience, New York, 1941;   W. A. Sisson in E. Ott, *Cellulose and Cellulose Derivatives*, Interscience, New York, 1943.

explain the high melting point, the low solubility, and probably also the high tensile strength of well-oriented samples. One interesting result of the x-ray diffraction work is that cellulose and many of its derivatives can appear in polymorphic modifications which differ only in their crystal lattice.

Much work was done on cellulose derivatives, especially on cellulose nitrate, cellulose acetate, and cellulose xanthate. In no case has the analysis been brought far enough to provide quantitative data about interatomic and intermolecular distances, but all diagrams are compatible with structures which comply with the commonly used distances and angles. Cellulose and many derivatives can take water and other liquids into the lattice in a manner that resembles the behavior of certain silicates such as zeolite and analcim.

II. BEHAVIOR OF MOLECULES IN ELECTRIC AND MAGNETIC FIELDS

A. INTRODUCTION

If molecules are introduced in a uniform electric field, *two* effects are observable which provide important information on the internal structure of the particles.[1]

The *first* is that the negative charge clouds that surround the individual atoms of each molecule are displaced and deformed by the field. The result of this deformation is that the centers of gravity of the positive and negative charges of the system no longer coincide in space, so that an otherwise electically isotropic particle assumes in the field an *electric moment* which is responsible for its behavior toward other particles. The two charges are equal and opposite; hence the molecule as a whole remains neutral. Since the two poles exist only in the presence of the external field, the phenomenon is termed *electrical polarization* and the molecules are said to possess *induced* or *influenced dipole moments*. The stronger the field and the more mobile the charge clouds, the greater is the polarization of a molecule in a field of unit strength.

Second, there are molecules in which the centers of gravity of the positive and negative charges are not coincident by reason of internal structure; they possess an *electric moment* independent of the existence of an external field, *i.e.*, they carry with them a *permanent electric dipole*. Such particles are *oriented* in a uniform electric field by trying to align themselves with the dipole axis parallel to the direction of the field. The final result of this directional effect depends upon the strength of the field, the magnitude of the permanent dipole moment, and the temperature. The irregular thermal motion tends to disturb the orientation of the dipole axes parallel to

[1] Compare for this paragraph, *e.g.*, P. Debye, *Polar Molecules*, Chemical Catalog Co., New York, 1929; C. P. Smyth, *Dielectric Constant and Molecular Structure*, Chemical Catalog Co., New York, 1931; C. P. Smyth, "Determination if Dipole Moments," in A. Weissberger, *Physical Methods of Organic Chemistry*, 2nd ed., Vol. I, part II, Interscience, New York, 1949, chapter 24.

the field, so that macroscopically a stationary state is observed in which the individual molecules are drawn in a certain direction by the field and continually randomized by the Brownian movement.

Since both phenomena afford important information on molecular structure we will consider them one after the other.

B. POLARIZABILITY

If the negative charge cloud of a molecule is equally polarizable in all directions, the induced moment, μ_i, can be taken as independent of direction and as proportional to the field strength E producing it:

$$\mu_i = \alpha E$$

In this case the proportionality factor α is characteristic of the molecule and equal in all directions; it is termed the *polarizability* of the substance and has the dimension of volume.[2]   To determine it experimentally one starts with the dielectric constant ϵ of the substance to which α is related under certain generally valid suppositions by the Clausius-Mosotti equation:

$$[(\epsilon - 1)/(\epsilon + 2)][M/\rho] = (4\pi/3)N\alpha = P \qquad (II.1)$$

where ρ = density of the substance; M = molecular weight; N = number of molecules per mole (Avogadro's number); α = polarizability of the molecule; and ϵ = dielectric constant of the substance.

In deriving this equation it should be remembered that the polarized molecules exert forces *on one another*, which cause a certain degree of mutual polarization, and that the whole effect therefore arises from the *external* field acting *and* the *internal* field resulting from the polarized molecules.

Equation II.1 holds only for isotropic phases—gases, solutions, liquids, and regular crystals—but not for anisotropic liquids or for noncubic crystals.   In this equation P is termed the *molar polarization*.

If one introduces the square of the refractive index n instead of the dielectric constant, one arrives at the Lorentz-Lorenz equation, which relates the *electronic polarizability* α_E with the refractive index:

$$[(n^2 - 1)/(n^2 + 2)][M/\rho] = (4\pi/3)N\alpha_E = R \qquad (II.2)$$

[2] Compare, *e.g.*, N. Bauer and K. Fajans, "Refractometry," in A. Weissberger, *Physical Methods of Organic Chemistry*, 2nd ed., Vol. I, part II, Interscience, New York, 1949, chapter 20.

The right-hand side of equation II.2 is termed *molar refraction* and is denoted by R. For ideal gases under normal conditions, M/ρ can be taken as 22.4×10^3 cc., the term $(n^2 + 2)$ can be replaced by the value 3 since the refractive index of most gases is nearly unity, and a simplified equation valid for ideal gases is obtained.

$$\alpha_E = 2.94 \times 10^{-21}(n^2 - 1) \qquad (II.3)$$

It has been found that the molar refraction R at a given wave length can be computed additively from the atomic refractions by considering that double bonds, triple bonds, rings, etc. manifest themselves by *increments*. The additivity is fulfilled even better if, following Fajans and Knorr,[3] characteristic refractions are ascribed not to individual atoms but to bonds (*e.g.*, the C—C, C=C, or C=O bond). The superiority of the Fajans-Knorr method of calculation is founded on the fact that the components of the electronic shell in the molecule, which are specially subject to deformation, are no longer correlated with individual atoms, but are dependent, rather, upon the nature of the bonds between them.

The discussion of refractions showing exceptions to additivity has long been a valuable aid in elucidating the structure of more complicated organic molecules and to discover the presence of double bonds, conjugated systems, aromatic rings, etc. Table II-1 contains a few atomic refractions which can be used in the computation of molar refractions.

TABLE II-1

REFRACTIONS OF ELEMENTS AND BONDS IN ORGANIC MOLECULES FOR λ = 5890 Å.

Element or bond	Refraction	Element or bond	Refraction
Carbon	2.418	Bromine	8.865
Hydrogen	1.100	Iodine	13.900
Oxygen as ether	1.525	Increment for double bond	1.733
Oxygen as hydroxyl	1.643	Increment for triple bond	2.398
Oxygen as carbonyl	2.211	C—H	1.705
Nitrogen, primary	2.322	C—C	1.209
Nitrogen, secondary	2.499	C=C	4.151
Nitrogen, tertiary	2.840	C≡C	6.025
Chlorine	5.967		

We have hitherto considered the polarizability of a molecule to be a scalar quantity; actually, however, the polarizability of nonisotropic mole-

[3] K. Fajans and F. Knorr, *Ber.*, **59**, 256 (1926).

cules differs in different directions. Molecules having axial symmetry possess two polarizabilities, asymmetrical molecules possess three. Obviously, in measuring polarization by refractive index, this anisotropy is not perceptible because the molecules of the substance concerned are randomly arranged and there is no net effect. Anisotropy of polarizability is only observed if the individual particles are fixed in definite directions. This is the case in noncubic crystals and in gases or liquids exposed to an electric field (Kerr effect: compare Sect. F2).

C. APPLICATIONS OF POLARIZATION MEASUREMENTS

Molar refraction has long been an important aid for determining the constitution of organic molecules. Since there seems to be a growing tendency toward its use in polymer chemistry, it will be useful to summarize the most important relationships between molar refraction and molecular constitution.

In the optical sense, an increase in molar refraction always means a relaxation of the negative charge clouds of the atoms constituting the molecule. If, for example, it is proved that there is no change in molar refraction on ring closure of an open aliphatic chain, we may assume that there is also no relaxation of the charge clouds which represent the separate principal valence bonds in the chain and in the ring. On the other hand, where considerable ring tension is observed, increases in molar refraction are known to occur, as, for example, in cyclobutane and cyclopropane. This obviously implies that the forcibly compressed electron clouds of the homopolar valence bonds are loosening each other up, and perhaps this is likewise true for the neighboring nuclear charges. In the cyclopropane ring this effect extends so far that its molar polarization approaches that of the aliphatic double bond.

The aliphatic double bond, as well as the $C{=}O$ and $N{=}O$ bonds, show a considerable increase of polarizability above the corresponding single bond; this is easily understood inasmuch as the four-electron charge cloud of a double bond is more easily deformed and displaced by the field of the incident light wave than the considerably more rigid structure of a two-electron single bond. Conjugated double bonds show an enhanced effect, which was used to establish the presence of conjugated systems. The influence of conjugation has recently been illustrated by experiments of R. Kuhn and his co-workers, who showed that, with accumulation of conjugated double bonds, relaxation of the electron clouds finally can proceed so far that the compounds absorb light in the visible region and therefore appear colored. Moreover, the quantum-mechanical discussion of conditions obtaining in *polyene compounds* makes a mutual relaxing effect of double bonds intelligible.

On the other hand, in aromatic compounds, particularly in benzene and its derivatives, a *decrease* in the molar refraction can be observed. This *depression* is specific to the aromatic character and is consistent with the fact that, on account of the ring arrangement of the three double bonds within the nuclear framework, a peculiar distribution of negative charge density occurs in which the excess electrons representing the double bonds can no longer be definitely localized between two individual carbon atoms, but are distributed over the whole nuclear framework of the molecule. The same consequence was deduced from quantum-mechanical considerations by Hückel, Pauling, and Slater[4,5]; it signifies a peculiar stability associated with the system of three conjugated double bonds in the ring.

This is in accord with the view that the benzene ring—with regard to chemical behavior—should be represented neither by the simple Kekulé formula nor by those proposed by Dewar, Claus, and Ladenburg; the truth is probably most nearly approached if the molecule is conceived as being essentially an assemblage of the two spatially possible "Kekulé" structures, K_1 and K_2, of equal potential energy:

$$K_1 = \hexagon \qquad K_2 = \hexagon$$

and the three possible "Dewar" structures (also of equal potential energy),

$$D_1 = \hexagon \qquad D_2 = \hexagon \qquad D_3 = \hexagon$$

K_1 and K_2 are present in the same proportion, and D_1, D_2, and D_3 are likewise equal in amount. In the final superposition of the five forms the Kekulé properties are more pronounced than the Dewar contributions. This conception is supported by all methods of attack, such as x-ray diffraction, electron diffraction, and Raman effect.

The further discovery that *cumulative double bonds* give smaller exalta-

[4] See the comprehensive treatise by E. Hückel, *Z. Elektrochem.*, **72**, 657 (1936).

[5] See also a series of very interesting publications of R. S. Mulliken, *J. Chem. Phys.*, **7**, 339, 353, 356, 364 (1939).

tions of refraction and dispersion is in accord with the quantum mechanical idea of the nature of the double bond.[6]

Attention may also be drawn to some interesting experiments on the optical behavior of isomeric compounds. Generally, it is found that those isomers whose shape permits a denser packing exhibit the higher molecular refractions. As examples may be cited $trans$-1,2-dibromoethylene (MR_D = 26.16) and its cis isomer (MR_D = 25.64), as well as p-dibromobenzene (MR_D = 42.78) and o-dibromobenzene (MR_D = 41.81). The internal molecular interaction between the positive nuclear charges and the electron clouds of the neighboring atoms is enhanced by their closer proximity, and apparently produces a fixation of the spatially dispersed negative electricity similar to that in the theory of the solutions of strong electrolytes.

The generally additive character of molar refraction and heat of combustion causes the quotient of the two magnitudes to be a constant under normal conditions, amounting in paraffins to 33.2 and in olefins to 32.3.

Interesting qualitative conclusions have been drawn from refractive index measurements of certain macromolecules, particularly in the oriented state. Many polymers such as cellulose and its derivatives, polyesters, polyamides, native rubber, and polyvinyl derivatives show strong birefringence if the chain molecules are oriented. In general the refractive index for light vibrating parallel to the direction of the chain is greater than for the perpendicular component. This is in good agreement with Silberstein's theory of induced polarizability. In all such cases the stretched sample (fiber or film) shows positive birefringence. In some instances, however, such as nitrocellulose or certain proteins, one has negative double refraction because of the strongly polarizable side groups which extend essentially perpendicular to the chain and are responsible for the larger refractive index of the light vibrating in this direction.

The degree of birefringence of a fiber or a film can be used as a measure of the orientation and the uniformity of orientation and has been successfully applied to discover fluctuations of orientation along a filament. It is also interesting to note that the orientation of stained or dyed high polymers does not lead only to $birefringence$ but also to $dichroism$. This phenomenon has been used by Land to produce strongly polarizing sheets (Polaroid) of relatively faint color and large area.

---

[6] More details are given in the two mentioned books of Hellmann and Pauling, in the comprehensive paper of E. Hückel and furthermore K. W. F. Kohlrausch, *Phys. Z.*, **37**, 58 (1936); J. H. Hibben, *Chem. Rev.*, **18**, 7 (1936); L. Simons, *J. Applied Phys.*, **9**, 781 (1938).

The refractive index itself has proved to be a valuable means of following the progress of vinyl-type polymerization in bulk or in solution, because the monomer usually has a higher specific refractivity than the polymer owing to the replacement of the strongly polarizable double bond by two less polarizable single bonds during this type of polymerization. Finally, it may be mentioned that the temperature dependence of the refractive index of macromolecular substances in bulk shows a distinct change in magnitude at the so-called *second order transition point* and that this has been used by several authors to determine this point experimentally.

D. DIPOLE MOMENT

Molecules with *permanent* electric moments are termed *polar* molecules or *dipole* molecules; their electric moments are usually larger than the induced moments discussed in the previous section.

In a uniform electric field, dipole-free molecules orient themselves with the axis of greatest polarizability parallel to the field (induction effect), whereas dipole molecules orient themselves with the axis of their permanent moment in the direction of the field (direction effect). If both influences exist in one and the same molecule, it is of great interest to separate them from one another. In order to do that, Debye pointed out that the induction effect is essentially independent of temperature, while the orientation effect depends on temperature because the oriented dipoles are always again thrown into disorder by thermal agitation.

According to Debye,[7] the Clausius-Mosotti equation (II.5) has to be expanded for dipole molecules to:

$$[(\epsilon - 1)/(\epsilon + 2)][M/\rho] = (4\pi/3)N[\alpha_E + (\mu^2/3kT)] \qquad (II.4)$$

where μ = permanent dipole moment; k = Boltzmann constant; T = absolute temperature; and α_E = polarizability at infinite frequency. If we denote the left side of the equation as $f(\epsilon)$ it can be expressed as a linear function of the reciprocal absolute temperature:

$$f(\epsilon) = A + (B/T) \qquad (II.5)$$

[7] P. Debye, *Polar Molecules*, Chemical Catalog Co., New York, 1929; C. P. Smyth, *Dielectric Constant and Molecular Structure*, Chemical Catalog Co., New York, 1931; also C. P. Smyth in R. E. Burk and O. Grummitt, *Chemical Architecture* (*Frontiers in Chemistry*, Vol. 5), Interscience, New York, 1948.

where $A = (4\pi/3)N\alpha_E$, and $B = (4\pi/3)N(\mu^2/3k)$. The two magnitudes A and B can now be determined separately by measurements of $f(\epsilon)$ at several temperatures. If we insert numerical values for π, N, and k, we obtain:

$$\mu = 0.0127 \times 10^{-18} \sqrt{B} \text{ in electrostatic units} \times \text{cm.}$$

The unit 10^{-18} e.s.u. cm. is termed one "debye."

This procedure holds strictly only for gases because they alone satisfy the condition of completely random distribution and of negligible interaction between the individual molecules. In the liquid phase orientation effects exist even in the absence of an external field due to the mutual interaction of the molecular dipoles. Restriction to gases is sometimes troublesome in experimental practice because of the small effects obtainable; the measurements are difficult and actually only substances with high vapor pressure can be investigated. Consequently one often determines the dipole moments of molecules in the *dissolved* state, chooses dipole-free solvents of small polarizability, and works at very low solute concentrations in order to reduce the mutual interaction of the dipole moments of the solute molecules on one another.

It is best if the values of μ obtained at different concentrations are extrapolated to infinite dilution. The moment obtained from the polarizability of the solvent is determined by control measurements and subtracted. Comparison of the moments obtained in different solvents is useful in this connection. By this means fairly satisfactory agreement has been reached between measurements in the dissolved and in the gaseous state.

E. APPLICATION OF DIPOLE MEASUREMENTS IN DETERMINING MOLECULAR STRUCTURE

In classifying the available experimental material, it is convenient, as a first approximation, to ascribe to individual groups of atoms in a molecule *characteristic dipole moments*, the so-called *group moments*. Figures for a few important group moments in organic molecules are summarized in Table II-2. Their magnitudes are not strictly independent of the atoms or bonds surrounding them, so that, as in the valence distances and valence angles, allowance must be made for a certain influence of the molecular environment on group moments.

As long as the surrounding of a polar group, such as OH, CO, NO_2, CN, etc., does not contain other polar groups or easily polarizable configurations, such as multiple bonds or conjugated systems, the dipole moment of a given group is remarkably constant. Thus, the moment of the hydroxyl group in methanol is 1.66 debyes and the corresponding moments of all other aliphatic alcohols up to C_{16} are between 1.60 and 1.70. The same is true for the CO group ($\mu = 2.73$ debyes in formaldehyde), the CCl group ($\mu = 1.86$ debyes in methyl chloride), the CN group ($\mu = 3.94$ debyes in acetonitrile), and the NO_2 group ($\mu = 3.95$ debyes in nitromethane).

TABLE II-2

DIPOLE MOMENTS FOR A FEW IMPORTANT ATOMIC GROUPS

Bond	Dipole moment $\times 10^{18}$	Bond	Dipole moment $\times 10^{18}$
N—O	0.1	O—H(methanol)	1.68
C—H	0.4	O—H(phenol)	1.56
O—CH₃	1.23	O—H(H_2O)	1.58
C—I	1.62	N—H(NH_3)	1.66
C—Br	1.80	C=O	2.73
C—Cl	1.86	N=O	3.22
NH₂	1.54	NO_2	3.95
		C≡N	3.94

If the individual dipoles of a larger molecule are sufficiently far apart, it has been found that the moment of the whole molecule can be obtained by simple vectorial addition of the individual group moments, taking into account their magnitude, direction, and sign. The result is that molecules containing several polar groups may be nonpolar, as a whole, if there is internal compensation of the various polar components. Thus, experience shows that methane and carbon tetrachloride, for example, are nonpolar, whereas it is indicated in Table II-2 that both the C—H and the C—Cl bond possess measurable moments.

The most impressive application of this principle has been made for di-substituted benzene derivatives, in which the *para* derivatives of difluoro-, dichloro-, dibromo-, diiodo-, dinitro-, and dicyano-benzene show no measurable moments.[8]

This is additional good experimental evidence for the fact that the valence directions in the benzene ring all lie in the plane of the ring and that the *para* substituents are directed exactly opposite to each other.

This principle has found the following interesting application in polymer chemistry: polystyrene is a plastic material of excellent mechanical and electrical properties, but has, unfortunately, a heat distortion point below 100°C. It was found that introduction of chlorine in the ring increases the

[8] Compare here, *e.g.*, G. E. K. Branch and M. Calvin, *Theory of Organic Chemistry*, Prentice-Hall, New York, 1941.

softening point substantially but still provides for good molding properties and sufficient chemical stability. However, introduction of *one* chlorine atom to produce *p*-chloropolystyrene leads to a material of relatively high dielectric constant and power losses because each monomer unit in the macromolecule carries a dipole of about 1.90 debyes, which undergoes orientation in a static and oscillation in an alternating field. However, if one introduces *two* chlorine atoms in *para* position in each benzene ring and polymerizes 2,5-dichlorostyrene, a polymer of high softening point, low dielectric constant, and low power factor is obtained, because the two chlorines in *para* position in each monomeric unit compensate each other and the resulting group moment of each monomer is comparatively small (about 0.5 debye). The same holds for the poly-2,4,6-trichlorostyrene, which has a still higher softening point and exhibits a low dielectric constant and a small power factor.

If two polar groups, such as F, Cl, Br, NO_2, CN, etc., are introduced in *ortho* or *meta* position in the benzene ring or in any other aromatic system and the vectorial addition rule is applied, one finds noticeable deviations from the experimental values. This is because the two individual polar groups are now rather close to one another (about 2.0–2.5 Å.) and interact by virtue of their moments. This interaction will, in general, be a repulsion between the two groups; the valence angle between them will be increased and the theoretical total moment will be smaller than the experimental one.

TABLE II-3

SEVERAL DIPOLE MOMENTS OF *p*-SUBSTITUTED BENZENE DERIVATIVES

Substance	$\mu \times 10^{18}$ (observed)	$\mu \times 10^{18}$ calc. with angle at O atom = 110°	$\mu \times 10^{18}$ calc. without regard to angle
p-CH_3—C_6H_4—OH............1.50		1.60	2.10
p-CH_3—C_6H_4—OCH_3.........1.10		1.13	1.60
p-NO_2—C_6H_4—OCH_3.........4.80		4.35	2.60
p-Cl—C_6H_4—OH.............2.65		2.47	0.15

If the polar group is characterized by a certain valence angle, such as OH, OCH_3, etc., the proper position of the polar bond in the molecule has to be accounted for. Thus, in some *para* disubstituted benzene derivatives, the vectorial addition of the two competing group moments has to be carried out with consideration of the valence angle at the oxygen atom. Table II-3 shows for a few *p*-substituted benzene derivatives that in oxygen a valence angle of about 110° is indicated, which is in good agreement with that derived from x-ray and spectroscopic data. The dipole method accordingly supplements and expands our knowledge of the nuclear framework hitherto discussed, and has the advantage that even in the case of comparatively complex molecules significant results can be obtained with its aid.

The dipole method has also proved to be very useful in the investigation of *cis-trans* isomers because it allows of a simple and satisfactory differentiation between the two forms. As shown in Table II-4, the moments of all *trans*-dihalogenated ethylenes are zero, while the *cis* compounds have measurable moments. Similar conditions hold for other isomers of analogous nature.

TABLE II-4

DIPOLE MOMENTS OF *cis*- AND *trans*-DIHALOGENATED ETHYLENES

Substance	$\mu \times 10^{18}$ (observed)	Boiling point, °C.
Ethylene..........................	0	−103.9
cis-Dichloroethylene.................	1.8	59
trans-Dichloroethylene...............	0	48
cis-Dibromoethylene.................	1.35	112
trans-Dibromoethylene...............	0	108
cis-Diiodoethylene...................	0.75	188
trans-Diiodoethylene.................	0	190.5

Very interesting contributions were made by dipole measurements to the question of resonance in organic molecules. Although these results do not directly refer to macromolecules, they are of importance for the understanding of the stability or reactivity of monomers such as propylene and butadiene, and for the mechanism of radical-type activation, inhibition, and copolymerization. It may therefore be appropriate to enumerate a few examples in which dipole measurements indicate the existence of resonating structures, which in turn permits conclusions concerning the reactivity of molecules and of radicals which are derived from them.

It has already been mentioned (compare Table II-2) that the CCl bond in aliphatic compounds is characterized by a dipole moment of about 2 debye units. Specifically, ethyl chloride carries a dipole moment of 2.03, *tert*-butyl chloride of 2.13, etc. On the other hand, the dipole moment of chlorobenzene is only 1.72 debyes, which is substantially smaller than the aliphatic value. This is presently explained by assuming[9] that five reso-

[9] Compare, *e.g.*, G. W. Wheland, *The Theory of Resonance*, Wiley, New York, 1944, p. 126; C. P. Smyth in R. E. Burk and O. Grummitt, *Chemical Architecture (Frontiers in Chemistry*, Vol. 5), Interscience, New York, 1948; E. Bergmann, *Isomerism and Isomerization of Organic Compounds*, Interscience, New York, 1948.

nating structures are contributing to the properties of chlorobenzene.   Two
of them are "Kekulé" configurations with normal CCl dipoles; the other
three of them are ionic structures, which are produced by the donation of
one electron from the chlorine atom to the ring and can be characterized by:

$$Cl^+ \qquad\qquad Cl^+ \qquad\qquad Cl^+$$

The additional dipole moment of these structures is opposed to the original
moment of the CCl bond and, therefore, causes the decrease of the net total
from a value of about 2.05 to a value of about 1.75.   A similar case is nitrobenzene, in which the following contributing structures have to be considered:

$$O \quad O^- \qquad {}^-O \quad O^- \qquad {}^-O \quad O^- \qquad {}^-O \quad O^-$$
$$N^+ \qquad\qquad N^+ \qquad\qquad N^+ \qquad\qquad N^+$$

In this case, the value of the dipole moment of the NO_2 group is elevated
above that of aliphatic nitro compounds by the resonating ionic configurations.   The NO_2 group withdraws an electron pair from the ring and
charges the *ortho*, *viz.*, *para* position positive.   In fact, the dipole moment
of nitrobenzene vapor is 4.25 debyes, whereas that of 2-nitro-2-methylpro-
pane vapor is only 3.71.[10]

Polar structures seem also to be involved in the resonance of aliphatic
hydrocarbons that contain double bonds or conjugated systems.   While all
saturated hydrocarbons have only very small dipole moments, propylene
has a moment of 0.35 and methylacetylene one of 0.72 debye.   As explanation is offered the existence of three polar resonating structures for propylene of the form:

$$H^+H_2C=CH-C^-H_2$$

Butadiene does not show any measurable moment, as should be expected
from its symmetrical structure, but 1- and 2-methylbutadiene both have
appreciable dipole moments (0.68 and 0.38 debye).

[10] C. P. Smyth, *loc. cit.*, p. 42; E. Bergmann, *loc. cit.*, p. 1.

Another case of aliphatic resonance has been found in vinyl chloride, the moment of which (1.44 debyes) is much smaller than that of ethyl chloride (2.05 debyes). This can be explained by resonance of structures of the type:

$$H_2C=CHCl \quad \text{and} \quad H_2C^--CH=Cl^+$$

Another important monomer is acrylonitrile; its dipole moment (3.88 debyes) is somewhat smaller than that of propionitrile (4.04 debyes), which seems to call for the existence of resonating structures of the form:

$$H_2C=CH-C\equiv N \qquad H_2C^--CH=C=N^+$$

Thus, the dipole method has had a considerable share in the deduction of those principles which have to be employed to understand the reactivity of unsaturated organic molecules.

In the field of high polymers the concept of polar groups in a molecule has been used to great advantage, especially by measuring and interpreting the dielectric constant of polymers in bulk over a wide range of frequencies, at different temperatures and with different plasticizer content. The principle of this approach is based on Debye's theory[11] of the relaxation time of polar molecules and was exemplified for macromolecules by Busse, Fuller and Baker, and particularly by Fuoss and his collaborators.[12]

If one subjects ordinary polar molecules, such as water or alcohol, to an alternating electric field, they are capable of following the oscillations of the field up to rather high frequencies (10^{10} to 10^{12} per second). As a consequence, the dielectric constant of such materials does not depend upon frequency in the usually applied range from zero to about 10^7 or 10^8. However, if the dipoles are rigidly connected with large molecules, it will not be possible for them to follow the field as fully and as rapidly as before, because they cannot move *alone*. They have to carry with them those segments of the chain molecule to which they are firmly bound by strong chemical forces. Considering always the material in its bulk phase, the internal mobility is therefore slowed down considerably. If all dipoles in a polymer like polyvinyl chloride would follow an alternating field up to a certain frequency, and could not move sufficiently rapidly to follow the field above this frequency, the dielectric constant of the material would have a certain value at low frequencies and a lower value at high frequencies. This phenomenon is known as *dispersion of dielectric constant*. If

[11] R. M. Fuoss, *J. Am. Chem. Soc.*, **63**, 378 (1941).

[12] R. M. Fuoss, "The Electrical Properties of High Polymers," in *Chemistry of Large Molecules* (*Frontiers in Chemistry*, Vol. I). R. E. Burk and O. Grummitt, eds., Interscience, New York, 1943, pp. 191–218.

the rate of motion of all the dipoles in the material can be characterized by a single time constant (known as the *relaxation time*), the decay in dielectric constant from its upper to its lower value will occur in approximately two cycles of logarithmic frequency, as was first shown by Debye (see Fig. II-1). In larger molecules the decay in dielectric constant occurs over many cycles of logarithmic frequency, indicating a distribution of relaxation times (Fig. II-2).

This occurs since there are certain dipoles which can move more easily because of local conditions, whereas others are more severely impeded and

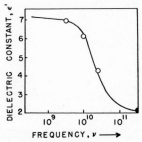

Fig. II-1. Dependence of dielectric constant of isobutyl bromide at 25° on the logarithm of the frequency. The solid curve is the theoretical curve for dielectric dispersion arising from a single relaxation time which clearly fits the data very well. (After E. J. Hennelly, W. M. Heston, and C. P. Smyth).

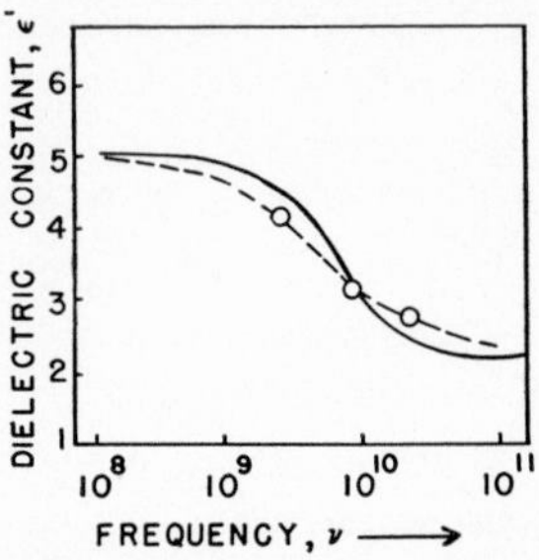

Fig. II-2. Same effect for *n*-octyl bromide. The solid curve is the theoretical curve for dielectric dispersion arising from a single relaxation time. The experimental data do not fit this curve because this larger molecule has a distribution of relaxation times.

need more time to follow the field. The distribution in relaxation times can be mathematically related to dispersion curves of the type shown in Figure II-2.

This calculated relaxation time spectrum is obviously of great importance for the electrical behavior (such as dielectric constant, power losses, etc.) of high polymers in the technical frequency range; it reflects the resistance that is offered by the entangled macromolecules to motions of small portions of them, and amounts therefore to a local viscosity measurement at different frequencies. Hence it is noticeably influenced by temperature in that the curve of Figure II-2 shifts to higher frequencies (shorter relaxation times) and flattens out slightly. This is demonstrated in Figure II-3, which shows measurements with Buna-NX rubber at temperatures of 20, 40, and 60°C.

The same effect can also be obtained by the addition of a plasticizer or softener at constant temperature, because its presence essentially decreases the viscosity of the polymer and hence reduces the relaxation time of the individual dipoles. That plasticizer is most efficient which at a given concentration causes the largest shift of the dielectric constant versus frequency curve. If, on the other hand, a cross-linking agent is introduced and the individual chain molecules are tied together by strong chemical

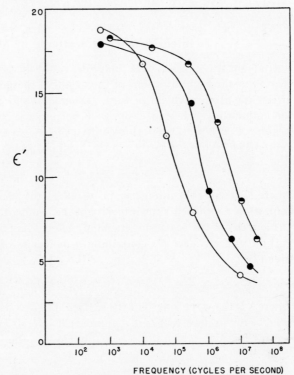

Fig. II-3. Dielectric constant versus logarithmic frequency for a vulcanized copolymer of butadiene and acrylonitrile (Ph.D. thesis of W. C. Schneider at Princeton University, 1945): (O), 20°; (●), 40°; and (◐), 60°C.

FREQUENCY (CYCLES PER SECOND)

bonds, the structure of the polymer is consolidated and the curve of Figure II-2 is shifted to lower frequencies (higher relaxation times). Sometimes one is interested in changing the over-all rheological properties of a material, such as moldability or extrudability without affecting the local viscosity as indicated by the ease of dipole motion. This has been accomplished in certain cases by a careful balance of plasticizing and cross linking. The dielectric method has been very valuable in such cases to check on the distribution curve of relaxation times while the various steps of plasticizing and curing are carried out.

F. SCATTERING OF LIGHT BY MOLECULES

Analysis of the light scattered by individual molecules in the gaseous and dissolved state has recently led to the development of very effective means of drawing far-reaching conclusions regarding the size and shape of the investigated molecules.[13,14] Essentially, there are 4 phenomena which permit conclusions on molecular size and shape: the *intensity* of the laterally scattered light, its *angular distribution*, the *Kerr effect*, and the *depolarization of the scattered light*.

1. Intensity of Light Scattered by Molecules

If a light wave passes over molecules in the gaseous, liquid, or solid state it produces forced vibrations of the negative charge clouds around and between the atoms, which, in turn, act as light sources and cause a certain amount of the incident intensity to be scattered in directions off the primary beam.   This lateral scattering of the primary wave can be formally interpreted as a certain *turbidity* τ of the medium, which is defined by:

$$I/I_0 = e^{-\tau l} \tag{II.6}$$

where I_0 denotes the intensity of a parallel light beam which enters the system, while I represents the intensity of the beam after it has passed through the length l of the scattering medium.   According to electrodynamics[15] the turbidity of an *ideal gas* containing n molecules of the polarizability α is given by:

$$\tau = (8\pi/3)(2\pi/\lambda)^4 n\alpha^2 \tag{II.7}$$

where λ is the wave length of the scattered light.   Equation (II.7) has been used to determine Avogadro's number; Table II-5 shows that one obtains figures for $N_{Av.}$ which are reasonably close to the best presently accepted value.[16]

[13] Compare, *e.g.*, H. A. Stuart, *Molekülstruktur*, Springer, Berlin, 1934; G. E. K. Branch and M. Calvin, *Theory of Organic Chemistry*, Prentice-Hall, New York, 1941; J. Cabannes, *Diffusion moléculaire de la lumière*, Presses Universitaires de France, Paris, 1939; P. Debye, *J. Applied Phys.*, **15**, 338 (1944); also H. Mark in R. E. Burk and O. Grummitt, *Chemical Architecture* (*Frontiers in Chemistry*, Vol. 5), Interscience, New York, 1948.

[14] Compare M. Born, *Optik*, Springer, Berlin, 1933; P. Debye, *J. Applied Phys.*, **15**, 338 (1944).

[15] Lord Rayleigh, *Phil. Mag.*, **41**, 107, 274, 477 (1871).

[16] H. Mark, "Light Scattering in Polymer Solutions," in *Chemical Architecture* (*Frontiers in Chemistry*, Vol. V).   R. E. Burk and O. Grummitt, eds., Interscience, New York, 1948, pp. 121–173.

If one considers in a similar manner the scattering from *liquids,* one has to take care of the mutual interaction between the individual molecules. Einstein,[17] Smoluchowski,[18] and Raman and Ramanathan,[19] have shown that the light scattering by a pure liquid can be considered to be caused by its *thermal density fluctuations* which provoke fluctuations in refractivity which in turn render the medium turbid. This turbidity is closely connected with the compressibility of the liquid and has been used to determine compressibilities and their temperature dependence experimentally.

TABLE II-5

AVOGADRO'S NUMBER FROM LIGHT-SCATTERING MEASUREMENTS[16]

Method	$N_{Av.} \times 10^{-23}$
Light scattering from a mixture of 91% argon, 8.7% nitrogen, and 0.3% oxygen	6.90
Light scattering from ethyl chloride vapor	6.50
Light scattering from water vapor	6.40
Presently accepted value	6.06

Einstein and Raman have also shown that turbidity of a *solution* depends on *fluctuations* of *solute concentration* and is therefore related to its osmotic pressure. On this effect Debye has recently based a new, important method to determine the weight and shape of macromolecules.[20,21] Introducing van't Hoff's law for the osmotic pressure, he found that the turbidity of a solution containing solute molecules which are small as compared with the wave length of the scattered light is connected with the molecular weight M_p of the solute of concentration c by:

$$\tau = HM_pc \qquad (II.8)$$

where H is given by:

$$H = (32\pi^3/3)(\gamma^2 n^2/\lambda^4)(1/N_{Av.}) \qquad (II.9)$$

$N_{Av.}$ = Avogadro's number $\gamma = \partial n/\partial c$
n = refractive index of the solvent c = solute concentration

In the case of macromolecules it is necessary to use a somewhat more complicated relation between osmotic pressure and molecular weight, which leads to:

[17] A. Einstein, *Ann. Physik,* **33,** 1275 (1910).

[18] M. v. Smoluchowski, *Ann. Physik,* **25,** 205 (1908).

[19] C. V. Raman and K. R. Ramanathan, *Phil. Mag.,* **45,** 113 (1923); C. V. Raman, *Indian J. Phys.,* **2,** 1 (1927).

[20] P. Debye, *J. Applied Phys.,* **15,** 338 (1944); *J. Phys. & Colloid Chem.,* **51,** 18 (1947).

[21] P. M. Doty, B. H. Zimm, and H. Mark, *J. Chem. Phys.,* **12,** 144 (1944); **13,** 159 (1945).

$$\frac{Hc}{\tau} = \frac{1}{M_p} + \frac{2B}{RT}c \qquad (II.10)$$

where H, τ, M_p, and c have the same meaning as in (II.9), and where B is characteristic for a given solvent–solute system at a given temperature. It describes the interaction of an individual segment of the macromolecule with the surrounding solvent molecules and can be obtained from the slope of a plot of osmotic pressure π divided by solute concentration c *versus* solute concentration (compare the more detailed discussion in Chapter

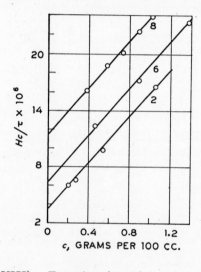

Fig. II-4. Values of Hc/τ of three polystyrene fractions in toluene *vs.* solute concentration.[16]

VIII).   Equation (II.10) has been used by several authors to determine molecular weights of macromolecules.[22]   Its results appear to be in fair agreement with figures obtained by other methods such as osmotic pressure, sedimentation, and diffusion.   Figure II-4 shows a plot of Hc/τ *versus* c of three polystyrene fractions in toluene and demonstrates that the experimental points fall approximately on straight lines, as equation (II.10) requires;   their intercepts can be used to determine the molecular weight of the solute, whereas the slopes describe the segment–solvent interaction. Table II-6 contains a few numerical values: the molecular weights (M_p) as determined by turbidity agree reasonably well with those found by osmotic pressure measurements;   also the μ-values as obtained by the two

[22] Compare, *e.g.*, reference 24 and P. P. Debye, *J. Applied Phys.*, **17**, 392 (1946); R. S. Stein and P. M. Doty, *J. Am. Chem. Soc.*, **68**, 159 (1946);   B. H. Zimm, *J. Chem. Phys.*, **16**, 1093 (1948).

TABLE II-6

OSMOTIC AND LIGHT-SCATTERING MEASUREMENTS OF POLYSTYRENE FRACTIONS IN TOLUENE
AT 25°C.[1] '

Fraction No.	M_p		μ	
	Osmotic	Turbidity	Osmotic	Turbidity
2	200,000	285,000	0.44	0.43
6	127,000	137,000	0.43	0.44
8	100,000	88,500	0.45	0.43

different methods are in satisfactory agreement with each other; μ is connected with B by the relation:

$$B = (0.5 - \mu)/V_0 d_p^2$$

where V_0 is the molar volume of the solvent, and d_p is the density of the solute.

Equation (II.10) holds only as long as the scattering molecules are small compared with the wave length of the scattered light; in this case, the intensity of the latter depends only slightly upon the angle of observation and is symmetrical in the forward and backward directions. As soon, however, as any dimension of the solute molecules becomes comparable (say one-fifth or one-fourth) with the wave length (which is usually around

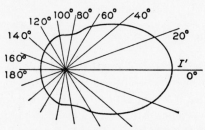

Fig. II-5. The radii of the curve are proportional to the intensity of the scattered light in the direction of the radius. The envelop shows a considerable dissymmetry in favor of forward scattering.[16]

5000 A.), there is *more* scattering at small angles than at large ones and the intensity distribution becomes *dissymmetric*. The degree of this dissymmetry depends upon the size and shape of the dissolved macromolecules and can be used to determine their dimensions if one makes certain reasonable assumptions regarding their shape. This has been done for solutions of spherical, rodlike, and randomly coiled polymer molecules,[23] and has led to interesting data.   Figure II-5 shows the dissymmetry of light scattering for spherical particles with a diameter of the same order of magnitude as the wave length of the scattered light and demonstrates clearly a preponderant scattering in the forward direction.   Table II-7 gives the dimensions of cellulose acetate molecules of different molecular weights (varying from 65,000 to 163,000) as determined from the dissymmetry coefficient $(z - 1)$, where z is the ratio of intensity of light scattered at 50° to light scattered at 130°.   It can be seen that the smaller molecules (MW $\simeq$ 65,000) are almost completely extended chains, whereas the larger ones show a coiling to

TABLE II-7

MOLECULAR WEIGHT AND MOLECULAR DIMENSIONS OF SEVERAL NITROCELLULOSE SAMPLES
FROM LIGHT SCATTERING[a]

Sample	$\overline{M}_w$ from light scattering assuming the molecule is a:			Molecular dimension (in Å.):			
	sphere	rod	coil	d for sphere	l for rod	R for coil	extended length, L
S-3,4	35,000	35,000	35,000	605	805	645	630
P-3,2	87,000	89,000	93,000	800	1210	960	1670
P-4,2	298,000	312,000	319,000	1080	1690	1250	5700
Rayonnier B	356,000	370,000	400,000	965	1450	1120	6550

[a] R. M. Badger and R. H. Blaker, *J. Phys. & Colloid Chem.*, **53**, 1056 (1949). $\overline{M}_w$ = weight average molecular weight. d = diameter of the particle assumed to be a sphere. l = length of the particle assumed to be a rod. R = root mean square separation of the ends assuming the particle is a random coil. L = extended length calculated on basis of random coil molecule.

about one-third of their extended length.   It should be added here that the scattering of light in polymer solutions opens a wide field for experimental and theoretical work, in which very interesting progress has recently been made by studying systems with 3 components (1 polymer and 2 solvents) and by investigating systematically the solutions of polyelectrolytes.[24]

2. The Kerr Effect

If a gas, liquid, or solution is introduced between the plates of a charged condenser, the molecules tend to orient themselves with the axis of their

[23] Compare, *e.g.*, reference 20 and also B. H. Zimm, R. S. Stein, and P. M. Doty, *Polymer Bull.*, **1**, 90 (1945);   R. S. Stein and P. M. Doty, *J. Am. Chem. Soc.*, **68**, 159 (1946);   G. Oster, P. M. Doty, and B. H. Zimm, *J. Am. Chem. Soc.*, **69**, 1193 (1947); B. H. Zimm, *J. Chem. Phys.*, **16**, 1093 (1948).

[24] Compare R. H. Ewart, C. P. Roe, P. Debye, and J. R. McCartney, *J. Chem. Phys.*, **14**, 687 (1946);   P. M. Doty, *J. Chem. Phys.*, in press;   J. J. Hermans, International Conference on Macromolecules, Amsterdam, September, 1949;   G. Oster, *loc. cit.*

maximum polarizability, or if a permanent moment exists, with the axis of this moment parallel to the direction of the electric field. Because of the thermal agitation, however, this orientation is actually established only to a very small extent: the previously isotropic medium now exhibits anisotropy which can be detected by its double refraction. This birefringence caused by the presence of the external field is called the *Kerr effect*. The phenomenon is measured by the difference $\Delta\lambda$ between the wave length of the beam polarized in the direction of the field and that polarized perpendicular hereto; it is given by:

$$\Delta\lambda = K(lE^2/\lambda) \tag{II.10}$$

where l is the length of the cell, E the voltage, and λ the wave length. The constant K is characteristic for the substance investigated at given concentration (pressure) and temperature, and is known as the *Kerr constant* (compare Table II-8). The theory of this effect, which holds for ideal gases and dilute solutions, was essentially developed by Lord Rayleigh,[25] Born, and Langevin. It represents K as:

$$K = 3\pi N_{Av.}(\theta_1 + \theta_2) = K_1 + K_2 \tag{II.11}$$

$N_{Av.}$ is Avogadro's number, while θ_1 and θ_2 are complex functions of the dipole moments and polarizabilities of the molecule. The constant can be split into two terms of which one (K_1) expresses the anisotropy of the polarizability and the other (K_2) represents the effect of the permanent dipole moments. The two terms differ from each other in their dependence upon temperature; the Kerr effect of dipole free molecules is proportional to $1/T$, that of dipole molecules to $1/T^2$.

TABLE II-8

KERR CONSTANTS FOR A FEW SIMPLE ORGANIC COMPOUNDS

Molecule	Kerr constants	Molecule	Kerr constants
CH₄	1.0	p-Xylene	22.6
CCl₄	2.30	Chlorobenzene	385
Hexane	1.73	Nitrobenzene	6000
Cyclohexane	2.30	p-Nitrotoluene	6400
Benzene	12.1		

It is mainly through this difference in temperature dependence that the two contributing effects represented by the two terms can be separated. If one knows both Kerr constants and is able to make plausible assumptions

[25] Lord Rayleigh, *Scientific Papers*, Vol. VI, p. 540.

regarding the symmetry of the investigated molecule, one can occasionally arrive at rather far-reaching conclusions regarding its shape.   Since this is usually possible only in conjunction with the degree of depolarization of the scattered light, we shall briefly discuss this phenomenon before passing on to the discussion of these results.

3. Degree of Depolarization of the Scattered Light

If light is diffracted by isotropic molecules, the transverse nature of the electromagnetic waves has the consequence that the light scattered normally to the primary beam will be *linearly polarized*.   If, however, scattering experiments are actually carried out on gases, liquids, or solutions, there is found in most cases a noticeable *depolarization* of the radiation scattered at 90°.   This is due to the fact that the diffracting molecules are not isotropic with respect to their polarizability.   The classical theory of light scattering as developed by Lord Rayleigh, Gans and Born[26] allows to establish a relationship between the degree of depolarization and the anisotropy of the polarizability, *viz.*, the three axes of the ellipsoid of polarizability.

If one wants to arrive at definite results it is useful to work with molecules having axial symmetry because they have only *two* main polarizabilities, namely, parallel and perpendicular to the axis.   These two can be calculated from the average polarizability determined by the refractive index (see page 40) and from the degree of depolarization, so that two equations are available for the two unknowns.

TABLE II-9

DEGREE OF DEPOLARIZATION OF THE SCATTERED LIGHT IN PER CENT

Molecule		Molecule	
Methane	0	Isobutanol	0.8
Benzene	4.2	*tert*-Butanol	0.7
Toluene	4.6	CO_2	9.8
m-Xylene	4.6	N_2O	12.5
n-Butanol	1.7		

Table II-7 contains a few figures about the degree of depolarization of several compounds and shows that the magnitude of the effect increases as the molecules become more anisotropic.

Depolarization of the laterally scattered light has also been observed in

[26] Lord Rayleigh, *Phil. Mag.*, **41**, 107, 274, 477 (1871).   R. Gans, *Ann. Physik*, **37**, 881 (1912); **62**, 331 (1920); **65**, 47 (1921).   M. Born, *Optik*, Springer, Berlin, 1933.

polymer solutions and was used by Doty and Kaufman[27] to draw interesting conclusions on the shape of dissolved macromolecules. They investigated fractions of cellulose acetate in acetone, found a noticeable degree of depolarization (from 1.7 to 4.5%) and concluded that the solute molecules are not tightly coiled up, but exist in a fairly extended shape. On the other hand, fractions of polyvinyl chloride in methyl ethyl ketone exhibit only slight depolarization, which points to the fact that these molecules have a tendency to form more or less tightly coiled entities in this particular solvent. Finally, it was found that the shape of polystyrene molecules in toluene and methyl ethyl ketone depends not only upon the molecular weight of the fraction but also upon the temperature at which the material was polymerized. Polystyrene prepared at 100°C. appear to be smaller and more isotropic than molecules prepared at 70°C.

Let us now pass to a brief discussion of the results which can be obtained on molecular structure if one combines measurements of the *total polarizability*, the *degree of depolarization* and the *Kerr constant*. As one has now three independent measurements, it is possible to compute individually the three axes of the ellipsoid of polarizability.

TABLE II-10

POLARIZATION ELLIPSOIDS OF SEVERAL MOLECULES ACCORDING
TO H. A. STUART[28]

Substance	Formula	$\alpha \times 10^{25}$	$b_1 \times 10^{25}$	$b_2 \times 10^{25}$	$b_3 \times 10^{25}$	Position of optical axes and electric moments; structure of molecule
Acetylene.........	C_2H_2	99.9	51.2	24.3	24.3	b_1 axis of symmetry linear molecule
Methane.........	CH_4	78.3	26.1	26.1	26.1	Regular tetrahedron
Carbon tetra-chloride.......	CCl_4	315	105	105	105	Regular tetrahedron
Methyl chloride...	CH_3Cl	137	54.2	41.4	41.4	b_1 axis of symmetry
Ethyl chloride....	C_2H_5Cl	192	66.0	50.1	75.9	Angular molecule
Benzene..........	C_6H_6	309.6	123.1	63.5	123.1	b_2 axis of symmetry
Toluene..........	$C_6H_5CH_3$	367.8	136.6	78.4	156.4	Plane molecule; b_2 perpendicular to plane of molecule
Pyridine..........	C_5H_5N	285	118.8	57.8	108.4	Same

Table II-10 shows the polarizabilities for a number of important molecules in three directions. It is evident that acetylene is particularly easily polarizable parallel to the triple bond, that methane and CCl_4 behave sym-

[27] P. M. Doty and H. S. Kaufman, *J. Phys. Chem.*, **49**, 583 (1945).
[28] See H. A. Stuart, *Ergeb. exakt. Naturw.*, **10**, 159 (1931).

metrically, that CH_3Cl possesses an axis of symmetry, and that higher aliphatic chlorides are asymmetrical. Benzene behaves like an uniaxial platelet, while toluene and pyridine are asymmetrical.

An investigation of the simplest ethers demonstrated clearly that the valence angle at the oxygen atoms is about 110°, in complete agreement with the values obtained by previously mentioned methods.

There has not yet been reported any coordinated application of refractive index, depolarization, and Kerr constant measurement for macromolecules, but it is obvious that it would lead to interesting results.

III. MOLECULAR SPECTRA

A. OSCILLATIONS AND ROTATIONS IN MOLECULES

It has already been emphasized that the nuclear framework of molecules must not be conceived as a rigid structure, formed of fixed, immobile parts. Rather, the individual atoms or atom groups execute various motions under the influence of the forces between them and of temperature. Knowledge of these motions is just as important to understanding the molecular behavior as is the knowledge of the nuclear framework itself, because the study of these internal motions throws light on the nature of the forces which hold the molecules together and determine their physical and chemical properties.

The internal motions of a molecule may be divided into two types: *oscillations* and *rotations*. However, it must be pointed out that in some cases oscillations go over into rotations and vice versa. Hence a sharp differentiation between these two types of movements is not significant.

Extensive studies of the *atomic oscillations* in a molecule have revealed that it is practical and advantageous to distinguish between two different types: *valence oscillations* and *deformation* (break or kink) *oscillations*. The former consist of a periodic motion of the involved atoms *in the direction* of the main valences linking them together; they cause a periodic extension and contraction of the bond distances. In the kink or break vibrations, on the other hand, the movements of the atoms are perpendicular to the bond direction and cause a periodic increase and decrease of the valence angles. Both oscillations have the consequence that the nuclear frame-study of these internal motions throws light on the nature of the forces work of a molecule is actually not rigid, but undergoes periodic, rapid, but small, changes; at any particular instant it is distorted according to the magnitude and direction of the instantaneous elongations of the individual atoms. In organic molecules the elongations are, at room temperature, between 0.05 and 0.10 Å. units, which amounts to 4–8% of the bond length.

The *rotation* of individual groups or parts of a molecule plays an important role in organic molecules, in which the principle of free or almost free

63

rotation about the single covalent bonds allows the components of a molecule to move without appreciable changes in the potential energy of the particle. These rotations and oscillations at constant or nearly constant potential energy are the result of thermal collisions which the particles undergo with their environment; their amplitudes increase with rising temperature. The mutual interaction of the various atoms within an organic molecule causes the rotations in most cases not to be entirely free but somewhat restricted by energy barriers. If these barriers between different configurations are large as compared with the average kinetic energy, RT, there will be no complete rotation, but the mobile parts of the molecule will merely oscillate about the positions of minimum energy. If, however, the various configurations of a molecule are separated from one another only by energy barriers of the magnitude of the average thermal energy, then each arrangement is assumed equally often and the rotation about certain valence directions will be essentially free.

It is therefore the internal molecular field of force that determines the oscillations and rotations inside of a molecule, and their study has led to interesting aspects of the dynamics of molecules. These general remarks on the significance of oscillations and rotations, will now be followed by a description of the most important methods for investigating the internal motions in molecules.

After the elucidation of the atomic spectra by the Rutherford-Bohr-Sommerfeld theory, one of the principal services of the improved and expanded quantum mechanics has been to give a complete explanation of the highly complex molecular spectra.[1]

The frequencies of the lines of an atom spectrum can all be represented as differences in energy states of the atom, so that each state is characterized by a definite arrangement of the electrons in the atom, *i.e.*, by a definite distribution of its negative charge cloud. A line is emitted if the atom passes from one state to another; its frequency v is calculated from the liberated energy difference ΔE according to the Einstein-Bohr equation:

$$v = \Delta E/h \qquad \text{(III.1)}$$

where h is Planck's constant.

In a molecule the energy of a given state is determined *not only* by the distribution of the *electrons, but also* by the particular state of its *atomic nuclei.*

[1] Compare, e.g., G. Herzberg, *Molecular Spectra and Molecular Structure*, Prentice-Hall, New York, 1939; W. West, "Spectroscopy and Spectrophotometry," in A. Weissberger, *Physical Methods of Organic Chemistry*, 2nd ed., Interscience, New York, 1949, part II, p. 1241.

In addition to the energy characteristic of the electronic state, there are now energy contributions arising from the individual states of vibration and rotation of the various atoms in the molecule. This explains why the spectrum of a molecule consists in general of many more lines than that of an atom; atomic spectra can properly be described as *line spectra*, molecular spectra as *band spectra*.

Experimental examination of band spectra has made extraordinary advances in recent years and the ideas of wave mechanics have made it possible to arrive at a satisfactory fundamental interpretation in terms of molecular structure.[2]

Generally, the frequency of any line of a molecular spectrum is due to the superposition of *three* energy contributions. First, in the emission of a line, the electronic state of the whole molecule is altered just as in the emission of a line of an atomic spectrum; this liberates the energy E_1. In addition, however, the state of oscillation of the various atoms of the molecule can also change by one or more vibrational quanta, thus liberating the additional energy E_2; this term must be added to that of the electron transition, with a positive or negative sign according to whether the molecule is passing from a higher state of oscillation to a lower, or vice versa. There is finally the possibility of a change in the state of *rotation* of the whole molecule or of one of its parts, giving rise to a rotational energy term E_3, which again must be added with the appropriate sign to the two other values. Thus, we should expect that the frequency of any individual line of a band spectrum may be expressed by an equation of the form:

$$\nu = (E_1 + E_2 + E_3)/h \qquad (III.2)$$

The energy changes involved in electronic transitions are of the order of magnitude of 10^{-11} to 10^{-12} erg per transition, the corresponding frequencies ($\nu = 10^{15}$ sec.$^{-1}$) are in the ultraviolet or visible range; the energy differences for changes in vibrational levels amount to 10^{-13} to 10^{-14} erg per molecule, the frequencies corresponding to them ($\nu = 10^{14}$ sec.$^{-1}$) are in the near infrared. The change in energy of a molecule on assuming different states of rotation is, however, only of the order of 10^{-15} to 10^{-16} erg per molecule and pure rotational frequencies therefore occur in the range of ($\nu = 10^{12}$ to 10^{13} sec.$^{-1}$) the far infrared.

If one wants to observe molecules in the unexcited electronic ground state, one must work in the domain of infrared radiation. In fact, the accurate study of infrared absorption spectra of simple molecules in the

---

[2] Compare, *e.g.*, G. Herzberg, *Infrared and Raman Spectra of Polyatomic Molecules*, Van Nostrand, New York, 1945; H. Sponer, *Molekülspektren*, Springer, Berlin, 1935.

gaseous state has contributed much valuable information to our basic knowledge of molecular structure.

If electronic transitions occur as well, it is possible to make observations in emission spectra. Owing to the larger energy quanta liberated, the spectra shift toward the visible or ultraviolet. The investigation of these spectra is simpler from the experimental point of view because spectroscopically this region is more easily accessible than the infrared, but the interpretation of these spectra is more involved, and there is the added difficulty that the molecule is always in a state of electronic excitation. The result is that in complicated molecules—particularly in high polymers—emission spectra cannot properly be observed and analyzed. Here one has to rely essentially on infrared absorption.

In 1926, Raman found that the oscillation and rotation spectra of molecules are also revealed in the light which they scatter laterally.[3] Whereas classical optics requires that light scattered laterally by a molecule must

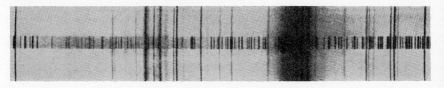

Fig. III-1.   Raman spectrum of phenol.

have the same frequency as the primary radiation, experiment shows that other frequencies—displaced lines or Raman lines—appear in addition to the original frequency. The differences in frequency between normal and displaced lines correspond to the oscillation and rotation frequencies of the molecule and afford a relatively convenient means of measuring these magnitudes in the visible or ultraviolet instead of the more difficultly accessible near or far infrared. Figure III-1 shows the Raman spectrum of phenol and it can readily be seen that the displaced lines are numerous and sharp; they can therefore be measured with considerable accuracy and reliability.

Absorption spectra in the infrared, emission spectra in the visible, and ultraviolet and Raman spectra together provide a very broad and reliable experimental foundation for the analysis of oscillations and rotations in molecules.

In addition, heat capacity and its dependence upon temperature also allows the quantitative study of slow oscillations and rotations in larger

[3] C. V. Raman and K. S. Krishnan, *Nature*, **121**, 501 (1928). Compare also A. Smekal, *Naturwiss.*, **11**, 873 (1923).

molecules.   In recent years an important development has taken place by evaluating heat capacity measurements of organic molecules containing deuterium instead of hydrogen in certain positions.   This procedure has been applied particularly to elucidate the internal mobility of ethylene and ethane.[4]

It has been shown in discussing the geometry of the nuclear framework of organic molecules that several methods independent of one another and based on different physical principles can give concordant results.   It has thus been possible to approach the same problem from different angles, to secure good control of the individual approaches and to assure the reliability of the final results.

It is the same with internal molecular movements.   Again, there are several experimental methods available based upon different physical principles, and the greatest possible use has been made of them to secure reliability of the results by independent proof.

B. MOMENTS OF INERTIA, NUCLEAR DISTANCES, AND DISSOCIATION ENERGIES

Among the experimental results, prominence may be given to the determination of *moments of inertia* and *interatomic distances* from the investigation of molecular spectra, since these afford another important contribution to the geometry of a molecule.   In discussing Tables I-2 to I-3 it was mentioned that atomic distances in simple molecules could also be ascertained from band spectra.   This is possible by analyzing the rotational part of the spectrum and arriving at the moment of inertia I of the molecule. For diatomic molecules this is connected with the masses m_1 and m_2 of the atoms and with their distance d by the equation:

$$I = [(m_1 m_2)/(m_1 + m_2)]d^2 = \mu d^2 \qquad (III.3)$$

$$\mu = \text{reduced mass}$$

If the masses are known, the nuclear distance can be computed.   A few nuclear distances ascertained in this way are given in Table III-1.   Gen-

---

[4] *E.g.*, J. R. Partington, *Proc. Roy. Soc.*, **A 100**, 27 (1922); A. Eucken and F. Luěde, *Z. physik. Chem.*, **B5**, 413 (1929); A. Eucken and A. Parts, *Z. physik. Chem.*, **B20**, 161 (1933); A. Eucken and K. Weigert, *Z. physik. Chem.*, **B23**, 265 (1933); A. Eucken and A. Bertram, *Z. physik. Chem.*, **B31**, 361 (1936); J. B. Howard, *J. Chem. Phys.*, **5**, 442 (1937); G. B. Kistiakowsky and F. Nazmi, *J. Chem. Phys.*, **6**, 18 (1938); G. B. Kistiakowsky, J. R. Lacher, and F. Stitt, *J. Chem. Phys.*, **6**, 407 (1938); G. B. Kistiakowsky and W. W. Rice, *J. Chem. Phys.*, **7**, 281 (1939); G. B. Kistiakowsky, J. R. Lacher and F. Stitt, *ibid.*, **7**, 289 (1939); F. Stitt, *ibid.*, **7**, 297 (1939).

erally, complete evaluation of the rotational fine structure of a molecular spectrum is possible only in di- and triatomic molecules. The remarkable agreement between spectroscopic atomic distances and those obtained from diffraction studies should be emphasized.[5]

TABLE III-1

ATOMIC DISTANCES COMPUTED FROM MOMENTS OF INERTIA

Bond	Molecule	Distance	Bond	Molecule	Distance
C—H....	CH_4	1.09	C—H....	Ethylene oxide	1.0802
N—H....	NH_3	1.02	C—D....	Ethylene oxide	1.0819
O—H....	H_2O	0.96	C=C....	Ethylene	1.35
C—C....	Ethylene oxide	1.4728	C≡C....	Acetylene	1.19
C—O....	Ethylene oxide	1.4363	C—C....	Benzene	1.40

TABLE III-2

DISSOCIATION ENERGIES FROM MOLECULAR SPECTRA

Bond	Dissociation energy, cal.	Bond	Dissociation energy
H—H$^+$	60,260	I—I	35,305
H—H	102,442	C—H	80,500
Li—Li	26,220	N—H	96,600
Na—Na	17,480	O—H	101,200
N≡N	169,050	Cl—H	101,200
P≡P	115,184	C≡O	220,800
O=O	117,070	N=O	121,900
S=S	102,350	S=O	116,219
Cl—Cl	56,764	C≡N	154,100
Br—Br	45,103		

It may be observed here that important conclusions have been drawn from the rotational fine structure of molecular spectra, using equation (III.3), regarding the presence and proportions of isotopes, a circumstance that led to the discovery of the isotopes of nitrogen and oxygen.[6]

In addition to this geometrical evidence, the band spectra allow further conclusions regarding the *dissociation energy* of diatomic molecules. Here one considers the *vibrational spectrum*, which, for large quantum numbers, is known to lose its intensity gradually and finally to disappear. At the

[5] Compare G. L. Cunningham, A. W. Boyd, W. D. Gwinn, and W. I. LeVan, *J. Chem. Phys.*, **17**, 211 (1949).

[6] See W. F. Giauque and H. L. Johnston, *Nature*, **123**, 318, 831 (1929); also S. M. Naude, *Phys. Rev.*, **34**, 1499 (1929); **36**, 333 (1930).

point at which the lines of the vibrational spectrum vanish the molecule is obviously no longer capable of oscillations and is therefore considered dissociated. The dissociation energy is the energy difference between the lowest vibrational state and the convergence limit of the higher vibrational states. Thus the dissociation energies of diatomic molecules can be found by ascertaining directly or by calculating the convergence limit of the vibrational states of the molecule.

Table III-2 gives a few relevant data to which are added, in Table III-3, some dissociation energies determined thermally for the purpose of comparison. It is evident that the two different methods give concordant results. Attention may be called to the point that the nuclear distances and dissociation energies of structures such as H_2^+, Li_2, CH, NH, OH, etc. can be investigated spectroscopically, although these groups cannot in the ordinary chemical sense be considered as stable molecules.

C. NUCLEAR VIBRATIONS AND GROUP FREQUENCIES

The ultimate aim of molecular spectrum analysis is to reduce the vibrations observed in the infrared, visible, and ultraviolet band spectrum, as well as in the Raman spectrum, to a definite model, locating exactly the individual atoms on one hand and specifying quantitatively the forces between them on the other. It is relatively easy to attain the former object from data on internuclear distances and valence angles, while the latter is a difficult problem as yet unsolved. In interpreting band spectra, it was first attempted to assume that among all atoms of a molecule, including those not directly united with each other, forces exist which depend essentially upon the distances between the various atoms.

Such *central force* systems have been used, for example, by Dennison[7] to explain the vibrational spectrum of multiatomic molecule. The potential energy of the molecule has a relatively simple form, but the results are not always in accord with experimental results.

TABLE III-3

SOME THERMALLY MEASURED HEATS OF DISSOCIATION

Molecule	D, cal.	Molecule	D, cal.	Molecule	D, cal.
H_2	95,000	Na_2	16,800	Br_2	46,200
Li_2	23,400	Cl_2	57,000	I_2	35,670

[7] D. M. Dennison, *Phys. Rev.*, **41**, 304 (1932); *Proc. Roy. Soc. London*, **148**, 250 (1935).

Accordingly, Bjerrum[8] has proposed another approach. As a first approximation in describing the internal molecular field of force he assumes that *forces dependent upon distance* exist only between chemically linked atoms and that there exist in addition elastic forces which resist changes of the valence angles. A chemical bond is, therefore, in this concept of valence, a force defined by *two* elastic constants. One of them corresponds to a tension in the direction of the bond, the other to a resistance against any deflection of the bond off this direction. It is understandable that this picture is particularly well suited to describe the internal field of force in organic molecules; actually it has proved valid even for rather complex molecules, giving results which show reasonably good agreement with the experimental data.

Generally, much greater forces are required to stretch a primary valence lengthwise than to deflect it from its normal direction. Preliminary information has already been given in Tables I-7, I-8, and I-9 and in Chapter I (Sect. J.). We shall now discuss the interatomic forces in more detail.

Kohlrausch[9] and Mecke[10] attempted to establish a relationship between the vibrations of a molecule and its valence field starting with the simplest case of a diatomic molecule which undergoes harmonic oscillations of frequency ν. The force constant, k, characterizing the vibration is given by the equation:[11]

$$k = 4\pi^2\mu^2\nu^2 \qquad (III.4)$$

Since μ is known and ν can be measured, k can be computed. Another measure for the resistance of a bond against elongation has been introduced by Mecke[10] as the so-called *bond constant* ϵ, which indicates the amount of work required to double the distance between the atomic nuclei in the molecule, assuming the validity of Hooke's law over the whole range. The bond constant is defined by:

$$\epsilon = 2\pi^2\mu\nu^2 r_0^2 \qquad (III.5)$$

r_0 = atomic distance in the rest position

[8] N. Bjerrum, see especially in K. W. F. Kohlrausch, *Der Smekal-Raman-Effekt*, Springer, Berlin, 1938, p. 62 et seq.; J. H. Hibben, *Chem. Rev.*, **18**, 1–232 (1936); J. H. Hibben, *The Raman Effect*, Reinhold, New York, 1939.

[9] K. W. F. Kohlrausch, *Der Smekal-Raman-Effekt*, Springer, Berlin, 1938, pp. 53 et seq.

[10] See, *e.g.*, R. Mecke, *Z. Physik*, **104**, 291 (1936).

[11] See, *e.g.*, K. W. F. Kohlrausch, *Der Smekal-Raman-Effekt*, Springer, Berlin, 1931; J. H. Hibben, *Chem. Rev.*, **18**, 1 (1936); also J. H Hibben, *The Raman Effect*, Reinhold, New York, 1939.

The two quantities, k and ϵ, correspond essentially to a modulus of elasticity of a given chemical bond and measure its resistance against being stressed along its own direction; they afford very interesting information about the nature of the various bonds.

TABLE III-4

FORCE CONSTANTS, INTERNUCLEAR DISTANCES, AND FREQUENCIES FOR
SINGLE, DOUBLE, AND TRIPLE BONDS OF CARBON[a]

Bond	Frequency (wave numbers)	Internuclear distance, Å.	Force constant k (dynes cm.$^{-1}$)
C—C	993	1.54	4.6×10^5
C—O	1030	1.43	5.0
C—N	1033	1.47	4.9
C=C	1620	1.33	10.6
C=O	1700	1.21	11.6
C=N	1650	1.27	10.4
C≡C	2120	1.20	15.8
C≡O	2146	1.10	18.5
C≡N	2150	1.15	17.5

[a] J. H. Hibben, *The Raman Effect and Its Chemical Applications*, Reinhold, New York, 1939.

TABLE III-5

COVALENT RADII IN ANGSTROM UNITS FOR ATOMS[a]

Element	Single bond	Double bond	Triple bond
H	0.29–0.37		
B	0.88	0.76	0.68
C	0.771	0.665	0.602
N	0.70	0.60	0.547
O	0.66	0.55	0.50
F	0.64	0.54	
Si	1.17	1.07	1.00
P	1.10	1.00	0.93
S	1.04	0.94	0.87
Cl	0.99	0.89	
Ge	1.22	1.12	
As	1.21	1.11	
Se	1.17	1.07	
Br	1.14	1.04	
Sn	1.40	1.30	
Sb	1.41	1.31	
Te	1.37	1.27	
I	1.33	1.23	

[a] L. Pauling, *The Nature of the Chemical Bond*. Cornell Univ. Press, Ithaca, 1940.

Table III-4 shows the frequencies, internuclear distances, and force constants for some single, double, and triple bonds involving carbon. It is interesting to note that the force constants for single, double, and triple bonds are approximately in the ratio 1:2:3 and not very markedly dependent on what particular atom is involved in the bond with carbon. The

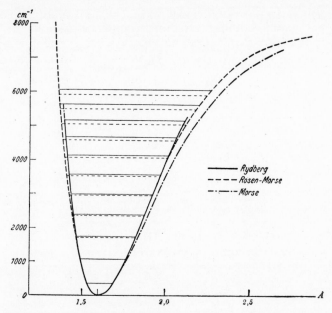

Fig. III-2.   Potential curve for the O_2 molecule.   Energy in cm.$^{-1}$.

values (in angstrom units) of the covalent bond radii for single, double, and triple bonds of various elements are given in Table III-5.

Figure III-2 shows the potential energy curve of the O=O linkage plotted from the vibrational spectrum of this bond. The abscissa measures the distance between the two oxygen nuclei, while the ordinate gives the negative potential energy of the molecule (in cm.$^{-1}$)*; large restoring forces or high bond constants indicate that the radius of curvature of the potential energy curve in the neighborhood of the equilibrium position is small, so that the potential trough has steep walls. Figure III-3 gives in one diagram the potential energy curves of the single, double, and triple

* In order to obtain the energy value in ergs, one must multiply the value on the ordinate first with the velocity of light (3×10^{10}) to arrive at the frequency of the vibration, and then with Planck's constant (5.6×10^{-27}).

carbon-carbon bonds; the various nuclear distances, dissociation energies, and bond constants can be conveniently compared.

If the diatomic vibrational system considered up to now is incorporated in a larger molecule, its frequencies and consequently its characteristic constants will be changed by the new environment in which it is placed.

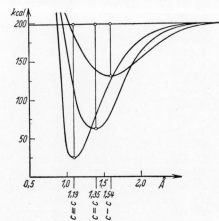

Fig. III-3. Potential curve for the C—C, C=C, C≡C bond. Energy in kilocalories.

TABLE III-6

INFLUENCE OF ENVIRONMENT ON C—H FREQUENCY

Molecule	Wave number, cm.⁻¹	Molecule	Wave number, cm.⁻¹
$H\cdot CO\cdot CCl_3$	2867	$H\cdot CCl_3$	3018
$H\cdot CO\cdot NH_2$	2882	$H\cdot CBr_3$	3021
$H\cdot CO\cdot H$	2945	$H\cdot C_6H_5$	3050
$H\cdot CO\cdot OH$	2951	$ClHC{=}CHCl$	3078
$Cl_2HC\cdot CHCl_2$	2984	$Cl_2C{=}CHCl$	3082
$Cl_3CC\cdot HCl_2$	2985	$HC{\equiv}C.N$	3213
$Br_2HC\cdot CHBr_2$	2986	$HC{\equiv}C.H$	3320

In general, it is impossible to foretell theoretically the extent of this change and whether, within a large molecule, the physical identity of an individual bond will be practically lost. However, experiments show that this is frequently not the case. Although substituents attached to the vibrating atoms exert a definite effect on their frequencies, these variations are systematic and keep within moderate limits. This is of great importance for the application of vibrational analysis to organic chemistry and is brought out in Table III-6, which shows the relatively moderate influence

TABLE III-7

GROUP FREQUENCIES: $R = C_nH_{2n+1}$; $Ar = C_6H_5$

Group	Wave number, cm.$^{-1}$	Molecule
C—I	~480	$R_3C \cdot I$
C—I	~490	$R_2HC \cdot I$
C—I	~500	$R \cdot H_2 \cdot C \cdot I$
C—I	522	$H_3C \cdot I$
C—Br	~510	$R_3C \cdot Br$
C—Br	~530	$R_2HC \cdot Br$
C—Br	~560	$RH_2C \cdot Br$
C—Br	594	$H_3C \cdot Br$
C—Cl	~570	$R_3C \cdot Cl$
C—Cl	~610	$R_2HC \cdot Cl$
C—Cl	~650	$RH_2C \cdot Cl$
C—Cl	710	$H_3C \cdot Cl$
C—C	750–1100	Paraffin chains
C—C	992	$H_3C \cdot CH_3$
C—C	802	Cyclohexane
C—C	886	Cyclopentane
C—C	~960	Cyclobutane
C—C	1184	Cyclopropane
C—OH	1032	$H_3C \cdot OH$
C—NH_2	1037	$H_3C \cdot NH_2$
C=N	1560–1660	Various
C=O	1650–1800	Various
N=O	~1640	$R \cdot O \cdot NO$
C=C	1621	$H_2C=CH_2$
C=C	~1642	$R \cdot HC=CH_2$
C=C	~1658	$R \cdot HC=CH \cdot R$, *cis*
C=C	~1674	$R \cdot HC=CH \cdot R$, *trans*
C=C	1676	$R_2C=CR_2$
C≡C	1973	$HC≡CH$
C≡C	~2118	$RC≡CH$
C≡C	~2235	$R \cdot C≡CR$
C≡N	~2245	$R \cdot C≡N$
C—H	2700–3000	$R \cdot CH_3$
C—H	3000–3100	$C=CH_2$
C—H	3113	$H \cdot CN$
C—H	~3310	$R \cdot C≡CH$
N—H	3310–3370	$R \cdot NH_2$
N—H	~3330	R_2NH
N—H	~3335	$C=NH$
O—H	~3400	$R \cdot OH$

of different substituents on the C—H frequency.   The same holds for other bonds so that it seems to be legitimate to speak of *group frequencies*, whose appearance in a molecular spectrum indicates the presence of a certain atomic group in the molecule.   Table III-7 gives a series of such group frequencies; the influence of the various substituents is again readily seen.

A possibility of applying this fact to high polymeric substances is exemplified by studies of Signer and Weiler,[12] and of Mizushima, Morino, and Inoue,[13] who followed the polymerization of styrene with the aid of the Raman spectrum.   Monostyrene has a distinct and characteristic Raman spectrum in which a wave number at *ca.* 1630 cm.$^{-1}$, due to the aliphatic double bond, is clearly observable beside that of the aromatic bond at about 1600 cm.$^{-1}$.   The ratio of the intensities of these lines is about 2:1.   If the substance is now polymerized, this ratio is displaced gradually in favor of the aromatic wave number 1600 cm.$^{-1}$, until ultimately in high polymeric samples nothing further is to be seen at 1630 cm.$^{-1}$.   The Japanese authors have found an intensity ratio 1:5 for a product in a moderate state of polymerization and have calculated from it an average polymerization degree of 10, which corresponds to a molecular weight of 1040.   Cryoscopic determination indicated 1150.

Determination of the average degree of polymerization of highly polymerized substances would, of course, not be easy by this method, unless one has a device to measure very low intensities by a special experimental arrangement.   Similar experiments have been carried out by Monnier, Susz, and Briner,[14] who followed the polymerization of acrylic ester with the aid of the Raman effect and by Kienle and his coworkers,[15] who applied the infrared absorption spectrum to the polycondensation of glycerol and dicarboxylic acids.

We will now turn our attention to *the break or kink vibrations* which are produced by a rapid succession of increases and decreases of the valence angles.   It is to be expected from the evidence of Table I-9 that much smaller forces are operating here and hence lower frequencies will be observed.   This is, in fact, the case.

Table III-8 represents the various vibrations of the CO_2 molecule. There exist two valence vibrations and one break vibration; the frequency of the latter is considerably smaller than those of the two former.   The lower frequencies point to smaller values for the restoring force and for the bond constant as compared with valence vibrations.   This is shown in

[12] R. Signer and H. Weiler, *Helv. Chim. Acta*, **16**, 115 (1932).

[13] S. Mizushima, Y. Morino, and R. Inoue, *Bull. Chem. Soc. Japan*, **12**, 136 (1937).

[14] D. Monnier, P. A. Susz, and E. Briner, *Helv. Chim. Acta*, **21**, 1349 (1938).

[15] R. H. Kienle, P. A. van der Meulen, and F. E. Petke, *J. Am. Chem. Soc.*, **61**, 2258, 2268 (1939); **62**, 1053 (1940); **63**, 481 (1941).

TABLE III-8

FUNDAMENTAL VIBRATIONS OF THE CO_2 MOLECULE

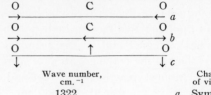

Wave length, cm. $\times 10^{-4}$	Wave number, cm. $^{-1}$	Character of vibration
7.65	1322	a. Symmetrical
4.267	2363	b. Asymmetrical
14.78	667.9	c. Asymmetrical

TABLE III-9

FREQUENCIES, FORCE CONSTANTS, AND NUCLEAR DISTANCES OF DIATOMIC MOLECULES

Molecule	Wave number	$k \times 10^{-5}$	r, Å.	Molecule	Wave number,	$k \times 10^{-5}$	r, Å.
H—H	4405	5.68	0.75	H—I	(2323)	3.14	1.62
H—D	3817	5.68	0.75	Cl—Cl	565	3.32	1.98
D—D	3117	5.68	0.75	O=O	1579	11.7	1.22
H—F	4141	9.55	0.92	N=O	1907	15.9	1.15
H—Cl	2989	5.06	1.27	C≡O	2181	19.1	1.15
H—Br	2650	4.06	1.41	N≡O	2359	22.8	1.09

TABLE III-10

VALENCE FORCES (k), DEFORMATION FORCES (d), VALENCE ANGLES (α), AND NUCLEAR DISTANCES (r), OF SEVERAL TRIANGULAR MOLECULES

Molecule	$k \times 10^{-5}$ (dyne cm. $^{-1}$)	$d \times 10^{-5}$ (dyne cm. $^{-1}$)	α	r, Å.
O=S=O	9.56	1.60	120°	1.46
H—O—H	7.55	1.37	105°	0.96
D—O—D	7.75	1.38	105°	—
H—S—H	3.91	0.90	92°	1.35

TABLE III-11

VALENCE FORCES, DEFORMATION FORCES, VALENCE ANGLES, AND NUCLEAR DISTANCES OF SYMMETRICAL CHAIN MOLECULES

Molecules			$k \times 10^{-5}$	$d \times 10^{-5}$	α	r_{12}, Å.
1	2	3				
$H_3C\cdot$	O	$\cdot CH_3$	4.53	0.68	116°	1.43
$H_3C\cdot$	NH	$\cdot CH_3$	4.24	0.64	114°	1.48
Cl$\cdot$	CH_2	$\cdot$Cl	2.61	1.09	108°	1.8
Br$\cdot$	CH_2	$\cdot$Br	2.13	0.82	113°	2.0
I$\cdot$	CH_2	I	1.76	0.55	114°	2.2

TABLE III-12

VALENCE FORCES, DEFORMATION FORCES, VALENCE, ANGLES AND NUCLEAR
DISTANCES FOR PYRAMIDAL MOLECULES XY_3

Molecule	$k \times 10^{-5}$	$d \times 10^{-5}$	α	r, Å.
NH_3 . . . . .7.09	1.36	108°	1.01
PH_3 . . . . .3.36	0.75	100°	—
AsH_3 . . . . .2.80	0.53	96°	—
PF_3 . . . . .4.56	2.14	100°	1.64
AsF_3 . . . . .3.90	0.80	97°	1.80
PCl_3 . . . . .2.11	0.62	102°	2.14
$AsCl_3$ 2.01	0.46	96°	2.24
$SbCl_3$ 1.75	0.34	94°	2.30
$BiCl_3$ 1.17	0.20	93°	2.46
PBr_3 . . . . .1.62	0.54	104°	2.31

TABLE III-13

VALENCE FORCES, DEFORMATION FORCES, AND NUCLEAR DISTANCES FOR
TETRAHEDRAL MOLECULES

Molecule	$k \times 10^{-5}$	$d \times 10^{-5}$	r, Å.
CH_4 . . . . .4.75	0.814	1.1
CCl_4 . . . . .1.89	0.348	1.76
$SiCl_4$ 2.72	0.206	2.1
$TiCl_4$ 2.48	0.110	2.3
$SnCl_4$ 2.35	0.110	2.3

Tables III-9, III-10, and III-11 in which data for a series of diatomic, triatomic, and polyatomic molecules are assembled; in every instance, the
deformation force d is smaller than the valence force constant k.   The
nuclear distances and the valence angles in the equilibrium positions are
also inserted.   A few data for pyramidal molecules are given in Table III-
12, and for tetrahedral molecules in Table III-13.   The deformation force
constants are noticeably influenced by substituents; in larger molecules
they gradually lose their simple and precise meaning and are represented by
a whole spectrum of lines.

Figure III-4 illustrates the principal simplicity but the actual complexity
of the vibrational spectrum of larger molecules represents the Raman
spectra of aliphatic hydrocarbons which all contain only one chlorine atom.
The hydrocarbon part of the molecules varies in length from CH_3 to $C_{10}H_{21}$
and includes a number of complicated branched structures.   All molecules
contain essentially three covalent bonds: C—H, C—C, and C—Cl.   Consequently the Raman spectrum contains three ranges of valence frequencies,

78   III. MOLECULAR SPECTRA

one between 2800 and 3000 wave numbers for the C—H vibrations, one
between 800 and 1400 for the C—C bonds, and one between 500 and
700 for the C—Cl vibrations. In the simplest case of methyl chloride

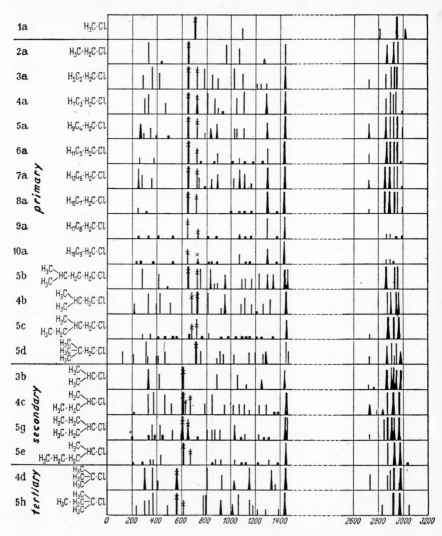

Fig. III-4. Raman spectra of homologous compounds of the aliphatic chlorinated
hydrocarbon series (frequencies in cm.⁻¹). When comparing spectra of 2a to 10a, note
that the lines belonging to the valence frequencies are fixed in the same place, while the
break frequency lines (around 400) are shifted.

there is actually only *one* strong line around 700 discernible for the C—Cl bond, and one around 2950 for the C—H vibrations.   As the molecules become more and more complex, these lines split into multiplets and, at the same time, a series of new lines appear in the range between 200 and 600 and between 1000 and 1200;   they are kink frequencies of the C—C and C—H vibrations and in the lowest range (around 200 and below), probably torsional frequencies of the long hydrocarbon chains.

Thus we pass gradually from the sharp high-frequency vibrations of the primary valence bonds by way of the kink frequencies into the domain of torsional vibrations and finally into the range of moderately hindered rotations.

D. APPLICATION OF MOLECULAR SPECTROSCOPY TO MACROMOLECULES

All spectroscopic methods have been used frequently in recent years to obtain information about the presence of certain groups in macromolecules and many questions of great interest have been answered in this way. Qualitatively the presence of such groups can be tied in with the chemical behavior of high polymers, particularly with their performance in aging, fatiguing, and degradation; quantitatively, such groups can be used to determine molecular weights if it is known that they occur only at the end or ends of the chain molecules; they can serve to distinguish between different reaction mechanisms and make it possible to predict the behavior of macromolecules during their formation and degradation.   A considerable amount of interesting information has been accumulated during the last few years, and it seems adequate, therefore, to review the various types of high polymers separately.

1. Polyhydrocarbons

Polyethylene was subjected to a thorough infrared and Raman analysis by several authors.[16]   The result was that the presence of carbonyl groups, ether groups, and aliphatic double bonds in small quantities could be established.   These groups are probably produced by the oxygen or peroxide which are used as catalysts or initiators in the polymerization reac-

---

[16] Compare, *e.g.*, C. W. Bunn and T. C. Alcock, *Trans. Faraday Soc.*, **41**, 317 (1945); W. M. D. Bryant, *J. Polymer Sci.*, **2**, 547 (1947); also K. H. Meyer, *Natural and Synthetic High Polymers (High Polymers*, Vol. IV), Interscience, New York, 1941; H. W. Thompson and P. Torkington, *Trans. Faraday Soc.*, **41**, 248 (1945);   J. J. Fox and A. E. Martin, *Proc. Roy. Soc. London*, **A175**, 226 (1940).

tion.   More interesting is that methyl groups have been found to be present in various amounts depending upon the mode of preparation of the polymer.

Polyethylene made by the decomposition of diazomethane or by the reaction of $2H_2$ with CO and likewise samples withdrawn from laboratory runs of high pressure ethylene polymerization at low conversions contain only one methyl group in a hundred methylene groups or more, whereas normal commercial specimens can have a ratio of CH_3 to CH_2 as high as one in thirty.   Parallel with the methyl group content goes a drop in melting point, a decreased tendency to crystallize, and an improved moldability and extrudability.   Bryant suggested as explanation for this behavior that each methyl group indicates the existence of a branch of a certain length, that these branches interfere with the regular dense packing of the chains and act as internal plasticizers to become responsible for the above-mentioned phenomena.   Experiments with polarized infrared radiation[17] have shown that in a highly oriented sample the methyl group are oriented parallel to the chains, which indicates that the branches have a length of at least five or six methylene groups.

Polystyrene has been investigated repeatedly by infrared and Raman spectroscopy.   This disappearance of the aliphatic double bond in polymerizing monostyrene has been used to follow the course of the polymerization reaction; the relative frequency of the CO absorption in a polymer which was initiated by benzoyl peroxide made it possible to show that ester-type fragments of the catalyst are attached to the ends of the macromolecules[18] and the study of various polystyrene samples revealed the existence, in small quantities, of accidental groups such as CO, CH_3, and $-CH=CH_2$. These groups are apparently connected with the individual reaction steps of initiation, branching, chain transfer, and termination (see Chap. XII).

Polybutadiene, polyisoprene, polyisobutylene, and copolymers of these monomers with styrene were rather thoroughly investigated during the last few years.[19,20]   The interest revolves essentially about two questions. Which proportion of the diene or diene component has been incorporated into the chain according to the 1,2 addition and which proportion according to the 1,4 addition.   Infrared absorption spectroscopy was capable of distinguishing between a $-CH=CH_2$ and a $-CH=CH-$ double bond and the estimate of an approximately 1 to 3 ratio for 1,2 and 1,4 addition in poly-

[17] E. J. Ambrose, A. Elliott, and R. B. Temple, *Proc. Roy. Soc.*, **A199**, 183 (1949).

[18] H. F. Pfann, V. Z. Williams, and H. Mark, *J. Polymer Sci.*, **1**, 14 (1946).

[19] Compare H. W. Thompson and P. Torkington, *Trans. Faraday Soc.*, **41**, 246 (1945); *Proc. Roy. Soc. London*, **A184**, 3, 21 (1945).

[20] G. B. B. M. Sutherland and A. V. Jones, *Nature*, **160**, 567 (1947).

butadiene has been confirmed independently by chemical methods, such as ozonization with subsequent hydrolysis. The other question was the occurrence of accidental groups in the various rubbery polymers under consideration. Again it was found that they all do contain carbonyl

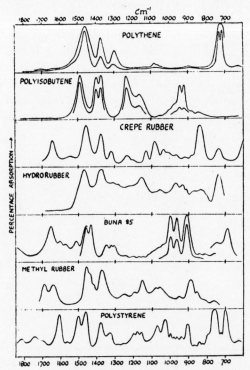

Fig. III-5.   Infrared absorption spectra of several polyhydrocarbons.[19]

groups, ether links, and hydroxyl groups which probably, together with the many double bonds in the chains, are responsib'e for the relatively high reactivity of these polymers toward oxygen in the presence of light and heat. Figure III-5 shows a few infrared absorption spectra of polyhydrocarbons; it reveals that the spectrum of polyethylene is of relative simplicity and that the spectra of different polymeric hydrocarbons exhibit characteristic differences.

2. Polyvinyl and Polyacrylic Derivatives

A large number of these polymers were studied by various authors in the course of the last five years[19,20] with the intention of determining whether a contribution could be made by the infrared absorption method to the question of "head-to-tail" or "head-to-head, tail-to-tail" sequence of the monomer units along the length of the chain. Comparison of polyvinyl acetate and polymethyl acrylate with a number of low molecular esters led Thompson and Torkington to the conclusion that these macromolecules are essentially built up according to the "head-to-tail" sequence. Essentially the same result was found for polyvinyl chloride and polyvinylidene chloride; here the conclusion of a preponderant "head-to-tail" sequence is in good agreement with the well-known chemical investigations of Marvel and his school[21] and with the results of x-ray analysis.

During these studies it was again found that accidental groups, such as —C≡C—, C═O, —O—, and OH are present in these polymers in small quantities.

3. Polyesters and Polyamides

Polyesters of adipic acid and ethylene glycol have been investigated with the result that one finds a sharp and pronounced absorption at the normal position of the carbonyl and ester frequencies, indicating that the configuration:

$$
\begin{array}{ccc}
 & \mathrm{O} & \\
\mathrm{H} & \| & \mathrm{H} \\
-\mathrm{C}-\mathrm{C}-\mathrm{O}-\mathrm{C}- & \\
\mathrm{H} & & \mathrm{H}
\end{array}
$$

is not disturbed either by the surrounding CH_2— groups or by mutual interaction. On the other hand it is interesting to note that the infrared absorption spectrum of polyamides, particularly in the highly oriented state, shows a distinct displacement of the carbonyl absorption to smaller wave numbers (from 1730 cm.$^{-1}$ to 1630 cm.$^{-1}$). This is commonly interpreted as an interaction between adjacent amide groups in the polymer and may well indicate the frequent existence of hydrogen bonds between the individual macromolecules. Infrared absorption spectra of phenol and cresol formaldehyde polycondensation products promise to permit conclusions as to the relative frequency of *ortho* and *para* condensation in these systems.

[21] Compare, *e.g.*, C. S. Marvel in R. E. Burk and O. Grummitt, *The Chemistry of Large Molecules* (*Frontiers in Chemistry*, Vol. I), Interscience, New York, 1943, p. 219; also *J. Am. Chem. Soc.*, **61**, 3241 (1939).

4. Various Other Polymers

Cellulose shows strong infrared absorption because of its many hydroxyl groups.[22] There is indication for hydrogen bonding, inasmuch as the OH frequency is noticeably disturbed. In certain samples the characteristic carboxyl frequencies have been observed and it seems possible to use the infrared absorption spectrum for carboxyl group determination in oxycellulose. Cellulose esters and ethers show the expected infrared absorption spectrum[23]; the amount of residual free hydroxyl groups may be estimated from the intensity of the stretching vibration of the O—H bond. Much experimental work has been done with infrared absorption in the protein field, but the spectra are, in general, rather complicated. Recently, however, Sutherland[24] succeeded in obtaining a remarkably simple infrared absorption curve from a copolymer which was obtained by Woodward and Schramm[25] by copolymerization of the carboxy amino anhydrides of leucine and phenylalanine. This spectrum is reproduced in Figure III-6, and shows very clearly the absorption frequencies of the C=O, C—N, C—C, C—H, and N—H bonds.

E. INTERNAL MOLECULAR POTENTIAL ENERGY AND FREE ROTATION

Since the time of van't Hoff, the principle of *free rotation* about the single carbon-carbon bond has been a cornerstone of stereochemistry of organic molecules; it must be invoked to understand why it is impossible to prepare a large number of isomers which could exist if it were not valid, and it gives simple explanations for numerous facts concerning the reactivity of organic molecules. It is remarkable that in this respect as well as in those of constant valence distances and valence angles, organic and physical chemists have succeeded in developing early an essentially correct picture merely through intuitive grasp of general relationships. In consequence, the more modern development consists largely of adding *quantitative* data and putting finishing touches to the qualitative picture already existing for many years. It will be seen that physical methods have, in fact, succeeded in developing many interesting numerical relationships concerning internal molecular mobility, so that today we possess a fairly detailed picture of the torsional

[22] J. W. Ellis and J. Bath, *J. Am. Chem. Soc.*, **62**, 2859 (1940).

[23] J. W. Rowen, C. M. Hunt, and E. K. Plyler, *J. Research Natl. Bur. Standards*, **39**, 133 (1947).

[24] S. E. Darmon and G. B. B. M. Sutherland, *J. Am. Chem. Soc.*, **69**, 2074 (1947).

[25] R. B. Woodward and C. H. Schramm, *J. Am. Chem. Soc.*, **69**, 1551 (1947).

rigidity of single and double bonds and of the influence of substituents on it.

It appears to be advantageous to start with the discussion of a relatively simple case, namely, ethane, to pass gradually to more complex conditions and, finally, to discuss the behavior of long-chain substances in so far as this is now possible.

The purely empirical assumption of free rotation around the simple C—C, C—O, or C—N bond has received full confirmation by the quantum

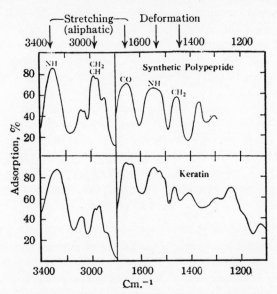

Fig. III-6.   Infrared absorption spectra of a synthetic polypeptide and keratin.[24]

theory of the covalent bond.   The present concept of such a bond, say the carbon-carbon covalent bond, is that the two valence electrons merge into a negative charge cloud, which surrounds the two bonded nuclei and has rotational symmetry with reference to the line joining them, *i.e.*, the axis of the bond.   Nothing prevents free rotation of the two atoms around this axis, any position taken up by them in the course of such rotation being equal in potential energy to any other.

However, conditions change if the three remaining valences of the two atoms are saturated by substituents such as hydrogen or fluorine atoms, as is the case in ethane or hexafluoroethane, because these substituents exert forces of attraction or repulsion on one another, the potential energy of which depends upon the azimuth of the two methyl or trifluoromethyl groups in the molecule. Quantum mechanics does not yet allow exact calculations of this interference, but does permit a more or less rough estimate of it.[26] Eyring[27] has first computed the potential energy of the two methyl groups in ethane as a function of their relative position and has summarized the results of his estimate in a diagram reproduced as Figure III-7, in which the potential energy of the ethane molecule is represented as a function of the azimuth, φ, of the methyl groups capable of rotating about the axis of the molecule. In the position $\varphi = 0$, represented diagrammatically in Figure III-8, all hydrogen atoms of the two methyl groups are

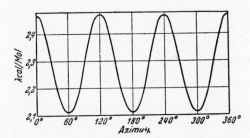

Fig. III-7. Internal molecular potential of ethane (energy in kilocalories per mole) as a function of the azimuth φ. Calculated by H. Eyring.

arranged directly above each other in such a way that two of them are always coplanar. All six H atoms lie in three planes, which pass through the molecule axis and make angles of 120° with each other. In this particular position the negative charge clouds of the H atoms interfere with each other to a noticeable extent and produce a maximum of potential energy. As they are negatively charged, a repulsion results between them making this configuration (azimuth = 0) one of maximum potential energy and hence unstable. The same is true for $\varphi = 120°$, 240°, and 360° as shown in Figure III-7. If one keeps one of the two methyl groups fixed and permits the other to rotate, the repulsion between the spheres of influence of the hydrogen atoms will cause it to turn away from the $\varphi = 0$ position until it has reached half the way to the next maximum ($\varphi = 120°$). There, at

[26] Compare, e.g., F. London and W. Heitler, Z. Physik, **44**, 455 (1927); L. Pauling, Phys. Rev., **40**, 891 (1932); J. C. Slater, Phys. Rev., **38**, 1109 (1931); E. Hückel, Z. Physik, **60**, 423 (1930); **70**, 204 (1931); **75**, 628 (1932). See also particularly R. S. Mulliken, Phys. Rev., **41**, 751 (1932); J. Chem. Phys., **7**, 14, 20, 121, 339, 353, 356, 364 (1939).

[27] H. Eyring, J. Am. Chem. Soc., **54**, 3191 (1932).

$\varphi = 60°$, is a minimum of potential energy caused by a comparatively favorable accommodation of the hydrogen atoms of the two methyl groups with respect to each other. Figure III-9 shows schematically that the hydrogen atoms are now staggered as one views them parallel to the axis of the molecule, and Figure III-9b again represents the photograph of a model, indicating that the covering spheres of the hydrogen atoms are now interfering with each other less than in the $\varphi = 0$ arrangement. As a consequence, the configurations with $\varphi = 60°$, $180°$ and $300°$ are minima in the potential energy curve, as shown in Figure III-7, and, therefore, correspond to configurations of the molecule, the thermal stability of which depends upon the depth of the minima between the separating maxima.

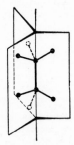

Fig. III-8. For $\varphi = 0$, the H atoms of both methyl groups lie directly over one another in the three planes drawn.

Fig. III-9. Ethane molecule for $\varphi = 60°$ seen parallel to the C—C bond. The methyl groups are rotated about one another and the H atoms are no longer directly above one another, but are staggered.

If the difference between the maxima and minima of the potential energy curve is large as compared with the average kinetic energy (kT per molecule or RT per mole), three stable isomers should exist, which, in the present case, would naturally be chemically indistinguishable because of the identity of the hydrogen atoms in the two methyl groups. This shows that under such conditions there is no free rotation in ethane, although the actual structure of the carbon-carbon bond itself permits it. However, there are the repulsive forces between the substituents which prevent the two methyl groups to rotate freely in respect to each other and favor the positions of minimum potential energy. On the other hand, if the height of the energy barriers between the minima in the molecule is comparable or smaller than kT, each collision possessing the average kinetic energy of the random thermal motion will be able to bring the methyl groups from one configuration to another and we shall have virtually free rotation. The only effect of the interaction of the substituents will now be that the velocity of rotation is not uniform but that the methyl groups will rotate around each other with periodically variable speed. No kind of isomerism is to be expected under these conditions.

It seemed first[28] as if heat capacity measurements would confirm Eyring's original value for depth of the minimum in Fig. III-7, which amounts to *ca.* 300 cal. per mole. This would have meant that there exists essentially free rotation about the carbon-carbon bond in ethane and consequently about the corresponding bonds in normal paraffin chains.

However, more recent investigations by Kistiakowsky,[29] Pitzer, and their collaborators[30] on the molecular spectra and heat capacities of C_2H_6 and C_2D_6, have shown that the general shape of the potential energy curve as given in Figure III-7 is correct, that it can be essentially represented by a function:

$$E = \tfrac{1}{2}E_0(1 - \cos 3\varphi)$$

but that E_0 is of the order of magnitude of 3000 cal. per mole instead of 300. This produces a noticeable hindrance of the free rotation about the carbon-carbon bond in ethane and indicates that at normal temperatures *torsional vibrations* around the axis of the molecule are carried out as the main motion and that there are only occasional jumps over the potential barrier. This high value of the energy barrier between adjacent minima in the ethane molecule has been explained by Lassettre[31] and is caused by a quadrupole moment interaction between the two methyl groups. The inhibition of free rotation in this case has nothing to do with the nature of the single carbon-carbon bond itself, but is caused by the interaction of the substituting hydrogen atom. This has recently been confirmed very clearly by the fact that in dimethyl ether, dimethyl sulfide, and dimethylacetylene the methyl groups do not hinder each other in their free mobility because they are farther apart and the covering spheres of the hydrogen atoms do not interfere noticeably with each other. On the other hand it has been found that the potential energy barrier which hinders the free rotation in hexafluoroethane is noticeably larger than in ethane, namely, about 5000 cal. per mole.

[28] A. Eucken *et al., Z. physik. Chem.,* **B20,** 184 (1933); **B40,** 307 (1938).

[29] G. B. Kistiakowsky and collaborators, quoted on p. 67.

[30] K. S. Pitzer, *J. Am. Chem. Soc.,* **70,** 2140 (1948).

[31] E. N. Lassettre and L. B. Dean, *J. Chem. Phys.,* **16,** 151, 553 (1948); **17,** 317 (1949).

We shall now pass to the discussion of (symmetrical) 1,2-dichloroethane, which has been recently investigated thoroughly by Bernstein[32] on purely geometrical grounds; there should exist three preferred configurations.

> The *"trans"* form in which the two Cl atoms lie in one plane but are on *opposite* sides of the axis of the molecule ($\varphi = 0°$).

> The *"cis"* form in which the two Cl atoms lie in one plane and are arranged on the *same* side of the axis of the molecule ($\varphi = 180°$).

> The "gauche" form in which the two Cl atoms are in two planes that form an angle of 120° with each other ($\varphi = 120°$).

Figure III-10 represents the potential energy of this molecule as a function of the azimuthal angle and shows that there is a deep minimum at the *trans* position ($\varphi = 0$) and two secondary minima in the two gauche positions ($\varphi = 120°$); these two rotational *isomers* are separated from each

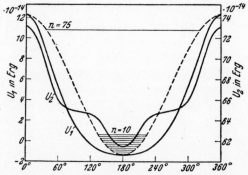

Fig. III-10. Internal molecular potential of symmetrical dichloroethane. Energy in ergs per molecule as a function of the azimuth φ. For the *cis*-position, $\varphi = 0$ and $360°$. For the *trans*-position, $\varphi = 180°$.

other by an energy barrier of about 2810 cal. per mole. Between the two gauche configurations rises a maximum of almost 9000 cal. per mole; the energy difference between the two isomers was found to be 1100 cal. per mole. This three minima potential energy curve can be represented by:

$$V = 0.733(1 - \cos \varphi) + 1.123(1 - \cos 3\varphi) +$$
$$0.197(1 - \cos \varphi)(1 - \cos 3\varphi) \text{ kcal. per mole}$$

Stuart[33] has carried out interesting calculations on a number of disubstituted benzene derivatives; he considers the various possible interactions

[32] H. J. Bernstein, *J. Chem. Phys.*, **17**, 256, 258, 262 (1949).
[33] H. A. Stuart, *Phys. Rev.*, **38**, 1372 (1931).

of the substituents and calculates the potential energy of the molecule; this is then compared with the deviations of the heats of combustion of these compounds from the additivity rule, with the result that considerable repulsion potentials are shown to exist in *ortho* compounds, which practically disappear in the *meta* and *para* derivatives.

The results are particularly interesting with the three xylenes, in which an internal potential energy of about 3000 cal. per mole is obtained from the difference in the experimental values for the heats of combustion of the *cis* and *trans* compounds, respectively. Translated to butane, this means that

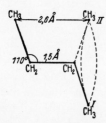

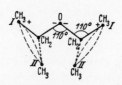

Fig. III-11. *Cis* (II) and *trans* (I) positions of normal butane (after H. A. Stuart).

Fig. III-12. Preferred position (I) of the diethyl ether molecules (after H. A. Stuart).

as in ethane and dichloroethane—the *cis* position (see Figure III-11) is relatively unstable, while the *trans* position is stabilized by the repulsion of the methyl groups by an energy minimum of 2000–3000 cal. per mole. The molecule is characterized by highly restricted free rotation, *i.e.*, vibrations of about 10^9 per second about the *trans*-position, with about 1000 jumps over the barrier per second.

Similar results have been obtained with ethers and ketones, which Stuart[34] has studied by measuring the Kerr constant and the degree of depolarization. In diethyl ether the preferred position is denoted by *I* in Figure III-12; around it torsional vibrations of large average amplitude (70°) take place; the same holds for diethyl ketone and for other ethers and ketones.

The Raman effect also affords interesting and important information on the question of free rotation. According to Kohlrausch,[35] it is to be expected that a continuum of configurations with equal energies should give rise to a diffuse band in the Raman spectrum and that inhibited rotation

[34] Compare, *e.g.*, H. A. Stuart, *Molekülstruktur*, Springer. Berlin, 1934, pp. 92 et seq.
[35] K. W. F. Kohlrausch, *Der Smekal-Raman-Effekt*; *Ergänzungsband*, Berlin, 1938; p. 155 and pp. 169 et seq.

should lead to a broadening of the Raman lines. Actually, diffuse Raman lines have been observed in several instances, where a high degree of internal mobility of the investigated molecule should be expected. On the other hand, a very thorough investigation of numerous monochloro paraffins in the liquid state has produced results which are not entirely in harmony with the existence of stable *trans* positions and vibrations about them. Thus it has been observed that other symmetrical arrangements see n to be preferred in addition to the planar *trans* configuration of normal paraffin chains, particularly in larger molecules such as $C_{10}H_{21}Cl$ and the like. If we consider that these molecules, especially in the liquid phase, are subject to strong interaction and tend to form molecular aggregates, we should refrain at the outset from comparison with results obtained in the gaseous state or in dilute solutions. It will be convenient to consider these results later in the discussion of the liquid state.

As we are particularly concerned with the study of chain molecules, the following experiments should be mentioned, which, by the aid of electron diffraction and dipole moment measurement, have contributed important information on the internal flexibility of such molecules.

Wierl[36] has investigated, by means of electron diffraction, the vapors of normal hydrocarbons up to hexane and has found only two characteristic atomic distances (1.5 and 2.5 Å.). This means that the chains possess sufficiently high mobility—not necessarily completely free rotation—that all larger distances capable of occurring between more widely separated carbon atoms are not sharp and, therefore, do not appear in the diagram. Measurements on the vapor of 1,5-dichloropentane also point to a considerable flexibility of the paraffin chain. If the chain of this molecule were rigid, the two chlorine atoms at the ends would have a well-defined distance of about 7 Å. from one another, which, because of the high scattering power of chlorine, should give rise to a distinct diffraction ring in the neighborhood of the primary beam. In spite of a careful search, however, such a ring could not be found. More recent studies of Pauling and Brockway[37,38] on a whole series of chlorinated and brominated paraffins up to ten carbon atoms have confirmed these findings and have placed the idea of a certain internal mobility in normal paraffin chains on a sound experimental basis.

Considering molecules of this type, we should not think in terms of mod-

---

[36] R. Wierl, *Ann. Physik*, **8**, 521 (1931); **13**, 453 (1932); compare also H. Mark and R. Wierl, *Die experimentellen und theoretischen Grundlagen der Elektronenbeugung*, Steinkopff, Leipzig, 1933; and H. de Lazlo, *Nature*, **131**, 803 (1933).

[37] L. Pauling and L. O. Brockway, *J. Chem. Phys.*, **2**, 8671 (1934).

[38] L. Pauling and L. O. Brockway, *J. Am. Chem. Soc.*, **57**, 2684, 2693 (1935).

els made of wooden spheres connected by wire rods which have so long been used for spatial demonstration of problems in stereochemistry. They do demonstrate very well symmetry relationships and possible isomerisms, but give an inaccurate picture of the space requirements and of the mutual hindrance caused by adjacent atoms in a molecule. Actual conditions are much better illustrated by wooden models as introduced by Stuart and as constructed according to Fischer, Hirschfelder, and Taylor and marketed by the Fisher Scientific Company, which give within the limits of possibility a fairly good representation of the true shape of organic molecules. A long, unsubstituted paraffin chain has about the shape, internal mobility, and softness of a large caterpillar, which with limitations as to sharp bends and twists, must be regarded in its entirety as a fairly flexible structure— very different in its behavior from a pencil of the same length and diameter.

A very instructive study of the torsional mobility of long-chain paraffins has been reported by Müller.[39] He investigated the dielectric behavior of two diketones, $C_{10}H_{18}O_2$ and $C_{11}H_{20}O_2$, in the neighborhood of their melting points. The structure of these compounds is such that the two carbonyl groups point in the same direction in one case, but in the opposite direction in the other. In both cases they are separated by a chain of 6 or 7 methylene groups. Mueller found that the two compounds show very different electrical properties in the crystalline state (as to be expected from their structure if they are rigid), but are indistinguishable above their melting points. He concludes from this fact that the hydrocarbon chain, which links the two carbonyl groups, exhibits a high degree of torsional flexibility.

The same conclusion was reached on the basis of dielectric measurements with other long-chain molecules.

Tiganik and Fuchs[40] have derived a formula which permits the computation of the total moment of a molecule having two individual dipoles with the moments, μ_1 and μ_2, which are able to rotate freely about certain axes fixed in space. By the application of this formula to substituted benzenes it is possible to decide whether the rotation of the polar groups or parts of them is free or inhibited. In *meta* and *para* derivatives, such as the chlorophenols, bromophenols, nitrophenols, etc., there occurs essentially free rotation of the OH dipole about the C—O bond, while in the corresponding

[39] A. Müller, *Proc. Roy. Soc. London*, **A174**, 137 (1940); D. R. Pelmore, *ibid.*, **A172**, 502 (1939); also A. Turkevitch and J. Y. Beach, *J. Am. Chem. Soc.*, **61**, 303, 3127 (1939); B. L. Crawford and W. W. Rice, *J. Chem. Phys.*, **7**, 437 (1939); **8**, 273 (1940); E. Gorin, J. Walter, and H. Eyring, *J. Am. Chem. Soc.*, **61**, 1876 (1939).

[40] R. Tiganik, *Z. physik. Chem.*, **B14**, 135 (1931). Cf. also W. Kuhn, *Kolloid-Z.*, **68**, 2 (1934); L. Onsager, *J. Am. Chem. Soc.*, **58**, 1486 (1936).

ortho derivatives the mutual interaction of the substituents is so considerable that the rotation is strongly inhibited. There is experimental evidence to show that rotation can be considered to be practically free if the energy barriers do not exceed 10 T cal./mole; at higher values inhibited rotation is to be expected which is perceptible from the fact that the dependence of the electric moment on temperature deviates from a straight line. Dipoles with a moment of the order of one to two debyes (OH, CCl, NH, etc.) interfere with one another appreciably only if they are separated in the molecule by a distance not greater than 3 Å. This agrees with the fact that *meta* and *para* substituents have practically no effect on each other.

The carboxyl group is characterized by strong interaction between its two constituent groups, the CO and OH dipoles. Measurements of Zahn[41] show that its actual moment is about 1.51 debyes, which suggests, according to Stuart, that the group assumes essentially the configuration

$$
\begin{array}{ccc}
\text{O} & & \text{H} \\
\diagdown\!\!\!= & & / \\
 & \text{C}-\text{O} & \\
/ & & \\
\text{R} & &
\end{array}
$$

and carries out slow vibrations about it; the other position:

$$
\begin{array}{ccc}
\text{O} & & \\
\diagdown\!\!\!= & & \\
 & \text{C}-\text{O} & \\
/ & & \diagdown \\
\text{R} & & \text{H}
\end{array}
$$

would give a moment of 3.9 debyes, whereas for free rotation of the OH dipole about the C—O bond, a moment of 3.5 debyes is calculated. Neither in formic acid nor in other fatty acids could dependence of the moment upon temperature be found.

Table III-14 gives some informative data of Zahn, Greene, and Williams[42] on the internal mobility of simple ethane derivatives. In all cases there is a significant dependence of the moment upon temperature, which means that around the *trans* position, which has no electric moment, vibrations are executed which increase with rising temperature. In no instance, however, is a value of the total moment attained which could correspond to free rotation.

Of special interest for the behavior of long-chain molecules and consequently for the properties of polymers are such cases as first discussed by

[41] C. T. Zahn, *Phys. Rev.*, **37**, 1516 (1931); *Physik. Z.*, **33**, 400 (1932).
[42] E. W. Greene and J. W. Williams, *Phys. Rev.*, **42**, 119 (1932).

TABLE III-14

EFFECT OF TEMPERATURE ON MOMENTS OF SEVERAL ETHANE DERIVATIVES

Substance	Formula	T, °K.	$\mu \times 10^{18}$ (observed)	$\mu \times 10^{18}$ calc. for free rotation
Dichloroethane........	ClH_2C-CH_2Cl	305–554	1.12–1.54	2.54
		298–588	1.27–1.57	
Dibromoethane.......	BrH_2C-CH_2Br	339–436	0.94–1.10	2.54
		347–449	0.97–1.04	
Chlorobromoethane....	BrH_2C-CH_2Cl	339–436	1.09–1.28	2.54
Diacetyl[a].............	OCH_3C-CCH_3O	329–504	1.25–1.48	3.20
Chloroacetone[a]........	ClH_2C-CCH_3O	336–454	2.17–2.24	3.0

[a] The structures are:

$$
\begin{array}{ccc}
CH_3 & & O \\
\diagdown & & \diagup \\
 & C-C & \\
\diagup & & \diagdown \\
O & & CH_3
\end{array}
\qquad
\begin{array}{ccc}
CH_3 & & Cl \\
\diagdown & & \diagup \\
 & C-C-H & \\
\diagup & & \diagdown \\
O & & H
\end{array}
$$

Diacetyl   Chloroacetone

Ebert[43] and more accurately investigated later by Smyth and Walls,[44] Eyring,[45] Devoto,[46] and W. Kuhn[47] in which a long chain molecule carries either a dipole or a free charge at each end, so that because of the length and the partial mobility of the individual members of the chain the influence of the terminal groups upon one another is negligible.[48]

The two moments then behave as if they were connected by a long, flexible thread, that is, they are limited in their motions only by the maximum length of the chain. If the two moments are equal and have the magnitude μ, the total moment of the molecule is given by:

$$\mu_{total} = \mu \sqrt{2}$$

Measurements of Smyth and Walls with normal paraffins carrying two equal dipoles at their ends have shown in fact that, within the limits of error of the method, the total moment was $\sqrt{2}$ times the moment of the individual dipole at each end of the chain (Table III-15). These molecules are clearly not rigid, planar zig-zag chains in the dissolved or gaseous state, but exhibit a certain degree of internal mobility.

[43] L. Ebert, in *Leipziger Vorträge*, Hirzel. Leipzig, 1929, p. 47.
[44] C. P. Smyth and W. S. Walls, *J. Am. Chem. Soc.*, **53**, 527, 2115 (1931).
[45] H. Eyring, *Phys. Rev.*, **39**, 746 (1932).
[46] G. Devoto, *Z. Elektrochem.*, **40**, 490 (1934).
[47] *E.g.*, W. Kuhn, *Kolloid-Z.*, **68**, 2 (1934).
[48] Compare also E. Guth and H. Mark, *Monatsh.*, **65**, 93 (1934).

TABLE III-15

MOMENTS OF SEVERAL LONG CHAIN MOLECULES

Substance	Formula	Total moment, $\mu \times 10^{18}$	Group moment, $\mu \times 10^{18}$
Decamethylene glycol............	$HO \cdot CH_2 \cdot (CH_2)_8 \cdot CH_2 \cdot OH$	2.5	1.67
Decamethylene bromide..........	$Br \cdot CH_2 \cdot (CH_2)_8 \cdot CH_2 \cdot Br$	2.4	1.8
Sebacic acid diethyl ester.........	$H_5C_2OOC \cdot (CH_2)_8 \cdot COOC_2H_5$	2.49	—
Hexadecamethylene dicarboxylic acid diethyl ester..............	$COOC_2H_5(CH_2)_{16}COOC_2H_5$	2.49	—

Observations and measurements by Bridgman[49] on omega-hydroxy-carboxylic acids and their polycondensation products have added another fact indicating the tendency of chainlike molecules to fold and curl to a certain extent. By self-esterification of ω-hydroxydecanoic acid, long chains of molecular weight between 900 and 14,000 were obtained and careful measurements of refraction and polarization were made on this material in dilute benzene solution over a wide range of frequencies. These molecules contain dipolar groups regularly spaced along the molecular chain, in contrast to the type of molecules which have dipoles only at the ends. The behavior of these molecules in an alternating electrical field can best be explained by considering that the electrical unit orienting in the applied field is but a small portion of the entire molecule. This type of molecule shows a definite contribution to the polarization due to the orientation of dipoles, but shows no variation of dielectric constant with frequency in the region where dispersion should occur if the entire molecule were being oriented by the field. On the other hand, dispersion of dielectric constant does occur in frequency regions corresponding to local motions of chain

TABLE III-16

DIPOLE MOMENTS OF CONDENSATION PRODUCTS OF
ω-HYDROXYDECANOIC ACID

Molecular weight	n (monomer units)	$\mu \times 10^{18}$ calc.	$\mu \times 10^{18}$ observed
13,900	82	16.4	19.0
9,070	53	13.3	15.7
7,780	46	12.4	12.4
4,140	24	9.1	10.2
2,120	12	6.6	6.7
905	5	4.2	5.0

[49] W. B. Bridgman, *J. Am. Chem. Soc.*, **60**, 530 (1938).

segments. Furthermore the dipole moments of the molecules as a whole were found to be proportional to the *square root* of the molecular weight (Table III-16). This can result only if the molecular chains are flexible and randomly kinked, so that the dipoles are more or less randomly oriented to one another. The vector addition of randomly oriented vectors is a classical problem known as Rayleigh's problem of random flights and was first applied to the dipole moment of long chain molecules by Eyring. The same problem applied to the calculation of the end-to-end length of long chain molecules will be discussed in section G of this chapter.

Experiments of Wyman and McMeekin[50] on polypeptides of glycine up to heptaglycine are also in agreement with the above. The increase in dielectric constant of water in the presence of dissolved polypeptides was determined and it was considered that for flexible chains the increase should be proportional to the increase in molecular weight. This held with reasonable accuracy for the higher members of the series, indicating that these chains do not behave like rigid rods but much rather like flexible threads.

F. THE DOUBLE BOND AND *cis-trans* ISOMERISM

At present, the best quantum mechanical concept of the aliphatic double bond is[51,52] that it is caused by *four valence electrons* which are shared by the two bonded atoms. Two of them form a charge cloud having rotational symmetry around the axis of the bond, while the two others form a charge cloud of planar symmetry, the plane of which is so placed relative to the nuclear framework that the two residual valences at each carbon atom are perpendicular to it (see Figure III-13). By this evidence, quantum mechanics confirms and interprets the concept originated by organic chemists many years ago regarding the spatial structure of the aliphatic double bond and the deductions possible from it.

The absence of axial symmetry has the consequence that the two carbon atoms and their substituents are now no longer free to rotate about the bond, but are supposed to form a system of considerable rigidity. The

[50] J. Wyman, *J. Am. Chem. Soc.*, **58**, 1482 (1936); **60**, 328 (1938); *J. Phys. Chem.*, **43**, 143 (1939). Cf. also W. B. Bridgman and J. W. Williams, *J. Am. Chem. Soc.*, **59**, 1579 (1937); J. H. van Vleck, *J. Chem. Phys.*, **5**, 556 (1937); J. Wyman and McMeekin, *J. Am. Chem. Soc.*, **55**, 908 (1933); J. G. Kirkwood, *Chem. Rev.*, **24**, 233 (1939).

[51] Compare E. Hückel, *Z. Physik*, **60**, 43 (1930); R. S. Mulliken, *J. Chem. Phys.*, **7**, 14, 20, 121, 339, 353, 356, 364 (1939); L. Pauling, *Phys. Rev.*, **40**, 891 (1932); J. C. Slater, *Phys. Rev.*, **38**, 1109 (1931).

[52] E. Teller and K. Weigert, *Nachr. Ges. Wiss. Göttingen*, **2**, 218 (1933).

reason is that, to effect any changes in the configuration as shown in Figure III-13, portions of the negative charge clouds corresponding to the double bond must be brought closer together, which is possible only by performing work against their mutual repulsion and results in an increase in potential energy of the molecule.

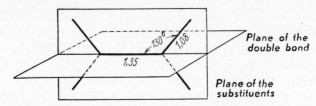

Fig. III-13.   Geometric arrangement of valences in the double C=C bond.

The effect of temperature on the heat capacity of ethylene reveals the existence of a torsional vibration of fairly high frequency (750 cm.$^{-1} \approx 10^{13}$ per sec.), indicating that this molecule must be considered as a one-dimensional oscillator of considerable rigidity.   On this depends the stability of the two isomers and the possibility of isolating them by the methods of organic chemistry.

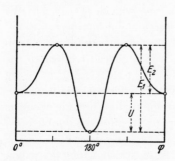

Fig. III-14.   Schematic curve of the internal molecular potential in the case of a *cis-trans* isomerism.   In the *trans* position, $\varphi = 180°$. In the *cis* positions, $\varphi = 0$ and $360°$.

The potential energy curve characteristic of an aliphatic double bond is shown in Figure III-14.   There are two distinct minima of potential energy, which represent stable configurations, the *cis* position ($\varphi = 0°$) and the *trans* position ($\varphi = 180°$).   Due to unequal distances between the substituents, they are not of equal depth; between them rises an energy barrier guaranteeing their stability, and arising from the superposition of double bond rigidity and the interaction of the substituents.

The energy difference between the minima of the two troughs is the heat of conversion of the two modifications into one another; it is responsible for the proportion of the isomers in an equilibrium mixture and can be calculated from the effect of temperature on this equilibrium. It has been determined experimentally for the dichloroethylenes by Ebert and Büll.[53] At about 300°C. the *cis* form is the more stable configuration and contains about 63% of all molecules, the energy difference being about 500 cal. per mole.

Stuart has attempted to compute the interaction between the two CCl dipoles in the two forms and has found that the *cis* form should be preferred; the numerical value of 1150 cal. per mole that he obtained is somewhat larger than that given by experiment.

In other cases—maleic and fumaric acids, cinnamic acid, etc.—the *trans* form is probably more stable due to free rotation within the CH_2COOH groups.

The energy differences, E_1 and E_2, between the minima of the two potential troughs and the peak of the energy barrier separating them are the activation energies for the transition from *cis* to *trans* and from *trans* to *cis*. They determine the thermal stability of the two forms and can be calculated from the effect of temperature on the rate of isomerization. This has been done for a number of systems by Kistiakowsky and his co-workers,[54] with the results that the activation energies for the conversion from the *cis* to the *trans* form are around 40,000 kcal. per mole if aromatic systems such as stilbene or cinnamic derivatives are involved. Eyring[55] has recently given a detailed analysis of the electronic states which are involved in a rotation about the double bond and has pointed out that two types of isomerization should be expected, one having an activation energy around 25,000 and one requiring about 40,000 cal. per mole. This appears to be in remarkable agreement with the experimental findings.

G. INTERNAL MOLECULAR DYNAMICS AND STATISTICS

The quantum mechanical treatment of simple diatomic molecules is fairly straightforward and consequential. One introduces an appropriate expression for the potential energy in the Schroedinger equation and arrives with it at the stationary states of the molecule and at the possible transitions between these states. They lead to the frequencies of the various

[53] F. Ebert and R. Büll, *Z. physik. Chem.*, **A152,** 451 (1931). Compare also R. J. Corruccini and E. C. Gilbert, *J. Am. Chem. Soc.*, **61,** 2925 (1939).

[54] M. Nelles and G. B. Kistiakowsky, *J. Am. Chem. Soc.*, **54,** 2208 (1932); G. B. Kistiakowsky and W. R. Smith, *ibid.*, **56,** 638 (1934); **57,** 269 (1935); **58,** 766, 2428 (1936).

[55] J. L. Magee, W. Shand, Jr., and H. Eyring, *J. Am. Chem. Soc.*, **63,** 677 (1941).

vibrations which the molecule carries out and provide a fairly complete
description of the dynamics of the system.   As one proceeds to more complicated molecules, containing three, four, or more atoms, it becomes necessary to apply approximations and simplifications which become more and
more dubious as the complexity of the molecule increases and therefore this
dynamic treatment of molecules can only be extended to relatively simple
organic molecules.   It refers essentially to rapid vibrations and rotations of
individual atoms or atomic groups which are accompanied by noticeable
changes of the potential energy of the molecule.

There exist, however, other internal motions, particularly in very large
and flexible molecules, which do not arise from the action of intramolecular
forces but which are such that, during their execution, the potential energy
of the whole molecule remains virtually constant.   These motions are
caused by the thermal energy of the individual parts of a macromolecule
and can best be compared to the random motion of the molecules in a per-

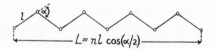

Fig. III-15.   Extended form of a normal paraffin chain.

fect gas or to the diffusional movements of solute molecules in a dilute solution.   It is natural, therefore, in studying this kind of internal molecular
movements to employ statistical methods that have proved successful in
the treatment of gases, liquids, and solutions.

In order to show the tendency of this approach, let us first discuss the
conditions in a long-chain molecule of simple paraffinic character as represented in Figure III-15.   For the purpose of a first approximation it is
sufficient to assume that geometrically different configurations exist in
which the whole molecule has essentially the same potential energy and
that these configurations can be converted into each other by simple rotations around the various single bonds of the chain.   These configurations
are evidently separated from each other by certain energy barriers, but they
will frequently be materialized as long as these barriers are low enough to
permit not too rare transitions from one arrangement into the other within
a period which is short as compared with the time of the experiment.   By
twisting and distorting the individual single bonds in the backbone chain
about comparatively small angles, a macromolecule can be brought into a
large number of configurations, which, in general, will have very odd and
bizarre shapes.   Given the direction of one terminal carbon-carbon bond,

for example, that of the adjacent bond will be limited by the interaction of the hydrogen atoms, to the neighborhood of essentially three directions as explained in section E, and as indicated in Figure III-7. The possible directions of the next bond along the chain are equally restricted in regard to the second bond but less so in respect to the first, there being more different orientations of essentially equal potential energy possible for it; as one passes on to the fourth and fifth bonds along the chain, the specific position of the terminal bond will have less and less influence on their direction. As long as it is not necessary to consider in detail the position of each individual bond, it will be permissible to treat the macromolecule as a chain in which each link can rotate about its axis, and to apply the conventional methods of statistics to count the number of configurations which are compatible with certain external conditions such as a prescribed distance between the two ends of the chain, a maximum extension of the molecule in a given direction, and so on.

The application of statistical methods in the treatment of long chain molecules and the explanation of their mechanical properties has been introduced by Eyring,[56] Guth and Mark,[57] and Kuhn,[58] after Wöhlisch,[59] Meyer,[60] and their collaborators had already shown that there was good experimental evidence to consider thermal motion as the significant cause for the contraction of muscle fibers and of stretched rubbery polymers. This so-called *kinetic theory* of *rubber elasticity* has recently been expanded by contributions of many authors and it is only fair to say that it represents, today, a well-founded part of the knowledge of the mechanical behavior of macromolecules (see Chapter X).[61]

The *fully extended* form of a paraffin chain represented in Figure III-15 is only *one* of many forms having equal energy, for we can perform con-

[56] H. Eyring, *Phys. Rev.*, **39**, 746 (1932).

[57] E. Guth and H. Mark, *Monatsh.*, **65**, 93 (1934); compare also H. Mark, *IX. Congr. Chim. Madrid*, **5**, 197 (1934).

[58] W. Kuhn, *Kolloid-Z.*, **68**, 2 (1934).

[59] E. Wöhlisch and R. de Rochemont, *Z. Biol.*, **85**, 406 (1927).

[60] K. H. Meyer, G. v. Susich, and E. Valkó, *Kolloid-Z.*, **59**, 208 (1932); H. Mark and E. Valkó, *Kautschuk*, **6**, 210 (1930).

[61] W. Kuhn, *Kolloid-Z.*, **76**, 258 (1936); **87**, 3 (1939); W. and H. Kuhn, *Helv. Chim. Acta*, **26**, 1934 (1943); **29**, 830 (1946); T. Alfrey and H. Mark, *Rubber Chem. Tech.*, **15**, 462 (1942); F. T. Wall, *J. Chem. Phys.*, **10**, 132, 485 (1942); **11**, 67, 527 (1943); L. R. G. Treloar, *Trans. Faraday Soc.*, **38**, 293 (1942); **40**, 109 (1944); P. J. Flory and J. Rehner, Jr., *J. Chem. Phys.*, **11**, 512 (1943); H. M. James and E. Guth, *J. Chem. Phys.*, **11**, 455 (1943); **15**, 669 (1947); compare also a comprehensive article of E. Guth, H. M. James, and H. Mark in H. Mark and G. S. Whitby, *Advances in Colloid Science*, Vol. II, Interscience, New York, 1946.

siderable rotations about any one of the n single carbon-carbon bonds—while preserving the tetrahedral angle—without having to perform any work. Since the chain in gas or in solution (*i.e.*, in the free state) is in thermal equilibrium with its surroundings and is subject to random impacts from all directions, it will assume in course of time—in accordance with the fundamental laws of thermodynamics—all configurations of equal potential energy and will actually perform all motions compatible with its flexibility just as the molecules of an ideal gas subjected to mutual thermal impacts will occupy any space made available to them.

Hence it is evident that it is quite meaningless to speak of a definite shape of such a chain if, by that, we mean a configuration that remains temporarily fixed over a long period. It would be just as inappropriate to speak of a fixed location of an individual molecule in a gas. In fact, these are always moving and, equally, the chain is in constant, sinuous motion. In all statistical treatments of gases we abandon any attempt to assign definite states to the individual molecules, but rather consider all these "micro-states" belonging to a given "macro-state" capable of being defined and reproducibly measured by macroscopic parameters. In a perfect gas, volume can be chosen as one of these parameters; in a long-chain molecule with a certain degree of internal free rotation there are several possibilities for choice; with regard to the later application of these considerations to the elasticity and viscosity of long-chain substances, we shall take either the distance between the two ends or the distance of the furthest point of the randomly coiled chain from one end point as a parameter which characterizes a definite macrostate.

In order to start with the simplest possible conditions, we shall consider an isolated unbranched hydrocarbon chain with n links, *i.e.*, with $(n + 1)$ carbon atoms (see Fig. III-15), where n is a number between 100 and 10,000. This model is actually a considerable simplification as compared with natural or synthetic rubbers because double bonds in the chain and substituents along the chain are absent, but it serves for the immediate study of the principal properties of such a system. Later on we shall have to remember that the free rotation assumed for such a chain does not actually exist and that different chains in a macroscopic specimen impede one another by intermolecular forces.

According to the information given in Chapter I, the individual carbon-carbon bonds are 1.54 Å. long and the angle, β, between the valences is about 109°.* If we extend the chain completely it assumes the shape illustrated in Figure III-15; its length is given by:

* The angle β discussed here is the supplement of the angle α in Figure III-15.

$$L(\text{extended}) = nl \cos (\alpha/2) \qquad\qquad (\text{III.6})$$

This extended length of the chain, as is immediately evident from the illustration, can be attained only under *one* condition, namely, that all the bonds are arranged in the same plane and form a zig-zag strip.

If, however, we permit the ends of the chain to be at some other distance apart, *e.g.*, a distance r, where $r < L$, this can be effected in a number of different ways because of the internal mobility of the chain. Obviously, we can arrange the individual links in many different ways and still have the two terminal carbon atoms separated by the given distance, r.

If we imagine a large number—say 1000—of such chains scattered at random on the floor, measure for each of them the distance between the ends and count the various configurations, it will be rather unlikely that the maximum possible distance, L, between the end will be found frequently, since it can be obtained only in one single way; any shorter distance can be obtained by a number of configurations and will, consequently, be found more frequently in actual conditions.

To each distance r between the ends of the chain there belongs a definite number of possibilities of materialization, which can be computed by the laws of probability. If l denotes the length of a single bond, n the number of links, and α, the supplement of the valence angle as shown in Figure III-15, and if we assume free rotation, then the probability that the ends of such a chain will be separated by the distance r, is given by:

$$W(r)\, dr = (4b^3/\pi^{1/2}) r^2 e^{-b^2 r^2}\, dr \qquad\qquad (\text{III.7})$$

where: $\qquad\qquad 1/b^2 = {}^2/_3\, nl^2 [(1 + \cos \alpha)/(1 - \cos \alpha)]$

It is easily shown from equation (III.7) that the most probable distance λ between the two chains ends is equal to $(1/b)$. The root mean square distance between the chain ends, R_0, which is the quantity most frequently used to characterize the dimensions of a randomly kinked chain, is:

$$R_0 = \sqrt{3/2}\, (1/b) = \sqrt{3/2}\, \lambda \qquad\qquad (\text{III.8})$$

If one considers flexible chains of a somewhat more complicated nature than a simple paraffin chain, such as actually occur in the various natural and synthetic rubbers, equations (III.7) and (III.8) are still valid except that b has a somewhat different value. Since R_0 is simply related to b by equation (III.8) it will suffice to show in Table III-17 the values of R_0 and also the maximum lengths for certain representative flexible chains. It should be noted that in all cases R_0 is proportional to $\sqrt{n}$ and the maximum length is proportional to n.

TABLE III-17

VALUES OF R_0 AND MAXIMUM LENGTHS FOR VARIOUS POLYMER CHAINS[a]

Type of polymer chain	R_0	Maximum length
Freely rotating chain of n links with fixed angle α between successive links (l = length of link)	$l[(1 + \cos \alpha)/(1 - \cos \alpha)]^{1/2}\sqrt{n}$	nl cos ($\alpha/2$)
Freely rotating chain of n links with no fixed angle between successive links	$l\sqrt{n}$	nl
Chain of n links with fixed angle α between successive links and partially restricted rotation (the parameter a is defined in reference c below)	$l[(1 + \cos \alpha)/(1 - \cos \alpha)]^{1/2} \cdot [(1 + a)/(1 - a)]^{1/2}\sqrt{n}$	nl cos ($\alpha/2$)
Paraffin chain, l = 1.54 Å., α = 70.5°	$2.18\sqrt{n}$ (Å.)	$1.21n$ (Å.)
Natural rubber chain (*cis*-polyisoprene)	$2.01\sqrt{n}$ (Å.)	$1.14n$ (Å.)
Gutta-percha chain (*trans*-polyisoprene)	$2.90\sqrt{n}$ (Å.)	$1.27n$ (Å.)

[a] H. Eyring, *Phys. Rev.*, **39**, 746 (1932); F. T. Wall, *J. Chem. Phys.*, **11**, 67 (1943); H. Benoit and C. Sadron, *J. Polymer Sci.*, **4**, 473 (1949).

For n = 30, $W(r)dr$ is shown as a function of r in Figure III-16. Like the well-known Maxwell-Boltzmann distribution curve, it is asym-

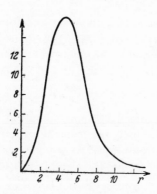

Fig. III-16. Distribution function for n = 30. Ordinate is $W(r)dr$.

metrical and has a considerable breadth because of the comparatively small number of statistically independent elements. The result is that we cannot regard the most probable value as the only one likely to be present, as we would in the ordinary statistical treatment of a gas.   Rather, we must also consider neighboring values and attach much greater significance to fluctuation phenomena than in gas statistics.

The above considerations invite the assumption that a chain in thermodynamic equilibrium with its surroundings—and subject to thermal impacts from all sides—always assumes that state which corresponds to the greatest number of possibilities for realization.   This is not more than the application of the Boltzmann principle to a single macromolecule and will meet with no serious objections as long as there are sufficient independent elements present for statistical treatment.   It has just been mentioned that the situation is not as favorable as the one existing in the statistics of gases, in which the number of independent systems in one mole is of the order of 10^{23}; a chain of 3000 to 4000 links will consist only of about 500 to 600 strictly independent elements because, after about seven or eight links, the influence of the first link will certainly have become so negligible that the ninth link may be regarded, practically, as the beginning of a new statistical chain element.

With these limitations, we may now, according to Boltzmann, ascribe to an isolated chain molecule an entropy:

$$s = k \ln W \qquad\qquad (III.9)$$

and try to derive its various properties from it.   It is obvious that such a chain will, of itself, change only to a state of higher entropy, *i.e.*, of greater probability, and that work must be performed to put it into a state of lesser probability.   If, therefore, we are dealing with a chain whose ends are separated by r and wish to extend it to the maximum length $L = r_{max.}$, we must perform an amount of work, A, corresponding to the entropy difference $s_L - s_r$.   This expenditure of work results in a heating of the chain on rapid extension by an amount:

$$A = T[s_r - s_L] = kT[\ln W(r) - \ln W(r_{max.})] \qquad (III.10)$$

This corresponds exactly to work done on an ideal gas on isothermal compression, during which there is an entropy loss because space previously accessible to the gas is now no longer available.   The decrease in volume reduces the number of possible configurations and hence the probability of the system.

The pressure p of a gas is exerted by random molecular impacts against the walls, which seek to enlarge the volume available to the gas and consequently to increase the number of configurational possibilities, which means an increase in entropy. Exactly in the same way the retractive force tending to shorten an extended macromolecule is caused by the random thermal motion of the individual links because the shorter length has more configurational possibilities:

$$p = +(\partial s/\partial V)_T T$$
$$Z = -(\partial s/\partial r)_T T \tag{III.11}$$

In ideal gases the internal energy E is independent of volume; consequently, in a rubber, a region may be defined as "ideal" in which the internal energy is independent of length. Experiments have shown that in slightly vulcanized elastomers the internal energy is, in fact, but little dependent upon elongation. In real gases and in rubber samples which do not conform with these special conditions, the properties differ, and, because of intermolecular forces, the internal energy becomes dependent upon volume or upon elongation.

We shall now attempt to establish an equation of state for an isolated macromolecule by analogy with an ideal gas. We start with equation (III.11); introduce $k \ln W$ for s; substitute for W; and with the aid of (III.7) we obtain:

$$Z = 6kT(1/nl^2)[(1 - \cos \alpha)/(1 + \cos \alpha)]\Delta L \tag{III.12}$$

$$\Delta L = \text{elongation of the chain}$$

$$Z = \text{force}$$

just as one gets for a molecule of an ideal gas the relation:

$$p = kT/V$$

Therefore we seem to be justified in interpreting equation (III.12) as the equation of state of an ideal rubbery molecule; it combines the tension with the elongation and represents the stress–strain curve of a single macromolecule.

Experimentally, however, one always deals with a macroscopic piece of material which is large enough to be handled, and we must therefore consider a volume element of rubber instead of a single chain. See Chapter X.

The kinetic treatment of long-chain molecules also permits a quantitative account of other important properties, such as melting point, solubility, swelling, etc., and it may be worth while to refer here briefly to the treatment[62] of the melting point of long-chain compounds.

[62] Compare H. Mark, *J. Applied Phys.*, **12**, 41 (1941); W. E. Garner, K. Van Bibber, and A. M. King, *J. Chem. Soc.*, **1931**, 1533; M. L. Huggins, *J. Phys. Chem.*, **43**, 1083 (1939).

Thermodynamics show that the temperature of fusion of a crystallized substance is given by:

$$T_f = \Delta H / \Delta S \qquad \text{(III.13)}$$

where ΔH represents all energy and ΔS all entropy changes which are involved during the transition from the solid into the liquid phase.

In long-chain molecules ΔH can generally be expressed by:

$$\Delta H = q_0 + nq \qquad \text{(III.14)}$$

where q_0 accounts for the influence of the end groups, while q is the increment of the heat of crystallization per elementary unit of the chain, n being the number of links. According to Garner and King the values of q are constant for a given homologous series and range between 610 cal. per methylene group (in the vertical forms of even hydrocarbons) and 1080 cal. per methylene group (in the tilted forms of even methyl esters of fatty acids). If n exceeds twenty, the influence of the end groups can be neglected without committing too great a mistake. For such long chains we may put:

$$\Delta H = nq$$

This would mean that, if constant entropy were involved, the melting point of long-chain compounds should increase with the chain length and should be proportional to the molar cohesion q of the elementary unit. However, this is only true in a limited range of n (according to Garner and King, if n is about between 10 and 30), while for longer chains the melting points tend to approach a convergence temperature. Careful experiments and calculations of Garner and King and recently of Hibbert and Lowell have shown that this convergence temperature lies in the range of between 380 and 410°K.

Taking into account the statistical theory of long-chain molecules, the following explanation may be suggested for this behavior.

The entropy of fusion of long-chain molecules will obviously have the form:

$$\Delta S = s_0 + s(n) \qquad \text{(III.15)}$$

where s_0 represents the entropy gain caused by the fact that the center of gravity of the molecules is set free and, instead of vibrating around a fixed equilibrium position in the solid state, carries out a Brownian movement in the liquid phase. This entropy gain will be, in first approximation, independent of n. The term $s(n)$, on the other hand, represents the entropy gain due to the fact that certain internal vibrations and rotations which were frozen-in in the crystal are activated in the melt. In the crystalline form, paraffin hydrocarbons may be assumed to exist in essentially one configuration, the extended planar zig-zag. On the other hand the total number of possible configurations of a long hydrocarbon chain of n links is 3^{n-2}. If these were all equally available in the liquid state, the configurational entropy of fusion, $s(n)$, for sufficiently long chains would be $nR \ln 3$. Actually the entropy of fusion for the vertical form of even paraffins is given by:[62]

$$\Delta S = 5.49 + 1.49n \text{ cals./deg. mole} \qquad (III.16)$$

The coefficient 1.49 appearing in equation (III.16) would arise if in the liquid state, due to restricted rotation and steric effects, each link had 2.13 available positions rather than all three theoretically accessible staggered configurations and contrasted to the *one* available position in the crystalline state.

For the temperature of fusion of even vertical paraffin chains of sufficient length, we have:

$$T_f = \frac{\Delta H}{\Delta S} = \frac{-1141 + 609n}{5.53 + 1.49n} \qquad (III.17)$$

This would give a convergence temperature of melting for large values of n of about 408°K.

In the case of linear high polymers that can crystallize, we have a temperature range in which crystallites are in equilibrium with amorphous material, and an upper limit of temperature beyond which all crystallites melt. If one wishes to raise the temperature of melting there are clearly two possibilities:

(a) *Increasing ΔH.* This can be accomplished by introducing groups with a higher molar cohesion into each (or at least nearly each) link of the chain. This influence accounts for the increased thermostability in the series: ethyl cellulose – cellulose acetate – cellulose.

(b) *Decreasing ΔS.* This means to reduce the entropy change during melting and thereby make the liquid state less probable and hence less desirable from the statistical point of view. This would occur in chains with a great deal of internal stiffness and is presumably why the upper melting temperature of polytetrafluorethylene is so high.

The presence of crystallites in a polymeric substance acts to prevent the substance from flowing. To fabricate crystalline polymers it is generally necessary to operate at temperatures above the upper melting temperature. Nevertheless it is often desirable to have a certain amount of crystallization at temperatures at which the polymers are used in order to impart strength and resistance to flow.

Linear polymers such as polystyrene which show little or no tendency to crystallize are generally called linear *amorphous* polymers. These exhibit two temperature regions of mechanical behavior, a lower temperature region in which they act "glassy," and an upper temperature region in which they act "rubbery." In the glassy state the rate of change from one randomly kinked molecular configuration to another is slow, and possibly some configurations are energetically more favored by an amount that thermal energy cannot easily overcome. In the rubbery state a large number of configurations are rapidly accessible and more or less uniformly populated. The temperature region of transition between glass and rubber is lower in flexible chains and in chains whose side groups have low molar cohesions.

All linear amorphous polymers in the rubbery state show a pronounced tendency to flow which increases with decreasing molecular weight. This can be almost completely suppressed by introduction of a small amount of chemical cross linkage which produces three-dimensional polymers.

IV. PRIMARY AND SECONDARY VALENCES

The first three chapters of this volume have given an outline of our present knowledge of the nuclear framework and the internal motions in organic molecules; it will now be appropriate to amplify and expand this information by a survey of our present concept of intramolecular and inter-molecular forces.   In organic substances, the intramolecular forces holding the atoms together and causing the existence of finite, well-characterized molecules are strong bonds, which need fifty to one hundred kilocalories to be dissociated.   They are normally referred to as *chemical bonds*, *main valence bonds*, or *primary valence bonds*, and have been studied extensively during the last two decades.   Physical methods and theories have contributed greatly to our present understanding of this kind of strong inter-action between individual atoms.[1]

The second type of forces is evidenced by the fact that, even after satura-tion of all primary valences and formation of a stable molecule, the resulting system is still able to exert further forces on other particles of the same or of different nature.   These forces are considerably weaker than the "chem-ical" bonds; they differ significantly in their mode of action and are usually termed *residual* or *secondary* valences.   These are the forces that unite molecules into associates, complexes, aggregates and micelles, and the macroscopic, condensed phases—liquids, mesophases, and crystals—owe their existence to them.   Although, as is the case in many branches of natural science, it is not always possible to draw a sharp dividing line be-tween these two types of bonds, and, although sometimes the question re-mains open whether a given group of atoms is held together by primary or secondary valences, the distinction between them has furnished so much in-sight into the many-sidedness of the phenomena, especially in the field of organic chemistry, that its usefulness is beyond doubt, even if it cannot be applied in all cases to the last detail.

We shall therefore accept this distinction of atomic and molecular inter-action as the basis of our further considerations and shall begin with the discussion of the primary valences.

[1] Compare particularly L. Pauling, *The Nature of the Chemical Bond*, Cornell Univ. Press, Ithaca, 1939.

A. PRIMARY VALENCES

In examining chemical compounds of high stability and large energy of dissociation one becomes aware of the fact that the nature of the interaction between atoms can be very different in kind even though its magnitude is of the same order.   All chemical and physical properties of such stable systems suggest that there are *several types of primary valence* forces which in some cases appear sharply defined and in others are more or less overlapping.   If we consider the three molecules NaCl, Cl_2, and Na_2, we have before us three representatives of those types of linkage which seem to cover the existing experimental data:

(1) the *heteropolar* linkage between oppositely charged ions;
(2) the *homopolar* linkage between neutral atoms;
(3) the *metallic* linkage between neutral atoms.

This classification has proved useful in considering isolated molecules but has assumed still greater importance in investigating crystals.   Since conditions in the condensed phases will be presented in greater detail in Chapter V, we shall turn our attention here mainly to the nature of these three types of bonding and try to show how far it is possible, within this classification, to formulate ideas regarding the origin, magnitude, and potential energy functions of those forces which unite atoms to form a molecule.

1. Heteropolar Bond between Oppositely Charged Ions

There are a great many chemical compounds which are known to consist of oppositely charged ions.   In the molten state or in aqueous solution they conduct an electric current by simultaneous movement of the ions into which they dissociate; they can be excited to carry out vibrations, in the course of which charged particles oscillate against one another; they form crystal lattices in which, according to evidence from diffraction experiments, charged ions are undoubtedly the elements of the lattice and they display, through a series of other properties, their heteropolar character.   NaCl, CaO, $CaCl_2$, and K_2PtCl_6 may be cited as examples.

We are indebted to Kossel[2] and Lewis[3] for the simple and successful theory that the ions possess inert gaslike, stable electronic shells which are produced from the atoms of the chemical elements by the loss of surface electrons (valence electrons) or by the acquisition of such electrons.   The

[2] W. Kossel, *Ann. Physik*, **49**, 229 (1916).

[3] G. N. Lewis, *Valence and Structure of Atoms and Molecules*.   Chemical Catalog Co. New York, 1923.

atoms lose their loosely bound electrons or replenish their incomplete electronic shells and are thereby converted into *positive* or *negative* ions, which attract each other by their opposite charges.   The essential point is that in the formation of such a bond one or more electrons are *exchanged* between the interacting atoms.

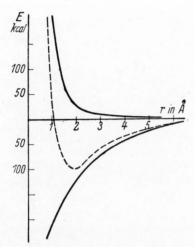

Fig. IV-1.   Potential energy E in kilocalories per mole as a function of r according to equation (IV. 1).

If the electronic clouds of these ions are not too large—as in the elements at the beginning of the periodic system—they may be considered as virtually rigid spheres which interact with each other essentially by electrostatic forces.   The equilibrium position of two such ions in a diatomic molecule or in a crystal lattice is produced by the cooperation of an attractive and a repulsive force, both of which may be derived from electrostatic potentials. The relationships can be appropriately illustrated by a potential energy curve, which represents the energy of the molecule as a function of the distance between the two ions.   A remarkably good interpretation of the experimental data is obtained if the attractive forces are based on Coulomb's law and the repulsion is expressed according to Born and Mayer[4] either by a higher negative power of the distance or, still better, by an exponential function in accordance with quantum mechanical considera-

[4] M. Born and J. E. Mayer, *Z. Physik*, **75**, 1 (1932); compare also M. Born and M. Goeppert-Mayer, *Handbuch der Physik*, 2nd ed., Springer, Berlin, 1933; Vol. 24, 2nd part, p. 722.

tions about the interaction of complete electronic shells.   The potential energy V for univalent ions then becomes one of the following functions of the distance r:

$$V(r) = -(e^2/r) + (b/r^n) \qquad \text{(IV.1)}$$

$$V(r) = -(e^2/r) + be^{-r/a} \qquad \text{(IV.2)}$$

where e is the electrical charge of the ions and n, b, and a are constants. It is represented graphically in Figure IV-1.   Equation (IV.1) gives accurate values for the atomic distances and dissociation energies of diatomic

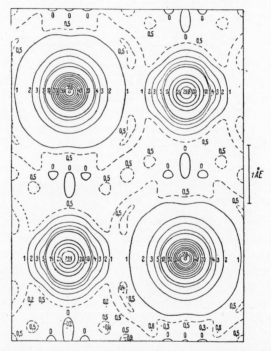

Fig. IV-2.   Electronic density in the NaCl lattice;   the large ions with the high charge density represent Cl, the others Na; between them the charge density is 0.

heteropolar molecules and has also proved to be very useful—as will be shown later in greater detail—in representing many properties of ionic lattices.

Fairly exact data regarding the spatial distribution of the negative charge clouds around the individual ions and between them has given experimental confirmation to the conditions expressed in equation (IV.1) by an actual contour map of the electronic density between bonded ions. By a remarkable increase in the precision of x-ray diffraction measurements, Grimm, Brill, Hermann, and Peters[5] have succeeded in determining very accurately the spatial electronic density distribution in ionic lattices. They found that in rock salt the positive atomic nuclei of sodium and chlorine keep their negative charge clouds very firmly around them and that there is only a very small electronic density discernible at the surface of the ions. The heteropolar bond is characterized by a complete exchange of electrons without any noticeable overlapping of electronic density. Figure IV-2 shows an electronic density contour map of the sodium chloride lattice and makes it evident that the density of the electronic clouds, at increasing distance from the atomic centers, falls off very rapidly and practically disappears between the two bonded ions.

In heavier elements, the charge clouds become larger and less rigid; this is particularly true for the negatively charged anions. As a consequence they are noticeably deformed by the electric field of the neighboring ions. This *polarization* or *deformation* of larger ions has been introduced by Lewis,[6] Langmuir,[7] Haber,[8] and Fajans,[9] and gives rise to additional attraction, the potential, ΔV, of which can be expressed by:

$$\Delta V(r) = -(\alpha e^2/r^4) - (2\alpha^2 e^2/r^2) \qquad (IV.3)$$

$$\alpha = \text{polarizability}$$

This term has to be added to the terms of equations (IV.1) or (IV.2).

Expanded potential functions of this type have been used successfully in calculating the dissociation energies of heteropolar compounds from the nuclear distances as given by x-ray data and spectroscopic measurements. In Table IV-1 are compared the actual dissociation energies of a number of ionic substances with the figures calculated theoretically; it can be seen that the agreement is quite satisfactory.[10]

The deformation of the electronic charge clouds in the individual ions

[5] H. G. Grimm, R. Brill, C. Hermann and Cl. Peters, *Naturwiss.*, **26**, 29, 479 (1938); *Ann. Physik*, [5] **34**, 393 (1939).

[6] G. N. Lewis, *Valence and Structure of Atoms and Molecules*. Chemical Catalog Co., New York, 1923.

[7] I. Langmuir, *J. Am. Chem. Soc.*, **41**, 868 (1919).

[8] F. Haber, *Verh. Phys. Ges.*, **21**, 750 (1919).

[9] K. Fajans, *Z. Elektrochem.*, **34**, 510 (1928); cf. also J. E. Mayer and M. Goeppert-Mayer, *Phys. Rev.*, **43**, 605 (1933); M. L. Huggins, *J. Chem. Phys.*, **5**, 143, 527 (1937).

[10] Compare here particularly F. Seitz, *Modern Theory of Solids*, McGraw-Hill, New York, 1940.

TABLE IV-1

EXPERIMENTAL AND THEORETICAL COHESIVE ENERGIES OF A FEW
IONIC SUBSTANCES

Substance	Repulsive exponent n	Cohesive energy, kcal./mole	
		Experimental	Theoretical
LiCl	7.0	198.1	193.3
NaCl	8.0	182.8	180.4
KCl	9.0	164.4	164.4
NaBr	8.5	173.3	171.7
KBr	9.5	156.2	157.8
AgF	8.5	223.0	207.9
CaF_2	8.0	618.0	617.7
ZnO	8.0	972	977
ZnS	9.0	857	816

and the potential energy functions describing them lead us gradually from the *pure heteropolar* bond, in which electrons are *exchanged* between the involved atoms, to the *typical homopolar* bond in which they are *shared*. The strongly deformed electronic charge cloud of a large ion represents an intermediate case in which first one or more electrons are exchanged and then the resulting charge clouds are deformed in a manner which amounts to a partial sharing of the exchanged electrons.[11]

2. Homopolar Bond between Neutral Atoms

In molecules of numerous elements—H_2, N_2, O_2, F_2, etc.—and in nearly all organic compounds, an entirely different type of linkage prevails. All properties of these substances in the solid, liquid, and gaseous states indicate that their molecules are built up of *neutral atoms*. The usual chemical representation of this type of linkage by a simple dash expresses in a diagrammatic but truthful manner the absence of heteropolarity and the preference for definite valence directions, in contrast to the spherical Coulomb field. Lewis, in his octet theory, has aimed at a refinement, in the sense that for each simple homopolar bond he invokes two electrons, each being contributed from one of the two bonded atoms. This aspect of homopolar bonding has been completely vindicated by subsequent quantum mechanical considerations. While the heteropolar valence concept could be developed into a quantitative theory without the use of quantum mechanical methods, the corresponding explanation of homopolar valence

[11] Compare L. Pauling, *The Nature of the Chemical Bond*, Cornell Univ. Press, Ithaca, 1939.

by the octet theory had to remain qualitative until Heitler and London[12] carried out a thorough wave mechanical study of the interaction between neutral hydrogen atoms and succeeded in explaining the existence and properties of the hydrogen molecule. The fundamental idea of the quantum mechanical treatment of homopolar bonding is the following. If two neutral hydrogen atoms approach each other to distances less than 2 Å. their electrons start to interact with each other. Whereas a sodium and a chlorine atom, on close approach, combine in such a way that the former loses its loosely bound electron and the latter fills up its incomplete shell, no such exchange of electrons can occur in the case of two H atoms because of their identity. Rather, an interplay sets in between the two nuclei and the two electrons, the result being that in the final molecule the two electrons are *shared* by both nuclei as a cloud of negative charge which welds them together into a coherent and symmetrical structure.

Mathematical treatment leads to a potential energy curve which, like equation (IV.1), expresses the energy of the molecule as a function of the distance between the two atoms; it can be calculated rigorously in the case of H_2^+, H_2 and Li_2^+ and with a certain approximation in a few somewhat more complicated cases. The agreement between theory and experiment is remarkably good. In the case of H_2, for instance, the dissociation energy D has been calculated[13] to be 4.722 e.v. and the radius in the equilibrium position to be 0.74 Å. The experimental values are $D = 4.72$ e.v., $r_0 = 0.7395$ Å. Since a rigorous computation of the potential energy function is possible only in the simplest cases and, even in these, involves rather time-consuming calculations, it is important that one can arrive at approximations that express the potential energy of a homopolar molecule just as equation (IV.1) does for a heteropolar system. Several authors have proposed algebraic expressions for such a function; one equation suggested by Morse[14] is frequently used with good success:

$$V(r) = D[e^{-2\alpha(r-r_0)} - 2e^{-\alpha(r-r_0)}] \qquad (IV.4)$$

It is remarkably simple and particularly illuminating because the two parameters D and r_0, represent the *dissociation energy* and the *nuclear distance* in the equilibrium position and have, therefore, a direct physical significance.* Other proposals, which have proved more or less satisfac-

* It may be mentioned that the corresponding constants b and n in the corresponding equation (IV.1) for the heteropolar bond have no such immediate meaning.

[12] W. Heitler and F. London, *Z. Physik*, **44**, 455 (1927).

[13] Compare, *e.g.*, S. Glasstone, *Textbook of Physical Chemistry*, 2nd ed., Van Nostrand, New York, 1946, p. 101 et seq.

[14] P. M. Morse, *Phys. Rev.*, (2) **34**, 57 (1929).

tory in certain cases, have been advanced by Morse and Rosen,[15] Teller and Pöschl,[16] and Rydberg.[17]   Figure IV-3 shows the general form of the potential energy function for a homopolar bond and indicates at the same

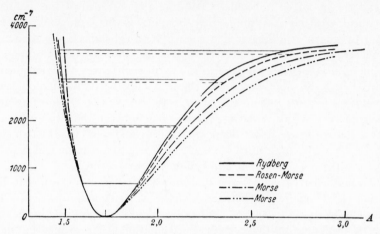

Fig. IV-3.   Potential energy curves for the homopolar linkage.

time how much the various mathematical expressions differ from one another.

Recently an interesting study of the potential energy curve of the single, double, and triple carbon-carbon bonds was made by Fox and Martin.[18] They start from an expression of the form:

$$V = D[n/(m - n)][(r_0/r)^m - (m/n)(r_0/r)^n] \qquad (IV.5)$$

where D is the energy of dissociation and is given by:

$$D = kr_0^2/mn$$

where r_0 = atomic distance in the equilibrium position, k = force constant from Raman spectrum, and m and n are constants.   For the various carbon-carbon linkages the potential function may be written as:

$$V = D(r_0/r)^{4.55}[4.55 \ln (r_0/r) - 1] \qquad (IV.6)$$

If the different values for D are put into this relation, the corresponding values of r_0 can be calculated from the minimum of V and compared with

[15] P. M. Morse and N. Rosen, *Phys. Rev.*, (2) **42**, 143 (1932).

[16] G. Pöschl and E. Teller, *Z. Physik*, **83**, 143 (1933);   cf. also P. M. Davidson, *Z. Physik*, **87**, 364 (1934).

[17] R. Rydberg, *Z. Physik*, **73**, 376 (1932).

[18] J. J. Fox and A. E. Martin, *J. Chem. Soc.*, **1938**, 2106;   **1939**, 884.

the experimental data.   Table IV-2 shows the result of this calculation and
manifests a very satisfactory agreement between theory and experiment.

TABLE IV-2

DISSOCIATION ENERGIES OF THE VARIOUS CARBON-CARBON BONDS

Bond	$k(10^5$ dynes/cm.)	r_0 (obs.), Å.	r_0 (calcd.), Å.
C≡C	15.6	1.20	1.208
C=C	9.8	1.33	1.326
C—C (arom)	7.6	1.40	1.395
C—C (aliph)	4.4	1.56	1.556

It should be especially emphasized that the quantum theory of homopolar linkage is not confined to the formulation of the potential energy function of a single carbon-carbon bond.   In the hands of Herzberg,[19] Hund,[20]
Hückel,[21] Mulliken,[22] Pauling,[23] and Slater[24] it has been successfully used
to explain the existence of spatially defined valence directions, the free
rotation round the single bond (Ch. III, Sect. E), the rigidity of the double
bond (Ch. III, Sect. F), and the nature of conjugated and aromatic systems.   These services of quantum mechanics to chemistry are described
very lucidly in the books of Pauling and Wilson[25] and of Hellmann,[26] and
are summarized in Pauling's book, *Nature of the Chemical Bond*.

The next step in the study of the homopolar bond leads to the actual distribution of the negative charge clouds of the two electrons which represent
the bond.   It is evident that as a result of the common electronic shell,
which constitutes the homopolar bond, a certain accumulation of negative
charge should occur along the axis of the molecule, halfway between the two
bonded atoms.   Actually Grimm and his co-workers[27] have shown, in a
thorough analysis of the electron density contour map of the diamond lattice, that along the direction of a carbon-carbon bond no region entirely

[19] G. Herzberg, *Molecular Spectra and Molecular Structure*, Prentice-Hall, New York,
1939.

[20] F. Hund, *Ergeb. exakt. Naturw.*, **8**, 147 (1929).

[21] E. Hückel, *Z. Physik*, **60,** 423 (1930); **70,** 204 (1931); **72,** 30 (1931); **76,** 628 (1931).

[22] R. S. Mulliken, *Phys. Rev.*, **40,** 751 (1932); *J. Chem. Phys.*, **7,** 339, 353, 356, 364
(1939).

[23] L. Pauling, *Phys. Rev.*, **40,** 891 (1932).

[24] J. C. Slater, *Phys. Rev.*, **38,** 1109 (1931).

[25] L. Pauling and E. B. Wilson, *Introduction to Quantum Mechanics*, McGraw-Hill,
New York, 1935; also L. Pauling in H. Gilman, *Organic Chemistry*, Wiley, New York,
1938.

[26] H. Hellmann, *Quantenchemie*, Deuticke, Leipzig, 1937.

[27] Compare footnote 5 on page 113.

free from charge is encountered. On the contrary, each pair of carbon atoms in the lattice which are 1.55 Å. apart from each other is linked by a charge bridge having an average charge density of 1.97 e.s.u. per Å.^{3}. This is clearly shown in Figure 4. In contrast to the isolated closed charge

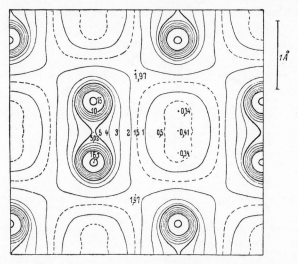

Fig. IV-4. The points of charge density 16.1 represent the positions of the centers of gravity of the C atoms in the diamond lattice.

clouds of the ions in NaCl or CaF$_2$, we have here two electron shells of adjacent atoms, blending with each other so that a definite direction of the bond is fixed by the fact that there is no point of vanishing charge along this direction in space. The charge clouds which thus produce homopolar bonds are fixed in space and are therefore responsible for the tetrahedral arrangement of the carbon atoms in the diamond lattice and for all other consequences of the tetrahedral character. The relative stiffness of the valence direction is caused by the repulsion of the electronic charge clouds representing the individual bonds.

This brief review of the homopolar bond brings us to the third primary valence linkage, $viz.$, the metallic bond.

3. Metallic Linkage

Metals do not follow the pattern of either heteropolar or homopolar valence; rather there exists a characteristic new form of linkage, about which we do not know too much as yet.   The metallic linkage is only little concerned with the organic high polymers to which this book shall serve as an introduction; but, at any rate, the following brief note may be given for the purpose of completeness.

Everything points to the fact that in a metal, positively charged ions are embedded in an electron gas distributed throughout the whole crystal. This type of linkage can be conceived as arising from the homopolar bond if we assume that the valence electrons abandon their orbitals around individual atoms and begin to permeate through the whole lattice.   They cannot, of course, be regarded actually as free, because they move in the three-dimensional periodic field of the ions which occupy the lattice points; however, they are not bound to any individual atom but are spread out over the whole lattice and, just for this reason, are the cause of the electronic conductivity which is so characteristic of the metallic state.

A potential energy function of the metallic bond has been worked out by Wigner and Seitz[28] for the case of alkali metals.   It represents satisfactorily the energy of dissociation and the distance between the atoms in the equilibrium position and corresponds to the functions (IV.1) and (IV.4) for the other types of linkage.   Table IV-3 shows that the formula of Wigner and Seitz is in fairly good agreement with the experimental data.

The idea of a spread-out electronic cloud in the lattice of metals has also been demonstrated experimentally through an accurate Fourier analysis of the electronic density distribution in metallic magnesium.   It was found that in such lattices a continuous electronic charge cloud extends throughout the whole system.

TABLE IV-3

SOME PROPERTIES OF THE METALLIC LINKAGE IN SODIUM

Property	Wigner and Seitz	Experimental
Heat of sublimation (cal./mole)	25.6	26.9
Lattice distance, Å	4.2	4.23
Compressibility, cgs	1.6×10^{-11}	1.0×10^{-11}

Those interested in a more detailed description of the metallic bond may be referred to Fröhlich,[29] Sommerfeld and Bethe,[30] Pauling,[31] and Seitz.[32]

[28] E. Wigner and F. Seitz, *Phys. Rev.*, **43,** 804 (1933); **46,** 509 (1934).

[29] H. Fröhlich, *Elektronentheorie der Metalle*, Springer, Berlin, 1936.

[30] A. Sommerfeld and H. Bethe, *Handbuch der Physik*, 2nd ed., Vol. 24, Springer, Berlin, 1936.

[31] L. Pauling, *The Nature of the Chemical Bond*, Cornell Univ. Press, Ithaca, 1939.

[32] F. Seitz, *Modern Theory of Solids*, McGraw-Hill, New York, 1940, p. 348.

B. SECONDARY VALENCES

While the heteropolar and the metallic linkages possess the ability to build up entire crystals from single units, such as NaCl or Na, the same forces serving to add more and more new particles to the existing system, it is characteristic of the homopolar bond, in most cases, that it ceases to act after the union of relatively few atoms and that the aggregate becomes saturated. Therefore, such forces usually give rise to finite molecules, which—as we shall see in considering high polymeric substances—may be fairly large in certain cases and are held together by strong bonds.

Experience shows, however, that even after saturation of all primary valences inside the resulting molecules, forces still remain operative which are generally known as *residual* or *secondary* valences or as *intermolecular* forces. The first quantitative statements about these intermolecular forces were made by van der Waals in his theory of real gases when he introduced the attraction constant a by means of an internal pressure, a/V^2; hence we frequently speak of *van der Waals' forces*.

The present state of our knowledge indicates that these van der Waals' forces between chemically saturated molecules owe their existence essentially to three different effects: (*1*) the *orientation* effect of *rigid dipoles* to which Keesom[33] first directed attention; (*2*) the *induction* effect of *polarizable molecules*, especially considered by Debye and Falkenhagen;[34] and (*3*) a *quantum mechanical interaction* of *intramolecular electronic motions*, investigated by London and Eisenschitz[35] and by Slater and Kirkwood.[36]

1. Orientation Effect of Rigid Dipoles

A dipole molecule (Ch. II, Sect. D) behaves at large distances (10 Å. and more) like a neutral system. However, on approach sufficiently close to be comparable with the distance between the two charges in the molecule, say at 3 or 4 Å., the separation between these charges becomes significant. At such small distances the particle reveals its polarity and influences similar particles by attraction between the unlike poles of each.

The equations for dipole-dipole interaction can be derived from purely electrostatic considerations as soon as the effective dielectric constant of the medium is known, and it will suffice here to describe the two extreme

---

[33] W. H. Keesom, *Physik. Z.*, **22**, 120, 643 (1921); **23**, 225 (1922).

[34] P. Debye, *Physik. Z.*, **21**, 178 (1920); **22**, 302 (1921).

[35] F. London and R. Eisenschitz, *Z. Physik*, **60**, 520 (1930).

[36] J. C. Slater and J. G. Kirkwood, *Phys. Rev.*, **37**, 682 (1931).

cases in which the dipoles are arranged parallel, *viz.*, anti-parallel to each other (see Fig. IV-5). In the former case the potential energy V as a function of the distance r is given by:

$$V_p(r) = -(\mu_1\mu_2/r^3) \qquad \text{(IV.6)}$$

in the latter by:

$$V_a(r) = -(2\mu_1\mu_2/r^3) \qquad \text{(IV.7)}$$

In the derivation of these equations it is supposed that the distance r between the two molecules is larger than the distance d between the charges in any individual molecule. For $r = 5d$, the error in using equation (IV.6) amounts to about 4%; at $r = 2d$ it increases to about 30%.

The meaning of this can be shown in an example: the dipole moment of the water molecule amounts to about 1.8 debyes; on dividing the unit charge by 4.8×10^{-10}, we obtain, according to equation $\mu = ed$ a value of about 0.4 Å. as the effective distance d between the positive and negative poles in H_2O; we can therefore calculate the interaction of two water molecules at distances of 3–5 Å. with tolerable accuracy from equations (IV.6) and

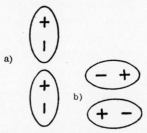

Fig. IV-5. Different positions of two dipoles with mutual attraction: (*a*) parallel — eq. (IV.6); (*b*) anti-parallel — eq. (IV.7).

(IV.7), with the proviso, of course, that there are no other forces acting between the two molecules. Were the centers of gravity of the molecules able to approach to within 1.5 or 2.0 Angström units, which is impossible owing to the repulsion of the charge clouds, it would no longer be legitimate to employ equation (IV.6) and we should have to use another, somewhat more complicated, relation.

Since the orientation or alignment established under the influence of dipole forces is always counteracted by thermal agitation, the net result of the orientation effect is highly dependent upon temperature.

2. Induction Effect

This concerns the influence of the molecular polarizability, as explained in Chapter II, Section B. A molecule containing readily mobile charges acquires an induced moment if placed in a field F, such that:

$$\mu_i = \alpha F$$

where α = polarizability. Due to this induced moment (either alone or in conjunction with other existing moments), there results an interaction between the polarized molecules. Usually, the permanent dipole of another molecule serves as inducing field; in this event the following relations hold:

(a) The inducing dipole is parallel to the induced; in this case the potential energy is given by:

$$V_p(r) = -2(\mu^2\alpha/r^6) \tag{IV.8}$$

(b) The inducing dipole is perpendicular to the induced; then one has

$$V_{pp}(r) = -{}^1\!/_2(\mu^2\alpha/r^6) \tag{IV.9}$$

This component of the van der Waals' forces generally is less dependent upon temperature than the orientation effect between permanent dipoles.

3. Quantum Mechanical Interaction of Virtual Dipoles (Dispersion Effect)

If one continues the quantum mechanical calculations which lead to the explanation of the homopolar bond, one arrives, in second approximation, at a further force between structures already saturated with respect to primary valences. From their magnitude and their dependence upon distance, these forces must be classified as secondary valences. Since they are related to the scattering of different wave lengths by the molecule, i.e., to the effect of frequency upon polarizability (dispersion), they are frequently called *dispersion forces*. Their potential as functions of distance has been expressed by London and Eisenschitz[37] as:

$$V(r) = -{}^3\!/_4(\alpha^2 I/r^6) \text{ volt} \tag{IV.10}$$

An equivalent relation was derived independently by Slater and Kirkwood:[38]

$$V(r) = -7.07 \times 10^{-21}(\alpha^{3/2}n/r^6) \text{ volt} \tag{IV.11}.$$

where I = ionization energy, α = polarizability, and n = number of electrons in the outermost shell.

In the derivation of these equations it is assumed that the interaction occurs between unexcited molecules and that the particles act on one another at a distance r, which is large as compared with their own diameter.

[37] F. London and R. Eisenschitz, Z. Physik, 60, 520 (1930); F. London, Z. physik. Chem., (B) 11, 22 (1930).

[38] J. C. Slater and J. G. Kirkwood, Phys. Rev., 37, 682 (1931).

If, as frequently happens, we wish to determine the interaction between larger molecules—paraffins, condensed ring systems, or macromolecules—we must resolve the total effect into the forces between separate, adjacent parts of the interacting molecules and recognize that the equations are applicable only if the distance of these segments from one another is greater than the cube root of the polarizability of the involved atomic groups.

Since, in most of the groups concerned—CH, CCl, CO, etc.—the polarizabilities are between 2 and 5×10^{-24}, we see that for a mutual approach of 3–5 Å. (equilibrium distance of secondary valence forces) this condition is sufficiently approximated to permit a fair calculation of the mutual interaction between homopolar molecules or parts of them.

In fact, if formula (IV.10) is applied to the forces of attraction between atoms of the inert gases, there is a remarkable agreement with experiment. Certainly these forces, in view of the spherical symmetry of the charge clouds in the rare gases, can be attributed neither to orientation nor to induction phenomena; in them we have the pure dispersion effect, and the principle of its calculation can be tested fairly rigorously by comparison of the theoretical data with the experimental values. A glance at Table IV-4 shows that from He to Xe the increase of the van der Waals' constant a is represented very satisfactorily, and that even the numerical data of the theoretical computation agree remarkably well with experiment. We should remember that no other constants than polarizability and energy of ionization have been used in this calculation.

TABLE IV-4

VAN DER WAALS' ATTRACTION CONSTANTS FOR THE INERT GASES

Gas	$\alpha \times 10^{24}$	I, volts	$a_{theor.} \times 10^{-4}$	$a_{exp.} \times 10^{-4}$
He..........0.20		25.5	4.8	3.5
Ne..........0.39		25.6	25.8	21
Ar..........1.63		17.5	144	135
Kr..........2.46		14.7	254	240
Xe..........4.00		12.3	432	410

Since these two magnitudes are constants specific to the molecule itself, the dispersion effect is not noticeably dependent upon temperature.

4. Superposition of the Three Types of Intermolecular Attraction

In the majority of cases attraction between molecules will not be caused by a single one of the three special types of interaction just mentioned, but will be a complicated superposition of all of them. The integrated effect, then, is the sum of one component virtually independent of temperature, of another component slightly dependent upon temperature, and of a third, which depends strongly upon temperature. The general character of the individual contributions is summarized in Table IV-5. We see that the

TABLE IV-5

CONTRIBUTIONS OF THE DIFFERENT TYPES OF VAN DER WAALS' FORCES

Forces:	Dispersion	Induction		Orientation	
Appearing in:	All molecules	Dipole mol.	Quad. mol.	Dipole mol.	Quad. mol.
Contribution to potential depends on..	$-r^{-6}$	$-r^{-6}$	$-r^{-8}$	$-r^{-3}$	$-r^{-5}$
Dependence on temperature..........	Nil	Slight		Fairly marked	

interaction between rigid dipoles decreases by a lower power of r than the other two effects; at greater distances, therefore, the former will predominate, whereas at smaller distances the induction and dispersion forces will become more and more noticeable.

TABLE IV-6

VAN DER WAALS' ATTRACTION CONSTANTS FOR SOME MOLECULES

1	2	3	4	5	6	7
				$a \times 10^{-6}$		
Substance	$\alpha \times 10^{24}$	b_0, cc./mole	I, volts	van der Waals'	Calc. by London	Calc. by Slater
HCl.......2.71		53.5	13.7	3.66	2.12	2.56
HBr.......3.85		58.9	13.3	4.42	3.83	3.93
CO.......1.99		51.5	14.3	1.44	1.24	1.86
N_2O.......3.00		58.8	11.23	3.77	1.59	3.82
H_2S.......3.78		57.3	10.42	4.43	2.95	3.93
NO.......1.78		34.6	14.4	1.29	1.46	2.42
N_2.........1.74		52.8	17	1.34	1.09	1.45
O_2.........1.57		42.5	13	1.36	0.89	1.81
Cl_2.......4.60		73.0	18.2	6.32	6.03	5.48
CO_2.......2.86		57.1	15.45	3.61	2.50	3.60
CH_4.......2.58		57.0	14.5	2.24	1.92	2.23
C_2H_2.......3.32		68.4	12.25	4.39	2.22	3.02
C_2H_4.......4.10		76.3	12.2	4.45	3.10	3.84
C_2H_6.......4.50		85.3	12.75	5.39	3.42	4.53

A calculation by London and Eisenschitz[39] of the van der Waals' attraction constant for a series of molecules shows that even in the case of fairly

[39] F. London and R. Eisenschitz, Z. Physik, 60, 520 (1930).

high polarity the dispersion effect always supplies a considerable share of the total attraction.

Table IV-6 gives the van der Waals' attraction constants for a number of important molecules as calculated from equations (IV.10) and (IV.11) and compares them with the experimental values; there is always fair agreement between the measured and calculated a constants. The ratio of induction to dispersion effect can be judged for a few molecules from Table IV.7; it is evident that even in the case of a strong dipole molecule like water, the mutual polarization amounts to only about 20% of the dispersion

TABLE IV-7

RATIO OF INDUCTION TO DISPERSION EFFECT

Substance	$\mu \times 10^{18}$	$\alpha \times 10^{24}$	I, volts	Induction Dispersion
CO...........	0.12	1.99	14.3	0.0008
HBr..........	0.78	3.85	13.3	0.020
HCl..........	1.03	2.71	13.7	0.048
NH₃..........	1.50	2.21	16	0.106
H₂O..........	1.84	1.48	18	0.20

forces. The orientation effect of the permanent dipoles in such molecules largely exceeds the two other contributions. It is therefore not surprising that one was inclined for a long time to attribute the van der Waals' forces of such molecules solely to the interaction between permanent dipoles.

Figure IV-6 shows the coaction of all three effects in HCl, H_2O, NH_3, and

TABLE IV-8

RATIO OF ORIENTATION TO DISPERSION EFFECT

	HCl	H₂O	NH₃	H₂S	HCN
$\dfrac{\mu^2 r^3}{\alpha^2 I} 0.617 \times 10^{12}$........0.29		1.53	1.02	0.164	1.64

SO_2 and demonstrates that at short distances the dispersion effect becomes increasingly apparent and that the induction component plays only a subordinate role in these particular molecules. The ratio between orientation and dispersion effects can be easily calculated for simple molecules; it is evident from equations (IV.7) and (IV.10) that it depends essentially upon the magnitude of the ratio:

$$Q = 0.617 \times 10^{12} \frac{\mu^2 r^3}{\alpha^2 I}$$

Table IV-8 shows values for this quotient; if they are small compared with unity, the dispersion effect is predominant; if they reach unity or more, the influence of the permanent dipoles prevails.

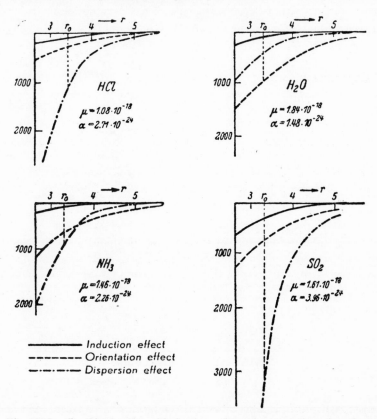

Fig. IV-6. Combined action of induction, orientation, and dispersion effects.

In small, difficultly polarizable molecules, having strong, easily accessible moments—H_2O, SO_2, HF—the orientation can become so prominent that it causes the formation of double molecules.

Particularly intense interactions also take place if strong, permanent dipoles approach molecules having easily polarizable parts.   The permanent dipoles induce dipoles in the interacting molecules and attract them. In such cases it has been observed that there exists a distinct tendency for the formation of stable molecular complexes, which sometimes are stoichiometrically well defined. This kind of intermolecular attraction plays an important role in the interaction of plasticizers with polymers[40] and in the explanation of the important phenomena of adhesion between macromolecules, of tackiness of elastomers and of the spinnability of polymer solutions.[41]

Although it is customary in the kinetic theory of gases, and is certainly justifiable in the mathematical treatment of ideal gases, to regard individual molecules as rigid elastic spheres, it is in no way legitimate to do so if we are considering their interaction at short distances. On the contrary, we must bear in mind in this case that molecules—in close enough proximity—have a complicated and differentiated structure and are extraordinarily deformable and readily changed. They have no less than three different possibilities of interacting with each other, and it will be the purpose of the next section to explain in more detail the finer features which determine the formation of pairs of molecules, of larger, stable aggregates, and, finally, the growth of entire crystals.

C. GENERAL REMARKS ON THE FORMATION OF MOLECULAR AGGREGATES

We shall begin by discussing some cases, in which there is good reason to suspect the existence of more or less stable aggregates of molecules in the gaseous and liquid phase even without it being possible to isolate well-defined molecular addition compounds. The association brought about by the action of the intermolecular forces is, in these cases, so quickly destroyed by thermal agitation that any two specific molecules remain only momentarily in close proximity and are unable to form an aggregate vibrating for a longer period about a definite position of minimum potential energy. In spite of this, the tendency for association as such may be quite appreciable, because, if a given group of molecules breaks up, each of the components immediately joins another group and does not remain isolated. Any given molecule thus nearly always finds itself in one of the molecular aggregates but never in the same one for long. Groups of closely bonded

[40] Compare, e.g., "Symposium on Plasticizers" at the University of Buffalo in June, 1947; *J. Polymer Sci.*, **2**, 113 (1947). A. K. Doolittle, *Ind. Eng. Chem.*, **36**, 239 (1944); **38** 535 (1946).

[41] Compare D. Josefowitz and H. Mark, *India Rubber World*, **106**, 33 (1942).

molecules are always present but they rapidly interchange their components in space and time.

1. Aggregate Formation by Dipole Forces

Equations (IV.6) and (IV.7) in Section B express the potential energy of two interacting permanent dipoles in the parallel and anti-parallel arrangements as a function of the distance between the two molecules. They control the conditions under which the two dipoles prefer to assume the parallel position, and hence are able to promote chain formation, and those under which they prefer to assume the anti-parallel arrangement and form pairs only.

The ratio r_p^3 (parallel arrangement) to r_a^3 (anti-parallel arrangement) is decisive. It depends upon whether the centers of the two interacting molecules can be brought nearer together by one arrangement or the other. Conditions for H_2F_2 are illustrated in Figure IV-7 according to Briegleb; in this case $r_p^3 \simeq 2r_a^3 (44 \simeq 43)$ so that the question cannot be decided in the

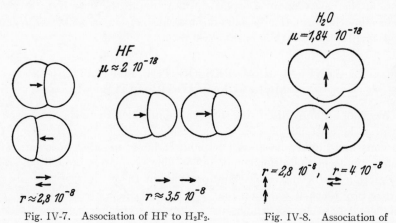

Fig. IV-7.   Association of HF to H_2F_2.

Fig. IV-8.   Association of H_2O to double molecules.

absence of further information; on the other hand, in water there is a distinct preference for a chain arrangement of the dipoles; here $2r_a^3 > r_p^3$ (128 > 22). In fact, Jona[42] was able to confirm this conclusion by measuring the molar polarization of water vapor at low temperatures, where the molecules are partially associated (see Figure IV-8). Briegleb[43] succeeded

[42] M. Jona, *Physik. Z.*, **20**, 14 (1919).

[43] G. Briegleb, *Zwischenmolekulare Kräfte und Molekülstruktur*, Enka, Stuttgart, 1937, p. 52 et seq. *Naturwissenschaften*, **29**, 420 (1941).

in obtaining data on the depth of the potential energy trough, through which such favored positions are stabilized in the parallel and anti-parallel positions. For water the attractive energy at a distance of 2.8 Å. between the centers of gravity was found to be 3500 cal. per mole of dipole pairs. We arrive at similar values for H_2F_2, while methyl fluoride, on account of the increase in distance caused by the CH_3 group, shows a weaker association tendency. Recently it has even been established that at sufficiently low temperatures, HF forms surprisingly long chains containing up to 10 individual HF molecules. They are not excessively stable but can be

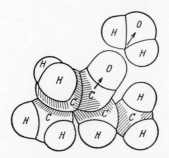

Fig. IV-9.   Position of water on diethyl ketone.

isolated in the form of a white powder mass at low temperatures. Briegleb[43] has estimated the dissociation energy of the bond that produces these chains to be about 10 kcal. per mole.

If we pass to larger molecules, such as methyl chloride, ethyl chloride, etc., the anti-parallel arrangement prevails more and more on geometrical grounds.

The addition of water to ketones, which, according to Stuart,[44] Wolf,[45] and Meerwein[46] should conform to the pattern shown in Figure IV-9, is of interest because it may be related to the water-binding capacity of macromolecules which contain carbonyl and carboxyl groups, and to the interaction of ester type plasticizers with macromolecules containing hydroxyl groups.

If the polar group of a molecule, e.g., CO, OH, NH_2, is surrounded by bulky homopolar groups such as CH_3, C_2H_5, and $C(CH_3)_3$, it may happen that the minimum distance within which the polar groups of two molecules can approach each other is so large that the orientation effect between the

[44] H. A. Stuart, Z. Physik, 51, 490 (1928).
[45] K. L. Wolf, Z. physik. Chem., B2, 39 (1928).
[46] H. Meerwein, Ber., 62, 999 (1929); 66, 411 (1932).

two shielded dipoles becomes less consequential than the dispersion effect between the homopolar groups which are much closer together than the centers of gravity of the permanent dipoles.

The properties of the molecules involved then resemble those of the corresponding hydrocarbons. An excellent example of this behavior is given in Table IV-9, which contains, according to Briegleb, boiling points of the isomeric butyl alcohols as a measure of intermolecular forces.

TABLE IV-9

BOILING POINTS OF THE ISOMERIC BUTANOLS

Substance	Boiling point
C_4H_9OH	
normal	117
secondary	99
tertiary	83
C_5H_{12}	37

Under the influence of a sufficiently strong dipole, the electron clouds of symmetrical molecules (CCl_4, $SnCl_4$, etc.) can be deformed so much that a considerable dipole moment results. Ulich[47] was able to demonstrate the existence of a noticeable dipole moment (about 2.5 debyes) in liquid $SnCl_4$, while in the gaseous state the substance has no measurable dipole moment and exhibits tetrahedral symmetry. The same is true with Al_2Cl_6, $TiCl_4$, and other metal halides. Moreover, highly symmetrical molecules which carry polar groups may deform one another if they are sufficiently close together, as we may infer, for example, from the lattice of the monoclinic modifications of CBr_4.[48]

Figure IV-10, shows, according to Briegleb, the angular deformation that occurs in $BeCl_2$ under the influence of a polar organic molecule when the two particles are in close proximity; the CO group is taken as the deforming dipole; its influence ceases as soon as the spheres of influence of CO and Be make contact with each other.

The symmetry of the electronic cloud of a molecule is more easily altered by the field of a polar molecule than the nuclear framework. The consequence is the induction of an electric moment with all the resulting phenomena already discussed. Occasionally, however, deformations of this type proceed further and lead to transition phenomena, which are intermediate between the linkages previously outlined. According to Meer-

[47] H. Ulich, *Angew. Chem.*, **44**, 750 (1931).
[48] H. Mark, *Ber.*, **57**, 1820 (1924).

wein,[49] they may play an important role on account of their peculiar re-activity in homogeneous catalysis through the formation of intermediate highly reactive compounds.

Onsager has suggested that, in the association of two alcohol molecules according to the scheme of anti-parallel configuration:

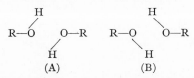

a quantum mechanical resonance phenomenon can develop because the two arrangements (A) and (B), which result from an exchange of the hydrogen atoms between the molecules, have the same potential energy and the same arrangement of all atomic nuclei in the molecule and differ only from each other by the geometrical arrangements of some of the valence electrons. Resonance only develops if the two systems remain sufficiently long in

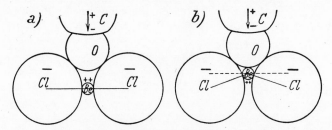

Fig. IV-10.   Angular deformation in $BeCl_2$ by a polar molecule.

favorable geometrical position, which the dipole forces serve to achieve. As a result of this resonance, we may expect a particular stability of the complex and a noticeable perturbation of the two hydroxyl groups.   Actually, it has been observed that the Raman lines of the OH frequency in alcohols are diffuse if one observes them in the condensed state.

Similar conditions prevail, according to Gillette and Sherman,[50] in the interaction of two carboxyl groups leading to the formation of the well-known double molecules of fatty acids.   The two possible configurations of a pair of carboxyl groups indicate that, by the exchange of two hydrogen atoms, it is possible to arrive at two arrangements of the atoms which are geometrically and energetically equivalent and differ only in the position of

[49] H. Meerwein, *J. prakt. Chem.*, **141**, 123 (1934).
[50] R. H. Gillette and A. Sherman, *J. Am. Chem. Soc.*, **58**, 1135 (1936).

the chemical bonds between oxygen and hydrogen. In terms of quantum mechanics, this corresponds to the case that several eigenfunctions (possibilities of geometrical arrangement of the valence electron) belong to the same eigenvalue (total energy of the system). The result of such a degeneration is that a linear combination of the eigenfunctions actually prevails which corresponds to an intermediate state consisting of both arrangements depicted above. This compromise state has a lower energy and hence a higher stability than either of the contributing configurations. According to Sidgwick,[51] this intermediate state may be considered as a system in which the two hydrogen atoms are continually changing places between the two molecules at a definite frequency. The dipole attraction contributes to this effect inasmuch as it produces the arrangement represented above and maintains it over a sufficiently long period in face of the destroying influence of thermal agitation. This type of bond, the so-called hydrogen bond or hydrogen bridge,[52] can be considered as a case in which dipole forces and quantum mechanical resonance cooperate to form a strong link between the two molecules.[53]

In 1936, a very interesting survey on the occurrence and properties of hydrogen bonds was given by Huggins.[54] Table IV-10 gives brief informa-

TABLE IV-10

DISSOCIATION ENERGY OF HYDROGEN BONDS

Bond	Dissociation energy, kcal./mole	Bond	Dissociation energy, kcal./mole
F—H—F	6.2	N—H—F	6.0
O—H—O	5.9–10.15	C—H—O	4.1–6.0
C—H—N	6.1–7.8	N—H—O	6.0–6.8

tion regarding the energy of dissociation needed to break hydrogen bridges between different atoms; Table IV-11 contains figures regarding the length of these bridges. It seems that hydrogen bonds not only play an important role in the formation of molecular compounds but also influence to a certain degree the cohesion and symmetry of normal crystals and of high polymers.

[51] N. V. Sidgwick, *Electronic Theory of Valency*, Oxford Univ. Press, London, 1927.
[52] L. Pauling, *The Nature of the Chemical Bond*, Cornell Univ. Press, Ithaca, 1939, p. 277.
[53] Compare W. M. Latimer and W. H. Rodebush, *J. Am. Chem. Soc.*, **42** 1431 (1920).
[54] M. L. Huggins, *J. Org. Chem.*, **1,** 407 (1936); compare also G. Briegleb, *Z. Elektrochem.*, **50,** 35 (1944); R. Brill, *ibid.*, p. 47.

There is, in fact, ample experimental evidence that the softening points solubilities and swelling properties of many polymers are essentially due to hydrogen bridges that are established in the polymer and to those that can be formed between the macromolecules and the molecules of a plasticizer

TABLE IV-11

LENGTH OF HYDROGEN BRIDGES

Bridge	Length, Å.	Bridge	Length, Å.
F—H—F	2.25–2.51	N—H—F	2.63
O—H—O	2.50–2.30	N—H—O	2.76–2.88
N—H—N	2.65		

solvent or swelling agent.   Infrared absorption and x-ray analysis indicate that in the crystalline domains of cellulose, all hydroxyl groups in the lattice are linked with each other by hydrogen bonds and that even in the disordered areas hydrogen bridges between the hydroxyl groups of adjacent molecules are still frequent.   If one wants to reach the hydroxyl groups of cellulose to form esters, ethers, or other derivatives, it is necessary first to liberate them from their mutual hydrogen bonding.   This is usually achieved by the action of hydrogen bond opening reagents such as strong acids or bases and manifests itself in a considerable swelling of the cellulose under the influence of these "catalysts."   Polyvinyl alcohol seems to be so strongly hydrogen bonded in the crystalline state, that its highly oriented films or filaments do not exhibit solubility in water.

Hydrogen bridges seem also to play an important role in forming and maintaining the structure of natural proteins and of synthetic polypeptides and polyamides.   The high melting point of nylon, its difficult solubility and even its high tenacity in the drawn state have been traced back to the existence of hydrogen bridges between the NH groups of one chain and the CO groups of adjacent chains.   These hydrogen bonds extend throughout the lattice perpendicular to the direction of the macromolecules and produce strong lateral cohesion between them.[55]

A considerable deformation of the electronic clouds of molecules like BF_3, $AlCl_3$, and $AlBr_3$ seems to occur under the influence of strong dipoles, in the sense that through this additional polarization the bonds between the central metal atom and the halogens become more polar.   Thus, according

[55] Compare C. S. Fuller and W. O. Baker, *J. Am. Chem. Soc.*, **62**, 3275 (1940); **65**, 1120 (1943); R. Brill, *Naturwissenschaften*, **29**, 200 (1941); M. Bergmann, I. Fankuchen, and H. Mark, *J. Text. Res.*, **18**, 1 (1948).

to Klemm,[56] by addition of NH_3 to $AlBr_3$, the character of the AlBr bond is shifted to the polar side, so that ultimately, by the entrance of more NH_3 components, the molecular addition compound $AlBr_3 \cdot NH_3$ is converted into an ionic complex compound $Al(NH_3)_3{}^{+++}Br_3{}^{---}$.

Briegleb and Lauppe[57] were able to establish a similar effect in the molecular association between $AlCl_3$ and ethers with the aid of the Raman spectrum.

2. Aggregate Formation by Dispersion Forces

It has previously been mentioned that dispersion and induction forces decrease with the distance between the interacting molecules more rapidly than the forces between permanent dipoles; they can therefore be effective only if the interacting groups have a chance to get sufficiently close together. Experience confirms this expectation. While, as explained above, the forces between dipole molecules in the gaseous state and also in the state of more or less dilute solutions sometimes cause the formation of permanent associations, the corresponding action of dispersion forces is restricted to the production of very transient aggregates in the liquid state, possibly also in concentrated solutions.

Briegleb, in his book, suggests that the individual particles in molecular aggregates, the composition of which fluctuates rapidly in space and time, must on the average always arrange themselves parallel to the axes or planes of highest polarizability. Under such conditions, molecular interaction will be favored by close proximity of the favorably packing rod- or plate-shaped molecules. Later (compare Chapter VII), in discussing the liquid phase, we will describe in greater detail the experimental facts on which present ideas about liquid structure are based; in anticipation it may be observed that x-ray diffraction, electron diffraction, Kerr effect, and degree of depolarization provide good experimental evidence for the existence of molecular clusters and show that nonpolar chain molecules (e.g., paraffins, olefins, etc.) orient themselves parallel to their long axes, whereas flat ring systems (e.g., benzene, naphthalene, etc.) arrange themselves parallel to the plane of the ring.

De Boer[58] estimated the magnitude of the dispersion forces between benzene molecules. If we calculate, from quantum mechanical postulates, the interaction between two benzene molecules in the position of Figure IV-

[56] W. Klemm, *Z. anorg. allgem. Chem.*, **200**, 367 (1931).
[57] G. Briegleb and J. H. Lauppe, *Z. physik. Chem.*, **B28**, 154 (1935).
[58] J. H. de Boer, *Trans. Faraday Soc.*, **32**, 10 (1936).

11, we must assume—on the basis of the effective radii of the H atoms given in Table I-10—that the distance between the centers of the two rings is about 2.5 Å. At the same time we should remember that there exists here an easily mobile and highly polarizable charge cloud near the center of the ring which corresponds to the equivalent of about two electrons per ring, and is connected with the aromatic character of the molecule. These negative charge clouds cannot approach each other very closely and are screened from one another by the stable periphery of the ring. If, however, the two rings are placed in the position of Figure IV-12, their centers

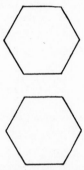

Fig. IV-11.   This position of the two benzene rings is not favorable to the formation of an *association configuration*.

Fig. IV-12.   Most favorable position of two benzene molecules for formation of a group preferred on energy grounds.

can approach each other to within a distance of about 2.6 Å. and the easily polarizable components of both charge clouds can be arranged directly opposite each other.

An estimate shows that the energy of interaction in the position of Figure IV-12 is about three times that of Figure IV-11 and amounts to about 1000 cal. per mole.[59]   The formation of groups or clusters having a certain short average lifetime of existence of stacked up benzene rings is thus feasible. De Boer has suggested that in polystyrene the benzene rings in close spatial proximity favor the parallel arrangement as shown in Figure IV-12 and that through their mutual attraction the original flexibility of the polymethylene chain is inhibited and only very restricted rotation around the carbon-carbon bond is possible at ordinary temperatures.   Polystyrene does, indeed, possess rubberlike properties at higher temperatures where the inter-

[59] J. H. de Boer, *Trans. Faraday Soc.*, **32**, 10 (1936); also E. Hückel, *Z. Physik* **70**, 204 (1931); **75**, 628 (1932).

action of the benzene rings in the molecule is reduced by their thermal vibrations.

In conclusion, a few rules governing boiling points of organic compounds may be mentioned. The boiling points of saturated normal hydrocarbons are known to increase with the length of the chain and to decrease as one passes to branched chains having the same number of carbon atoms, because, on branching, the molecule becomes more bulky and on purely geometrical grounds a dense packing of the interacting groups becomes difficult. The effect of dense packing on the boiling points of paraffins is shown in Table IV-12 in which the boiling points of normal hydrocarbons are compared with those of the corresponding ring systems. The open chains possess a certain degree of free rotation, which is opposed to a regular parallel arrangement of the molecules; in the cycloparaffins, however, it is to be expected that the free mobility of the methylene groups is greatly restricted by the existence of the ring and is limited merely to vibrations of moderate amplitude. Therefore the ring-shaped molecules should be more densely packed and more likely to form aggregates than the open chains. A glance at Table IV-12 shows that experiment confirms this expectation.

TABLE IV-12

BOILING POINTS OF PARAFFIN CHAINS AND RINGS

Substance	B.p., °C.	Substance	B.p., °C.
Pentane	37°	Cycloheptane	118°
Cyclopentane	50°	Nonane	150°
Hexane	69°	Dicyclononane	170°
Cyclohexane	80°	Heptadiene	107°
Heptane	98°	Cycloheptadiene	118°

We have tried in the foregoing to enumerate a few cases in which the action of intermolecular forces leads to the formation of unstable and transient aggregates; now we shall proceed to discuss a few instances in which these forces lead to the existence of relatively stable molecular compounds that can be isolated and characterized.

D. INTERMOLECULAR FORCES AND INTERMOLECULAR COMPOUNDS

From the large number of intermolecular compounds, we shall, in this section which is merely a preliminary to the discussion of the properties of high polymers, select two groups and discuss them in some detail: (1)

molecular associaton compounds involving aromatic systems;   and (2) molecular associations of carboxylic acids.

Recently a very interesting new type of adduct between aliphatic chain molecules and polar molecules, such as urea, thiourea, and formamide, was discovered by Bengen and thoroughly studied by Schlenk.[60]

1. Molecular Association Involving Conjugated and Aromatic Systems

We shall first discuss the molecular associations of organic nitro compounds with unsaturated hydrocarbons, familiar since the time of Pfeiffer[60] and more recently studied in detail particularly by Briegleb,[61] Bruni,[62] Hertel,[63] Lennard-Jones,[64] and others.   All evidence indicates that the easily mobile charge clouds of aromatic and unsaturated aliphatic hydrocarbons are polarized by the strong dipoles of the nitro groups.   There results an attraction between the two molecules and their electronic charge clouds are brought into closer proximity.   This, in turn, has the conse-

TABLE IV-13

ENERGY OF FORMATION OF THE MOLECULAR ASSOCIATIONS OF TRINITRO-
BENZENE WITH AROMATIC HYDROCARBONS IN CCl_4

Hydrocarbon	Energy of formation, kcal.	Av. mol. polarizability $\times 10^{24}$
Naphthalene	3.4	18.2
Phenanthrene	4.0	26.4
Anthracene	4.4	30.8
Styrene	1.81	14.18
Phenylbutadiene	2.15	18.85
Diphenylbutadiene	2.88	32.6

quence that dispersion forces come into play and produce the stability of the associated complex.   The relatively far-reaching dipole fields bring the molecules together to form a complex and the dispersion forces then stabilize the arrangement.

This view receives support from the data in Table IV-13, for which we are

[60] M. F. Bengen, *Experientia*, **5**, 200 (1949).   W. Schlenk, Jr., *Ann.*, **565**, 204 (1950).

[61] P. Pfeiffer, *Organische Molekülverbindungen*, 2nd ed., Enke, Stuttgart, 1927.   G. Briegleb, *Z. physik. Chem.*, **B31**, 58 (1935); **32**, 305 (1936).

[62] G. Bruni, *Gazz. chim. ital.*, **34**, 474 (1904); **35**, 304 (1905).

[63] E. Hertel, *Z. physik. Chem.*, **B11**, 59, 90 (1930).

[64] J. E. Lennard-Jones, *Trans. Faraday Soc.*, **32**, 1, 37 (1936).

TABLE IV-14

HEATS OF FORMATION OF MOLECULAR ASSOCIATIONS AS AFFECTED BY THE
NUMBER OF NITRO GROUPS

Compound	U, kcal.	Compound	U, kcal.
s-Trinitrobenzene-acenaphthene	2.45	m-Dinitrobenzene-naphthalene	1.6
m-Dinitrobenzene-acenaphthene	1.35	Nitrobenzene-naphthalene	Very small
Nitrobenzene-acenaphthene	Very small	s-Trinitrobenzene-anthracene	3.6
s-Trinitrobenzene-naphthalene	3.4	m-Dinitrobenzene-anthracene	1.5
		o-Dinitrobenzene-anthracene	2.9

indebted to Briegleb and his co-workers.[65] They show that the energy of
formation of the molecular association compound between trinitrobenzene
and various aromatic hydrocarbons increases with the average polarizabilities of the substances, upon which the induction and dispersion effects
depend. The stability of the resulting molecular association compounds as

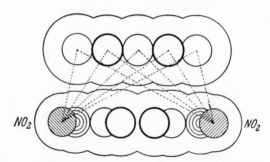

Fig. IV-13.   Side view of the complex naphthalene (above)-p-dinitrobenzene (below).
The ranges of action are indicated by the faint outlines.

given in Table IV-13 agrees with expectation in order of magnitude; a
dipole of the strength of about 4 debyes, as in the nitro group, interacts,
according to Briegleb, with about 2000 cal. per mole, with a molecule of an
average polarizability of 20×10^{-24} cc., such as occurs in the unsaturated
hydrocarbons, at a distance of 3 Å.

It has also been found that the number of nitro groups in the nitro compound has an important influence on the dissociation energy of the resulting

[65] Cf. G. Briegleb, *Zwischenmolekulare Kräfte und Molekülstruktur*, Enka, Stuttgart,
1937, table 13 on p. 106 and table 14 on p. 107.

molecular associate; Table IV-14 contains measurements of Halban and Zimpelmann[66] and of Briegleb and Schachowsky[67] which have established this fact. From these experimental data, which give the stability of the various association compounds, it is possible to derive some ideas regarding the spatial arrangement of the two components of such a molecular complex. The action of the forces involved will certainly reach its maximum if the planes of the two interacting ring systems are arranged parallel to each other. Figure IV-13 and IV-14 of Briegleb probably express the most

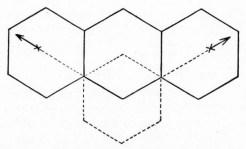

Fig. IV-14.   Complex anthracene (heavy line)-*m*-dinitrobenzene (broken line) seen from above.

favorable arrangement for the association of dinitrobenzene with naphthalene and anthracene, respectively. We may infer from the first figure, which represents the atoms of the two molecules and their spheres of action in the proper proportions, that such a position ensures the closest proximity of the inducing dipole and the polarizable charge cloud; any oblique position of one or other partner would considerably increase the distances involved for interaction. Figure IV-14 shows again that in this arrangement the permanent dipoles of the nitro groups attain very close proximity to the easily polarizable charge clouds near the centers of the benzene rings and can therefore polarize them effectively.

Before we pass to the discussion of molecular associations of aliphatic carboxylic acids it may be observed that the peculiar capability of aromatic systems for the formation of such associations is probably due to the fact that on ring closure the free rotation of the individual CH groups is eliminated and, that, again through ring closure, charge clouds of high polarizability are closely condensed in space, thus becoming readily susceptible to the deforming influence of strong dipole fields.

[66] H. v. Halban and E. Zimpelmann, *Z. physik. Chem.*, **A117,** 461 (1925).
[67] G. Briegleb and Schachowsky, *Z. physik. Chem.*, **B19,** 255 (1931).

Remarkably stable associations of trinitrobenzene with stilbene and with polyenes are known; the number of associated nitro groups is generally equal to the number of the phenyl residues in the molecule. Kuhn and Winterstein[68] conclude from this that—in the sense of the above discussion—the nitro aromatics prefer interaction with benzene nuclei to that with aliphatic polyene chains.

Briegleb attempted to estimate the bond strength of a series of molecular compounds on the basis of the charge distribution and polarizability of the aromatic ring systems or the aliphatic polyene chains and arrived at the data given in Table IV-15. Comparison with figures determined experimentally confirmed this estimation and gives confidence in the accuracy of other calculated energies of formation, at least with regard to their order of magnitude.

TABLE IV-15

DISSOCIATION ENERGIES OF A FEW MOLECULAR ASSOCIATIONS BETWEEN NITRO AROMATICS AND CONDENSED RING SYSTEMS

Association compound	Kilocalories	
	Observed	Calculated
s-Trinitrobenzene with		
Benzene...........................ca. 0.6		1.8
Styrene............................. 1.8		2.6
Naphthalene........................ 3.4		3.1
Anthracene......................... 4.4		4.6
Anthracene with		
o-Dinitrobenzene.................... 3.0		2.9
m-Dinitrobenzene................... 1.6		1.5
p-Dinitrobenzene.................... 1.45		1.2
s-Trinitrobenzene................... 4.4		4.6

In conclusion, it may be mentioned also that molecules other than nitro compounds, having a large permanent moment or carrying strong group moments, e.g., $AlCl_3$, quinones, phthalic anhydride, nitriles, etc., can produce molecular associations of remarkable stability, with molecules possessing easily polarizable domains. It is probable that these molecular compounds owe their existence to the same cause as discussed above for the interaction between nitro compounds and aromatic hydrocarbons.

The attraction between strong dipoles, such as NO_2, CN, CO, etc., and other similar groups, or their interaction with easily polarizable domains of

[68] R. Kuhn and H. Winterstein, Helv. Chim. Acta, 11, 144 (1928).

another molecule plays an important role in the formation of association compounds, of macromolecules with small molecules, such as solvents or plasticizers. Nitrocellulose, *e.g.*, forms relatively stable compounds with molecules having strong dipoles (*e.g.*, camphor, cyclohexanone), aromatic ketones and esters (*e.g.*, benzophenone, tricresyl phosphate), and the like. Esters, ketones, and chlorinated hydrocarbons are in general good solvents and plasticizers for many polymers because they interact with permanent dipoles and polymerizable parts of the macromolecules, and surround them with a layer of solvent or plasticizer molecules which separates the large molecules from each other and provides for plasticity, swelling, and finally for solubility. Polymer-solvent (or plasticizer) interaction has to compete in this respect with polymer-polymer interaction; if the latter prevails we shall have precipitation and insolubility.

Polar attraction between macromolecules, such as in polyvinyl acetate, polyvinyl chloride, nitrocellulose, etc., can usually be overcome by polar plasticizers or solvents.[69] If, however, the large molecules are linked together by hydrogen bridges, such as in polyamides, polyesters, polyacrylonitrile, cellulose, or proteins, only molecules with a strong hydrogen bond capacity will act as plasticizers or solvents. Such molecules are formic acid, benzyl alcohol, phenol, dimethyl formamide, butyrolactone, etc.

2. Molecular Associations between Carboxylic Acids

The existence of double molecules of carboxylic acids has been recognized for a long time. Fenton and Garner[70] and Coolidge[71] have proved their existence in the gaseous state by vapor pressure measurements. Molecular weight determinations in dilute solutions were carried out some time ago by Trautz and Moschel[72] and by a number of other authors with identical results; numerous exceptions to the Trouton-Eötvös rule in the liquid state are additional qualitative proof for the existence of such association compounds.

It was mentioned in Ch. III (Sect. C) that preliminary polar attraction between two carboxyl groups leads to an arrangement that favors the establishment of resonance, which, in turn, is probably responsible for the existence of dimers in all carboxylic acids with chains of not too great length. Actually, Pauling and Brockway[73] have confirmed experimentally the existence of such arrangements in lower members of the carboxylic acid

[69] Compare a series of articles collected in *J. Polymer Sci.*, **2**, 113 (1947).

[70] M. Fenton and W. E. Garner, *J. Chem. Soc.*, **1930**, 694.

[71] A. S. Coolidge, *J. Am. Chem. Soc.*, **50**, 2166 (1928).

[72] M. Trautz and W. Moschel, *Z. anorg. allgem. Chem.*, **155**, 13 (1926).

[73] L. Pauling and L. O. Brockway, *Proc. Natl. Acad. Sci. U. S.*, **36**, 430 (1930).

series by electron diffraction.   Moreover, the extensive studies of Müller, Trillat, Langmuir, and others[74] with x-ray and electron diffraction techniques show that the interaction of suitably arranged carboxyl groups provides for a strong intermolecular bond.

This view is also supported by the fact that on esterifying this group the tendency to form molecular associations is completely lost.   In terms of the information given in Ch. III there are two reasons for this.   First, by steric hindrance, the effect on the dipole field of the COOR group is diminished, and, second, in the absence of a mobile hydrogen atom any resonance between the molecules is impossible; the hydrogen bond is cut out on replacing the hydrogen by an alkyl group.

Table IV-16 contains a few data on the energy relationships.   It is evident, at least in acids with short chains, that the energy of formation of the double molecule decreases on enlarging the nonpolar component of the molecule, the reason being that its presence prevents close approach of the interacting carboxyl groups.

TABLE IV-16

ENERGY OF FORMATION OF DOUBLE MOLECULES OF SIMPLE CARBOXYLIC ACIDS

Substance	B.p., °K.	E, kcal.
Formic acid	374.3	14.3
Acetic acid	391.3	13.8
Heptoic acid	496.3	7.05
Benzoic acid	—	5.6

To what extent the nonpolar components of long-chain hydrocarbon molecules screen the effect of the polar groups and finally become themselves essentially responsible for intermolecular attraction cannot be stated with certainty.   However, it is very probable that the COOH group is responsible, in the sense discussed above, for the presence of double molecules of benzoic acid in benzene, whereas for the association effect in water it is rather the interaction of the benzene nuclei, because in aqueous solution the COOH groups are probably extensively hydrated.

Moreover, the well-known experiments of Langmuir,[75] Rideal,[76] Adam,[77]

[74] Cf. A. Müller, *Proc. Roy. Soc. London*, **A154**, 624 (1936);   J. J. Trillat and H. Motz, *Ann. Physik*, **7**, 161 (1928).

[75] I. Langmuir, *Colloid Chemistry*, New York, 1926.

[76] E. K. Rideal, *Surface Chemistry*, 2nd ed., Cambridge Univ. Press, London, 1930.

[77] N. K. Adam, *Physics and Chemistry of Surfaces*, Oxford Univ. Press, London, 1938.

and others on the spreading of fatty acids and other long-chain compounds on the surface of water show that, after adsorption of the COOH groups by the water surface, the mechanical properties of the resulting films are determined chiefly by the parallel orientation of the homopolar chains under the influence of nonpolar dispersion forces and depend in a characteristic fashion on chain length and on the extent of branching. In addition, Traube's rule on the heats of adsorption of homologous fatty acids confirms the influence of the lipoid fraction of these molecules. We shall return later to the very marked interaction between different types of molecules in the liquid phase in the section on liquids and solutions. Here, in concluding the discussion of well-defined molecular compounds, the above data may be sufficient.

3. Calculation of Molecular Cohesion

A few quantitative data have already been given regarding the magnitude of intermolecular forces, which show that, generally speaking, secondary valences possess the order of 500–5000 cal. per atom or atomic group, while the chemical primary valences are found to amount to 50,000–100,000 cal. per mole.

Table III-2 on page 68 contains figures on the dissociation energy of a number of primary valence bonds and it would obviously be desirable to have a similar table for intermolecular bonds. Such a table has actually been worked out by Dunkel,[78] who computed the intermolecular attraction for various characteristic groups—a quantity which K. H. Meyer termed *molar cohesion* if expressed in calories per mole.

For the data in Table III-2 the dissociation energies of the primary valence bonds, *i.e.*, the heats of combustion, had to be used; now, we must consider the energy necessary to overcome molecular cohesion, which is measured by the heats of sublimation and vaporization or by the van der Waals' attraction constant a. For the latter, and for the Sutherland constant closely allied to it, van Laar[79] long ago established certain additive relationships. These are expressed even more definitely in the well-known Traube rule for the heats of adsorption of homologous series, which, according to Eucken,[80] are closely related to the heats of vaporization.

Heats of vaporization certainly represent the best experimental material for deducing such relationships. Dunkel collected such data and estimated

[78] M. Dunkel, *Z. physik. Chem.*, **A138**, 42 (1928).
[79] J. J. van Laar, *J. chim. phys.*, **14**, 3 (1915).
[80] A. Eucken, *Z. physik. Chem.*, **A134**, 280 (1928).

from them the molar cohesion of typical groups in organic molecules. The difficulty that arises here in contrast to the Fajans-von Weinberg[81] calculation for primary valence bonds is due to the fact that, because of the large absolute values in the first case, the effect of temperature on these forces, *i.e.*, the influence of specific heats and of the chemical constants, can be ignored, whereas the experimental vapor pressure curves would lead to completely erroneous heats of vaporization if the influence of the specific heats and chemical constants were neglected. Measurements at very low temperatures would be of great value for a correct evaluation of the vapor pressure data, but they are unfortunately very scanty. Dunkel therefore attempted to separate semiquantitatively the contribution of certain groups to the heats of vaporization, and proceeded in the following way.

The vapor pressure of a substance is determined by two factors: the energy increase on evaporation and the ratio of phase volume at absolute zero, which are available to a molecule in the solid and gaseous state, respectively. The first factor comprises the heats of vaporization whose temperature dependence is determined by the difference between the specific heat of the vapor and the condensate. The second factor measures the ratio of the *a priori* probabilities to encounter a molecule in the con-

TABLE IV-17

MOLAR COHESION OF DIFFERENT ORGANIC GROUPS

Group	Molar cohesion, cal./mole	Group	Molar cohesion, cal./mole
$-CH_3$ $=CH_2$ }	1780	$-COOC_2H_5$	6,230
$-CH_2-$ $=CH-$ }	990	$-NH_2$	3,530
		$-Cl$	3,400
		$-F$	2,060
$-O-$	1630	$-Br$	4,300
$-OH$	7250	$-I$	5,040
$=CO$	4270	$-NO_2$	7,200
$-CHO$	4700	$-SH$	4,250
$-COOH$	8970	$-CONH_2$	13,200
$-COOCH_3$	5600	$-CONH-$	16,200

densed or in the free state and is related to the vibrations and rotations of the molecule under consideration. The boiling point rules and the other regularities mentioned above makes it reasonable to suppose that in homologous series each of the factors can be computed additively, as can

[18] K. Fajans and A. v. Weinberg, *Ber.*, **53**, 1347, 1519 (1920); **55**, 2828 (1922).

many other properties of such molecules.   In fact, within certain limitations there exists a satisfactory additivity of the two terms in the vapor pressure formula.   Table IV-17 records the molecular cohesion in terms of calories per mole of interacting groups for the most important groups in organic compounds.   With these figures and with appropriate additive terms corresponding to the chemical constants, the boiling points in homologous series can be calculated in fair agreement with experiment.

The limitations previously referred to are related to the mutual disturbance and interaction of individual groups in a molecule; the additive behavior is then liable to be eventually overshadowed by the mutual interaction of the functional groups.   Thus it is not possible to make up the molar cohesion of the carboxyl group additively from those of the hydroxyl and carbonyl groups, although it is possible, according to Eucken,[82] to do this for the dipole moment to a first approximation.   For the increment of the heat of vaporization, however, not only the moment of rigid dipoles, but to a large extent also the polarizability of the groups which are formed by association, must be taken into consideration.

The modern experimental methods of investigating dipole molecules and the evaluation of the results by the Debye theory have greatly extended our understanding of the connection between chemical constitution, dipole character and intermolecular attraction.   As long as we compare only homologous or polymer homologous series with one another, it is possible to compute to a fairly good approximation the molar cohesion of such compounds additively from individual group contributions.   Consequently, in such series, with increasing molecular weight, the molar cohesion increases almost proportionally to the molecular weight.

From the relation between dipole character, polarizability, and constitution it follows that isomeric compounds with the same or similar atomic arrangement cannot differ very greatly in their molecular attraction because the component dipole moments that exist in organic molecules all are between 1.5 and 4.0 debyes; they can at one time be somewhat strengthened by superposition and at other times weakened, but not to the extent that there is a very considerable difference in their external effect.   The polarizabilities of all groups concerned are also of the same order of magnitude: 10–20×10^{-24}.   If, therefore, two substances of the same empirical composition are on the one hand soluble and volatile, and on the other hand insoluble and incapable of distillation, we must conclude from our present general knowledge of intermolecular forces that the molecular weights of the two substances has to be distinctly different.

[82] A. Eucken, *Physik. Z.*, **30**, 397 (1930); *Z. Elektrochem.*, **28**, 6 (1922).

Should we wish to ascribe large differences in molar cohesion to a different arrangement of the individual groups in a molecule, we would have to assume *ad hoc* a new type of intermolecular force, previously unknown, although there is no other evidence for existence in organic chemistry.

E. INTERMOLECULAR FORCES, POLYMER TEXTURE, AND POLYMER PROPERTIES

The attractive forces between macromolecules play an important role in the physical texture of polymer samples and are of decisive influence on the ultimate mechanical and thermal properties of these materials. It has become evident that the nature of the monomer and the way in which the monomers in each individual chain are linked together determine, to a large extent, the physical behavior of polymers, and it seems appropriate to insert here a short paragraph on the importance of intermolecular forces for polymeric materials.

The investigations of the last two decades indicate that high polymers, in general, exhibit a rather intricate two-phase or even multi-phase nature.* Certain areas of a given sample possess a high degree of internal geometrical order or organization; one usually refers to them as "crystallites" or "micelles." In fact, they have many properties commonly found in ordinary crystals. They diffract x-rays and electrons of medium wave length, so that regular fiber or powder diagrams are produced. They exhibit birefringence and show distinct anisotropy of swelling. In other respects, however, these crystallized areas are unlike the crystals of normal organic substances. They do not have well-defined plane boundaries or sharp symmetrical edges. Their sizes seem to vary widely; in some cases, such as proteins or vinyl copolymers, they are very small; normally they are rodlike or ribbonlike, have an average length between 200 and 2000 Å., and an average width between 50 and 600 Å. In some cases it has been observed that they grow to comparatively large homogeneous domains of dimensions up to 10^5 or 10^6 Å.

These "crystallites" in a polymeric material should not be compared with the completely shaped and independent individuals of a crystal sugar powder, but rather with the grains of a polycrystalline metal, which also show many typical properties of normal crystals (x-ray pattern, birefringence, anisotropy) but, like the crystalline domains of an organic polymer, do not have plane boundaries and sharp edges. It seems, in general, that investigators of organic polymers can utilize with advantage the methods

* The word "phase" is not used here in Gibb's sense.

developed for and applied in metallography. Cellulose "crystallites" or rubber "micelles," then, will be taken to mean small areas of somewhat indefinite size and shape, inside of which the monomeric units are regularly arranged in a three-dimensional periodic pattern. The individual macro-molecules are longitudinally and laterally ordered.

But high polymers do not consist entirely of such well-organized domains. They always contain a certain amount of disordered and randomly entangled chains, which are usually referred to as the "amorphous" or "disordered" areas and which apparently contain the chains in a less perfect arrangement due to the fact that some irregularity has prevented them from reaching the proper equilibrium positions of the crystallized state. Macromolecules of a polymerization degree of about 1000 and more have an extended length of several thousand angstrom units. This is much longer than the average length of the crystalline areas. It is, therefore, the belief that one and the same chain can go through a crystalline domain, enter an amorphous area, go through it, enter another crystallite, and so on. This takes account of the fact that there is no sharp boundary between the crystallized and disordered areas, but that the chains of a certain crystal become somehow disordered, degenerate into fringes, and finally reach a completely disordered arrangement. Hence it may be appropriate not to make a sharp distinction between "crystallized" and "amorphous," but to consider various degrees of disorder, just as more than one crystallized modification of different high polymers have been observed. Baker, Fuller, and Pape[83] proposed to consider "mesomorphous" phases in quenched polyamides, and Taylor[84] has repeatedly pointed out that chains with regularly distributed centers of attraction are unlikely to curl up in a completely irregular way.

There seem to be even different degrees of randomness in a substance like rubber, as indicated by its thermal properties, particularly by the existence of second-order transition points at several different temperatures as established by Bekkedahl and Wood.[85] Transition points of higher orders are, in fact, a rather general feature in high polymers with chains of a certain internal flexibility and foldability, such as polystyrene, polyethylene, polyisobutylene, and polyacrylates. Theoretical considerations about a certain degree of regular folding in amorphous rubber were proposed several

[83] C. S. Fuller, W. O. Baker and N. R. Pape, *J. Am. Chem. Soc.*, **62**, 3275 (1940); **64**, 776 (1942).

[84] H. S. Taylor, compare, *e.g.*, lecture given at the ACS meeting in Memphis, Tenn., 1941.

[85] N. Bekkedahl and L. A. Wood, *J. Research Natl. Bur. Standards*, **23**, 571 (1939).

years ago by Kirchhoff[86] and by Fikentscher and Mark,[87] and were later improved by Mack,[88] who even based on them a theory of the elastic properties of rubber.

Polystyrene, polyvinyl acetate, and polyacrylic esters of polymerization degrees between 1000 and 2000 have not yet been forced into a definite crystalline structure by any mechanical or thermal treatment, although strongly anisotropic samples can be prepared by stretching. All these polymers show distinct transition points above room temperature. According to experiments of Davis and Whyte[89] they all exhibit amorphous x-ray diagrams in which, however, sharpness and intensity distribution of the diffuse halo can be influenced by appropriate pretreatments.

All this shows that even in chainlike (or slightly branched) hydrocarbons, or other polymers, where the intermolecular forces are weak and geometrically diffuse, various degrees of disorder exist and contribute to the mechanical behavior of the material.[90]

The tendency for a certain regularity in the curled-up state seems to be distinctly more pronounced if groups with attractive forces, such as permanent dipoles, easily polarizable bonds, or hydrogen bonding groups, are regularly distributed along the chain. Proteins, polyesters, polyurethans, and polyamides are examples for such systems. In accordance with these considerations, one has to distinguish between the "internal" crystallization of a single chain which is regularly folded back on itself and the "external" crystallization between two different chains. Cold drawing of polymers can in many cases be visualized as converting internal crystallization (regular curling up of the different individual chains) into external crystallization (parallelization of straightened-out chains). This picture of the conversion of folded-up chains having a certain degree of internal regularity into straightened-out chains having a high degree of lateral organization seems to be one molecular mechanism which accompanies most mechanical deformations of long-chain polymers.

Whether the free energy has its absolute minimum in the initial, relaxed

[86] H. Kirchhoff, *Kautschuk*, **1**, 119 (1930).

[87] H. Fikentscher and H. Mark, *Kautschuk*, **1**, 2 (1930).

[88] E. Mack, Jr., *J. Phys. Chem.*, **41**, 221 (1937).

[89] A. L. Davis and D. Whyte, unpublished observations made during their thesis work at the Polytechnic Institute of Brooklyn, 1943–45.

[90] Compare H. Mark, *Physik und Chemie der Zellulose*, Springer, Berlin, 1932; also H. Mark in E. Ott, *Cellulose and Cellulose Derivatives* (*High Polymers*, Vol. V), Interscience, New York, 1943; K. H. Meyer, *Natural and Synthetic High Polymers* (*High Polymers*, Vol. IV), Interscience, New York, 1950; T. Alfrey, *Mechanical Behavior of High Polymers* (*High Polymers*, Vol. VI), Interscience, New York, 1948.

state (curled-up chains) or in the final extended arrangement of the system (mutual crystallization of the chains) depends upon the molecular attraction between the chains, upon their geometrical fitting into the crystal lattice, upon temperature, and upon external forces.

(1) If the intermolecular attraction is small and the chains are difficult to fit laterally into a latticelike structure, then at a given temperature and stress the material will show a distinct tendency to return into its curled-up, relaxed state. Such conditions are typical for *rubbers*.

(2) On the other hand, if the molar cohesion is strong and the fine structure of the chains provides for easy lateral fitting into a latticelike arrangement, a state of high external crystallinity is favored and the material is a typical *fiber*.

(3) In intermediate cases, in which the forces are moderate and the geometry of the chains is moderately favorable for crystallization, the behavior of the material will depend greatly upon external conditions such as temperature and external mechanical forces. Such systems are typical *plastics*.

These qualitative considerations show that rubbers, plastics, and fibers are not intrinsically different materials. Their difference is rather a matter of degree and is produced by the way in which the intermolecular forces between the long chains and their general tendency to curl and fold cooperate in forming a certain mixture of crystallized and disordered portions in a given sample of the material.[91]

In general, it can be said that under given conditions such as temperature and external forces applied to the sample the tendency to crystallize is brought about by two different factors, which to a certain extent conflict with each other:

(a) *The forces between the individual macromolecules.* This influence corresponds to the ΔH term in the expression for the free energy change during crystallization. If the forces are strong (above 5000 cal. per mole of the group involved), then they will, at ordinary temperatures, preponderantly determine the behavior and we can expect the material to behave more or less as a typical fiber. This seems to be true for cellulose, proteins, nylon, terylene, Orlon, etc.

(b) *The geometrical bulkiness of the chains.* This influence corresponds to the $T \Delta S$ term in the expression for the free energy change during crystallization. Chains that fit easily into a crystal lattice (polyethylene, *trans*-polydiolefins) crystallize under the influence of comparatively weak forces and hence, in general, have a tendency to appear more fiberlike than would be expected if the forces alone were considered. On the other hand, materials which have bulky and irregular chains do not crystallize even if the intermolecular forces are quite strong. Hence they will be more rubberlike than one would expect on taking into account only the intermolecular forces (vinyl copolymers, cellulose mixed esters, etc.).

Table IV-18 illustrates the applicability of this consideration. The first

[91] H. Mark, *Ind. Eng. Chem.*, **39**, 1343 (1942).

column lists macromolecules ranging from polyhydrocarbons with small molar cohesion to polyamides and polyesters having strong van der Waals' forces between the chain.   The next column shows the type of covalent bond which links the different monomers together in each single chain. The approximate dissociation energies of these bonds are all above 70,000 calories per mole, which corresponds to strong primary valencies.   It has been calculated that the force needed to rupture such links would correspond approximately to a tensile strength of one hundred and fifty grams per denier, which is far above any experimentally observed value.   The highest tenacities of fibers actually measured are about ten grams per denier.   This shows that rupture of a fiber does not preponderantly involve rupture of the individual chains, but rather their slipping along one another and finally breaking the van der Waals' bond between them.

TABLE IV-18

EFFECT OF INTERMOLECULAR FORCES ON MECHANICAL BEHAVIOR OF VARIOUS POLYMERS

Substance	Covalent bond along chain	Groups responsible for lateral attraction	Specific molar cohesion, cal.
Polyethylene	C—C	CH_2	1000
Polyisobutene	C—C	CH_2, CH_3	1200
Rubber	C—C, C=C	CH_2, CH_3	1300
Polychloroprene	C—C, C=C	CH_2, CCl	1600
Polyvinyl chloride	C—C	CH_2, CCl	2600
Polyvinyl acetate	C—C	CH_2, $COCH_3$	3200
Polystyrene	C—C	CH_2, C_6H_5	4000
Polyvinyl alcohol	C—C	CH_2, OH	4200
Cellulose acetate	C—C, C—O	OH, $COCH_3$	4800
Cellulose	C—C, C—O	OH, COC	6200
Polyamides	C—C, C—N	CH_2, CONH	5800
Silk fibroin	C—C, C—N	CHR, CONH	9800

The fourth column of the table lists the groups mainly responsible for the mutual attraction of the chains as a consequence of the different types of van der Waals' forces (compare Table IV-17).   In the case of hydrocarbons the attraction is essentially caused by dispersion forces between methylene or methyl groups with cohesive energies of about 1000 cal. per mole of these groups; in the case of polyamides one has CONH groups, which are hydrogen-bridged from chain to chain and represent an attraction of about 8000 cal. per mole.

The forces of all attractive groups along the length of the chains add up and provide for a certain molecular cohesion per unit length.   The last column of Table 1V-18 contains the values of this cohesion calculated in calories per mole for a length of 5.0 Å. under the assumption that each chain is surrounded by four others; this quantity has been termed the specific molar cohesion.   The figures of the last column show that all typical rubbers (natural rubber, neoprene, polybutadiene, polyisobutylene) have specific molar cohesions between 1000 and 2000 cal.   The only exception is polyethylene, where the forces are also small, but where the rubberlike properties are not specifically pronounced.   This may be explained by an exceedingly good fitting of the straight, smooth, and comparatively not too flexible zigzag hydrocarbon chains in the crystal lattice.

If the specific molar cohesion as listed in the last column assumes values above 5000 cal., the substances behave like typical fibers with a high modulus of elasticity (10^{11} to 10^{12} dynes per square centimeter) and considerable tensile strength.   It seems again that the ease with which a given chain can be arranged in a lattice determines the position of the material among the fibers.   Thus, nylon is generally stronger and tougher than silk, although its specific molar cohesion is smaller.

In cases where the specific molar cohesion as listed in column 4 is between 2000 and 5000 cal., the material behaves like a plastic; it becomes soft or rubberlike at elevated temperatures, but shows crystallization at normal temperatures without stretching.   Polyvinyl alcohol, which has particularly smooth chains, shows a tendency to exhibit fiber properties, although according to its intermolecular attraction it should be a typical plastic.

It must be understood that Table IV-18 represents only a crude and preliminary attempt to correlate the properties of rubbers, plastics, and fibers from the point of view of intermolecular attraction because it considers essentially the intermolecular forces and does not sufficiently take into account the entropy changes during crystallization.

V. CRYSTAL STRUCTURE AND CRYSTAL FORCES

In the classification and systematization of our knowledge of crystal structure it became evident that there exist essentially *two* useful guiding principles: the *nature* of the *forces*, which hold the lattice together, and the *symmetry* of the lattice itself.

In course of time *two* approaches of studying and interpreting the properties of solids were developed, one with the emphasis on the *type of lattice-forming forces*, the other considering mainly *lattice symmetry*. At first it seemed as if there were no relation between these two approaches because lattices with the same symmetry can be held together by entirely different forces and, conversely, forces of the same nature can produce lattices of different symmetry. On further investigation, however, it became evident that the two ways of classifying crystal lattices complemented each other in a very successful manner.

Therefore, it appears advisable in the present discussion to describe both classifications of crystal lattices in some detail and to emphasize their cooperation whenever the structure of high polymeric substances is involved.

A. CLASSIFICATION OF CRYSTALS FROM THE ASPECT OF FORCES

The following types of forces can be responsible for keeping crystal lattices together: (*a*) heteropolar main valences between oppositely charged ions; (*b*) homopolar main valences between neutral atoms; (*c*) metallic valences; and (*d*) van der Waals' (secondary) forces and hydrogen bonds between saturated molecules.

Conditions are simplest if the same type of force is effective in *all three* directions of a crystal. In this case, true *ionic, atomic, metallic*, and *molecular* lattices are formed. It may happen, however—and these cases will later be shown to be of special interest—that in one and the same lattice different types of forces prevail in the different directions in space, and result in *mixed lattices* and *transition states* which will be discussed after the simple cases.

The fundamental nature of each of the four forces has already been

153

TABLE V-1

CLASSIFICATION OF CRYSTAL LATTICES ACCORDING TO GRIMM

Bond type	Lattice type (class of compound)	Compounds AB		Compounds AB₂		Further examples of different lattice types
		Lattice type	C.N.[a]	Lattice type	C.N.[a]	
Ionic linkage............	Ionic lattice (salts)	CsCl	8	CaF_2	8.4	AlF_3
		NaCl	6	TiO_2 (Rutile)	6.3	ZrF_4
Metallic linkage........	Atomic lattice (metals)	CuZn	8	—	—	K
		TiC	6	LaC_2	—	Cu_5Zn_8
Atomic linkage.........	Atomic lattice	ZnS (wurtzite)	4	SiO_2	4.2	Al_2O_3
(homopolar linkage)...	(diamond lattice)	ZnS (zincblende)	4	OCu_2	4.2	Si_3N_4
Van der Waals' linkage between the molecules; atomic linkage within the molecule........	Molecular lattices	CO	1	CO_2	2.1	CCl_4
		Cl_2	1	—	—	$CO(NH_2)_2$

[a] C.N. = Coordination number.

mentioned or described in the discussion of intra- and intermolecular attraction. It remains, therefore, only to show here what happens if a continuous crystal lattice is formed by each of these forces. As an introduction, Table V-1 gives a summary of pure lattice types, arranged according to the lattice forces acting.

1. Ionic Lattices

The development of the experimental techniques for investigating crystal structures with x-rays led first to the study of the simplest inorganic substances, such as NaCl, $CaCO_3$, SiO_2, MgO, and to the elucidation of their lattice structure. The abundant data thus obtained were naturally an inducement to a search for general relationships.

TABLE V-2

IONIC RADII OF VARIOUS ALKALIES AND ALKALINE EARTHS

Ion	Ions radius calculated		
	From the fluoride	From the chloride	From the bromide
Li^+	0.68	0.76	0.79
Na^+	0.98	1.00	1.01
K^+	1.33	1.33	1.33
NH_4^+	—	1.36	1.49
Ion	From the oxide	From the sulfide	From the selenide
Mg^{++}	0.78	0.80	0.81
Sr^{++}	1.27	1.19	1.21

Bragg[1], Fajans[2], Grimm[3], and Pauling[4] have investigated the fundamentals of these laws, and the extensive work of Goldschmidt and his coworkers[5] has formulated them comprehensively and confirmed them by many new experimental data. The principal results of this *ionic crystallo-chemistry* are:[6]

[1] Compare, *e.g.*, W. H. and W. L. Bragg, *The Crystalline State*, Macmillan, New York, 1934.

[2] K. Fajans, *Naturwiss.*, **11**, 105 (1923); *Z. Krist.*, **61**, 18 (1925).

[3] H. G. Grimm, cf. esp. his article in *Handbuch der Physik*, Springer, Berlin. 2nd edition 1936, Vol. 24, part 2.

[4] L. Pauling, *The Nature of the Chemical Bond*. Cornell Univ. Press, Ithaca, 1939.

[5] V. M. Goldschmidt, *Die Gesetze der Kristallchemie*, Oslo, 1925; *Naturwiss.*, **14**, 477 (1926); *Ber.*, **60**, 1263 (1927).

[6] Compare also P. Niggli, *Der feste Körper*, Leipzig, 1938.

(*a*) To a first approximation, the individual ions in a crystal lattice behave like *rigid spheres*. Each of them, such as the univalent Na^+ ion, the
divalent Ca^{++} ion, etc., possesses a definite radius which persists practically unchanged in the passage from one lattice to another. Table V-2
gives a few examples which demonstrate that the radii of the various ions
in crystal lattices are to a great extent independent of the partners with
which the ions build up the lattice. Deviations from this rule amount on
an average only to about 1–2% if the lattice types compared are similar to
one another (commensurable structures).

With this concept of rigid spherical ions, Goldschmidt could show that
the ratio of the radii of those ions which build up a lattice is of decisive importance for the appearance of one or the other lattice type in binary salts.
He applied an idea first used by Magnus[7] to explain the different coordination numbers of elements, namely, that a system of spheres of different
sizes is stable if the smaller spheres *exactly fill* the space formed by the
larger ones.

Figure (V-1a) shows, for example, that the space between four Cl ions,
which have radii of 1.8 Å., is filled exactly by the quadrivalent positive

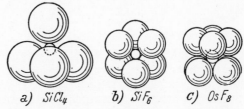

a) $SiCl_4$ b) SiF_6 c) OsF_8

Fig. V-1. Geometric explanation of the different
co-ordination numbers (according to A. Magnus).

silicon ion with the radius 0.4 Å., while the space formed by six chlorine
ions would be too great for one silicon ion; it would not fit firmly into it but
would "rattle." In contrast, six fluorine ions with the radius 1.3 Å., in
forming an octahedron, provide the exact space required by a silicon ion,
as shown in Figure V-1b. If eight fluorine ions are combined in cubic
arrangement, the resulting space is too large for the silicon ion, but is exactly filled by the larger osmium ion, as shown in Figure V-1c. Magnus
explained in this simple way the increase in coordination number from 4 to
6 and 8 by the ratio of the radii of the various ions involved. The application of this idea to crystal lattices has led Goldschmidt to a classification of

[7] A. Magnus, *Z. anorg. allgem. Chem.*, **124**, 291 (1922).

ionic structures which is in remarkable agreement with most experimental facts. Table V-3 contains a number of atomic radii as deduced from crystal structures.

TABLE V-3

IONIC RADII OF SEVERAL ELEMENTS IN ÅNGSTRÖM UNITS[a]

				Li+	Be²+	B³+	C⁴+	N⁵+	O⁶+	F⁷+
				0.60	0.31	0.20	0.15	0.11	0.09	0.07
				0.78	0.34	—	~0.2	0.1–0.2	—	—

N³⁻	O²⁻	F⁻	Na+	Mg²+	Al³+	Si⁴+	P⁵+	S⁶+	Cl⁷+
1.71	1.40	1.36	0.95	0.65	0.50	0.41	0.34	0.29	0.26
—	1.32	1.33	0.98	0.78	0.57	0.39	0.3–0.4	0.34	—

P³⁻	S²⁻	Cl⁻	K+	Ca²+	Sc³+	Ti⁴+	V⁵+	Cr⁶+	Mn⁷+
2.12	1.84	1.81	1.33	0.99	0.81	0.68	0.59	0.52	0.46
—	1.74	1.81	1.33	1.06	0.83	0.64	~0.4	0.30–0.34	—

As³⁻	Se²⁻	Br⁻	Rb+	Sr²+	Y³+	Zr⁴+	Nb⁴+	Mo⁶+
2.22	1.98	1.95	1.48	1.13	0.93	0.80	0.70	0.62
—	1.91	1.96	1.49	1.27	1.06	0.87	0.69	—

Sb³⁻	Te²⁻	J⁻	Cr+	Ba²+	La³+	Ce⁴+
2.45	2.21	2.16	1.69	1.35	1.15	1.01
—	2.11	2.20	1.65	1.43	1.22	1.02

[a] The two values are obtained in two independent ways.

(b) To a second approximation, there are certain small but systematic deviations from the behavior of ions as rigid spheres: the ionic radius depends upon the coordination number and generally increases with increasing coordination number. As a consequence it is conceivable that an increase in the number of like ions within a coordination sphere can, by their mutual repulsion, leave a larger cavity for the central ion, so that a larger ion would fit into it. This has actually been observed, and Table V-4 gives an idea of the magnitude of this effect, which, as a matter of experience, has not too much influence on the general crystal properties, such as melting point, hardness, and refractive index, and does not greatly affect the strength of the bond between the central and the coordinated ions.

(c) In addition to the above-mentioned purely geometrical aspects, there exists a dynamic property of ions which has a considerable influence on crystallochemical behavior, namely, their *polarizability* or *deformability*. If a large negative ion with easily displaceable electrons (iodine, for example) is exposed to the field of a small positive ion (lithium, for example) the charge cloud of the former will be attracted by the positive ion, the nucleus will be repelled, the large ion is deformed and will be characterized not only by its negative *charge*, but also by an *induced dipole moment*. Whereas the interaction between two rigid spherical ions can be described by Coulomb's law we must now take into account the axial dipole field of the deformed ion because a fraction of the negative charge of the deformable ion is now shifted in the direction of its positively charged partner.

TABLE V-4

CHANGE IN DISTANCE ON CHANGE IN COORDINATION NUMBER

Transition from coordination number	To coordination number	Reduction in distance of
8	6	3%
6	4	5–7%
12	8	3%
12	8	3.5%

Goldschmidt, using an extensive experimental material, has shown that in the absence of polarization, highly symmetrical arrangements are preferred, while—due to the lower symmetry of the deformed ion—the result of increasing polarization is always a less symmetrical lattice type.   Consequently, lattice forces are obtained of different magnitude in different directions, the rigid or at least approximately rigid ionic radii lose their significance, and the behavior of a given ion is to a high degree dependent on its neighbors, their size and polarizing action.   Compounds with highly polarizable constituents form an entire series of lattice types, which exhibit a wide range of physical and chemical properties;   their melting points, hardnesses, solubilities, etc., differ even in orders of magnitude from one another.   Table V-5 gives a few examples for the influence of polarization on lattice structure and crystal properties.

TABLE V-5

RELATION BETWEEN HARDNESS AND LATTICE STRUCTURE

Compound	Ionic distance	Hardness	Compound	Ionic distance	Hardness
BeO	1.65	9	ZnTe	2.64	3
ZnO	1.97	5	CdTe	2.80	2.8
ZnS	2.35	4	CC	1.54	10
ZnSe	2.48	3–4	SiC	1.89	9.5
CdSe	2.63	3	SiSi	2.35	7
HgSe	2.63	2.8	GeGe	2.43	6

These simple principles show that to a first approximation every ion in a crystal lattice can be characterized by a *charge* and a *radius*. To a second approximation, however, this radius is not a fixed magnitude, but depends somewhat upon the *number* of the surrounding oppositely charged ions. Larger ions with softer electronic clouds, such as heavy metal ions or the

TABLE V-6

CALCULATION OF LATTICE DISTANCES AND COMPRESSIBILITIES
ACCORDING TO LENNARD-JONES

Salt	NaF	NaCl	NaBr	NaI
$d_{calc.}$, Å	2.30	2.85	2.99	3.19
$d_{obs.}$, Å	2.31	2.81	2.97	2.23
$\chi \times 10^{12}$				
Calc.	—	3.88	4.51	5.18
Obs.	—	4.20, 4.3	5.08, 5.3	7.1
Salt	KF	KCl	KBr	KI
$d_{calc.}$, Å	2.63	3.13	3.24	3.47
$d_{obs.}$, Å	2.66	3.14	3.28	3.52
$\chi \times 10^{12}$				
Calc.	—	6.23	7.92	8.17
Obs.	—	5.63, 5.2	6.70, 6.4	8.54, 8.8
Salt	RbF	RbCl	RbBr	RbI
$d_{calc.}$, Å	3.37	3.24	3.43	3.58
$d_{obs.}$, Å	3.66	3.27	3.42	3.65
$\chi \times 10^{12}$				
Calc.	—	8.10	7.72	9.26
Obs.	—	7.3	7.94, 8.2	9.58, 9.3
Salt	CsF	CsCl	CsBr	CsI
$d_{calc.}$, Å	2.97	4.21	4.34	4.56
$d_{obs.}$, Å	3.00	4.12, 4.30	4.29	4.56
$\chi \times 10^{12}$				
Calc.	—	7.71	8.58	9.31
Obs.	—	5.9	7.0	9.3

higher halides, do not behave like rigid spheres but exhibit a certain deformability of their negative charge cloud.[5] The fact that ions exist of almost any size and polarizability, leads to inorganic lattices of the most diverse structural types having widely differing physical properties.

The application of these ideas by Goldschmidt has furnished not only a classification of existing lattice types but has also led to the prediction of several new ionic compounds, some of which have been prepared subsequently, and which actually did have the physical properties predicted by the laws of crystallochemistry.

Now, passing to the formulation of quantitative relations between the lattice parameter and the character of the lattice forming ions, it has been found that the following equation expresses the potential energy of a lattice with rigid spherical ions:

$$V(r) = -(e^2/r) + (b/r^n) \qquad (V.1)$$

The first term expresses the Coulomb attraction between the oppositely charged spherical ions, and the second provides for the repulsive forces that arise as soon as the two electronic charge clouds begin to overlap each other;

TABLE V-7

RHOMBOHEDRAL ANGLE IN CALCSPAR TYPE
ACCORDING TO W. L. BRAGG

Substance	Rhombohedral	$\alpha_{calc.}$	$\alpha_{obs.}$
$MgCO_3$.....................	4.61 edge in Å.	103° 28′	103° 21.5′
$ZnCO_3$.....................	4.64	103° 18′	103° 28′
$TlCO_3$.....................	4.70	103° 6′	103° 4.5′
$MnCO_3$.....................	4.77	102° 52′	102° 50′
$\frac{1}{2}(MgCa)CO_3$..............	4.78	102° 44′	102° 53′
$CdCO_3$.....................	4.92	102° 15′	102° 30′
$CaCO_3$.....................	4.96	102° 4′	101° 55′

TABLE V-8

LATTICE ENERGIES OF SILVER AND THALLIUM HALIDES

	Lattice energy, E (in kcal./mole), for						
	AgF	AgCl	AgBr	AgI	TlCl	TlBr	TlI
Theoretical....	219	203	197	190	167	164	159
Observed......	217.7	205.7	201.8	199.2	170.1	165.6	160.8
Difference...	−1.3	2.7	4.8	9.2	3.1	1.6	1.8

values between 9 and 11 are obtained for n.   Table V-6 computed by Lennard-Jones[8] shows that the lattice constants d and the compressibilities χ for simple ionic crystals can be calculated with the above equation with remarkable success.

In the case of rhombohedral crystals, Bragg has succeeded in calculating

[8] J. E. Lennard-Jones, *Trans. Faraday Soc.*, **24**, 100 (1928); **28**, 333 (1932).

the theoretical angles of the elementary cells; Table V-7 shows that the predicted values agree well with the data observed for several carbonates. The change of the lattice constants with pressure was also computed in fair agreement with the experiment.

The lattice energy—closely related to the heat of sublimation—is equally susceptible to theoretical approach. To obtain good agreement, one must take into consideration the *exchange forces* between electronic shells in close proximity and the *zero point energy*, in addition to the two purely electrostatic terms of equation (V.1). Born and Mayer[9] have done this for the halides of thallium and silver and have found very satisfactory agreement with experimental data, as shown in Table V-8.

The conditions are not as simple in lattices with polarizable ions. For such cases Born and Heisenberg[10] have derived a potential energy function that gives the lattice energy and distances in fair agreement with experiment. The contribution of polarizability to the total effect is between 10 and 20%. With the aid of this expanded theory it is also possible to compute the vibrational frequencies of the various ions with reasonable accuracy.

Calculations of the cohesive energy of ionic crystals have been carried out recently by quantum mechanical methods. Landshoff[11] reported for NaCl a value of 183 kcal. against 183 kcal. measured and Hylleraas[12] computed a value of 218 kcal. for LiH, whereas a value of 218.5 kcal. had been observed experimentally.

If a lattice consists of one small and rigid ion and one large and easily polarizable ion, the influence of deformation may be so great that the bond loses its heteropolar character to a large extent, with the resulting lattice almost resembling a molecular lattice in its properties.

Hund[13] investigated such cases and found that so-called *layer lattices* are formed in which the electronic charge cloud of the larger ion is strongly displaced toward the center of the smaller one.

Another interesting hybrid lattice is formed if, in alkali salts of organic acids such as sodium benzoate or potassium stearate, a small positive metallic ion forms a lattice together with a relativeley large negative organic residue, because in such cases the ionic charges may be separated

[9] M. Born and J. E. Mayer, *Z. Physik*, **75**, 1 (1932); M. L. Huggins and J. E. Mayer, *J. Chem. Phys.*, **1**, 643 (1933).
[10] M. Born and W. Heisenberg, *Z. Physik*, **23**, 388 (1924).
[11] R. Landshoff, *Phys. Rev.*, **52**, 246 (1937).
[12] E. A. Hylleraas, *Z. Physik*, **63**, 772 (1930).
[13] F. Hund, *Z. Physik*, **34**, 833 (1925).

so far from each other in the lattice that the dispersion forces between the homopolar parts of the anions prevail and determine the character of the structure.   Such lattices are highly anisotropic with regard to mechanical properties because strong forces act in certain directions and much weaker ones in others.

In conclusion it may be stated that simple lattices with purely electrostatic interaction between the participating ions can well be represented by equation (V.1) and that important transition cases in the direction of molecular lattices have been explained by progressive polarization and by the presence of homopolar constituents.[14]

2. Atomic Lattices

There exists lattices which cohere by primary covalent bonds in all three directions in space.   The fundamental character of this bond has already been discussed in Chapter IV; it has been mentioned that x-ray measurements have established the existence in the diamond lattice of a noticeable electron density between the carbon atoms, representing the charge cloud of the homopolar bond.[15]   From the point of view of symmetry, these lattices are usually very similar to ionic lattices, but Grimm and Sommerfeld have succeeded in establishing criteria to decide whether a given crystal forms an atomic or ionic lattice.   The atomic lattices under consideration are essentially of the *diamond* type and the very similar *wurtzite* type.   Elements crystallizing in these types are: C, Si, Ge, and Sn; compounds include MgN, SiC, AuS, and CdS.   On account of the high strength of the covalent bond, these substances form rigid, high melting, hard crystals, some of which have considerable technical importance. The absence of a simple, well-substantiated potential energy function in these lattices makes it difficult to predict the interatomic distances, angles, and lattice energies.   It has merely been possible, by comparison, to derive empirical rules relating atomic distances to bond strengths; they show that, under otherwise identical conditions, the stronger linkage corresponds to the smaller atomic distance.

3. Metallic Lattices

These lattices owe their existence to the metallic bond and show characteristic electronic conductivity, strong reflectivity, and, in general, high melting points.

[14] Compare here particularly the extensive treatment of this subject in F. Seitz, *Modern Theory of Solids*.   McGraw-Hill, New York, 1940.

[15] H. G. Grimm, R. Brill, *et al.*, *Ann. Phys.*, [5], **34**, 393 (1939).

Bernal divides the metallic elements in two groups, which he designates as *true* and *false* metals (see Table V-9), a distinction which is sharp in some cases but vanishes almost completely in others. True metals crystallize with a high degree of symmetry, possess high electrical and thermal conductivity, and show a *decrease* of these properties on fusion; false metals crystallize, as a rule, in lattices of low symmetry, and possess lower conductivity, which generally *increases* on melting. These latter substances represent a certain transition to atomic lattices.

TABLE V-9

DIVISION OF THE METALLIC ELEMENTS ACCORDING TO J. D. BERNAL

	True metals (Class 1)	Semi metals (Class 2)
Substance................	Alkali metals Alkaline earth metals Rare earths Ti–Cu (without Mn) Zr–Ag Hf–Au, Th, U	Zn, Cd, Hg, Ga, In, (Tl), Ge, Sn, (Pb), As, Sb, Bi
Crystal lattice............	Face- or body-centered or hexagonal close packing; coordination number 12 or 8	Loosely packed structures; coordination number 8
Change of properties on fusion	Decrease in electrical conductivity	Increase in electrical conductivity

The number of intermetallic compounds is very large and their x-ray investigation has revealed many interesting results, the description of which, however, would lead us too far afield in this volume.

The extent to which Wigner and Seitz[16] have succeeded in expressing the metallic linkage quantitatively has been mentioned in Chapter IV (Sect. A); an experimental analysis of the distribution of electronic charge clouds in magnesium crystals has been carried out by Grimm, Brill, Peters, and Hermann.[15]

In conclusion, a table compiled by Haber[17] may be added here as Table V-10. In it the lattice energies of highly symmetric metallic lattices are calculated, by analogy with ionic lattices, from the opposing effects of an attractive Coulomb force and a repulsive force, the repulsion exponent of which is determined from compressibility. It is interesting that, in contrast to the true ionic lattices, rather widely varying values (from 2.44 to 9.0) are obtained for these repulsion exponents. The reason is probably

[16] E. Wigner and F. Seitz, *Phys. Rev.*, **46**, 509 (1934).
[17] F. Haber, *Sitzber. Preuss. Akad. Wiss.*, **1919**, 506–990.

that in this case a two term equation of the type (V. 1) can only be considered as a formal expression without too much physical significance. Nevertheless, we do obtain good values for the lattice energies.

More recently, Seitz[18] has computed the cohesive energies of Li, Na, and K by a quantum mechanical calculation; he obtained the values 36.2, 24.5, and 16.5 kcal. whereas the corresponding observed values are 39, 26, and 23 kcal. Similarly, Herring and Hill[19] obtained 36–53 kcal. for beryllium, as compared with a measured value of 75 kcal., and Fuchs[20] found 33 kcal. for copper, which is much lower than the experimental figure of 81.

TABLE V-10

REPULSIVE FORCES AND LATTICE ENERGIES IN METALLIC CRYSTALS[a]
ACCORDING TO HABER

Values	Li	Na	K	Rb	Cs	Cu	Ag	Al
n from compressibility........	2.44	2.90	3.18	3.64	3.62	8.0	9.0	7.0
Lattice energy, calculated from n..................	6.51	5.69	5.04	5.02	4.68	11.73	10.50	8.56
Lattice energy found = heat of vaporization + heat of ionization................	—	5.87	5.13	4.88	4.56	10.69	10.17	8.71

[a] All energies are in 10^{12} ergs per molecule.

The three types of lattices discussed here have the common property that their cohesion is due to primary valences in all three directions of space; they may therefore be designated as *main valence lattices*. Because of the magnitudes of the lattice forces, they are all characterized by high heats of sublimation, high melting points, considerable hardness, and great ultimate mechanical strength. Entirely different properties are met with in the type now to be discussed, where secondary valences cause the cohesion of the lattice in all three directions of space.

4. Secondary Valence Lattices

These lattices are held together by van der Waals' forces and hydrogen bridges; in general, they have low melting points and low heats of sublimation; they are soft and have low ultimate strength. The majority of organic substances crystallize in this lattice type.

[18] F. Seitz, *Phys. Rev.*, **47**, 400 (1935); J. Bardeen, *J. Chem. Phys.*, **6**, 367 (1938).
[19] C. C. Herring and A. G. Hill, cited in F. Seitz, *Modern Theory of Solids*.
[20] K. Fuchs, *Proc. Roy. Soc. London*, **A157**, 444 (1936).

(a) Secondary Valence Lattices and Density

If a primary valence bond, for example, between carbon and carbon or carbon and oxygen, corresponds to a distance of 1.4–1.6 Å., it may legitimately be assumed that atoms not united by covalent bonds will maintain a greater distance from each other. In studying distances between adjacent atoms in neighboring molecules of secondary valence lattices it has been found that they are usually between 3.5 and 4.5 Å., *i.e.*, about 2–3 times larger, on the average, than the values corresponding to main valences. This reflects the characteristic difference between a covalent bond and a van der Waals' bond to which we already referred in discussing individual molecules (compare Chap. IV, Sect. B).

The distance of 3.0–4.5 Å. which corresponds to lattice forces in most organic crystals accounts for the fact that there is usually a strong x-ray diffraction in the patterns of such substances in the solid and liquid states indicating the existence of such a distance. For example, fatty acids show intensive reflections of planes, which are about 4 Å. apart because they contain the chain molecules and, consequently, are densely populated by diffracting atoms. Even in the melts, where the rigorous lattice order is lost, but where the average distances between the molecules are still determined by van der Waals' forces, we find frequently diffuse diffraction halos corresponding to distances of about 4 Å.

Finally, the well-known studies of Adam, Langmuir, Rideal, and others[21] on monomolecular films have shown that the distances between the molecules in such films of simple fatty acids amount to about 4–5 Å.

These facts make it possible to assign in lattices of organic substances—where covalent homopolar bonds and van der Waals' bonds exist—distances of 1.2–1.6 Å. to the main valences and values of 3.0–4.5 Å. to secondary valences. This assignment supplements the conventional structural formulas of organic chemistry by a quantitative element and permits the construction of molecular models that are a step nearer to reality than the normal formulas of organic chemistry. Considering also the dissociation energies and the cohesive forces of these two types of bonds it is possible not only to deduce from a structural formula the chemical behavior of the material but also to understand the physical properties of a lattice that is built up by molecules of a given structure. It will be remembered that Goldschmidt's crystallochemistry combines lattice properties with

[21] E. K. Rideal, *Surface Chemistry*, 2nd ed., Cambridge Univ. Press, London 1930; I. Langmuir, *Chem. Rev.*, **13**, 147 (1933). Cf. N. K. Adam, *The Physics and Chemistry of Surfaces*, 2nd ed., Oxford Univ. Press, London, 1938.

ionic structure in a similar way for inorganic substances. Just as in that case, we can employ distance rules in organic chemistry to show that certain molecules which would have been admissible by the classical structural formulas cannot actually exist.

A few remarks regarding the density of carbon compounds will explain the application of these rules.

We know that in the diamond lattice all distances between neighboring atoms are about 1.55 Å., whereas in the lattice of solid methane the distance between adjacent carbon atoms is about 2.5 times greater. Hence the density of diamond should be about 10 times that of methane. In an x-ray investigation of solid methane it has been found that the distances between two molecular centers is 4.2 Å.; the density of methane is 0.415 as compared with 3.51 for diamond The density ratio is about one to eight.

In graphite, the distances between adjacent atoms in the basic hexagonal plane are 1.45 Å., while perpendicular thereto the smallest distance amounts to 3.3 Å. We have before us a lattice which coheres in the two directions of the basic hexagonal plane by aromatic covalent carbon-carbon bonds and in the third direction along the hexagonal axis by van der Waals' bonds. Since the former are much stronger than the latter, graphite is a typical case of a layer lattice, with strong cohesion in the principal plane and weak cohesion perpendicular thereto. The densities of diamond and graphite, by reason of the identity of the atoms and the shorter C—C distance in the basic plane of graphite, should be in the ratio of 1.53:1; the actual density ratio is 1.52:1.

Proceeding from graphite, let us finally imagine a carbon lattice, which coheres in one direction through primary valences and in the two others by secondary valences. It is impossible to build up such a structure with singly bonded C atoms, but we can conceive of its being realized by a chain of continuous double bonds (cumulene). Its density, according to the distance law, would be between 1.1 and 1.3, depending upon the particular arrangement of the carbon atoms in the chains.

If we permit the presence of hydrogen atoms, as we did in the case of methane, we arrive at polyethylene as representing a lattice which is held together by covalent bonds in one direction and by weak dispersion forces in the two directions perpendicular thereto. According to the distance rules, its density should be around unity; in fact, it is about 1.1.

The smaller the domains of primary valence bonds in the lattice the greater is the specific volume and consequently the lower the density. Extreme values are represented by diamond (3.57) and methane (0.457).

The densities of all organic compounds containing only carbon, oxygen, nitrogen, and hydrogen are intermediate; layer lattices have densities between 2.0 and 2.4, chain lattices between 1.0 and 1.6. The ordinary molecular lattices, with individual molecules representing closed lattice units, have densities between 0.4 and 1.2. The result of the difference between primary and secondary valences in the lattices of normal organic substances is that the molecules that exist in the gaseous or dissolved state as kinetically independent units also remain clearly recognizable in the lattice as closely packed atomic groups; application of the molecular concept to the solid state of these substances, therefore, presents no difficulty. The case is entirely different for the layer and chain lattices. As in the ionic, atomic, and metallic crystals, it is impossible to delimit special atomic groups in the lattice, which correspond to the chemical molecules of the gaseous state. A new terminology is needed here to describe the existing conditions intelligibly. Such a terminology has been worked out by Weissenberg[22]; it will be briefly discussed in chapter VI.

(b)   Different Types of Secondary Valence Lattices

All three types of intermolecular forces are capable of building up crystal lattices; generally, each of them will contribute a definite amount to the total lattice energy and it will, as a rule, not be easy to separate them clearly from each other. However, there exist cases in which only one type of intermolecular force is essentially responsible for the lattice energy.

Dispersion forces alone are obviously responsible for the existence of the lattices of the rare gases. These substances crystallize in highly symmetrical arrangements such as the cubic, face-centered lattice. The dimensions of the elementary cells and the heats of sublimation have been determined experimentally. Eisenschitz and London,[23] have derived for the lattice energy U of such systems the expression:

$$U(r) = - \frac{59}{2} \frac{I \alpha^2 N}{r_0^6} \qquad \text{(V.2)}$$

where N = number of atoms in the crystal, I = energy of ionization of the atoms, α = polarizability of the atoms, and r_0 = distance of nearest neighbors in the lattice.

Table V-11 lists the heats of sublimation of various rare gases and other simple molecules as computed by this equation together with the experi-

[22] K. Weissenberg, Z. Krist., 62, 13, 52 (1925).
[23] R. Eisenschitz and F. London, Z. Physik, 60, 520 (1930).

mental values. The agreement is remarkable and was still further improved by Margenau,[24] who took into account the interaction of dipole and quadrupole terms.

TABLE V-11

COMPARISON OF CALCULATED AND OBSERVED HEATS OF SUBLIMATION

Substance	$\alpha \times 10^{24}$, cc.	Lattice energy, kcal./mole	
		Calculated	Obs. and extrap. to 0°K.
Ne	0.39	0.40	0.59
A	1.63	1.83	2.03
N_2	1.74	1.61	1.86
O_2	1.57	1.48	1.89
CO	1.99	1.86	2.09
CH_4	2.58	2.47	2.70
Cl_2	4.60	7.18	7.43
HI	5.40	6.50	6.21
HCl	2.63	4.04	5.05
HBr	3.58	4.53	5.52
NO	1.76	2.04	4.29

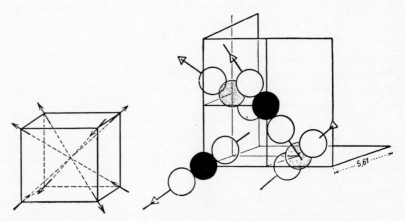

Fig. V-2. Lattice with cohesion due to dipole forces alone (Born and Kornfeld).

Fig. V-3. Elementary cell of the CO_2 lattice; black circles are C atoms, white are O atoms.

It is interesting that HCl and HBr, which already possess rather strong dipoles, show an appreciable deviation in the sense that the lattice energy

[24] H. Margenau, *Phys. Rev.*, **38**, 1785 (1931).

calculated on the basis of dispersion forces alone is too small. However, it must be pointed out that even in these lattices dispersion forces play an important role. This is evident from Table V-17 and also from calculations of Born and Kornfeld,[25] who have tried to work out a quantitative theory of the hydrogen halide lattices on the basis of dipole forces alone. Assuming the arrangement shown in Figure V-2 they arrived at the conclusion that it is not possible to obtain the observed heats of sublimation by dipole interaction alone. Their figures were too low, which shows that other types of attraction, namely, dispersion forces, must interfere.

The structure of carbon dioxide is shown in Figure V-3; the rod-shaped CO_2 molecules lie parallel to the space diagonals of a cube with $a = 5.63$ Å. in such a way that any two neighboring ones are perpendicular to one another. In this arrangement, the $C\!\!=\!\!O$ dipoles, which have moments of about 2.5 debyes, produce in molecules lying perpendicular to the dipole axis and separated by a distance of 3.5 Å. induced moments whose interaction with the permanent moments constitutes the main component of the lattice forces. The low boiling point of carbon dioxide (compared with H_2O or CS_2) is obviously due to the fact that the intermolecular interaction described above is relatively weak.

Sponer and Bruch-Willstätter[26] have computed the cohesive energy of carbon dioxide with consideration of dispersion forces and polar interaction; they arrive at 7 kcal. per molecule, whereas 8.24 has been observed.

The lattice of ice has been investigated with considerable accuracy. Its symmetry and heat of sublimation indicate, according to Bernal and Fowler,[27] the great importance of the interaction between the hydroxyl groups in ice.

Considering the similar situation in cellulose, starch, polyvinyl alcohol, etc., it may be permitted to discuss the structure of this lattice in some detail because, later, it will be possible to draw interesting conclusions regarding the behavior of high polymers that contain many hydroxyl groups.

At present three modifications of ice are known, a *hexagonal* type that is formed under normal conditions and two *rhombic* types that are stable at lower temperatures or at higher pressures. All have been investigated quite thoroughly with x-rays. The elementary cell of normal ice (ice 1) contains 12 molecules of H_2O; each of them is surrounded tetrahedrally by four others in such a way that the distances between the centers of gravity of the oxygen atoms are 2.74 Å.; Figure V-4 shows this arrange-

[25] M. Born and G. Kornfeld, *Physik. Z.*, **24**, 121 (1923).

[26] H. Sponer and M. Bruch-Willstätter, *J. Chem. Phys.*, **5**, 745 (1937).

[27] J. D. Bernal and R. Fowler, *J. Chem. Phys.*, **1**, 515 (1933).

ment, which can also be interpreted that each individual hydrogen atom appears to be united by a homopolar valence to a given oxygen. But there exists for each hydrogen atom a second oxygen atom toward which the hydrogen atom is especially inclined. Each O atom is therefore surrounded by four H atoms, which, are arranged, in the corners of a somewhat distorted tetrahedron, and every H atom is common to two such tetrahedrons; we thus obtain the correct ratio $H:O = 2:1$ and a three-dimensional tetrahedral framework of the formula $(H_2O)_n$. We shall see later that the different modifications of SiO_2 conform to the same structural principle. The structure of normal ice resembles most nearly that of tridymite. This configuration corresponds not to a close packing but to a rather loose arrangement of the lattice points.

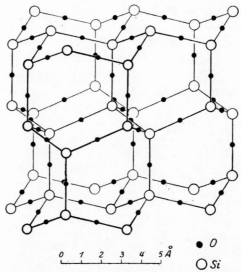

$\bullet\ O$

0   1   2   3   4   5 Å

$\bigcirc Si$

Fig. V-4.   Space-lattice of tridymite as pattern for the lattice of ice 1.

In the two rhombic phases we find similarly that a selected water molecule is surrounded by four others in tetrahedral arrangement, but there is again some deformation as compared with a regular tetrahedron; in ice 2 the distances between the centers of gravity of adjacent oxygen atoms are about 2.71 Å.; it is difficult to locate the H atoms, but one gains the impression that in these two lattices the molecular association is largely dissolved and the structure approaches that of an ionic lattice.

For liquid water, Bernal and Fowler assume that there exists a mixture of the three different configurations whose quantitative ratios depend upon temperature, and further that any one of the three persists only over a submicroscopic range and only for very short periods.

In the neighborhood of the melting point and up to $+4°$ a tridymite type of arrangement prevails, which is a remnant of the solid ice and which remains noticeable over a small temperature range, even though above the melting point. At higher temperatures (4–$200°$) a quartzlike modification becomes more and more apparent, and at still higher temperatures up to the critical point there exists essentially close packing. Further details of the interesting views regarding the structure of fluid water will be added in the section on liquids.

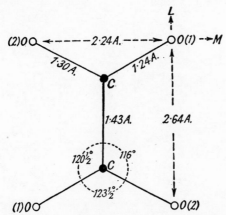

Fig. V-5.   Nuclear framework of the oxalic acid molecule
with H atoms omitted.

As an example of a molecular lattice in which cohesion is predominantly effected by hydrogen bonds, oxalic acid dihydrate may be discussed here, because it allows a certain insight into the role of the water of crystallization.

Hoffmann and Mark[28] determined some time ago the elementary cell and space group of this substance; more recently, Robertson and Woodward[29] carried out a complete Fourier analysis of the lattice and obtained the results shown in Figures V-5 and V-6. The six heavy atoms of the oxalic acid residue all lie in one plane. The carbon-carbon distance is 1.43

[28] H. Hoffmann and H. Mark, *Z. physik. Chem.*, **111**, 321 (1924).
[29] J. M. Robertson and I. Woodward, *J. Chem. Soc.*, **1936**, 1817; compare also J. D. Dunitz and J. M. Robertson, *ibid.*, **1947**, 142, 148.

Å.; it is distinctly smaller than usual (1.54) and almost approaches the distance of 1.39 Å. characteristic for the aromatic carbon-carbon bond. The reason for this probably lies in the proximity of the two conjugated carbonyl groups of the molecules. Figure V-6 shows the distances between the centers of gravity of a water molecule and the three nearest oxygen atoms of oxalic acid residues in a plane of the lattice. It can be seen that they are between 2.52 and 2.87 Å., corresponding to a typical hydrogen

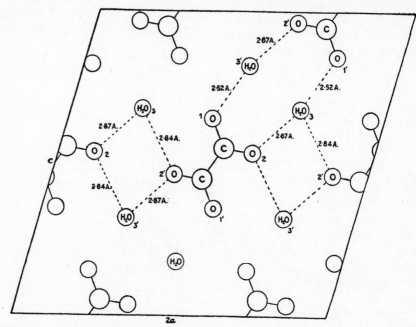

Fig. V-6. Arrangements of oxalic acid molecules in the lattice (H atoms omitted).

bridge. It appears, therefore, that the hydrogen atoms of the acid residues and those of the water molecules are essentially equivalent in the lattice and are arranged between the oxygen atoms of the water and the oxalic acid residue. In this sense the crystal could be regarded as oxonium oxalate with the formula:

$$(H_3O)^+ \; {}^-(OOC{-}COO)^- \; {}^+(H_3O)$$

each oxonium ion being linked with two oxalic acid ions by hydrogen bonds.

It is probable that here again the dipole forces first produce the configuration shown in Figure V-6 and that it is subsequently stabilized by quantum mechanical exchange forces which lead to the establishment of hydrogen bridges.

Interesting information regarding the details of van der Waals' forces can be derived from the lattice of hexamethylenetetramine which crystallizes in the cubic system (see Fig. V-7). The body-centered elementary cell of this substance and the location of the atomic centers in it was de-

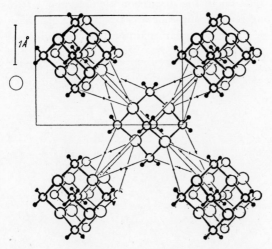

Fig. V-7.   Space lattice of hexamethylenetetramine.

termined some time ago by Gonell and Mark[30] and by Dickinson and Raymond[31]; later Grimm, Brill, Hermann, and Peters[15] established the exact distribution of the negative charge clouds in this lattice and found that, actually, certain regions between adjacent molecules of the composition $(CH_2)_6N_4$ are practically free of charge, whereas at other places charge bridges lead from one molecule to the other.

Their chief results are presented in Figure V-8, which shows that in the neighborhood of C (*i.e.*, between the two upper molecules of the figure) there is a large region in which the charge has declined practically to zero; here, the lattice displays a fairly large hole. At B a deep valley appears between the charge peaks of two adjacent molecules; the electronic density in the trough amounts to only 0.1 electron per Å.² . At A, however, a charge bridge leads from the upper left to the center molecule, which even at its

[30] H. W. Gonell and H. Mark, *Z. physik. Chem.*, **107**, 181 (1923).
[31] R. G. Dickinson and A. L. Raymond, *J. Am. Chem. Soc.*, **45**, 22 (1923).

lowest point still shows the considerable charge density of 0.9 electron per $\text{Å}.^2$.

These bridges are probably responsible for the attraction between the two molecules and the cohesion of the lattice.

(c) Molecular Lattices of Chain Molecules

Let us now pass on to the discussion of molecular lattices in which, on one hand, strong polar groups such as CO, OH, NH_2 are present, and, on the other hand, larger nonpolar chains exist which give rise to dispersion

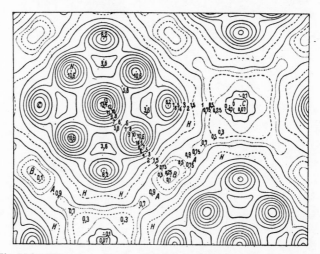

Fig. V-8.   Electronic density in the hexamethylenetetramine lattice.

forces.   By reason of the rod shape of their molecules, these substances will lead us gradually to the lattices of long chain polymers in which different forces provide for the cohesion in different directions.

The paraffins, aliphatic fatty acids, alcohols, amines, and ketones have been investigated thoroughly by Müller,[32] Trillat,[33] and by Brill and Meyer.[34]   The examination of paraffins from $C_{11}H_{24}$ to $C_{30}H_{62}$ revealed the interesting fact that, with increasing temperature, the lengths of the paraffin chains remain practically unchanged, whereas the lattice dimensions perpendicular to the chain axes exhibit considerable thermal expansion.

This anisotropy is due to the fact that along the chains strong covalent

[32] Cf. A. Müller, Proc. Soc. London, 114, 542 (1927); 120, 437 (1928).

[33] J. J. Trillat, Compt. rend., 180, 1329 (1925).

[34] R. Brill and K. H. Meyer, Z. Krist., 67, 570 (1928).

bonds are responsible for the cohesion, while perpendicular to the chains only relatively weak van der Waals' forces provide for the coherence of the lattice. They cannot withstand the thermal vibrations as effectively as the primary valence bonds.

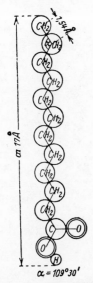

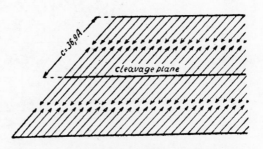

Fig. V-9. Individual lauric acid chain in the lattice (after Brill and Meyer).

Fig. V-10. Diagrammatic representation of the arrangement of the fatty acid chains in the crystal lattice.

It may be observed here, with respect to the conditions in cellulose and its derivatives to be discussed later, that most long chain aliphatic substances show a distinct tendency to exhibit polymorphism; two different modifications have been observed for paraffins and three for fatty acids. The high temperature modifications show cylindrical symmetry of the individual chain molecules in the lattice, while the chains themselves have elliptical cross sections; this can be understood by assuming that at elevated temperatures the paraffin chains in these lattices rotate about their long axes and, as a result, no longer exhibit elliptical symmetry perpendicular to the long axis, but show the higher axial symmetry of rotation. Actually at lower temperatures the chains resume their elliptical cross section and the free rotation degenerates into a vibration of the chain about an equilibrium position.[35]

[35] C. S. Fuller and C. J. Frosch, *J. Am. Chem. Soc.*, **61**, 2575 (1939).

Figure V-9 gives a picture of the molecule of lauric acid, and Figure V-10 shows the arrangement of the individual chains in the lattice of this substance; the carboxyl groups are linked together by hydrogen bridges as indicated on page 141 and cause the formation of double molecules in the lattice. Along the planes containing these groups cohesion is particularly strong, while only weak dispersion forces are acting along planes occupied by the terminal methyl groups; these planes cause the easy cleavage of the structure and its pronounced laminar behavior.

As a consequence of this lattice structure we should expect to find relatively simple additive relations in homologous and polymer homologous

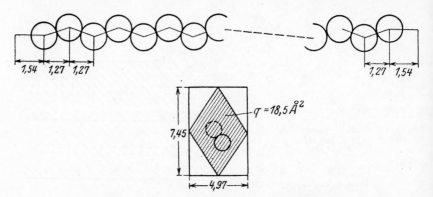

Fig. V-11.   Length and cross dimensions of a paraffin chain.

series.   In the crystalline state all paraffin chains have about the same cross section of 18.5 Å.^{2}; their length is made up of increments of 1.27 Å. represented in Figure V-11.

The volume of a single paraffin molecule with n carbon atoms is accordingly:

$$V = 18.5\,[3.1 + (n - 1)1.27] = 18.5[1.27n + 1.83]$$

Tables V-12 and V-13 show the application of this formula; they contain the densities and molar volumes calculated from these densities for several paraffins at 0° and 99°C.   Columns 4–5 give the molecular volumes calculated by the above formula for the various paraffins and those calculated from the density.   The lower hydrocarbons are compared at 0° in Table V-12, the higher ones at 99° in Table V-13.

The quotient of columns 4 and 5 remains constant, so that comparison at the same temperature is legitimate.   Inasmuch as the individual CH$_2$

TABLE V-12

CALCULATION OF DENSITIES FROM TRUE MOLECULAR VOLUMES

Molecule	Density at $0°$	Mol. wt.	Volume of molecule ($Å.^3$) from		Quotient of volumes
			Density	18.5 $(1.27n + 1.83)$	
Butane...............	0.60	58	159	128	1.24
Pentane..............	0.646	72	183	151	1.22
Hexane..............	0.677	86	208	175	1.19
Heptane.............	0.700	100	234	198	1.18
Octane...............	0.718	114	261	222	1.17
Nonane..............	0.733	128	286	245	1.17
Decane..............	0.745	142	313	269	1.16
Undecane............	0.755	156	339	292	1.16
Dodecane............	0.765	170	368	316	1.16
Tridecane............	0.771	184	391	339	1.15
Tetradecane..........	0.774	198	420	363	1.16

TABLE V-13

CALCULATION OF DENSITIES FROM TRUE MOLECULAR VOLUMES

Molecule	Density at $99°$	Mol. wt.	Volumes of molecule ($Å.^3$) from		Quotient of volumes
			Density	18.5 $(1.27n + 1.83)$	
Nonane..............	0.6541	128	320	245	1.31
Decane..............	0.6690	142	345	269	1.30
Undecane............	0.6816	156	374	292	1.28
Dodecane............	0.6930	170	402	316	1.27
Tridecane............	0.7008	184	429	339	1.27
Tetradecane..........	0.7078	198	459	363	1.27
Pentadecane..........	0.7136	212	487	386	1.31
Hexadecane..........	0.7197	226	522	410	1.27
Heptadecane.........	0.7245	240	543	434	1.25
Octadecane..........	0.7288	254	572	457	1.25
Nonadecane..........	0.7323	268	598	481	1.25
Eicosane.............	0.7363	282	628	500	1.25
Heneicosane..........	0.7400	292	654	528	1.24
Docosane............	0.7422	310	688	551	1.24
Tricosane............	0.7456	324	714	574	1.24
Tetracosane..........	0.7481	338	742	598	1.24

groups—which behave essentially as independent centers of attraction—exert approximately equal forces from group to group at any one temperature, equal distances between the molecules are to be expected.

If one does not restrict oneself to homologous or polymer homologous series only rather general view points can be advanced, such as the rule formulated by Gervaise-Le Bas that ring closure leads to a decrease in molecular volume[36] and that the bulkiness of a molecule is reflected in its specific gravity: asymmetric and irregularly shaped molecules have a greater specific volume than regular ones. An example is given by the following comparison.

Compound	$d_{19.5}°$	Volume of a molecule Å.^{3}
Cyclohexane	0.7788	175
Methylcyclopentane	0.7488	184

In liquids, molecular volume multiplied by a low power of the surface tension has been shown to be an additive quantity and has been termed the *parachor* by Sugden.[37]   Its additivity holds over a considerably greater range than the density relations themselves, which are true only within homologous series.

In many cases the form and habit of organic crystals is rather directly influenced by the shape of the individual molecules which build up the crystals.   Although it is not possible to make as valid and far-reaching predictions as in the case of ionic lattices, a number of qualitative relationships can be formulated.   Groth,[38] in his *Chemical Crystallography*, established a relation between molecular structure and crystal habit for molecular lattices, and Duden and Scharff[39] concluded from the cubic symmetry of hexamethylene tetramine crystals a high symmetry of the molecule itself, which was later confirmed by x-ray analysis.[30,31]

Another interesting example is the cubic symmetry of crystallized adamantane,[40] which is a cage molecule of the formula $C_{10}H_{16}$, having a carbon skeleton that corresponds completely to the arrangement of 10 adjacent carbon atoms in the lattice of diamond.

It has been mentioned previously that the individual methylene groups of a normal hydrocarbon chain act as independent centers of intermolecular attraction;   for each group a definite and equal amount of energy is liber-

---

[36] M. Gervaise-Le Bas, *Phil. Mag.* (6), **14**, 324 (1907);   **16**, 60 (1908);   compare also F. Lossen, *Ann.*, **214**, 81 (1882);   **254**, 42 (1889).

[37] S. Sugden, *J. Chem. Soc.*, **125**, 1167, 1177 (1924).

[38] P. Groth, *Chemische Kristallographie*, 5 vols., Engelmann, Leipzig, 1906–1919.

[39] P. Duden and M. Scharff, *Ann.*, **288**, 218 (1895).

[40] W. Nowacki, *Helv. Chim. Acta*, **28**, 1233 (1945);   compare also *ibid.*, **29**, 1798 (1946);   see also V. Prelog and R. Seiwerth, *Ber.*, **74**, 1644, 1769 (1941).

ated as the molecules are condensed from the gaseous to the liquid or solid state. In a normal paraffin chain, for example, molar cohesion (in kilocalories) is distributed over the individual groups as follows:

$$CH_3\text{—}CH_2\text{—} \ldots \text{—}CH_2\text{—} \ldots \text{—}CH_2\text{—}CH_3$$

$$1.8 \quad 1.0 \qquad\qquad 1.0 \qquad\qquad 1.0 \quad 1.8$$

Energy contributions of this order of magnitude are obtained if the chains are entirely surrounded by others, *i.e.*, if they possess four or six neighbors. If we consider only the mutual attraction of the two chains lying parallel to one another, the above amount has to be divided by four or six.

The energy liberated is much less if two chains are arranged "head to head," with only the terminal groups interacting with each other: it amounts to 1.8 kcal. per mole.

The parallel arrangement of the chains is therefore that for which the decrease of internal energy is a maximum; accordingly, it will correspond to the equilibrium state at low temperatures in crystals as well as in liquids, where the existence of clusters or bundles of molecules should be expected.

In fact, Stewart and Morrow have observed diffraction rings in liquid fatty acids and paraffins (see Chap. VII), which point to the existence of such bundles; also, the well-known studies on condensed monomolecular films of fatty acids on water surfaces confirmed that this phenomenon is due to the fact that the carboxyl groups of the acid stick to the surface of the water while the lipoid hydrocarbon chains emerge from the surface and form relatively tough thin layers, which have a very small surface tension on account of the small molar cohesion of the terminal methyl groups. Calculation of the surface tension of such a film from the molecular cohesion of CH_3 groups yields values between 10 and 20 dynes per centimeter, which agree satisfactorily with those determined experimentally.

Trillat[41] demonstrated, by careful experiments on the orientation of chain molecules on metal surfaces and other phase boundaries, that their parallel arrangement can also be detected in layers of adsorbed liquids and that it plays a decisive role in the physicochemical and technical properties of such films.

That long threadlike molecules are capable of forming oriented bundles or clusters even in the plain liquid phase is evidenced clearly by the existence of so-called liquid crystals or mesophases where the presence of oriented aggregates of molecules gives rise to interesting optical and x-ray phenomena. These systems constitute a transition from the liquid to the crys-

[41] J. J. Trillat, *J. phys. radium*, **10**, 32 (1929).

talline state such that any given molecule is neither completely free as in the former nor entirely fixed as in the latter; rather, it still possesses, according to the particular type of mesophase concerned (*smectic* or *nematic*), certain degrees of freedom of rotation or translation which make it to some extent independent of the surrounding molecules. Conditions in mesophases will be discussed later in more detail; here it may suffice to refer to a series of comprehensive articles by Vorländer,[42] Friedel,[43] Oseen,[44] and Zocher.[45]

If long chain molecules are oriented parallel in a latticelike arrangement, the two cases shown in Figure V-12 are possible. Simple hydrocarbons of

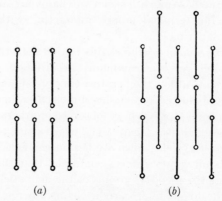

(a)   (b)

Fig. V-12. Chain molecules in different arrange-
ment in the crystal lattice.

regular shape are known to prefer arrangement *a* and consequently form preferably platelike crystals. The normal paraffins, naphthalene, anthracene, etc., are representatives of this type. If type *b* is assumed, the conditions are less clear; the products crystallize, as a rule, in needles (diphenyl, dibenzyl, etc.).

If, in addition to hydrocarbon residues, polar groups of higher molecular cohesion are present in a molecule, they generally exert a special influence on the arrangement in the lattice. The hydroxyl group (molar cohesion 7.2 kcal.), the carbonyl group, and, particularly, the carboxyl group (molar

[42] D. Vorländer, *Chemische Kristallographie der Flüssigkeiten.* Akadem. Verlagsgesellschaft, Leipzig, 1924.

[43] E. Friedel, *Z. Krist.*, **79**, 1 (1931).

[44] C. W. Oseen, *Die anisotropen Flüssigkeiten.* Berlin, 1929.

[45] H. Zocher, *Physik. Z.*, **28**, 790 (1927).

cohesion 8.97 kcal.) are examples of such cases. If there is only one such group in a molecule the formation of pairs of molecules frequently results; these pairs are often characterized by a center of symmetry. As soon as two or more groups of high molar cohesion are present, a chain- or netlike arrangement prevails which gives rise to particularly large cohesive forces in certain directions of the crystals, resulting frequently in needlelike habitus.

The first case is typical of the monobasic fatty alcohols and amines. In the lattice of these substances, two chainlike molecules are arranged with their polar groups to form double molecules which behave almost like paraffins of double length. These materials crystallize like paraffins in laminae and exhibit distinct tendencies for cleavage, which is caused by the low cohesion in those planes formed by the methyl groups. The second case is found in bifunctional molecules, such as hydroquinone, phthalic acid, adipic acid, and similar substances containing two polar groups; they have a tendency to form crystals of needlelike shape.

(d) Molecular Lattices and Symmetry of the Unit Cell

Most organic molecules exhibit low symmetry. It could therefore be expected that the *triclinic* system would be frequently met with. Actually most organic substances crystallize in the *monoclinic* system; their lattices possess digonal screw axes or gliding planes.

According to Reis and Weissenberg[46] the reason is as follows: the triclinic system is characterized by *parallel translation*. Such a parallel arrangement of molecules can only be expected if the areas of strongest attraction between the molecules are exactly opposite in direction to each other. In most cases, however, these directions form a certain angle with each other and the adjacent molecule deviates from the parallel position. If now, we assign to a third molecule the same position with regard to the second as the second has to the first, a symmetrical saturation of the intermolecular forces results. The first and third molecules are now parallel to each other and the arrangement can be continued indefinitely; it corresponds to a two-fold screw axis or a gliding plane, which, therefore, may be anticipated to occur frequently in organic crystals; they generally lead to the formation of needles or platelets.

The above consideration holds only for the aggregation of molecules from the gaseous state. In solution, solvation and desolvation of the

[46] A. Reis and K. Weissenberg, *Z. Physik*, **34**, 406, 420, 433 (1925).

molecules will interfere. Molecules containing hydrophylic and lyophilic groups, will have the former solvated in polar solvents, the latter in liquids of hydrocarbon character.

Naturally, the unsolvated (free) groups are the ones that determine the association of the molecules in the crystal lattice because their forces are still free to act.

In this way an explanation can be found for a phenomenon well known in organic chemistry that both the rate of crystallization and the shape of the crystals formed differ greatly from solvent to solvent. It may be cited as an example that the higher dibasic acids crystallize from water in laminae, whereas in benzene the different solvation relationships cause the growth of needles. Conversely, azobenzene, which crystallizes in platelets from most solvents, can be obtained in needles from dilute sulfuric acid. If the polar groups, hydroxyl, carbonyl, carboxyl, etc., serve as the principal centers of crystallization, it will be convenient to crystallize from media in which these groups are not solvated. This may be related to the fact that many oxygen-containing compounds crystallize particularly well from hydrocarbons and that even small amounts of moisture hinder crystallization to a noticeable degree.

The concept of a virtually constant space requirement of certain groups in organic molecules can also be applied to the problem of isomorphic replaceability in organic crystals. The vast experimental material accumulated by Bruni[47] can be coordinated and interpreted in the light of the concept of molecular and crystal structure. The formation of mixed crystals of phenanthrene and anthracene or naphthalene and dihydronaphthalene may be explained by the similar size and shape of the molecules concerned and by the similarity of their association forces. The same is true for the series stilbene, tolane, and azobenzene. Characteristic is also the formation of mixed crystals observed by Villiger[48] of 5-nitro-2,4-dichlorobenzoic acid and 5-nitro-4-hydroxy-2-chlorobenzoic acid. For isomorphic replaceability there is the obvious condition that the different atoms or atomic groups of the compounds crystallizing together occupy about the same space and that, in their interchange, the association forces of the whole molecule are not essentially influenced. This is generally the case if methyl is replaced by hydroxyl, or if hydroxyl is replaced by chlorine.

[47] G. Bruni, *Die festen Lösungen.* Stuttgart, 1902.
[48] V. Villiger, *Ber.*, **51**, 2596 (1928).

B. LATTICES WITH DIFFERENT FORCES IN DIFFERENT DIRECTIONS

Up to now we have described essentially lattices, the cohesion of which is effected by the same forces in all three directions in space and have pointed out only occasionally that transition cases also exist. Now we shall discuss substances in which different kinds of forces prevail in different directions of the lattice.

Let us first consider Figure V-13, which, according to Grimm, represents the conditions in a general and comprehensive manner. At the corners of a tetrahedron are arranged the four types of linkage described in the fore-

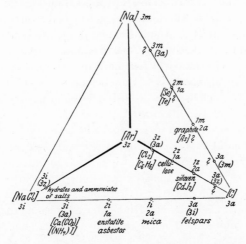

Fig. V-13. Systematic survey of crystal lattices in which different kinds of forces prevail in different directions of the lattice structure.

going sections; the transition lattices are then arranged along the edges of the tetrahedron. A glance at the figure reveals the interesting fact that the homopolar primary valence bond (*a*) participates in all transition lattices; the three edges that lead from 3*i* to 3*z*, from 3*i* to 3*m*, and from 3*m* to 3*z* are almost void (if we ignore the hydrates and ammoniates of ionic lattices). In contrast, we find a number of very interesting compounds on the other three edges.

We consider first the line connecting 3*i* and 3*a*, namely, substances in which the atomic and the ionic bonds participate in building up the lattice.

1. Lattices with Atomic and Ionic Linkages

Proceeding from the left side of Figure V-13, we find NaCl, CaO, CaF_2, etc., which are typical representatives of ionic lattices. But in compounds which contain radical or complex ions, the conditions are already different. Thus, for example, in $(NH_4)Cl$ it is true that the crystal lattice is built up in different directions by true ionic forces, but one of the two ions, $(NH_4)^+$ owes its cohesion to homopolar bonds. Since, naturally, the lattice forces are themselves codetermined by the size and polarizability of this ion, the atomic bond, in building up the structure of the lattice as a whole, participates, not directly, but indirectly, in this and in similar cases such as $CaCO_3$, $BaSO_4$, NaCN, etc. This is expressed in the diagram by inserting under the symbol $3i$ for the ionic linkage in three directions, the symbol $(3a)$ in parentheses for the atomic linkage inside the ion.

If we proceed in the direction to the atomic bond corner of the tetrahedron, we come to lattices which cohere in two directions by ionic forces and in the third by atomic forces; they belong to a certain group of silicates the structure of which will be discussed later in another connection (see page 203). Particular well-known representatives are: enstatite, $MgSiO_3$; diopside, $CaMg(SiO_3)_2$; and asbestos. The latter at once suggests by its marked fibrous habit that a particularly strong bond prevails in one direction. In this case it is the covalent bond that produces O—Si—O chains, while in the other two directions weaker ionic forces are active.

The next step leads to substances with *one* ionic and two atomic linkages; again, silicates provide particularly clear examples in the large groups of the *micas* and *chlorites*. Their essentially laminar structures show very definitely that strong atomic forces are effective in two directions, while, in the third, cohesion is produced by weaker ionic linkages.

Finally, we arrive at a class of compounds in which the lattice as such is welded together in all three directions by atomic forces, while ionic linkages produce finite small groups in the elementary cell; such substances are $CaTiO_3$, and most of the feldspars. Reis has coined the term *honeycomb* lattice for such structures because they exhibit very interesting swelling and shrinking properties.

Finally we come along the tetrahedron edge $3i$–$3a$ to the true atomic lattices which have their typical representative in diamond.

If we pass now on to the edge $3a$–$3m$, we come to lattices with atomic and metallic linkages.

2. Lattices with Atomic and Metallic Linkages

Substances in which lattice structure is caused in all three directions by homopolar bonds—while cohesion inside of the elementary cell is due to metallic bonds—may exist in certain intermetallic compounds although nothing definite can be said here regarding the exact type of linkages involved.

On the other hand we have in graphite, and probably also in Sb and Bi, elements in which homopolar bonds or strong dispersion forces are predominant in one direction in space while metallic bonds are responsible for the cohesion in the two other directions. This view is confirmed by the anisotropy of their mechanical optical and electrical properties.

According to Bernal the lattices of Se and Te are also characterized by the existence of metallic linkages in two directions and of atomic forces in the third. Many other semiconductors, some of which have very interesting and important technical properties, cannot yet be included in the above scheme with certainty, but are probably arranged in some manner along the tetrahedral edge $3a$–$3m$.

The last important edge leads us to lattices with atomic and van der Waals' bonds.

3. Lattices with Atomic and van der Waals' Bonds

These include, notably, the layer lattices that cohere in two directions by covalent bonds and in the third by secondary valences; examples, which we shall discuss later in greater detail, are CdI_2, MoS_2, AsI_3, talcum, graphitic acid, and siloxane. The anisotropy of the cohesion produces their distinct laminar habit and specific mechanical properties.

A type of special importance for natural and synthetic organic high polymers are the *chain lattices* which cohere in one direction by covalent bonds and in the two others by van der Waals' forces. The chief representatives of this class are cellulose, chitin, rubber, proteins, and a large number of synthetic polyvinyl- and polyacrylic derivatives, polyesters, polyamides, polyethers, polysulfides, polyurethans, etc.

The next step leads us to those compounds in which the lattice itself is held together in all three directions by secondary valence forces, but in which the lattice units are kept together by covalent bonds. We have here all molecular lattices consisting of compact units, such as Cl_2, CH_4, C_6H_6, and we arrive finally at the inert gases in the lattices of which there exist only van der Waals' forces.

This enumeration concludes the classification of crystal lattices on the basis of the cohesive forces and we shall now turn to the other classification, which depends mainly on considerations of symmetry.   It will appear in the course of the description how these two systems cooperate successfully in clarifying the behavior of crystals and the relationships between structure and properties.

VI. CRYSTAL STRUCTURE AND CRYSTAL SYMMETRY

A. GENERAL REMARKS ON SYMMETRY OF CRYSTAL LATTICES

It has been shown in the previous chapter that the study of organic and inorganic crystals has led to important general relationships between the forces of cohesion between atoms, ions, or molecules in the lattice and the distances separating them. Almost simultaneously with this approach, which was prosecuted largely by Bragg and Goldschmidt, another more geometrical method of treating the connection between cohesion and lattice structure was inaugurated by Reis and developed into a general theory by Niggli and Weissenberg. In a rational crystallochemical treatment of high molecular substances, it is advantageous to rely on both methods of consideration because only by applying all available approaches can a satisfactory elucidation of these complicated structures be attained. It will therefore be appropriate to outline briefly the general principles of symmetry concepts and to supplement the distance rules already mentioned by a more detailed discussion of the geometric theory of crystal structure.

The first aim of any crystal structure determination with x-rays, which can be nearly always attained with macroscopic crystals and often also with sufficiently oriented preparations of colloidal systems, is the determination of the *unit cell*. By this we understand the smallest volume from which the entire crystal can be built up merely by parallel displacement along three directions. The unit cell is determined if one knows the identity periods along the crystallographic axes and the angles between them. These identity periods are the distances which must be traversed along each of these preferred directions in the crystal in order to arrive at a lattice point identical with the initial one. If, in addition to these fundamental periods of the lattice, we also know the angles between the crystallographic axes, we can determine the volume V of the unit cell according to stereometric formulas.

If we multiply this volume V with the specific gravity ρ of the substance, we obtain the absolute weight of the unit cell in grams and, by dividing this by the weight of the hydrogen atom (H = 1.65×10^{-24} gram) the relative weight of the unit cell is found. If, as is often the case in molecular lattices, we know something about the molecular weight of the substance from observations in the vapor phase or in solution, we can ascertain the number of atoms or molecules present in the unit cell by dividing the weight of the cell by the molecular weight. Table VI-1 contains data calculated for a number of typical compounds; in the case of hexamethylenetetramine, for example, two molecules of the composition $C_6H_{12}N_4$ are building up the unit cell. It is known from the complete structure determination that each of these two molecules is in itself closely packed while they are separated from each other by distances of several angstrom units.

TABLE VI-1

UNIT CELLS OF SEVERAL MOLECULAR LATTICES

Substance	Density	Volume of unit cell, Å.³	Molecules in unit cell
Carbon dioxide	1.63	176	4
Benzene	1.09	471	4
Oxalic acid	1.90	302	4
$CO(NH_2)_2$	1.33	147	2
Pentaerythritol	1.39	329	2
Methaldehyde	1.27	442	9
Isatin	1.51	645	4
Hexamethylenetetramine	1.34	341	2
Stearic acid	0.94	1837	4
Anthraquinone	1.43	1931	8
Triphenylmethane	1.06	3050	8
Phthalocyanine	1.44	1200	2
Vitamin B	1.43	1648	4
Follicular hormone	1.22	1479	4

Since the unit cell combines in itself all the properties of the macroscopic crystal, it also possesses its symmetry. The spatial arrangement of the individual atoms in the unit cell is not random, but is controlled by the symmetry elements specific to the crystal. The geometric theory of three-dimensional space lattices permits an accurate counting and a complete description of all combinations of symmetry elements that are geometrically possible and shows that in three-dimensional space there are only 230 such combinations possible. Each of them is defined by a certain group of symmetry elements in specific relative positions. Such a group is termed a *space group*.

The above definition of the unit cell suggests a comparison with the conditions in the gaseous state on which the concept of a "molecule" is based. In a perfect gas, by progressive division, we arrive ultimately at *structural units* which cannot be further subdivided without loss of the chemical properties of the macroscopic phase constituted by them. These particles are moving kinetically independent of each other in space and are called the *molecules* of the substance. We can find in each one of them all chemical properties of the material because the assembly of many molecules to form the gaseous phase introduces no new factor inasmuch as the individual particles exert no forces on one another in this state. In the same way, by progressive subdivision of a crystal, we arrive ultimately at the *unit cell* as the *smallest structural unit*, embracing all the properties of the crystal; occasionally this has also been termed the *crystal molecule*. If, however, we compare the unit cell of the crystalline state with the kinetic molecule of the gaseous phase, we often find that it is a multiple of the latter. We can therefore state: in molecular lattices of organic substances, the smallest region which contains all chemical properties is usually smaller than that which in itself includes all properties of the crystalline state.

This can readily be understood. The chemical properties are given by the internal structure of the kinetic molecule in the isolated state, while the essential physical properties of the solid material (hardness, refractive index, conductivity, etc.) are determined by the mutual interaction between these molecules and by the architecture of the whole lattice. Accordingly, these properties can seldom be expressed by the properties of the single molecule but require the assembled qualities of a group of molecules in association.

If the unit cell is known, the next step in the elucidation of structure is to search for all its symmetry elements, *i.e.*, the determination of the *space group*. By its symmetry the geometrical conditions within the unit cell are defined. A full description of all symmetry elements and space groups would far exceed the scope of this treatise and we can only refer to the comprehensive literature on the subject, particularly Niggli's book and Weissenberg's papers.

However, in order to understand the idea of the geometric systematization it will be appropriate to explain the general character of symmetry elements by a simple example.

Figure VI-1 represents a crystal that possesses the property of self-coincidence on rotation through 180° about the axis AA'. This is termed the symmetry of a *two-fold* (*digonal*) axis of rotation; it is determined by the fact that in this crystal lattice all points are translated into one another on rotation through 180° about the axis AA', as shown in Figure VI-2; 1 is converted into 2, $1'$ into $2'$, etc.

In addition to the two-fold, there are three-, four-, and six-fold axes of rotation which, in turn, possess the property of allowing a given point to appear in three, four, and six different positions in the unit cell.

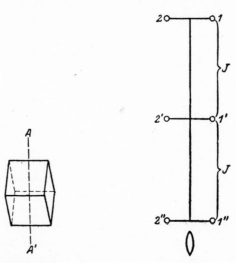

Fig. VI-1. Crystal with two-fold axis of rotation.

Fig. VI-2. Point arrangement in a two-fold axis of rotation.

If we now imagine, as shown in Figure VI-3, that the two points P_1, P_2— which, on account of the four-fold axis A, are a crystallographic group of points (equivalent lattice positions)—are bound together by a force, (*e.g.*, a primary chemical valence), then the four-fold axis is obviously an expression of the fact that all four points are joined together by equivalent forces. Parallel displacement applied to the individual cell results in the formation in the crystal of *closed groups*, each consisting of four equivalent points. There exist, therefore, symmetry elements, which, in conjunction with the specific translation periods pertaining to each crystal, permit the formation of *closed point groups* in the lattice (rotation axes, symmetry plane, center of symmetry). Such point groups have been termed *micro-units* or *islands* by Weissenberg; his method of sytematization consists first in counting up all micro-units that are possible in three-dimensional lattices.

Besides the above-named rotation axes, there exist other axial symmetry elements, the so-called *screw axes*.   Figure VI-4 represents the arrangement

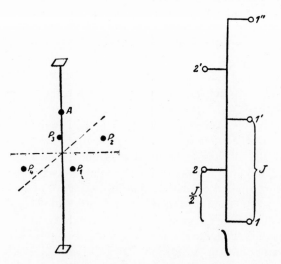

Fig. VI-3.   Point arrangement of a four-fold axis.

Fig. VI-4.   Point arrangement
of a digonal screw axis.

of points corresponding to a *digonal screw axis*; it is evident that the crystallographically equivalent points 1 and 2 are no longer capable of conversion into one another merely by rotation through 180°, but only by rotation and subsequent parallel displacement of the rotated points by half the identity period I parallel to the axis of rotation.   Thus, the coincidence movement here consists of *rotation plus translation*.   Since the translation extends through the entire crystal, an *infinite number of equivalent points* is produced by the screw axis from a *single given point*.

If we now assume a given force to be acting between the two points 1 and 2, the presence of the screw axis expresses the fact that the *same* force extends throughout the whole crystal parallel to the direction of this axis.

While a rotation axis leads to an assembly of *closed point groups*, the screw axis provides, by the same type of combination, a *chain of points traversing the entire crystal*.   Weissenberg has named such chains "*island chains*."   If two screw axes are present, we obtain *island networks* and in the presence of three digonal screw axes perpendicular to one another we obtain *island lattices*.

For the present purpose, therefore, we can divide the symmetry elements into two groups:

(*1*) Those which build up *closed point groups* (molecules) from one or more given points (atoms); they are rotation axes, symmetry planes, and centers of symmetry.

(*2*) Those which translate a given point into an *infinite number* of equivalent points. This class gives rise either to chains or networks which go through the whole lattice, or there results the whole three-dimensional crystal itself. Such symmetry elements are screw axes, gliding planes, and parallel translations.

In a lattice whose space group is known, the Weissenberg method allows us to find all possible *micro-units* and to indicate their symmetry. Their count leads us to all closed, finite atom groups possible in the crystal lattice investigated and permits us for the solid state, to make statements that are in a certain analogy with a molecular weight determination in the gaseous phase. It is evident that the micro-units will generally be smaller than the unit cell, for they possess only a part of its total symmetry, namely, symmetry elements of the first kind. The physical content of this theory is now the prediction that in all molecular lattices of organic compound the largest possible micro-units are identical with the kinetic molecules of the substance, a concept that can be tested by experiment and that has essentially been confirmed, with the exception of certain cases in which association exists in the lattice (metaldehyde, acetaldehyde ammonia, etc.).

Thus, for example, in the lattice of urea, the atomic group $CO(NH_2)_2$ is the largest that can be united in a micro-unit; this is consistent with the expectation emphasized particularly by Willstätter that in the lattices of organic substances the molecules always persist as clearly recognizable, closely packed groups. Thus the idea of closely packed atom groups in molecular lattices derived from distance measurements is supplemented and confirmed by the geometrical systematization of all possible micro-units.

This relation has also proved true in lattices of inorganic substances; here the micro-units are identical with the complex ions or with the molecules of the intermetallic compounds (*e.g.*, $ZnMg_2$, CO_3, $PtCl_4$, SnF_6). In the first case, metallic, and in the second, ionic bonds, are responsible for the existence of micro-units. It is evident from this that the purely geometrical demarcation of the micro-units tells us nothing about the physical nature of the forces holding these units together; it only affirms that the points capable of being linked together form a *closed group* in the crystal which is clearly separated from the other identical group.

However, by considering the symmetry elements of the second kind, Weissenberg's approach furnishes information on general structural principles for the building up of crystal lattices, for these symmetry operations enable a given point to be translated into an infinite number of other positions. Therefore one will conclude that the field of force whose point arrangement corresponds to a digonal screw axis is of such a nature that it will not be saturated by the assembly of only a finite number of atoms; rather, as soon as a new particle approaches there arises a force analogous to that existing previously and results in a further growth of the chain. We can therefore express the difference between the field of force corresponding to a digonal axis of rotation and to a digonal screw axis by saying: an axis of rotation is saturated after the assembly of a definite small number of atoms, a screw axis effects *growth* of an infinitely long chain in a certain direction. Nothing is said about the nature and magnitude of the prevailing forces.

If we are to understand the structure of a crystal lattice fully and are interested both in the geometrical arrangement of the atoms and the magnitude and nature of the forces, we must take into account the distance rules and the other properties of the substance in addition to the above-described geometrical considerations and try to merge both approaches into a complete picture of the system under investigation.

An example in which the conditions are simple and clear is the lattice of urea. Here, the ultimate structure determination shows that the group $CO(NH_2)_2$ is closely packed in itself but relatively distant from the next identical group; the Weissenberg tables indicate that this group is the largest possible *micro unit;* there is thus full concordance between the two available modes of consideration; both recognize the molecule $CO(NH_2)_2$ as a particularly stable group and everything leads to the conclusion that this molecule is held together in the crystal by primary valences, while the lattice forces are van der Waals' forces or hydrogen bonds.

The same is true for the majority of organic molecular lattices already discussed.

We see that the purely geometrical consideration of the prevailing symmetry, with particular regard to the existence of closed groups, leads to the same result as the consideration of the forces acting within a crystal; there are lattices that consist of isolated units firmly closed in themselves, there are lattices that are built up of chains and networks, and, finally, there are crystals in which no closed groups can be recognized either geometrically or dynamically; the whole crystal is held together by identical, generally very strong, forces, and forms one gigantic molecule. To complete the discussion on different kinds of lattices and to conclude the chapter on the solid state, we shall now discuss briefly the principal lattice types from the point of view of the existence of closed groups.

B. PRIMARY VALENCE LATTICES

The entire crystal is held together in all directions by identical forces and the demarcation of a definite closed region is impossible geometrically and dynamically. Such lattices are familiar among the metals in which cohesion is provided for by the *metallic bond* (*e.g.*, Na, Mg, Cu, W). They also exist as ionic lattices, such as NaCl, CaF_2, CaO, in which *heteropolar primary valences* determine and hold the structure together and there exist finally primary valence lattices with homopolar bonds: diamond, silicon carbide, zinc sulfide, and so on.[1]

It may be added that many natural and synthetic organic polymers also form three-dimensional networks which cohere at least partly by homopolar primary valences. In most of these cases, however, the regularity of the cross links is not sufficient to produce sharp and intense crystal diffraction patterns, but there can be no doubt that the substances concerned are to be classed as more or less deformed and randomized primary valence lattices with a smaller specific bond density than diamond.

A well-known case is hard rubber, in which the individual long chains of the original native rubber are reticulated by simple or multiple sulfur bridges into a framework that coheres strongly in all directions and that is nonfusible and nonsoluble. The so-called cyclized rubber also belongs to this type because it is very probable that heat treatment of natural rubber in the presence of condensing agents (such as $AlCl_3$, BF_3) does not only result in ring structures within the individual chains but also in cross linking between them.

Many polycondensation products of great importance are of the same kind. Elimination of water from polybasic acids and polyvalent alcohols, notably, glycerine, produces the so-called glyptals, which in the initial stages of condensation exhibit predominantly chain character, but, in the later stages of the reaction, show every indication of far-reaching three-dimensional reticulation. The same holds for condensation products of urea, melamine or phenol, and formaldehyde. Wherever the condensation process is carried far enough, one obtains solid, hard, nonfusible, and insoluble products of high resistance to impact and high specific gravity.

---

[1] See, *e.g.*, H. Mark, *Ber.*, **59**, 2991 (1926).

In conclusion, it may be remarked that many natural polymers, such as certain proteins and native resins—the keratin of nails, hairs and feathers, colophony, and others—form primary valence lattices which at times possess so much regularity that they even give fairly definite x-ray patterns.

The properties of primary valence lattices enumerated above—infusibility, insolubility, strength, and density—make it difficult to treat them with the classical methods of physical and organic chemistry, although these same properties are exceedingly important for their technical applications.

C. PRIMARY VALENCE SHEETS

Here, also, there appears to be a general gratifying concordance between geometric and dynamic systematization. Lattices in which, according to Niggli, Reis, and Weissenberg, one can build up infinite layers of atoms, ions, or molecules in two dimensions, and where conditions are therefore favorable for the development of lamellar lattices are usually held together by different forces in different directions. We are interested here especially in those cases where primary valence networks are formed through the action of homopolar bonds which traverse the entire crystal uniformly.

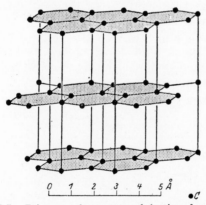

Fig. VI-5.   Primary valence network lattice of graphite.

Thus, for example, in the lattice of graphite the micro-unit is identical with the carbon atom, *i.e.*, no larger closed atomic group can be formed. If any two points lying in the basic plane (Fig. VI-5) are tentatively connected with each other by a bond, this same bond is extended by the symmetry elements along the whole plane, but in such a way that any two consecutive planes remain free of one another.

By applying the distance rules, one can identify the bonds in these planes with chemical primary valences, through which *primary valence layers* are formed. In the case of graphite the uniform bonds within the hexagonal plane are provided by conjugated double bonds and lead to an almost metallic linkage parallel to these planes. The planes themselves are bonded together with each other by much weaker van der Waals' forces. These conditions explain the laminar form, the easy slippage along the basic plane, the metallic conductivity, and various other properties of graphite.

There exist many other interesting layer lattices; the most closely allied is that of *graphitic acid*.

If graphite is treated with nitric acid or a mixture of concentrated HNO_3 and H_2SO_4, a definite swelling of the laminar crystals is observed. Hofmann and Frenzel[2] have found that most x-ray diffraction points remain unchanged; only the reflections of the basic plane become more diffuse and undergo a shift to smaller angles of diffraction. This corresponds to an increase of the lattice distance from the normal value of 3.37 Å. to 3.68 and 4.1 Å. On further swelling, the material changes color and becomes brown; the interplanar distance of the networks mounts to 7.9 A. Graphitic acid results if $KClO_3$ is added during the oxidation of graphite with HNO_3; it consists of green laminae which swell strongly in water. In the dry state, the distance between the layers is 6.4 Å., whereas in the presence of 60% water it increases to 11.3 Å. It is evident that we have here a definite layer lattice in which the separate basic planes—which are held together firmly in themselves by primary valences—can be easily displaced with respect to one another by the infiltration of a swelling agent.

Schleede and Wellmann[3] have obtained interesting products by the action of alkali metal vapors on graphite. X-ray data show that the atoms of the alkali metals—K, Rb, and Cs—penetrate between the basic lattice planes and increase their distances quite appreciably; identity periods of 21, 34, 18, 51, 22, 73 Å. were measured along the hexagonal axis; for graphite itself the identify period is 6.79 Å.

A case of similar interest is the structure of calcium silicide, which was described by Boehm and Hassel[4] as a primary valence lattice of six-membered silicon rings linked together by calcium bridges. Figure VI-6 shows the arrangement of the various atoms in this typical layer lattice, which is characterized by extreme laminar habitus.

[2] U. Hofmann and A. Frenzel, *Kolloid-Z.*, **61**, 297 (1932); **69**, 351 (1934); *Z. Krist.*, **86**, 340 (1933); **98**, 229 (1937).

[3] A. Schleede and W. Wellmann, *Z. physik. Chem.*, **B18**, 1 (1932).

[4] J. Boehm and O. Hassel, cf. footnote 5.

Another interesting layer lattice was described by Kautsky[5] in the reaction product of calcium silicide with water. He found that these systems can experience chemical substitution layer for layer without losing their shape and cohesion, a process which Freundlich has called a *permutoid reaction* of this crystalline material. It is a special case of a reaction which is confined to definite, spatially fixed points and which have been investigated by Kohlschutter and termed *topochemical*.

There exist many ionic lattices with typical layer lattice properties; there are heteropolar linkages acting parallel to the layer planes and perpendicular to them, but because of the polarizability of the various ions

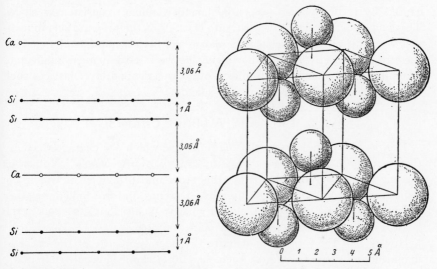

Fig. VI-6. Point arrangement in the layer lattice of calcium silicide (after Boehm and Hassel).

Fig. VI-7. Layer lattice of cadmium iodide.

the linkages are considerably stronger *in* a given plane than *perpendicular* to it. An example of such an ionic layer lattice is cadmium iodide, represented in Figure VI-7; its strongly anisotropic conductivity, solubility, etc., are readily understandable from the structure.

Recent studies of de Boer and his collaborators[6] on the intermicellar swelling of CaF_2 in cesium vapor are of a particular interest in this con-

[5] H. Kautsky, *Z. anorg. allgem. Chem.*, **139**, 135 (1925); **147**, 81 (1925); *Ber.*, **57** 1665 (1925).

[6] C. I. Dippel and J. H. de Boer, *Z. physik. Chem.*, **B21**, 278 (1933); **25**, 399 (1934).

nection. They show that CaF_2 prepared by sublimation is able to take up appreciable amounts of cesium and liberate it again by a completely reversible process.

The particular preference for a given plane is always characteristic of a *layer lattice*. Macroscopically it is usually evident as a cleavage plane and is particularly prominent by its intensity in the x-ray diagrams as the plane which gives the strongest reflections. Using deformed specimens of graphite and molybdenite, x-ray diagrams show, moreover, that the distance between the individual layer planes is not as constant as the atomic distances within them. On application of pressure the diffraction spots of the basic plane of graphite are broadened markedly, while the reflections caused by lattice planes perpendicular to it remain consistently sharp. This fact indicates that in the minute crystals of the preparations investigated the distance between layer planes has been somewhat changed by the stress, but that the primary valence network has remained unaffected. A similar phenomenon was found in other well-defined layer lattices such as molybdenum sulfide and calcium silicide.

D. PRIMARY VALENCE CHAINS

The next step leads us to the *chain lattices*, which are characterized by the presence of a parallel set of *screw axes* or *gliding planes*. Numerous organic molecular lattices possess this structural principle, in which the individual molecules form closely packed groups and are linked together to island chains by hydrogen bonds or van der Waals' forces, such as in the lattices of carbon dioxide, ice, oxalic acid, and urea.

However, if the forces which unite the micro-units are of the order of magnitude of chemical bonds, then we obtain chain molecules extending throughout the whole crystal, which are called *primary valence chains*.

If experience gained from layer lattices is applied to *chain* or *fiber* lattices, it is to be expected that the cohesion of the primary valence chains will impose their character on the whole structure and that permutoid reaction will be exhibited to a still higher degree than in layer lattices, because the strong cohesion due to primary valence bonds acts now only in a single direction. We may further assume that the diffraction effects of such primary valence chains will exhibit certain similarities to diffraction phenomena in linear lattices.

It is known that a system of equidistant points on a line irradiated perpendicularly with monochromatic x-rays gives a diffraction pattern on a flat plate which consists of curves resembling hyperbolas. Only by the juxtaposition of several linear lattices in a regular lateral arrangement do these hyperbolas break up into separated points due to the additional extinctions now occurring, and produce the familiar *layer lines*. Figure VI-8 represents the diffraction of a linear lattice and Figure VI-9 that of several linear lattices placed regularly beside one another.

If, now, the regular arrangement of the individual chains is disturbed by some influence, we may expect increasing width of the spots along the individual layer lines. Actually it was found (in asbestos, cellulose, and

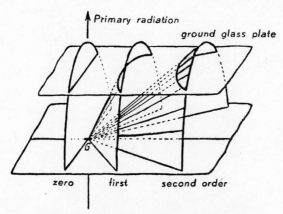

Fig. VI-8. Diffraction phenomenon in a linear point lattice; co-axial diffraction cones are produced.

polyvinyl derivatives—all belonging to the group of chain lattices) that such effects can be observed more or less clearly. Frequently the diagram of strongly mercerized or otherwise chemically treated cellulose shows definite diffuseness of the diffraction spots *along the layer lines*, a qualitative proof that the structure concerned belongs to the fiber lattice type. It will be shown in greater detail in the next section that all x-ray and chemical evidence points to the fact that typical fiber lattices of primary valence chains are characteristic for most high polymers.

The relations between molecular and chain lattices are clearly illustrated by diagrams which Hengstenberg[7] prepared at the suggestion of Mie and Staudinger on the paraffin $C_{35}H_{72}$ and were extended later by the systematic work of Müller[8] on $C_{29}H_{60}$ and $C_{30}H_{62}$. As already mentioned, investigations of lower and higher paraffins which form macroscopic crystals have

[7] J. Hengstenberg, *Z. Krist.*, **67**, 583 (1928); *Ann. Physik*, **84**, 245 (1927).

[8] A. Müller, *Proc. Roy. Soc. London*, **B120**, 437 (1928); **124**, 317 (1929); *Trans. Faraday Soc.*, **25**, 347 (1929).

indicated that the unit cell increases regularly in one dimension as one increases the length of the hydrocarbon chain but remains constant in the other two dimensions.[9] We concluded from this that the paraffin molecules in the unit cell are arranged with their long axis parallel to one of the crystallographic axes (c axis) as shown in Figure VI-10. If we reflect on a

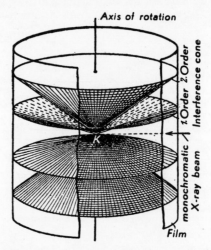

Fig. VI-9. Diffraction phenomenon in a linear point lattice taken on a cylindrical film; parallel layer lines are produced.

set of planes which are perpendicular to the paraffin chains and coincide with the gliding planes of the lattice, we obtain a diagram which allows us to calculate the identity period along the axis of the molecules. In the case of $C_{35}H_{72}$ it is 46.2 Å.

For measuring the two other (shorter) periods perpendicular to the chains, the crystal has to be adjusted with the chains parallel to the axis of the camera and rotated in front of a monochromatic x-ray beam. The resulting diagram shows that the a and b edges of the elementary cell have lengths of 7.4 and 4.97 Å., respectively, and that the crystal possesses rhombic symmetry.

Besides these three distances of 4.97, 7.4, and 46.2 Å., which form the elementary cell and are the identity periods of the lattice, another spacing appears with strong intensity in the diagram. It corresponds to a distance

[9] E. Shearer, *Proc. Roy. Soc. London*, **A108,** 655 (1925); A. Müller, *Proc. Roy. Soc.,* **A138,** 517 (1932); **158,** 292 (1937); A. R. Ubbelohde, *Trans. Faraday Soc.,* **34,** 292 (1938); J. W. H. Oldham and A. R. Ubbelohde, *Trans. Faraday Soc.,* **35,** 328 (1939).

of about 2.5–2.6 Å., which coincides closely with the distance between alternate carbon atoms in an ordinary zig-zag paraffin chain as represented in Figure VI-11.

While the three above-mentioned periods of 4.97, 7.4, and 46.2 Å. are to be regarded as the fundamental true identity periods of the lattice, the spacing of 2.5 Å. demonstrates the existence of a subperiodicity within the

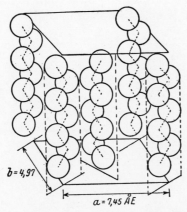

$b = 4,97$

$a = 7,45 \; \overset{o}{A} E$

Fig. VI-10.   Position of paraffin chains in the unit cell.

molecules themselves.   Figure VI-12 shows how diffraction spots close to the primary beam correspond to large spacing of the lattice, whereas spots that appear under a large angle correspond to the small distances within the molecule.   Similar results have been obtained with many well-defined long-chain compounds, such as fatty alcohols, ketones, and acids.   They give us a clear and reliable insight into the lattice structure of crystals, which are built up by chains of medium length and of complete uniformity.

If we now pass from pure substances with molecules of exactly equal length to mixtures of chains with slightly different length, the long spacings characteristic for the length of the molecule become less and less pronounced and finally disappear completely.   What is left are only the above-mentioned subperiodicities of the individual chain molecules.   Since this short distance now appears as the only observable identity period along the fiber axis, we are no longer measuring the length of the entire chain but only that of one of its repeating units.   Consequently, what we now interpret as the unit cell is much shorter than the molecule and the lattice has become a typical primary valence chain lattice.

Piper has actually observed that the reflections corresponding to the molecular lengths in a mixture of palmitic and stearic acids appear broadened and lie between the positions of the pure components, a behavior which is in line with the Vegard rule for mixed crystals of inorganic compounds.

Later, Hengstenberg[7] and Müller[8] demonstrated that in pure substances (e.g., $C_{35}H_{72}$) the long periods are always observable but that they disappear in mixtures of paraffins with not too different chain lengths. How-

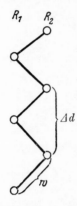

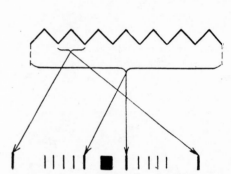

Fig. VI-11. The zig-zag structure of the fatty acid chains gives rise to an internal periodicity of the magnitude Δd.

Fig. VI-12. Because of the Bragg reflection law, large network plane distances correspond to small angles of diffraction and vice versa.

ever, these mixtures show very strongly a diffraction line, indicating the existence of a spacing of 2.5 Å., which corresponds to the short intramolecular periodicity of a zig-zag paraffin chain.

Synthetic long chain compounds from a certain molecular size on can no longer be separated into pure substances, that is, into fractions of exactly the same chain length. The x-ray diagrams of the lower, pure members show molecular lattices with well-developed long periods, whereas the patterns of the higher, impure preparations represent typical primary valence chain lattices. In a few cases, such as the polyhydroxymethylenes, the gradual disappearance of the diffraction spots of the long spacings has been experimentally confirmed. In these studies it was observed by Hengstenberg that after the disappearance of the large periods the small ones are not the only spacings to persist. There exist intermediate periodicity which in the polyhydroxymethylenes are about nine times as long as the short ones.   This intermediate value is presumably produced by a mutual lateral interaction of the chains.   Natural and synthetic high polymers with very long and heterogeneous chains only exhibit the reflections corresponding to the intramolecular periodicity, and, in general, no longer show the long spacings; they are typical main valence chain lattices.

Sometimes it is possible to obtain preparations of macromolecules of such high uniformity that the long spacings can be directly observed with x-rays.   Bernal and Crowfoot[10] have measured identity periods of 67 and 154 Å. directly in single crystals of pepsin using a particularly precise technique; a molecular weight of 40,000 was obtained with 12 molecules in the elementary cell.   A qualitative discussion of the intensities allows the conclusion that the protein particles are densely textured, spheroidal particles with a diameter of about 30 Å.

Clark and Corrigan[11] have found identity periods of 74.7 and 30.6 Å. in crystalline insulin and derived from them a molecular weight of about 39,000.   Similar results were obtained by Wyckoff and Corey[12] with hemoglobin and other proteins, and by Clark, Parker, Schaad, and Warren,[13] who measured spacings of about 440 Å. in collagen.

E. STRUCTURE OF SILICATES

There exists a group of important substances which exhibit almost all the lattice types described in the last section (Sect. D.)—primary valence lattices, primary valence networks and primary valence chains.   This is the species of the silicates whose structural principles were studied and elucidated by Bragg and his co-workers.[14]   It is well known that for these compounds the use of the normal structural formulas of inorganic chemistry proved to be inadequate.

The work of Bragg, Pauling,[15] and Machatschky,[16] which is based on the principles of crystal chemistry, led to the establishment of astonishingly simple pictures which render the structure and properties of these widely distributed important compounds rather easily intelligible.

The forces controlling the structure of these lattices are those between

[10] J. D. Bernal and D. Crowfoot, *Nature*, **133**, 794 (1934).

[11] G. L. Clark and K. E. Corrigan, *Phys. Rev.*, **40**, 639 (1932).

[12] R. W. G. Wyckoff and R. B. Corey, *Science*, **81**, 365 (1935).

[13] G. L. Clark, E. A. Parker, J. A. Schaad, and W. J. Warren, *J. Am. Chem. Soc.*, **57**, 1509 (1935).

[14] Cf. *e.g.*, W. L. Bragg and W. J. Warren, *Z. Krist.*, **69**, 168 (1928);   **76**, 201 (1930).

[15] L. Pauling, *Proc. Nat. Acad. Sci. U. S.*, **16**, 578 (1930).

[16] F. Machatschky, *Naturwiss.*, **26**, 67 (1938).

the silicon and oxygen atoms and are best considered to be essentially homopolar primary valences, although they probably contain a certain degree of heteropolar character. Accepting this basic assumption, it seems that the structure of all silicates can be based on the following principles: (a) each silicon atom is surrounded by four oxygen atoms in tetrahedral arrangement; (b) one oxygen atom can be chemically combined with one or two silicon atoms; and (c) two tetrahedrons built up of silicon and oxygen atoms may have one oxygen atom in common. These rules lead to two extreme cases:

(1) The lattice consists of charged SiO_4 tetrahedrons forming isolated lattice units which are held together by metal ions of various chemical nature and charge, each oxygen atom belonging to only one tetrahedron; the ratio of Si to O is 1:4.

(2) Each oxygen atom belongs to two tetrahedrons. Then a three-dimensional primary valence network of the composition $(SiO_2)_n$ is formed and the ratio of Si to O is 1:2.

All existing silicates can be placed somewhere between these two extreme cases, depending on whether more or less of the oxygen atoms belong to two Si atoms. In this way we obtain:

(a) The *ortho-silicates* with fourfold negatively charged SiO_4 ions. They possess the properties of normal heteropolar lattices with complex ions such as $CaCO_3$ or $BaSO_4$, Mg_2SiO_4, $ZnSiO_4$, and others belong to this class.

(b) Silicates which, through polymerization, contain a *finite* number of SiO_4 groups; they are formed if one or more oxygen atoms belong to two silicon atoms in the lattice. If, for example, *two* SiO_4 tetrahedrons have *one* oxygen atom in common, dimeric (Si_2O_7) ions result; they also represent isolated groups in the lattice; examples are $Sc_2Si_2O_7$ and $Pb_3Si_2O_7$. If *three* SiO_4 tetrahedrons condense with the elimination of three oxygen atoms to a ring-shaped ion (Si_3O_9), compounds such as $BaTiSi_3O_9$ result.

(c) Silicates with *infinite* SiO chains, which are formed when SiO_4 tetrahedrons linked successively in a given direction of the lattice, always have *one* oxygen atom in common. Here we have primary valence chains of the composition $(SiO_3)_n$. This structure is found in the pyroxenes $CaMg(SiO_3)_2$ or $MgSiO_3$. By association of two (SiO_3) chains, an infinite ribbon is produced which has the formula $(Si_4O_{11})_n$; such structures exist in the silicates of the *amphibole* and *serpentine* groups and are characterized by a distinct fibrous behavior (asbestos).

(d) Silicates with plane infinite SiO networks. By continuous linkage of (SiO_4) tetrahedrons, giant laminar anions can be produced in such a way that three oxygen atoms are always common to two SiO_4 tetrahedrons. They have the composition $(Si_2O_5)_n$ and are present, for example, in talcum, kaolin, and mica. All physical and chemical properties of these substances are in harmony with the presence of primary valence networks. The layers can cohere to each other by ionic or van der Waals' forces.

(e) Silicates in which each O atom belongs to two (SiO_4) tetrahedrons and which form primary valence lattices that have been designated *honeycomb* lattices; this class includes the various modifications of SiO_2 quartz, tridymite, and crystobalite, and the silicates of the feldspar and zeolite

TABLE VI-2

STRUCTURE OF THE SILICATES

Ratio Si : O	Composition and form of anion	Total charge of anion	Charge of one Si anion	Examples
1:4	(SiO_4), tetrahedron	-4	-4	$Mg_2(SiO_4)$, forsterite
2:7	(Si_2O_7), double tetrahedron	-6	-3	$Sc_2(Si_2O_6)$, tortveitite
1:3	(Si_3O_9), ring	-6	-2	$BaTi(Si_3O_9)$, bentonite
1:3	(Si_6O_{18}), ring	-12	-2	$Be_3Al_2(Si_6O_{18})$, beryl
1:3	$(SiO_3)_n$, chain	$-2n$	-2	$CaMg(SiO_6)_2$, diopside
4:11	$(Si_4O_{11})_n$, band	$-6n$	-1.5	$Ca_2Mg_4(Si_4O_{11})_2Mg(OH)_2$, tremolite
2:5	$(Si_2O_5)_n$, plane	$-2n$	-1	$Mg_2(Si_2O_5)_2Mg(OH)_2$, talc
3:10	$(AlSi_3O_{10})_n$, plane	$-5n$	-1.67	$KAl_2(Si_3AlO_{10})(OH)_2$, muscovite
1:2	$(SiO_2)_n$ space network	0	0	SiO_2, quartz
3:8	$(AlSi_3O_8)_n$ 3-dimensional	$-n$	-0.33	$K(AlSi_3O_8)$, orthoclase
1:3	$(AlSi_2O_6)_n$ giant anion	$-n$	-0.5	$Na(AlSi_2O_6) + H_2O$, analcite

groups. In these the exchangeable water molecules fit into the large cavities that occur between the incompletely formed SiO_4 tetrahedrons. Table VI-2 (Grimm[17]) summarizes this situation and gives a striking picture of the great variety of lattices encountered in this group, and indicates that the silicates, which are rightly classed as the high polymers of inorganic chemistry, extend in their properties over a wide range, appearing sometimes as needle-shaped or laminar, soft materials and sometimes as hard brittle substances.

[17] Cf. H. G. Grimm, *Handbuch der Physik.* Second edition, Springer, Berlin, 1936, Vol. 24, part 2.

In conclusion it may be pointed out that Pauling[18] has succeeded in the task of investigating in the same way the large class of hetero polyacids of W and Mo with regard to their lattice structure.

F. SHAPE AND INTERNAL MOBILITY OF MOLECULES IN RELATION TO LATTICE STRUCTURE

The idea that molecules can change their shapes is not alien to organic chemists. In ring closure in the 1,5 or 1,6 positions it is always assumed that the chain curls and that ends unite to form the ring. This concept has been represented symbolically by the formulas, but it can now be taken literally and evaluated morphologically.

The phenomena of polymorphism show clearly that the individual atoms in organic molecules assume different arrangements under changing external conditions. Thus, for example, in tetrabromomethane the individual molecule possesses tetrahedral symmetry above 45°C., while below this temperature it possesses a lower symmetry and crystallizes in the monoclinic form. Thus a change has occurred in the positions of the bromine atoms relative to one another and to the central carbon atom. Similar changes in the shapes of individual molecules are probably responsible for many other cases of polymorphism. As previously stated (see page 20), the tetrahedral angle is not strictly preserved in the transition from CCl_4 to $CHCl_3$ and CH_2Cl_2. Moreover, the optical activity of crystallized benzil and even of simple paraffins which vanishes in solution points to an atomic configuration within certain molecules which is different in the crystal lattice from that in the free state.

In solution and in the gaseous state the concept of approximately free rotation leads to the conclusion that, at temperatures which are not excessively low, open chains, such as hexane, heptane, and octane, do not possess the same rigid rodlike form as in the densely packed crystal lattices. Rather, the length and shape of the chains will undergo thermal fluctuations; the frequency of occurrence of a given form will be determined by its *a priori* probability and its energy content. An isolated long paraffin chain in the gaseous state, because of its heat capacity and also because of the van der Waals' forces exerted by the individual segments on one another, will assume a more or less coiled-up configuration, which is both lower in potential energy and at the same time statistically more probable than the straight chain. Therefore, the shape of the molecule in the gaseous state frequently differs from that in the crystal.

[18] L. Pauling, *Proc. Nat. Acad. Sci. U. S.*, **16**, 578 (1930); see also S. B. Hendricks and W. H. Fry, *Soil Sci.*, **29**, 457 (1930).

Particularly marked differences are to be expected for molecules which possess groups with strong dipole moments (OH, COOH, NH_2, CO). Here we know from the association of fatty alcohols and carboxylic acids in the vapor state that such groups exert strong intermolecular attraction. In the crystal lattice it was found that the molecules of normal dibasic acids are arranged parallel to one another, that the two carboxyl groups of each individual molecule are as far as possible removed from each other and that they are closely associated with the carboxyl group of a neighboring molecule. Undoubtedly, the isolated dicarboxylic acid molecules, such as sebacic or suberic acid, behave differently. Due to the attraction between the two terminal carboxyl groups, considerable curvature of the molecule to a ring-shaped structure is to be expected. In solution, the shape depends upon the solvent and differs in those liquids which solvate mainly the CH_2 groups and in those which solvate the COOH groups. In water, alcohols, and organic acids, the van der Waals' forces of the two carboxyl groups are to a large extent saturated by the solvent, but in dilute solution in benzene or other hydrocarbons conditions similar to those in the gaseous state should obtain.

The behavior of fatty acids in thin films on a water surface confirms this view experimentally. According to Langmuir and Adam it must be assumed that, in fatty acid films on water, the carboxyl groups are arranged in the surface, while the lipoid chains are floating on the water. As to their space requirement, dibasic long chain acids behave like two molecules of a monobasic acid, viz., there is folding or coiling of the chain.

For example, the space requirement of nonylic acid amounts to 25×10^{-16} cm.^{2} per molecule, that of sebacic acid 57×10^{-16} cm.^{2}. Similar relations exist in amino acids, hydroxy acids, polyhydroxyl compounds, etc.

It is clear that in low molecular weight compounds, such shape changes do not result in spectacular phenomena, but they do so in compounds in which the macroscopic physical and mechanical behavior is influenced by the configuration of the individual molecules. In this case the changes of molecular shape may be accompanied by noticeable changes of the physical, thermal and mechanical properties. This is particulary to be expected in compounds with *open chains*, since the relatively free internal rotation of such systems permits a change in shape without substantial energy changes. In molecules whose structure is stiffened by ring closure, such as cellulose and its derivatives, folding or curling occurs to a much lesser degree.

Many of these phenomena can be demonstrated very nicely with wooden molecular models, which were first, as it seems, used by Stuart and later improved and perfected by Fisher, Hirshfelder, and Taylor. Occasionally they can help to rule out certain suggested structural formulas and arrangements.

For instance, it may be shown that, of the anhydrides of 2,3,6-trimethylglucose which would be possible according to the normal formulas of organic chemistry and which are represented below by the formulas I and II, II cannot be reconciled with the requirements of the molecular models.

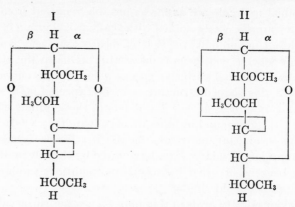

This can be seen readily in the space model of Figure VI-13 which was constructed with Bragg's atomic diameters and the tetrahedral carbon

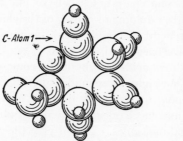

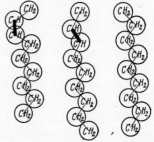

Fig. VI-13. Spatial model of β-glucose.

Fig. VI-14. Left, *cis* configuration; center, *trans* configuration; right, normal paraffin chains.

atom. It is evident that in the β configuration an anhydride bridge from 1 to 4 would have to go through the opening of the ring—which is geometrically impossible.

Moreover, it can be seen that an anhydride of cellobiose, which contains an oxygen bridge between carbon atom 1 of one ring and carbon atom 4 of the other ring, cannot be constructed without strain. This is important because such a formula has occasionally been assigned to certain degradation products of cellulose and is probably not correct.

In compounds of the type of camphor or cineol, *cis* and *trans* forms are possible from structural theory, but only one type of molecule has been found to date. The spatial model with the double ring system shows at once that only the *cis* configuration is possible in which the groups and atoms involved stand outside of the spherical system that forms the camphor framework.

Since the tendency to form mixed crystal and isomorphic systems is essentially due to the fact that foreign molecules of similar shape and association forces are incorporated in a lattice, the fact of mixed crystal formation can be utilized sometimes for determining constitution in otherwise doubtful cases, provided that at least the structure of one of the two compounds crystallizing together has been clearly elucidated. This method, frequently used by Bruni, gains considerably in conclusiveness through the modern concepts of molecular structure; it may be particularly applied to the problem of the *syn-anti* configuration.

As shown in Figure VI-14 the plane zig-zag structure of a normal paraffin is closely related to the *trans* configuration of a double bond, while the *cis* configuration has a totally different spatial arrangement. Therefore, it is to be expected that *trans* forms resemble the long chain paraffins physically and will be able to crystallize together with them. In fact, Bruni proved that elaidic acid crystallizes with stearic acid and deduces from this that elaidic acid is the *trans* form. This conclusion was later confirmed by Müller and Shearer,[19] who carried out an x-ray investigation of both acids. The resemblance between stearic and elaidic acid is also evident from their similar melting points as compared with the lower melting point of oleic acid. It is also known that gutta percha with *trans* configuration differs from rubber with *cis* configuration by having a higher melting point.

Bruni demonstrated in an analogous way the connection between crotonic and butyric acid; the *trans* form is indicated for crotonic acid and the *cis* form for isocrotonic acid. He further deduced, from the isomorphism of stilbene, benzal aniline, and azobenzene with dibenzil, the *trans* configuration of these compounds; x-ray examination clearly confirmed the *trans* form of stilbene. If it is possible in this way to establish the configuration of a double bond with the acid of a known, normal aliphatic chain, it is also possible to determine the configuration of a paraffin by crystallizing with an olefin of known structure.

[19] A. Müller and E. Shearer, *J. Chem. Soc.*, **123**, 3156 (1923).

When Bruni shows that dimethyl succinate crystallizes with dimethyl fumarate, it means that the succinic acid ester has a structure resembling the *trans* form, *i.e.*, it must have a zig-zag form, at least as long as it is incorporated in the fumarate crystal.

Isomorphism can also serve for elucidating constitution in really complicated cases; many years ago Garelli[20] concluded from the fact that tropanine and granatanine form solid solutions in naphthalene that they are simple binuclear substances without branches; Willstätter,[21] and Ciamician and Silber[22] proved this later by direct synthesis.

Similar consideration established for the sterols by Bernal and Crowfoot[23] are of special importance.   Definite proposals for the structural formulas of these substances have been made by chemists working in this field. especially by Windaus and Wieland, although preparative chemical methods have not succeeded in setting up a completely satisfactory structural formula.

TABLE VI-3

UNIT CELLS OF CERTAIN STEROLS

Substance	a (Å.)	b (Å.)	c (Å.)	β	Thickness of molecule
Cholesterol	14.0	10.3	2×19.6	117	—
Ergosterol + H_2O	9.75	7.4	2×19.6	115	4.95
Dihydroergosterol	3×10.3	7.4	2×21.6	127	4.1
α-Ergosterol + alcohol	12.0	5.81	2×17.8	95	—
γ-Ergosterol	10.0	6.9	2×18.5	90	5.0
Calciferol	2×10.4	7.15	2×17.8	95	5.2
Calciferol-pyrocalciferol	2×10.1	7.35	2×20.0	117	4.5
Suprasterol I	2×13.0	7.5	2×20.0	137	4.5
Suprasterol II	13.4	10.4	2×17.2	90	—
Lumisterol	2×10.2	7.25	20.4	120	4.3

Measurements on a series of sterols have supplied very informative data on the dimensions of their unit cells (see Table VI-3) and made it possible to calculate the thickness of the molecules and their spatial expansion in the molecular plane.   The result was that the formula preferred by organic

[20] A. Garelli, *Ber.*, **29**, 2972 (1896).

[21] R. Willstätter, *Ber.*, **29**, 393 (1896); *Ann.*, **312**, 204 (1901); **326**, 1 (1903).

[22] G. Ciamician and P. Silber, *Ber.*, **25**, 1601 (1892); **26**, 156, 2738 (1893); **29**, 481 (1896).

[23] J. D. Bernal and D. Crowfoot in J. M. Robertson, *Rep. Progr. Phys.*, **4**, 332 (1938).

chemists is incompatible with the evidence of the x-ray measurements. Bernal deduced from his measurements that a different, flatter structural formula, proposed for discussion by Rosenheim and King, was nearer the truth, a view that has now been accepted by all research workers in this field.

Thus, x-ray diffraction of molecules that are complicated even in the mind of an organic chemist has made significant contribution to the elucidation of the structure of an important class of compounds.

VII. LIQUIDS, MESOPHASES AND THE AMORPHOUS-CRYSTALLINE CHARACTER OF POLYMERS

A. GENERAL REMARKS ON THE ARRANGEMENT OF MOLECULES IN LIQUIDS

While a quantitative theory of ideal and real gases has been fairly well developed with the aid of statistical mechanics, and a rather complete quantitative theory of crystal structure has been worked out as a result of x-ray and electron diffraction, a really satisfactory theory of liquids has not yet been fully developed. There exist very interesting early contributions by Jäger,[1] who approached the liquid state from the state of highly compressed gases and actually succeeded to correlate certain properties of liquids in a quantitative manner, but precise evidence regarding the arrangement of the individual particles such as atoms and molecules in a liquid has only become available in recent years.[2]

The reason is obviously the following: the molecules of ideal gases are virtually independent of one another; they usually move without being influenced by any forces, and it is therefore possible to apply statistical methods to obtain data which, though summary, are sufficient to characterize the macroscopic state. In a crystal, on the other hand, the forces between the individual particles are so strong that these particles are permanently fixed in certain equilibrium positions and only carry out small vibrations about these positions. It is possible, therefore, to relate molecular structure and macroscopic properties in a purely dynamic way.

Forces are also prevalent in liquids, otherwise there would be no surface tension and no heat of vaporization, but they are not large enough to overcome completely the thermal motion of the molecules and to cause the formation of a well-organized lattice. Hence, in liquids, we have condi-

---

[1] G. Jäger, *Sitzber. Akad. Wiss. Wien*, **102**, 253, 483 (1893); **105**, 97 (1896); **111**, 697 (1902).

[2] Compare especially the excellent monograph of J. T. Randall, *The Diffraction of X-Rays and Electrons*, Wiley, New York, 1934.

214   VII. LIQUIDS, MESOPHASES, ETC.

tions that can be treated neither by purely statistical nor by purely dynamic methods; this has delayed the development of a quantitative theory for a long time.

Only in recent years has there been any significant progress, when Debye,[3] Eyring,[4] Frenkel,[5] Lennard-Jones,[6] and Prins and Born[7] made successful attempts to interpret the diffraction patterns obtainable from liquids with x-ray and electrons; they deduced quantitative relationships for the molecular arrangement of spherical particles. Later, other authors, particularly Raman and his co-workers,[8] Stewart,[9] Trillat,[10] and Kratky[11] studied theoretically and experimentally the conditions in liquids consisting of nonspherical particles and arrived at interesting results regarding the molecular arrangement in such systems.

As a consequence of these investigations it can be said that the individual particles of a liquid do not, like those of a perfect gas, assume at random all possible positions and orientations in space, but that their mutual arrangement resembles closely that of the crystalline state. In this sense we may conceive of a liquid as an aggregate of numerous very small crystals each of which is not perfectly ordered but has flaws and imperfections of all kinds. These small crystallites (consisting of 10–100 atoms) have only very short lives; they disband continually and re-form so that a given particle belongs for a moment to one of these small aggregates, then to none, then to a subsequent one that formed in the meantime, and so on. Kistler[12] has proposed for such transient groups the term "cyboma," and it seems to be reasonable to adopt such nomenclature in order to have a short expression for the situation just described.

In the gaseous state, the molecules travel undisturbed over relatively large distances, then suddenly collide with one another, thereby suffering a sudden change in direction; in the crystal lattice the individual atoms vibrate about fixed equilibrium positions; in a liquid the particles move slowly and randomly from place to place with persistent, irregular superimposed vibrations; they carry out a Brownian motion of very small free

[3] P. Debye, *Physik. Z.*, **31**, 348 (1930).
[4] H. Eyring, *J. Chem. Phys.*, **4**, 283 (1936).
[5] J. Frenkel, *Trans. Faraday Soc.*, **33**, 58 (1931).
[6] J. E. Lennard-Jones, *Proc. Phys. Soc.*, **43**, 471 (1931).
[7] J. A. Prins, *Z. Physik.*, **56**, 617 (1929). M. Born and H. S. Green, *Proc. Roy. Soc.* **A190**, 455 (1947).
[8] C. V. Raman, *Phil. Mag.*, **47**, 671 (1924).
[9] G. W. Stewart, *Rev. Modern Phys.*, **2**, 116 (1930).
[10] J. J. Trillat, *Trans. Faraday Soc.*, **29**, 495 (1933).
[11] O. Kratky, *Physik. Z.*, **34**, 482 (1933).
[12] S. S. Kistler, *J. Phys. Chem.*, **39**, 79 (1935).

path, during which their centers of gravity exhibit additional rapid vibrations, being always under the strong influence of the adjacent molecules.

The method which gave the best approach to the understanding of these relatively complicated conditions was the scattering of x-rays and electrons by liquids, which we shall now discuss briefly.

B. SCATTERING OF X-RAYS AND ELECTRONS IN LIQUIDS

Well-developed crystals were such convenient and attractive objects for the elucidation of structure by x-rays that much time elapsed before experiments on the scattering of x-rays and electrons in liquids were carried out with the necessary accuracy for a satisfactory theoretical treatment. Compared with the sharp and distinct diffraction spots and lines of crystals the patterns obtained from liquids did not, at first, seem very promising. For they consist, in most cases, only of a few blurred rings, the measurement of which at best gave two or three data, which had to suffice for theoretical interpretation. Conditions changed when Zernike and Prins[13] and Debye[14] showed that it was not sufficient to consider only the radius of the diffuse halos or rings but that one had to consider the dependence of the scattered intensity on the angle point by point. They demonstrated that the scattering of x-rays by liquids is made up of two components which must be considered separately if the total effect is to be interpreted quantitatively.

Debye, to whom, particularly, we owe the clear recognition and calculation of the two effects, has named them the *internal* and *external* diffraction.

The *internal diffraction* is produced by the scattering of the x-rays by the individual electrons in *each* atom. In a monatomic liquid, such as A, Kr, Xe, Hg, and Ga, the result is that on account of intraatomic destructive interference there exists a certain dependence of the scattered intensity upon the angle of diffraction. This influence is usually expressed by a factor that—because of its origin—is called the *atomic form* factor; its consequence is that more intensity is scattered in the directions near the primary beam than at larger angles, where destructive interference reduces the scattering.

If we are concerned with a molecule consisting of several atoms, such as H_2O, CCl_4, or C_6H_6, we have to consider that the individual atoms occupying definite positions in the molecule produce secondary waves which interfere with one another and cause a further change in the angular dependence of the scattered radiation; *intramolecular interference* is added to *intraatomic*

[13] F. Zernike and J. A. Prins, *Z. Physik*, **41**, 184 (1927).

[14] P. Debye, *Physik. Z.*, **31**, 384, 797 (1930).

interference, and a *molecular form factor* must be taken into account as well as an *atomic form factor*.

This *internal effect* is most clearly exhibited in the scattering of x-rays or electrons by molecules in the *gaseous* state and its study has provided much valuable evidence on molecular structure, as discussed in the first chapter.

If now, the atoms or molecules, which are entirely independent of one another in the gaseous phase, condense to a liquid, certain distance relationships are established between them. The result is that the secondary waves scattered by the different molecules interfere with one another and cause additional modification of the laterally scattered radiation. This external effect is caused by the special arrangement of the individual particles in the liquid, and it is therefore possible to deduce from it information about this arrangement. Conditions are naturally simplest in monatomic liquids, and the first quantitative results were obtained with them.

The extent to which the intermolecular phase relations change the angular intensity distribution may be seen by a comparison of Figure VII-1 and VII-2, both taken from a fundamental publication by Debye and Menke.[15] Carbon tetrachloride was irradiated with x-rays in the gaseous

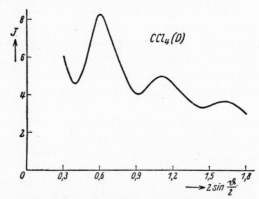

Fig. VII-1. Intensity curve of CCl_4 vapor.

and liquid states. The curve in Figure VII-1 shows the scattering of CCl_4 molecules while entirely independent of one another in the gaseous phase. It represents the pure *internal effect* and gives information on the symmetry of the distances in the carbon tetrachloride molecule.

The curve in Figure VII-2 shows entirely different conditions. The

[15] P. Debye and H. Menke, *Physik. Z.*, **31**, 797 (1930).

first maximum is displaced and appears now much closer to the primary beam, indicating the frequent occurrence of certain distances in the liquid which exceed the intramolecular distances between the individual atoms; for, according to Bragg's law, the sine of the angle of diffraction θ and the distance between the scattering particles d are reciprocal to one another. The appearance of intense rings in the neighborhood of the primary beam points relatively to large distances between centers of strong scattering, while lines, points, or bands under larger diffraction angles indicate smaller distances between scattering centers in the irradiated material.   On comparing the two diagrams, we see that the maximum of the *external effect* in Figure VII-1 corresponds to about half the value of the maximum of the *internal effect* (Fig. VII-2), and we may infer as a rough approximation that

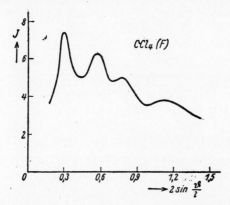

Fig. VII-2.   Intensity curve of CCl_4 liquid.

any distance occurring frequently in the liquid must be about twice the distance appearing within the individual molecules of carbon tetrachloride. Since the latter amounts to about 2 Å., we may deduce from a comparison of the two diagrams that a distance of about 4 Å. must occur very frequently in liquid carbon tetrachloride.   It is evidently plausible to consider this as the *average* intermolecular distance of individual molecules in the liquid phase and to obtain in this way an initial idea of its structure.

However, we shall not be content with such a rough average value, but will attempt to establish a more accurate distribution of the atoms or molecules in a liquid just as it has been possible to arrive at the fine structure of crystals from their x-ray diagrams.   The theoretical analysis of the scattering by randomly arranged particles has shown that it does not suffice to establish the existence of certain maxima—as seen in Figures VII-1 and

VII-2—and to derive from them, as was done there, the presence of definite average distances. It is necessary to establish the entire scattered intensity as a function of the angle and to deduce from it with a harmonic analysis the arrangement of the individual particles in the liquid.

Hitherto, it has only been possible to apply this method rigorously to *monatomic* liquids, but the results obtained permit drawing interesting analogies regarding the arrangement of molecules in liquids which do not consist of spherical particles.

1. Scattering of X-Rays by Monatomic Liquids

Two methods are possible for elucidating conditions in monatomic liquids, such as argon, krypton, mercury, and gallium. The first was used particularly by Prins,[16] Zernike,[17] Mark,[18] and Kratky.[19] Its principal assumption is that monatomic liquids possess structures that may be regarded as somewhat distorted hexagonal or cubic close packing, which would produce certain diffractions patterns that can be checked by experiment. The other method, which is stricter and more far reaching in its consequences, has been worked out by Debye and Menke,[20] Prins and Zernike[21] and Kirkwood.[22] It seeks to compute directly the spatial distribution of the scattering centers in the liquid by harmonic analysis of the experimental intensity distribution curve.

Since the first method has the advantage of simplicity and the latter that of mathematical exactness, we shall describe them both briefly and show how they complement each other.

Prins and Mark expressed the view that the arrangement of the atoms in liquid mercury may be regarded, to a fair approximation, as a hexagonal close packing strongly distorted by Brownian motion. This assumption is based on a very simple estimation. If we construct from mercury atoms the densest possible hexagonal packing with a specific gravity of 13.6, the distance between two neighboring atoms turns out to be 3.26 Å. On the other hand, the x-ray diagram of liquid mercury as represented in Figure VII-4, shows a particularly intense maximum, which must certainly be ascribed to the *external effect*, since a monatomic liquid is involved. If,

[16] J. A. Prins, *Physica*, **6**, 315 (1926).

[17] F. Zernike, *Z. Physik*, **41**, 184 (1927).

[18] H. Mark, *Z. Physik*, **54**, 505 (1929).

[19] O. Kratky, *Physik. Z.*, **34**, 482 (1933).

[20] P. Debye and H. Menke, *Physik. Z.*, **31**, 797 (1930).

[21] F. Zernike and J. A. Prins, *Z. Physik*, **41**, 184 (1927).

[22] J. G. Kirkwood, *J. Chem. Phys.*, **7**, 919 (1939).

as an approximation, we evaluate this maximum as representing the *average* distance between neighboring atoms, we obtain 3.26 Å. for this average value. To a fair approximation, therefore, the interatomic distances which prevail in hexagonal close packing also hold in the liquid phase.

Consideration of this average value alone will not suffice for a real thorough description and it is desirable to have a more accurate conception of the positions of the atoms in a monatomic liquid.   Kratky has extended

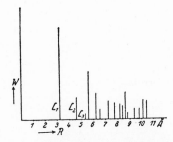

Fig. VII-3. Distribution of atomic centers of gravity in hexagonal close packing.

the view of Prins and Mark in several directions and has specifically discussed in greater detail the possible distortion of the hexagonal close packing which serves as the initial arrangement.   We arrive at a result most easily by assuming that all possible arrangements of the atoms in a liquid can be produced by starting with an ideal lattice and allowing each atom a definite displacement of its position relative to its neighbors.

The same is true for a vibrating crystal lattice, but in this case the displacements occur relative to a rigid, geometrically ideal framework (the point lattice at absolute zero).   In liquids, however, the displacements occur relative to the neighbors, which are likewise removed from their ideal positions; the result is that the relative displacement of two atoms increases with distance, while in the vibrating crystal the relative displacements from the equilibrium position are constant for all individual atoms.

We shall now imagine the origin of a system fixed in some individual atom and consider a lattice point at a distance r from it.   The displacement calculated for this lattice point on the basis of the above assumptions is then a measure for the distortion of the lattice at this point and at the same time is also a measure of the mobility of an atom at a distance r from the reference point.

To invest this method of consideration with formulas, we proceed from the above-mentioned reference atom and establish progressively in every direction in space the distances to the surrounding atoms. In this way we obtain the statistics of the interatomic distances in the liquid, the quantitative determination of which is the object of investigation.

It is convenient to imagine a thin spherical shell described around the origin, the radius of which is allowed to increase gradually so as to include, during the expansion, the atoms present in concentric spherical shells. The radii of these shells are then plotted as abscissas and the values W for the density of atoms situated in the shells as ordinates. If we establish, for example, that a shell of the radius r and the thickness dr contains n atoms, the density of atoms in the shell is:

$$W(r)\, dr = \frac{n}{4\pi r^2}\, dr \qquad\qquad \text{(VII-1)}$$

If we apply this consideration to a hexagonal close packing, we obtain a density distribution as shown in Figure VII-3. On moving out from the

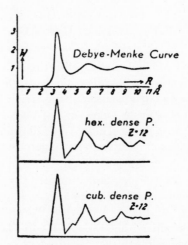

Fig. VII-4. Comparison of experimentally determined distribution curve of Hg with a distorted hexagonal or cubic spherical packing.

atom at the origin, we meet first with no other atoms because there is a characteristic minimum interatomic distance in this lattice. It amounts to 3.26 Å., as mentioned before, so that we come to the first neighboring atom only at this distance. The coordination number in the lattice of hexagonal close packing is 12, so that 12 atoms are present in the spherical shell of

r = 3.26 Å. This gives the first ordinate I in Figure VII-4. If we continue this construction, we obtain sharp lines at definite distances determined by the symmetry and the distances in the lattice, which indicate the presence of atoms in the appropriate shells. An inspection of Figure VII-4 shows that, actually, in the distortion of such an arrangement a distribution with several maxima results, the first of which, however, is predominant.

A more accurate treatment, also due to Kratky, indicates two further maxima, which, although not corresponding exactly in height to the experimental data, agree fairly well with them with regard to position. Figure VII-4 gives a comparison between the distribution function calculated by Debye and Menke from the experimental intensity distribution of the scattered radiation (upper curve), and the distribution derived by Kratky; the latter was calculated on the basis of a hexagonal close packing subject to a certain distortion of the arrangement (middle curve), and for a cubic close packing (lower curve). It is evident that there is good agreement with experiment, particularly for hexagonal close packing.

This comparison is illustrated even more clearly by Figure VII-5, where the actual distribution, according to Debye, is indicated by a heavy line,

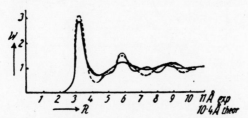

Fig. VII-5. Comparison of three curves for arrangement of atoms in a monatomic liquid.

the hexagonal close packing by a broken line, and the cubic close packing by a thin line. It is evident that at least as a first approximation, the concept of a distorted close packing for the arrangement of spherical atoms or molecules in a liquid is probably near the truth.

The procedure of Debye and Prins is still more rigorous. Here a mathematical relation is established between the scattered intensity I as function of the angle of diffraction θ and a distribution W as function of r, which indicates the degree of probability that, on proceeding from a given reference atom in any direction in space, another atom is met after traveling the distance r. W and I are related by an equation derived independently by Zernike and Debye:

$$N\rho(1 - W) = 2\frac{V}{\lambda^3}\int_0^\infty s\,[1 - E(s)]\sin 2\pi\rho s\,ds \qquad \text{(VII.2}$$

in which:

$$E(s) = \frac{2I(s)}{(1 + \cos\theta)N\psi^2} \qquad \text{(VII.3}$$

and $\rho = r/\lambda$; λ = wave length; $s = 2\sin(\theta/2)$; θ = angle of deflection N = number of atoms in the irradiated volume V; and ψ = atomic form factor.

Experiment supplies the I values corresponding to each value of s or θ. We can therefore compute E as a function of s (compare Fig. VII-6) and

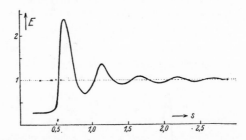

Fig. VII-6.   Experimental scattering curve $E = f(s)$ for Hg.

integrate the right-hand side of equation (VII.2) stepwise, either graphically or numerically. After performing this calculation, the right-hand side of (VII-2) represents a function of ρ, $viz.$ of r, from which the desired distribution function W may be calculated using equation (VII.2). We obtain

$$W(r) = 1 - \frac{F(r)\lambda}{Nr} \qquad \text{(VII.4}$$

By this process we obtain a continuous, smooth distribution function $W(r)$ as given by Debye and Menke for mercury in Figure VII-4. The distance from the reference atom is chosen as abscissa and is plotted directly in Ångström units in the figure. If we imagine a given atom in liquid mercury as fixed and a volume element combined with it at distance r the ordinate of the curve in Figure VII-4 represents the probability that the center of another mercury atom lies within that volume element.

Experiment gives a zero value for W close to the initial atom, because the atoms are unable to interpenetrate, owing to the repulsive forces acting between the negative charge clouds. The function represented by equation (VII-4) expresses a different behavior because the repulsive forces between the atoms have not been taken into consideration. In this region, therefore, the result of the computation is given simply by the abscissa. The distribution curve then rises steeply to the first maximum, to which, as we have seen, the 12 adjacent mercury atoms found in the first coordination sphere correspond. It then falls again to a minimum, indicating that there comes again a region not occupied by atomic centers. A second peak occurs at about 5.6 Å., and at large distances the probability that an atom will be found at a certain distance from the reference atom no longer depends upon r in any appreciable way.

In a rigid lattice, the sharp lines shown in Figure VII-3 replace the broadened maxima of Figure VII-4. In this case, the preference for certain distances is very definite; this eliminates the appearance of intermediate distances. The distribution curve of Figure VII-4 gives a quantitative idea of the extent to which a crystallike structure persists in a liquid in spite of the greater freedom of movement of individual atoms. Equation (VII.2) combines analytically the two functions represented in Figures VII-4 and VII-6 and may well be regarded as a satisfactory solution of the problem for the case of monatomic liquids.

Model tests with steel balls carried out by Debye and Menke and later by other authors using spheres as well as disks and rods give a pictorial impression of the above conception.

Table VII-1 gives a few relevant data for liquid alkali metals. It is

TABLE VII-1

AVERAGE DISTANCES IN LIQUID ALKALI METALS

Substance	Distance, Å., calcd. from liquid ring	d_{110} of solid metal
Sodium	3.01	3.04
Potassium	3.87	3.68
Rubidium	4.09	3.97
Cesium	4.51	4.28

evident that the average lattice spacings computed from the first peak increase with the position of the metal in the periodic system, just as would be expected from our general knowledge of atomic radii. A few data for argon, nitrogen, and oxygen are given in Table VII-2, from which it is evident that in liquefied gases, also, the most frequent average distances are of the order of magnitude of 3.5 Å.   Columns 3 and 4 show spacings for lattices of crystallized A, O_2, and N_2.   Comparison with the values in the liquids indicates, as is to be expected, that the identity periods of the unit cells are always greater than the distances of adjacent atoms in the liquid.

TABLE VII-2

AVERAGE PARTICLE DISTANCES IN LIQUEFIED GASES

Substance	Liquid d, Å.	Solid Lattice spacing	d for most intense lines
Argon	3.22	5.42	3.13
Nitrogen	3.59	5.66	4.01
Oxygen	3.24	$a = 5.50$ $b = 3.82$ $c = 3.44$	1.60 2.58 2.71

2. Molecular Structure of Water

After elucidating conditions in liquids with spherical particles, attempts have been made to treat cases in which accurate spherical shape and isotropy of the molecular forces are lacking, but with deviations from the spherical form not too great and the lattice of the crystalline phase well known.   A particularly important substance, whose behavior in the liquid state has long aroused great interest, is *water*.

It has been assumed that, because of strong dipole interaction between the individual molecules, a high degree of association prevails in liquid water, so much so that individual molecules in this liquid may not be regarded as in any way independent of one another.   X-ray diffraction of liquid water, has been extensively studied chiefly by Stewart[23] and Meyer,[24] whose experimental results have furnished the basis for a theoretical treatment of this problem.   The subject has been pursued by Bernal and Fowler,[25] who used the crystal structure of ice (see Chapter V), the x-ray diagram of water, and the known data for the water molecule to develop a pattern of the molecular arrangement in liquid water that represents in a remarkable way all known properties of this substance.

[23] G. W. Stewart, *Phys. Rev.*, **37**, 9 (1931).
[24] H. H. Meyer, *Ann. Physik*, **5**, 701 (1930).
[25] J. J. Bernal and R. Fowler, *J. Chem. Phys.*, **1**, 515 (1933).

Bernal and Fowler proceeded on the assumption that in ice there is a somewhat distorted tetrahedral arrangement of the individual water

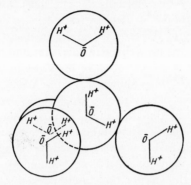

Fig. VII-7.   Tetrahedral arrangement of H₂O molecules in ice.

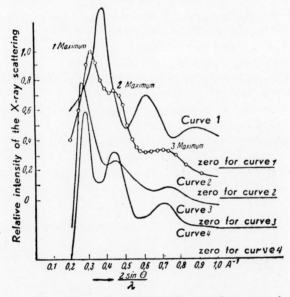

Fig. VII-8. Comparison of experimental scattering curve for water (circles) with different types of molecular packing.

molecules and that this also prevails in liquid water to a certain extent. Such a structure, with coordination number four, is far from close packing, and, as shown in Figure VII-7, considerably less compact.   In contrast to this bulky arrangement, liquids whose particles are spherical or have spherical fields of forces always show a distinct tendency for close packing. Were we to arrange water molecules in the most compact configuration possible, we would obtain a structure with a density of about 1.8.

To test the validity of the tetrahedral arrangement, Bernal and Fowler have discussed two configurations, one *quartzlike* and the other resembling *tridymite*. The intensity distribution of the x-ray diagram was calculated for both arrangements and is shown in Figure VII-8. Curve *1* gives the scattering of a closely packed water in which the molecules have a diameter of 2.76 Å. It is evident that this result is in complete disagreement with curve *2*, representing the experimental data. The first peak in the pattern of water appears considerably nearer to the direct beam and, because of the loose packing, corresponds to an average minimum distance of 3.24 Å; the first sharp and high peak for the closely packed structure would correspond to a distance of about 2.70 Å. Curves *3* and *4* of Figure VII-8 give the theoretical scattering for the two tetrahedral arrangements and evidently show considerably more resemblance to the experimental curve. A more accurate analysis of the conditions led Bernal and Fowler to the conclusion that in water three arrangements of the molecules are present which are continuously changing into one another.

α-water exists preferentially below 4° and has a tridymite like arrangement, which is a remnant of the structure of ice.

β-water is preferred at average temperatures up to about 200° and shows a *quartzlike* structure.

γ-water approximates the close packing and is stable at higher temperatures, up to the critical point (374°).

These three configurations do not pass into one another at sharp transition points, as would be expected in the case of distinct crystalline phases; rather, they are changing gradually with increasing temperature. The fact that the Raman spectrum of water undergoes considerable modification with temperature is in harmony with this view. Moreover, a mixture of quartzlike tetrahedral structure and close packing approximates very closely the scattering curve determined experimentally at 20°, as seen in Figure VII-9.

Finally, Bernal and Fowler calculated the heat of vaporization of water as represented by their model and found 11.5 kcal. per mole, while 11.81 is measured. Essentially, the attraction between the individual molecules is caused by hydrogen bonds.

From the angular width of the diffraction lines of water and their dependence on temperature, and from similar experiments carried out by

James[26] with CCl_4 it is possible to deduce the average size of the molecular clusters in the liquid phase.   Although no definite quantitative results are

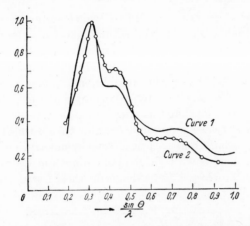

Fig. VII-9.   Curve 1: mixture of tetrahedral structure and close packing.   Curve 2: scattering curve determined experimentally.

yet available, we are probably not wrong in assuming an order of 10 for the number of members in such a regional group and a temperature effect such that the groups become smaller at higher temperatures.

3. Structure of Liquids with Chainlike Molecules

Although a quantitative theory of the structure of liquids with ellipsoidal particles is not yet available, it was possible, at least, to get a good qualitative idea of the molecular arrangement in liquids with rod- and disk-shaped particles.

The liquid paraffins from C_5 to C_{15} were examined with x-rays by Sogani and Stewart[27] and it was found that the most intense diffraction ring occurred at an angle corresponding to an average intermolecular distance of 4.6 Å.   The most reasonable explanation is that in these liquids long chains arrange themselves with their chain axes parallel to one another and form small groups or bundles, which, although constantly destroyed by thermal motion, reassociate again because they represent arrangements of minimum potential energy.   The chains in these bundles stiffen each other through mutual interaction and assume essentially the same zig-zag form as in the crystal lattice.   Because of the relatively high mobility of each

[26] R. W. James, *Physik. Z.*, **33**, 737 (1932).
[27] G. W. Stewart, *Phys. Rev.*, **31**, 174 (1928); **32**, 153 (1928).

individual chain in the liquid their cross section has axial symmetry similar to that established by Müller in the high temperature form of hydrocarbons in the crystalline state.

Katzoff,[28] Wilson and Ott,[29] and Pierce[30] have examined normal heptane with monochromatic radiation over a wide temperature range and carried out a Fourier analysis of the intensities. Markedly preferred distances of 1.4, 2.5, and 3.8 Å. are indicated. They are probably the intramolecular distances between a reference carbon atom and its first, second, and third neighbor. Then there is a maximum, corresponding to a distance of 5.2–5.5 Å., displaced at higher temperatures to 5.75 Å. It is caused by the average distance between individual paraffin chains which form bundles whose axes show arrangements of hexagonal symmetry.

Extensive experiments with the alcohols from C_1 to C_{11} were carried out by Stewart[31] and Morrow.[32] The diagrams show two definite peaks, one

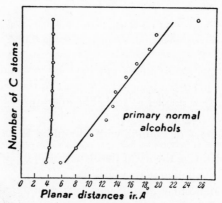

Fig. VII-10.   Relation between d_1 and d_2 and the
length of the alcohol molecules.

corresponding to 4.6 Å., which appears with equal intensity and sharpness in all cases. It represents the average separation of the chain molecules from one another. The second maximum is displaced with increasing number of carbon atoms (see Figure VII-10) from 6 to nearly 24 Å. It is

[28] S. Katzoff, *J. Chem. Phys.*, **2**, 24 (1934).
[29] D. A. Wilson and E. Ott, *J. Chem. Phys.*, **2**, 231 (1934).
[30] W. C. Pierce, *J. Chem. Phys.*, **3**, 252 (1935).
[31] G. W. Stewart, *Phys. Rev.*, **30**, 232 (1927).
[32] R. M. Morrow, *Phys. Rev.*, **31**, 10 (1928).

less intense and, according to Warren, originates from terminal hydroxyl groups that, owing to their attraction, arrange themselves in definite planes; the distances between these planes increase with the length of chains. Therefore, this weak diffraction line moves nearer to the primary beam as the chain length increases.

TABLE VII-3

TYPICAL LATTICE PLANE DISTANCES OF A FEW FATTY ACIDS

Acid	Number of C atoms	d_1, Å.	d_2, Å.
Formic	1	5.2	3.65
Acetic	2	5.9	4.17
Propionic	3	6.0	4.39
Butyric	4	8.5	4.64
Valerianic	5	10.2	4.54
Caproic	6	12.8	4.64
Heptoic	7	14.5	4.54
Caprylic	8	17.0	4.54
Pelargonic	9	18.4	4.54
Capric	10	20.3	4.59
Undecylic	11	22.0	4.54

Normal fatty acids have been studied very carefully in the liquid state, particularly by Katz,[33] Krishnamurti,[34] Morrow,[32] de Smedt,[35] and Sogani.[36] Table VII-3 shows experimental data in which the number of carbon atoms varies from 1 to 11; it indicates that, just as in the case of the alcohols, a feeble diffraction spot is observed resulting from the interaction between the terminal groups, which with increasing chain length moves toward the primary beam.

Another strong diffraction ring observed is independent of the number of carbon atoms of the molecules of the substance investigated; it corresponds to an average distance of about 4.5 Å. and, by its sharpness and intensity, shows that in the liquid state these substances form relatively well-defined bundles of parallel chains.

The existence of small transitory groups of oriented molecules is a consequence of space-filling requirements and is further promoted by the spatial forces of attraction between the molecules. Rehaag and Stuart[37] have

[33] J. R. Katz, Z. Physik, 45, 97 (1927); 46, 392 (1928).
[34] P. Krishnamurti, Indian J. Phys., 2, 355 (1928); 4, 449 (1930).
[35] J. de Smedt, Bull. soc. roy. Belge, 10, 366 (1924).
[36] C. M. Sogani, Indian J. Phys., 2, 491 (1928).
[37] H. Rehaag and H. A. Stuart, Physik. Z., 38, 1027 (1937).

demonstrated in a two-dimensional model the occurrence of groups of rod-shaped particles that always appear if the packing is so close that anisotropic space fillings become necessary.

If small brass rods are shaken in a flat dish, one obtains a virtually random arrangement as long as there are only few particles present. However, as soon as the density is increased the formation of definite bundles can be observed. In such experiments the bundle formation is evidently due to space-filling requirements only: it certainly will be increased by the attractive forces between the actual molecules.

C. DETERMINATION OF SIZE AND SHAPE OF SMALL CRYSTALS BY X-RAY DIFFRACTION

In the foregoing sections we discussed the arrangement of molecules in crystals and liquids and it became evident that x-ray diffraction is a very useful method in this field. It remains now to show that it is equally valuable for the determination of the average size and shape of small crystalline domains.

It can be demonstrated that the size and shape of the crystalline areas determine the angular width of the diffraction rings or spots that are produced by them. If we turn our attention not only to the *position* and *intensity* of the diffraction spots as before but also to their *breadth* and shape, it is possible to obtain a numerical relation between the angular width of an interference ring and the number (n) of the scattering particles responsible for it. The breadth of the spot increases as the number of the interacting lattice planes within the individual crystalline area decreases.[38]

A corresponding phenomenon is observed if the particles have anisometric shapes; in this case only a few lattice planes follow one another regularly in one direction and the diffraction of these planes appears broadened, while the diffraction spots of those lattice planes which are perpendicular to the long axis of the crystallite will be of normal sharpness.

The line broadening begins to be observable as soon as n drops below 1000, and can be studied most easily in the region between $n = 50$ and $n = 200$. Very diffuse diffractions can also be obtained, however, from crystalline domains in which only 4 or 5 lattice planes succeed one another periodically in the same direction.

The angular breadth of a diffraction line, as it appears in powder or fiber

[38] See for instance J. T. Randall, *Diffraction of X-Rays and Electrons.* Wiley, New York, 1934, p. 28 et seq.

diagrams, is determined essentially by two factors: (*a*) by the influence of the crystallite size and (*b*) by the thickness of the specimen. Since the latter can be controlled readily by the experimental setup, there remains the problem of separating the former in a suitable way. In a formula first derived by Scherrer[39] the term that depends upon the thickness of the sample, which is independent of the angle of diffraction, is simply added to the term caused by the crystal size, which depends upon $\cos \theta/2$. This is correct as long as one has a completely parallel beam and a nonabsorbing material. Under such conditions the sample, represented as a cylindrical rod, is projected on a cylindrical film having the same breadth under all angles (compare Fig. VII-11). If, however, there is a parallel beam and

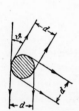

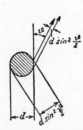

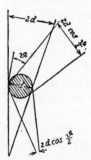

Fig. VII-11. Cylindrical rod; parallel light; non-absorbing substance.

Fig. VII-12. Cylindrical rod; parallel light; strongly absorbing substance.

Fig. VII-13. Cylindrical rod; divergent light; non-absorbing substance.

an absorbing substance, Figure VII-12 shows that the rod will appear to be broader at larger angles; this influence can be taken into account mathematically: it has been tested experimentally by Brill and Pelzer.[40]

If one works with a divergent beam and a nonabsorbing substance, as represented in Figure VII-13, Bragg's law requires that the rod appear broader at small angles of deflection than at larger ones, so that the angular width of the diffraction spot, which increases with increasing angle, counteracts the influence of the decreasing breadth of the rod. For this case, formulas were developed by Laue[41] which are more general than the Scherrer formula mentioned above. Considering all these conditions, it is possible to obtain fairly reliable data on the size and, under favorable circum-

[39] P. Scherrer, *Nachr. Ges. Wiss. Göttingen*, **1918**, 98.
[40] R. Brill and J. Pelzer, *Z. Krist.*, **72**, 398 (1929); **74**, 147 (1930).
[41] M. v. Laue, *Z. Krist.*, **64**, 115 (1926).

stances, the shape of the crystalline areas that produce the diffraction pattern, particularly if many reflections have been measured. In order to appreciate the accuracy and significance of such data, it is well to bear in mind the assumptions under which the various formulas have been derived. We will summarize and discuss them briefly: (*1*) all crystallites have the same size and shape; (*2*) they all have the same lattice structure; (*3*) the lattice is perfect in every individual particle; there are no lattice distortions or defects; and (*4*) the thermal motion does not cause a measurable broadening of the lines.

By comparing the width of the diffraction lines at normal temperature and at the temperature of liquid air, it can readily be established that the influence of temperature is usually negligible. This confirms the requirements of the Debye-Waller theory,[42] which, to a first approximation, calls only for a decrease in intensity and not for an increase in width of the diffraction spots[43] with increasing temperature.

On the other hand, it is important to consider carefully the influences arising from the three other points.

Actually, we shall never meet with exactly uniform particle size, and must therefore always take into consideration a certain crystal size distribution curve. Patterson[44] and Hengstenberg[45] have done this for a Maxwellian and a Gaussian distribution, respectively, and have found that neglecting particle size distribution causes an error of about 50% of the value obtained in the correct manner. Consequently, particle size determination with x-rays has significance only in terms of order of magnitude, but does not permit accurate calculations of the dimensions of the scattering domains.

As in the other two conditions, it must be admitted that there is still no satisfactory means of separating the broadening of the diffraction lines due to limited particle size from the broadening due to lattice defects or to differences in lattice structure. The case in which the lattice itself appears to be perfect in each individual crystallite but where different lattice constants exist in different particles seems to occur in certain metallic mixed crystals and need scarcely be considered here, but lattice distortion must be given special consideration.

A quantitative determination of existing lattice defects and distortions

[42] P. Debye, *Ann. Physik.*, **49**, 1 (1914); I. Waller, *Z. Physik*, **17**, 398 (1923).

[43] F. Halla and H. Mark, *Röntgenografische Untersuchung von Kristallen*. Leipzig, 1937, p. 317.

[44] A. L. Patterson, *Z. Krist.*, **66**, 637 (1928).

[45] J. Hengstenberg, *Z. Krist.*, **69**, 271 (1928).

in the crystalline domains of high polymers is not possible with the techniques now available, but it is possible to arrive at an estimate by comparing the intensity accumulated in the diffraction spots with that of the diffusely scattered radiation. Every atom displaced from its equilibrium position by lattice distortion contributes to the diffuse scattering and weakens the intensity of the sharp diffraction spots. In order to obtain an idea of the extent of lattice defects in native cellulose, Hengstenberg measured with monochromatized radiation the breadths of the equatorial and diatropic reflections of carefully degummed ramie fibers and estimated the radiation scattered diffusely along the equator and the perpendicular bisector line of the diagram. The scattering between the diffraction lines is rather small and did not show any anisotropy. He then found that the width of the diatropic lines was so small that there could not be much lattice distortion, otherwise a greater breadth would have been found. Since the diffuse radiation along the equator is not greater than that on the meridian of the diagram, the inference is that, in these fibers, lattice defects do not seem large enough to obscure the results of the determination of crystal size. Conditions are different in samples which have been treated chemically or mechanically by swelling or stretching; here, lattice defects undoubtedly influence the details of the diffraction pattern.

TABLE VII-4

PARTICLE SIZE OF VARIOUS IRON PREPARATIONS

		Particle size, Å.	
Preparation		Scherrer	Brill, Pelzer, and Laue
1.	Fe from Fe_2O_3...............................	230	$\begin{cases} 200 \\ 210 \end{cases}$
	After heating to 1000° for 10 hours..................	420	$\begin{cases} \infty \\ 1000 \end{cases}$
2.	Fe from Carbonyl............................	$\begin{cases} 77 \\ 75 \end{cases}$	100
	Fe from Carbonyl............................	60	90
	Fe from Carbonyl............................	100	110
	Fe from Carbonyl............................	120	100
3.	Electrolytic iron............................	230	$\begin{cases} 230 \\ 210 \end{cases}$

In several cases it was established that the results of the x-ray method were in good agreement with independent data on particle dimensions. Scherrer, in the work previously mentioned, found that the particle size of colloidal gold sols calculated by the use of his formula agreed satisfactorily with those obtained by the Zsigmondy method of direct counting.

Later, Brill compared the different relations available for the computation of particle sizes with one another and obtained for fine iron powders the data presented in Table VII-4. It includes a comparison of the relation originally given by Scherrer with the Laue formula modified by Brill and Pelzer. Various preparations of very fine iron powders, which are of importance for catalysis in the ammonia process, served as test material.

It can be seen that the agreement is not perfect but is fairly satisfactory from the point of view of order of magnitude.

Table VII-5 gives similar data for particle size determinations of gold sols and makes it evident that the various equations give values that agree with one another in order of magnitude. The last line in this table contains measurements with the ultracentrifuge and is of special interest. The ultracentrifuge data are generally higher than the x-ray values, a fact that is not surprising and should be expected in similar comparisons because it ought to be remembered that the x-ray method responds to those lattice domains within which strictly coherent scattering occurs. In contrast, the other methods—measuring rate of diffusion or of sedimentation—determine the size of those particles which move as kinetically independent units in the solution. They certainly cannot be smaller than the former and may indeed be greater because different circumstances may lead to the aggregation of the individual crystals into secondary particles.

TABLE VII-5

PARTICLE SIZES OF VARIOUS GOLD SOLS

Method of determination	Particle size, Å.				
	1	2	3	4	5
After Scherrer	—	—	47	62	81
After Laue	32	38.5	52	65	87
After Brill, Cu radiation	—	—	47	58	82
After Brill, Fe radiation	30.5	42	—	—	—
With the ultracentrifuge	40	61	100	149	225

In any case, the experiments with inorganic crystal powders described here show that the interferometric determination of particle dimensions gives essentially accurate results. Therefore, there is no reason to hesitate too much in applying these methods to the determination or, at least, to the estimation of the size and shape of the crystalline domains in polymeric materials.

Considering all previously mentioned experimental precautions, Hengstenberg calculated the data given in Table VII-6 for native fibers. They

may not be exact individually but they certainly indicate the correct order
of magnitude and agree satisfactorily with earlier estimations of Herzog.

TABLE VII-6
MICELLE DIMENSIONS IN CELLULOSE

Diameter of preparation, mm.	hkl	Dimension, Å.
0.75	101	56
0.75	002	56
0.75	004	53
1.0	002	59
0.4	002	57

D. OBSERVATIONS ON MESOPHASES AND LIQUID CRYSTALS

Having described our present knowledge of molecular arrangement in
liquids, we shall now discuss briefly the so-called *liquid crystals* or *mesophases*. The existence of such systems was discovered by Lehmann[46] as
early as 1889; their properties have been repeatedly and thoroughly investigated by numerous workers, notably by Schenck,[47] Vorländer,[48] and
G. and E. Friedel[49]; and different views have been expressed on the nature
of the liquid crystalline state mainly on the basis of the behavior in polarized light. A detailed discussion of this subject was instigated by P. P
Ewald, and has been published in a special volume of the *Zeitschrift für
Kristallographie*, which should be consulted for all details and for an account of the historical development.[50]

Here we shall give but a brief description of the observed phenomena and
their interpretation in terms of special molecular arrangements in mesophases.

1. Experimental Results in the Investigation of Mesophases

There are numerous organic substances that show remarkable anomalies
on melting. Upon fusion, their solid well-shaped crystals give a cloudy
and sometimes gelatinous melt, which displays optical anisotropy in polarized light and becomes a normal clear liquid only on further heating at a
definite temperature. In such systems, evidently, there exist two or more

---

[46] O. Lehmann, cf. Vol. 79 of the *Z. Krist.* devoted to the discussion of liquid crystals.
[47] R. Schenck, *Z. Krist.*, **79**, 269 (1931).
[48] D. Vorländer, *Z. Krist.*, **79**, 61 (1931).
[49] G. and E. Friedel, *Z. Krist.*, **79**, 1 (1931).
[50] P. P. Ewald, *Sonderband "Fluessige Kristalle," Z. Krist.*, **79**, 299 (1931).

liquid phases which, apparently, are characterized by cluster formations of the molecules. They can be converted reversibly to each other, as can polymorphous modifications of crystals.

The two liquid phases—the "amorphous" and the "crystalline" phase (occasionally several liquid crystalline phases have been observed)—differ from each other in many respects. While the amorphous phase is optically isotropic, the crystalline liquid phase usually exhibits noticeable birefringence and sometimes also pleochroism.

Numerous experiments have been carried out on their anomalous viscosity. Table VII-7, taken from Schenck, shows that crystalline liquids

TABLE VII-7

VISCOSITIES OF SEVERAL CRYSTALLINE LIQUIDS

Substance	1st m.p.	2nd m.p.	Existence range (diff.)	Viscosity (water = 100)	
				Cryst.	Amorphous
p-Azoxycinnamic ethyl ester....................249 °C.		141 °C.	108 °C.	>900	600
Cholesterol benzoate........178.5		145.5	33	890–620	420–218
p-Azoxybenzoethyl ester.....120		114	6	860–470	350–270
p-Azoxyanisole.............134		116	18	141–128	175–135
p-Methoxycinnamic acid.....186		170	16	106–91	159–117
p-Azoxyphenetole...........168		137	31	79–66	95–75

can be considerably more viscous than the corresponding amorphous phases of the same chemical composition. Sometimes, however, the reverse has also been observed.

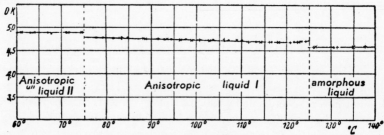

Fig. VII-14. Change of dielectric constant at transition points of a crystalline liquid.

The dielectric properties of liquid crystals have been studied especially by Kast,[51] who was able to show that their dielectric constant undergoes sudden changes at the various transition points. Figure VII-14 shows this

[51] W. Kast, Z. Krist., 79, 315 (1931).

effect for the diethyl ester of ethoxybenzal amino-α-methylcinnamic acid.

The magnetic susceptibility of liquid crystals also changes abruptly at the transition points, as shown in Figure VII-15.[52] Of special importance is the fact that, owing to the large size of the clusters in mesophases, it is possible to obtain practically complete orientation by rather weak magnetic fields. In such cases, the orienting effect of a magnetic field can be

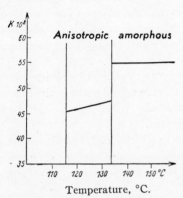

Fig. VII-15. Change of magnetic susceptibility at the transition points.

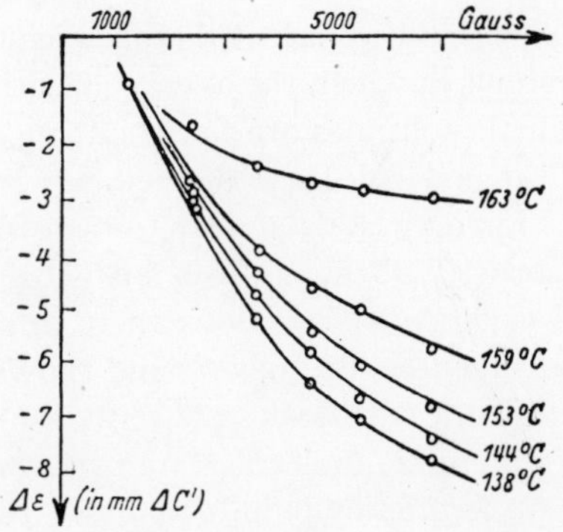

Fig. VII-16. Influence of magnetic field strength on dielectric constant.

determined readily by the dielectric constant. Figure VII-16 shows that the dielectric constant of crystalline liquid p-azoxyphenetol first decreases proportionally to the magnetic field and then approaches a saturation value. Other physical properties, such as electrical conductivity and opacity, vary in the same way.

The x-ray diffraction of crystalline liquids is particularly interesting and informative, as shown by investigations of Kast and Glamann[53] and of Hermann and Krummacher.[54] The principal result is that in liquid crystals the diffuse halos, which are characteristic for normal liquids, split in a magnetic field into a pair of crescents, while in the amorphous phase the influence of a magnetic field is inappreciable.

2. Molecular Arrangement in the Mesophases

These experimental results indicate that in crystalline liquids there is a considerable degree of association and orientation of the individual mole-

[52] G. Foëx, Z. Krist., **79**, 289 (1931).

[53] W. Kast and P. W. Glamann, Z. Krist., **79**, 210 (1931).

[54] K. Hermann and A. H. Krummacher, Z. Krist., **74**, 73 (1930).

cules intermediate between the complete order of a crystal lattice and the complete randomness of a true liquid.

In a crystal lattice every atom is permanently fixed at a given equilibrium position and executes about it more or less frequent vibrations of small amplitude; it is the mean positions of these vibrations that are fixed in a rigid three-dimensional lattice. It has been already mentioned that in long chain paraffins more or less free rotation about the chain axes can occur without apparent disturbance of the crystalline state. Thus we have systems in which the average positions of the centers of gravity of the individual molecules are fixed, but in which free rotation about the long axes of the molecules is permitted.

Liquid crystals appear to be a further step in the direction of increased disorder. Although it is not yet possible to give a final systematization of all existing observations there appear essentially to be *two* preferred arrangements: the *smectic* and the *nematic* states.

Smectic substances are crystalline liquids in which elongated filamentous or ribbonlike molecules are arranged in such a manner that all their ends lie preferably in definite planes. Figure VII-17 shows a diagrammatic rep-

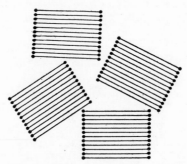

Fig. VII-17.   Diagrammatic representation of the smectic state.

resentation of this type. Apart from the restrictions imposed on the molecules by this grouping they are free to carry out certain motions: they can rotate about their axes and the number of the chains comprised in a bundle, as shown in Figure VII-17, can vary; molecules from one set can pass over to another, etc. The only thing fixed is the preference of certain planes which are separated from one another by a distance characteristic for the substance considered. De Broglie and Friedel[55] could detect diffraction lines in the sodium, potassium, and ammonium salts of oleic acid,

[55] See in G. and E. Friedel, *Z. Krist.*, **79**, 184 (1931).

which, owing to the considerable length of the molecules, were observable as narrow rings in the immediate vicinity of the primary beam.   From the angle of diffraction, the preferred interplanar distance was found to be about 43.5 Å.;   in ethyl azoxybenzoate it was about 20 Å.   Both figures are in fair agreement with the molecular dimension if we assume the formation of double molecules, which seems plausible on the basis of the information given in Chapter IV.

We may now go one step further toward entirely free mobility of the molecules and assume that the preferred arrangement of the ends in definite planes no longer holds, but that only the parallelism of the chains is preserved.   Then we arrive at an arrangement represented in Figure VII-18;

Fig. VII-18.   Diagrammatic representation of the nematic state.

the rod or ribbon-shaped molecules can rotate about their long axes, and their centers of gravity are displaceable in all three directions in space with merely the parallel orientation preserved.   Systems of this type have been termed *nematic* liquids by Friedel.   Their diffraction pattern is that of a linear lattice in which the strongest diffraction line is given by the average distance of the molecules from one another.

Hermann,[56] in a detailed investigation of the symmetry groups of amorphous and mesomorphous phases, developed a systematic treatment of all possible crystalline liquids equivalent to the space group theory of crystals and demonstrated that there are many different possibilities for the appearance of mesophases which behave characteristically in respect to x-ray diffraction and polarized light.

If we confine ourselves to the smectic and nematic states only, we can visualize the transition from a completely ordered solid crystal to an amorphous liquid in the following way:

(1) *Three-dimensional crystal.*   The centers of gravity of all lattice units are fixed (apart from vibration);   rotations are not possible.   Examples: hexamethylenetetramine, urea.

(2) *Crystal with rotating molecules.*   The centers of gravity of all lattice units are fixed;   rotation about one or more axes is possible.   Examples:

[56] C. Hermann, Z. Krist., 79, 337 (1931).

ammonium chloride, sodium stearate at higher temperatures.[57]

(3) *Smectic state.* The centers of gravity of the units are mobile in one direction; rotation about *one* axis is permitted. Examples: sodium oleate, allylester of phenetolazoxybenzoic acid at 72°.

(4) *Nematic state.* The centers of gravity of the units are mobile in *two* directions; rotation about *one* axis is permitted. Example: allyl ester of phenetolazoxybenzoic acid at 88°.

(5) *Amorphous liquids.* The centers of gravity of the units are mobile in three directions in space; rotation about three axes perpendicular to one another is possible. Examples: carbon tetrachloride, mercury.

An interesting experiment of the transition from the smectic to the nematic state was carried out by Hermann and Kupfermacher, who took x-ray diagrams of the allyl ester of phenetolazoxybenzoic acid at different temperatures in the presence of an orienting magnetic field.

Two rings were observed, one in the vicinity of the primary beam, which is characteristic for the smectic phase (see page 238), and the other at a somewhat greater angle of diffraction, which occurs in both phases and shows higher intensity; it is related to the thickness of the rod- or ribbon-shaped molecules. Table VII-8 shows the results of an x-ray examination of the amorphous, smectic, and nematic phases of the substance in the temperature range between 72° and 100°C. It is evident that the diameter of the outer ring is in all cases approximately the same and—evaluated according to Bragg's law—gives a distance between the molecular axes between 4.6 and 5.0 Å., which is in agreement with all knowledge of the dimensions of such molecules.

TABLE VII-8

ALLYL ESTER OF PHENETOLAZOXYBENZOIC ACID

State of substance[a]	D	$\vartheta/2$	d_a(Bragg), Å.
100° liquid, n. m.	32	8° 47′	5.0
88° nematic, n. m.	34	9° 18′	4.8
79.5° nematic, w. m.	34	9° 18′	4.8
75.5° smectic, w. m.	35	9° 33′	4.6
72° smectic, w. m.	35	9° 33′	4.6

[a] n.m. = no magnetic field, w.m. = with magnetic field.

The question of the properties that a molecule must possess to give rise to the phenomena of liquid crystals is of great interest. Here, we have the experimental material collected and sorted by Vorländer in systematic

[57] W. O. Baker and C. P. Smith, *J. Am. Chem. Soc.*, **61**, 2798 (1939).

researches over a number of years, which he summarizes by saying that the tendency for the formation of mesophases has a geometric as well as an energetic reason.

The geometric effect demands that the molecules shall be extended and rectilinear; a ribbonlike shape apparently has the advantage over a cylindrical one. Any internal mobility is undesirable; rigid or almost rigid molecules are most suitable. Zig-zagging within the chains and branching at their ends or in the middle influence adversely the formation of crystalline liquid phases. Table VII-9 of Vorländer shows the influence of the length of a chain inserted between two larger identical terminal groups.

TABLE VII-9

C_6 $>$CH$_2$ C_6	C_6 $>$CH$_2$ CH$_2$ $\backslash C_6$	C_6 $>$CH$_2$ CH$_2$ $>$CH$_2$ C_6	C_6 $>$CH$_2$ CH$_2$ $>$CH$_2$ CH$_2$ $\backslash C_6$	C_6 $>$CH$_2$ CH$_2$ $>$CH$_2$ CH$_2$ $>$CH$_2$ C_6
Noncrystalline liquid	Highly crystalline liquid	Noncrystalline liquid	Crystalline liquid	Barely crystalline liquid

There exists some empirical knowledge on the influence which certain structural units—double bonds, triple bonds, etc.—exert on the nature of crystalline liquids; they allow us to draw certain conclusions on the appearance of mesophases.

From the point of view of intermolecular attraction the simultaneous presence of strong dipoles and easily polarizable groups appears to be essential. Further, it seems advantageous if the dipole is located on the axis of the molecule and forms a right angle with it. Easily rotating or otherwise mobile polar groups at the ends of the molecule are of subordinate importance.

If we compare these conditions, determined purely empirically, for the preferred appearance of mesophases with the discussions in Chap. IV, we obtain the impression (a) that the aggregation of numerous particles over large regions is caused by the attraction of a dipole rigidly fixed on the axis of one molecule to the readily polarizable parts of another molecule, (b) further, that the dipole of the second attracts a third molecule and soon until a structure results that can be compared to a bundle of pencils. The arrangement and mobility of the molecules individually depends in a very sensitive way on their form, on the magnitude of the forces acting between them, and on the extent of thermal motion.

E. CRYSTALLINE-AMORPHOUS CHARACTER OF POLYMERIC MATERIALS

It was pointed out in Chapter I that polymeric materials can occur in different states of molecular order; it appears appropriate to add here a few additional facts and ideas on the structure and texture of macromolecules in the solid state.

Many polymers, if frozen from their melt, assume the properties of glasses or supercooled liquids: they do not exhibit signs of anisotropy, their x-ray diagram resembles that of a liquid, they soften gradually upon increase of temperature and harden reversibly on cooling, etc. Evidently the macromolecules are randomly and disorderly arranged in space; their mutual attraction provides for a very high viscosity of the system at sufficiently low temperatures and creates the impression of an elastic solid body although the material is, in fact, a very viscous liquid.

Many linear polymers and copolymers (such as polystyrene, polyacrylic esters, polyvinyl acetate, Buna S, Buna N) and most three-dimensional systems (such as phenol-formaldehyde, urea-formaldehyde, glycerol-phthalic anhydride, and others) occur primarily or only in this state; they display the properties of structureless resinous plastics which become brittle at low temperatures, and at elevated temperatures either soften gradually to form viscous melts ("thermoplastic" resins) or harden to form insoluble and infusible "thermosetting" resins.

Many linear polymers, however, show a distinctly different behavior. If cooled from a melt or precipitated from solution, the macromolecules of these substances exhibit a distinct tendency to establish arrays of lateral order in which the axes of the individual chain molecules are parallel to each other and in which a more or less pronounced periodicity exists as one passes through such a domain perpendicular to the chain axes. These laterally ordered areas are sometimes referred to as "crystallites" or "micelles," although they do not possess all properties which originally were embraced by the meaning of these words. Polymers that show a definite tendency toward the formation of these laterally ordered domains are, for example, polyethylene, polyesters, polyamides, cellulose, many proteins, and natural rubber. It seems that "crystallization" of macromolecules is always favored if the chains possess a smooth and regular structure, and if there are regularly distributed along them groups of strong molar cohesion such as OH, CO, CONH, etc. On the other hand, macromolecules with irregular chain structure, particularly random copolymers, favor the formation of amorphous polymers.

The "crystallites" of a polymer can be of very different size and shape; they may be oriented or not, and they are intimately connected with the amorphous "matrix" inasmuch as the same macromolecule may pass

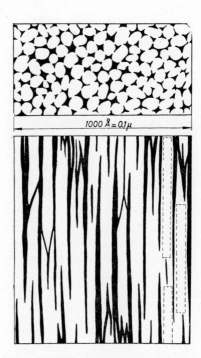

Fig. VII-19. Micellar structure.[58]

Fig. VII-20. Diagram of micellar texture of cellulose fibers after Frey-Wyssling.[60]

through several crystalline and disordered areas. Figure VII-19 gives a schematic idea of this concept; the parts of the chain molecules which are parallel and are drawn as heavy lines represent the laterally ordered domains, whereas the thinner lines in between are supposed to indicate the amorphous areas. Several chains go through more than one crystalline

[58] O. Kratky and H. Mark, Z. physik. Chem., B36, 129 (1937).

and amorphous region, one of them is accentuated by little circles; chain ends which are located inside of "crystallites" (such as the pair A–A') are thought to be of lesser importance as weak spots than chain ends which occur inside amorphous domains, because they are fixed and immobilized by the strong intermolecular cohesion prevailing inside a crystallite.[59]

Figure VII-20[60] gives a similar picture of a cellulose fiber according to Frey-Wyssling, indicating a fabriclike texture consisting of laterally ordered micelles and of "voids" between them.[61]

It was found in many cases, e.g., cellulose, cellulose acetate, polythene, nylon, Orlon, etc., that both the *degree of crystallinity* and the *orientation of the crystallites* are of preponderant influence on the mechanical properties of the sample; it may therefore be in order to give some information as to how these two quantities can be determined experimentally. If the crystallites in a specimen are in complete random distribution, all diffraction circles in an x-ray diagram of the material are uninterrupted (full circles as shown in Figure I-2, p. 7). If axial orientation prevails, some or all of these circles degenerate into arcs, which become shorter the higher the orientation. Figure VII-21 gives the outline of an x-ray diagram of a moderately oriented fiber of regenerated cellulose, whereas Figure I-14b represents the diagram of a highly oriented sample. If one traces with a densitometer the intensity distribution *along* the arcs of the individual diffraction lines, one can arrive at a quantitative measurement of the axial orientation of the crystalline domains with the aid of formulas developed by Berkeley, J. J. Hermans, P. H. Hermans, Kratky, and Sisson.[62] It has

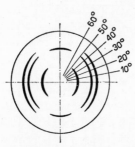

Fig. VII-21. Outline of x-ray diagram of an imperfectly oriented fiber (with cellulose II).[60]

[59] Compare here particularly the complete and lucid presentation in the book of P. H. Hermans, *Physics and Chemistry of Cellulose Fibers*, Elsevier, New York-Amsterdam, 1949, p. 26 *et seq.* Also O. Gengross and C. Hermann, *Z. physik. Chem.*, **B10**, 371 (1930), F. D. Miles, *Trans. Faraday Soc.*, **29**, 110 (1933), W. T. Astbury, *ibid.*, **29**, 193, 204 (1933), and O. Kratky and H. Mark, *Z. physik. Chem.*, **B36** 129 (1937).

[60] P. H. Hermans, *Physics and Chemistry of Cellulose Fibers*, Elsevier, New York-Amsterdam, 1949.

[61] Compare particularly A. Frey-Wyssling, *Morphologie des Protoplasma*, Berlin, 1938, p. 79.

[62] E. E. Berkeley, *Textile Research*, **9**, 335 (1939). J. J. Hermans *et al.*, *Rec. trav. chim.*, **65**, 427 (1947). P. H. Hermans, *Physics and Chemistry of Cellulose Fibres*, Elsevier, New York-Amsterdam, 1949, p. 250. O. Kratky, *Z. physik. Chem.*, **B50**, 255 (1941). W. A. Sisson, in E. Ott, ed., *Cellulose and Cellulose Derivatives* (High Polymers, Vol. V), Interscience, New York, 1943.

been found that the modulus of elasticity and the tensile strength of fibers and stretched films increase noticeably with increasing orientation in the direction of stretch, while at the same time decreasing perpendicular thereto.

Another important property of a polymer in the solid state is the degree of lateral order or the degree of crystallinity. A superficial inspection of the x-ray diagram of ramie, stretched rubber, or drawn nylon may create the impression that the entire material consisted only of crystallites because the sharp and intense accumulation of the scattered intensity in the directions of crystal reflections stands out clearly, whereas the scattering of the amorphous domains is diffusively distributed over the whole film. It is therefore necessary to compare quantitatively the "concentrated" and "diffuse" scattered intensities and estimate from this comparison the degree of crystallinity. Earlier exploratory work[63] of preliminary character was followed recently by the development of a new precision technique for quantitative x-ray diagrams of polymers, by P. H. Hermans and Ingersoll,[64] which seems to be applicable to most polymers and appears to give results agreeing with other methods for estimating the degree of lateral order.

Figure VII-22 shows the photometer tracing of the equator of a fictitious polymer giving the scattered intensity I as a function of the angle of de-

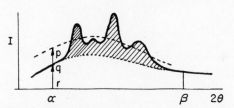

Fig. VII-22. Fictitious example of radial photometer curve of the x-ray diagram of a polymer.[65]

flection 2θ. The curve indicates the existence of a "continuous background" (white area below the lowest curve) and of superimposed "diffraction spots" (hatched area). In order to estimate the absolute amount of the disordered domains, which are responsible for the diffuse scattering, Goppel[66] proposes to compare the intensity curve of the crystalline

[63] J. Hengstenberg and H. Mark, Z. Krist., 69, 271 (1928). Gehman and Field, J. Applied Phys., 15, 371 (1944). H. Mark, J. Phys. Chem., 44, 764 (1940).

[64] P. H. Hermans and A. Weidinger, J. Applied Phys., 19, 491 (1948); J. Polymer Sci., 4, 135, 709 (1949). H. G. Ingersoll, J. Applied Phys., 17, 924 (1946).

[65] P. H. Hermans and A. Weidinger, J. Polymer Sci., 4, 710 (1949).

[66] J. M. Goppel, Applied Sci. Research, A1, 3 (1947); A1, 347, 462 (1949).

polymer with that of the melt, which is completely amorphous, and to take the ratio of the two areas or of two appropriately selected ordinates as the percentage of amorphous material in the investigated sample. The dashed line in Figure VII-21 represents the intensity curve obtained from the melt and the ratio (q/p) at point r gives a measure of the noncrystalline fraction of the sample. In cases in which the completely disordered state is not available, Hermans and Weidinger[67] propose using the ordinate of the diffuse scattering at its highest point as a measure of the fraction of disordered constituents. The application of both methods led to fair agreement in the case of partly crystallized natural rubber and polythene; for a polythene sample it was found that the crystallinity at 115°C. was 8%; that at 90°, 23%; and that at 18°, 54%. The same method gave for the crystallinity of four polyamide samples figures between 50 and 70%.

Probably the most thoroughly investigated polymer for the point of view of lateral order is cellulose, for which Ingersoll and Hermans established that the degree of crystallinity as determined by x-rays corresponds fairly well with that estimated from *density* measurements and from various methods involving the *reactivity* of cellulose. Native fibers like cotton, flax, ramie, and hemp show crystallinities up to 75%, whereas rayon and Cellophane lead to figures between 25 and 40%.[67] The degree of crystallinity of a given polymer is important not only for the mechanical properties of the sample, but also for its swelling, dyestuff absorption, and for its general chemical reactivity; it is therefore probable that an important field is still open here for quantitative intensity measurements.

[67] Compare P. H. Hermans, *Physics and Chemistry of Cellulose Fibres*, Elsevier, New York-Amsterdam, 1949, p. 262 *et seq.*

VIII. THERMODYNAMICS OF SOLUTIONS

The solution properties of chemical substances are of fundamental interest in physical chemistry because by interpretation of solution properties in the range of very high dilution it is possible to obtain the molecular weights of the dissolved substances. Solubility properties are also of importance from the point of view of separating and purifying various compounds. In the case of linear polymers, solution and fractional precipitation provides one of the few means of separating molecules of identical chemical structure but different molecular weight. Furthermore, molecules in the dissolved state are generally more accessible to chemical reagents than in the solid state. The solvent also acts as a vehicle for transportation of the dissolved substances, the body fluids being an outstanding example of such a vehicle.

In the case of linear polymers, concentrated solutions such as rubber cements, lacquers, dopes, etc., provide a means by which thin coatings of polymer can be spread over large surfaces. Also, artificial fibers are produced by forcing concentrated polymer solutions through small orifices into a precipitating medium, tension being generally applied to the extruded fiber.

The solution properties of linear polymer molecules do not differ in kind from those of low molecular weight materials. In general, macromolecules are more slowly and difficultly soluble than low molecular weight materials of the same chemical nature. When polymer and solvent are immiscible, two phases are formed, just as in the case of ether and water. Very often the polymer-rich phase will imbibe large quantities of the solvent. There is, however, a qualitative difference between solution properties of low molecular weight material and linear polymers on the one hand and the solution properties of three-dimensional polymers or gels on the other. Whereas the former will dissolve to unlimited extent in apt solvents, the latter will swell to a limited extent only.

There are two aspects to the theoretical treatment of solutions. First, there is the thermodynamic approach which relates all solution properties, such as vapor pressure, freezing point depression, osmotic pressure, solubility, etc., to thermodynamic quantities such as partial molar free energy, entropy, and enthalpy. Second, there is the statistical mechanical approach which attempts to derive the thermodynamic properties from molecular quantities.

A. COLLIGATIVE PROPERTIES OF SOLUTIONS

The colligative properties of solutions include vapor pressure, osmotic pressure, depression of freezing point, and elevation of boiling point. All of these properties can be used to calculate the molecular weight of the dissolved substance by extrapolation to infinite dilution, because at infinite dilution the colligative properties are closely related to the number of completely independently moving kinetic units in the solution. For this reason, if the solute is of heterogeneous molecular weight, the measurement of colligative properties provides a measure of the *number average molecular weight*.

All of these properties can be related to the free energy of dilution or to the activity of the solvent. The free energy of dilution $\overline{\Delta F_0}$ is the increase in total Gibbs free energy when one mole of solvent is added to a very large bulk of solution. Similar definitions apply for the entropy of dilution $\overline{\Delta S_0}$ and for the enthalpy (heat content) of dilution $\overline{\Delta H_0}$. These quantities are related to the partial molar quantities and to each other through the following thermodynamic expressions:

$$\overline{\Delta F_0} = \bar{F_0} - F_0^0 = RT \ln a_0 \qquad (\text{VIII.1})$$

$$\overline{\Delta S_0} = \bar{S_0} - S_0^0 \qquad (\text{VIII.2})$$

$$\overline{\Delta H_0} = \bar{H_0} - H_0^0 \qquad (\text{VIII.3})$$

$$\overline{\Delta F_0} = \overline{\Delta H_0} - T \overline{\Delta S_0} \qquad (\text{VIII.4})$$

where $\bar{F_0}$ is the partial molar free energy of the solvent in a solution of a certain concentration, and F_0^0 is the partial molar free energy (equal molar free energy) of the pure solvent. Similar definitions hold for $\bar{S_0}$, S_0^0, $\bar{H_0}$ and H_0^0. The activity of the solvent a_0 is defined by equation (VIII.1).

The heat of dilution can be determined calorimetrically, or from the temperature coefficient of the free energy by means of the equation:

$$\overline{\Delta H_0} = \frac{\partial [\overline{\Delta F_0}/T]}{\partial [1/T]_p} \qquad (\text{VIII.5})$$

The entropy of dilution can then be obtained from equation (VIII.4).

The colligative properties are related to the free energy of dilution and to the activity of the solvent by the following equations:

$$\overline{\Delta F_0} = RT \ln p/p^0 \qquad\qquad p = p^0 a_0 \qquad\qquad \text{(VIII.6)}$$

$$\overline{\Delta F_0} = -\pi V_0 \qquad\qquad \pi = \frac{-RT}{V_0} \ln a_0 \qquad\qquad \text{(VIII.7)}$$

$$\overline{\Delta F_0} = \frac{L_f}{T_f}\theta \qquad\qquad \theta = \frac{RT_f^2}{L_f} \ln a_0 \qquad\qquad \text{(VIII.8)}$$

where p is the vapor pressure of solvent above the solution, p^0 is the vapor pressure of solvent, π is the osmotic pressure, V_0 is the molar volume of the solvent, L_f is the latent heat of fusion of the solvent, T_f is its freezing point, and θ is the freezing point change produced by the solute.

For ideal solutions the activity is equal to the mole fraction. If the mole fraction of solvent is taken as x_0 and the mole fraction of solute is taken to be x_p, then for dilute ideal solutions:

$$\ln a_0 = \ln x_0 = \ln (1 - x_p) = - x_p = - \frac{V_0}{M_p} c$$

where c = concentration of solute in grams per cubic centimeters of solution, M_p is the molecular weight, and V_0 is the molar volume of the solvent. Equations (VIII.6) through (VIII.8) become:

$$p = x_0 p^0 \text{ (Raoult's law)} \qquad\qquad \text{(VIII.9)}$$

$$\pi = \frac{RT}{V_0} x_p = \frac{RT}{M_p} c \qquad\qquad \text{(VIII.10)}$$

$$\theta = - \frac{RT_f^2}{L_f} x_p = - \frac{RT_f^2}{L_f} \frac{V_0}{M_p} c \qquad\qquad \text{(VIII.11)}$$

It will be seen subsequently that, for sufficiently dilute solutions, equations (VIII.9)–(VIII.11) are valid even for the case of nonideal solutions such as polymer solutions. The difficulty that presents itself in the case of polymer solutions is that the limiting laws (VIII.9)–(VIII.11) become valid only in the range of extreme dilution, and so for this reason it is of great importance to have a theoretical foundation for interpretation of solution properties in a somewhat more concentrated region in order to give reasonable certainty to the extrapolation methods for getting at molecular weight from colligative properties. Furthermore, in the range of dilution at which the limiting laws are valid, the colligative effects to be measured are very minute for polymer solutions. Suppose we had a 1% solution (by weight) of polymer of molecular weight 200,000 dissolved in a solvent of molecular weight 200. This concentration would generally be considered to be far outside the range in which equations (VIII.9)–(VIII.11) apply. Nevertheless the vapor pressure lowering would be only 0.001%. If the molal freezing point depression of the solvent were 10°, which is very favorable, the freezing point depression of this solution would be 0.0005°C. If the molar volume of the solvent were 224 cc., the osmotic pressure of this solution at 0°C. would be 10.3 mm. of water. Both the vapor pressure lowering and the freezing point depression would be outside the limits of measurement by ordinary technique, but the osmotic pressure could be measured relatively easily. Osmotic pressure measurements are a satisfactory means of determining molecular weights for high polymer solutions in the range roughly between 20,000 and 500,000 molecular weight.[1] Freezing point depression measurements for determination of number average molecular weight are practicable thus far only in a molecular weight range up to 5000, where the method provides for one possible way of measuring molecular weights, whereas the chemical determination of end groups provides another.

B. ENTROPY OF DILUTION

1. Ideal Solutions

In the absence of thermal effects (no heat of mixing) two substances will tend to dissolve in one another because in this way a greater entropy (randomness) can be achieved. The calculation of configurational entropy is based on Boltzmann's relation between entropy and probability, W.

$$S = k \ln W \qquad (VIII.12)$$

where k is the Boltzmann constant.

A usual method for calculation of configurational entropy of mixing is the lattice site method. Thus, for a perfect solution of two molecules of equal size one considers that N_0 and N_p molecules of solvent and solute respectively, are mixed on a lattice. The number of possible configurations is:

$$W = \frac{(N_0 + N_p)!}{N_0! N_p!} \qquad (VIII.13)$$

---

[1] McGoury and Mark, in A. Weissberger ed., *Physical Methods of Organic Chemistry*, second edition, Part I, Chapter VIII, Interscience, New York, 1949.

The entropy of mixing becomes:

$$\Delta S_{mix} = k \ln W = -k(N_0 \ln x_0 + N_p \ln x_p)$$

$$= -R(n_0 \ln x_0 + n_p \ln x_p) \qquad \text{(VIII.14)}$$

where n_0 and n_p are the number of moles of A and B, respectively, and x_0 and x_p are the mole fractions.

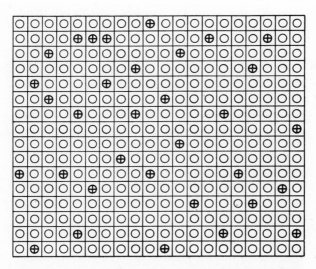

Fig. VIII-1.   The lattice model for molecules of equal size.

The entropy of dilution is given by:

$$\overline{\Delta S_0} = \frac{\partial \Delta S_{mix}}{\partial n_0} = -R \ln x_0 \qquad \text{(VIII.15)}$$

If we assume no heat of mixing, then from equation (VIII.4):

$$\overline{\Delta F_0} = RT \ln x_0 \qquad \text{(VIII.16)}$$

As previously noted, equation (VIII.16) expresses the entire content of the classical theory of ideal solutions.   Colligative properties of ideal solutions can all be obtained by substitutions of equation (VIII.16) in equations (VIII.6)–(VIII.8).

2. Nonideal Solutions

Ideal solutions which obey Raoult's law over the whole range of concentration have been found in only a few cases—such as ethylene dibromide

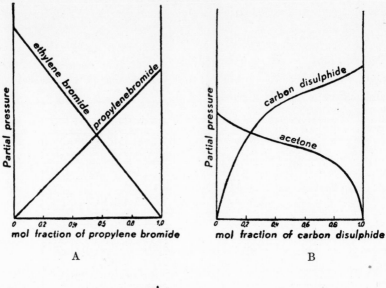

A

B

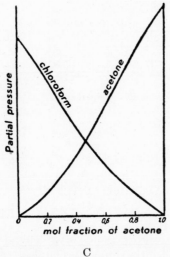

C

Fig. VIII-2. A, partial pressure diagram of an ideal mixture; the partial pressures are proportional to the mole fractions. B, the partial pressures of the components of this system are not proportional to the mole fractions. C, departures from ideal behavior are not very great here.

and propylene dibromide at 85°C., n-hexane and n-heptane at 30°C., and n-butyl chloride and n-butyl bromide at 50°C. In almost all of these cases the two components are very similar physically and chemically, $i.e.$, similar internal pressures, similar molar volumes, etc.

Deviations from ideality occur when the intermolecular solvent-solvent,

solvent-solute, and solute-solute interactions are different. This manifests itself most importantly as a nonzero heat of mixing. If unlike molecules attract more than like molecules, we have a specific solvation effect resulting in an exothermic heat of mixing. In most cases, however, unlike molecules attract less strongly than like molecules, so that we have a endothermic heat of mixing which opposes the solution process. Partial pressure *vs.* mole fraction curves are shown for ideal and nonideal systems in Figure VIII-2.

An important simplification of the problem of solutions was made by Hildebrand, who introduced the concept of a *regular solution*. One may define a regular solution as one in which it is assumed that the entropy of mixing can be calculated from geometrical considerations, neglecting the effect of the interactions between molecules in producing a nonrandom mixing. In other words, for a regular solution we can calculate the entropy of mixing independently of the heat of mixing.

The first question that obviously arises is: to what extent are we justified in assuming the validity of equation (VIII.14) for the entropy of mixing for regular solutions? The question concerning the applicability of equations (VIII.14) and (VIII.15) to *molecules of unequal size* was raised by Guggenheim,[2] Hückel,[3] and Fowler and Rushbrooke.[4] Meyer and co-workers[5,6] pointed out that solutions of long chain compounds dissolved in simple solvents such as carbon tetrachloride did show an important experimentally demonstrable deviation from equation (VIII.15). Meyer[7] suggested that the entropy of mixing of a long chain molecule with a small solvent could be calculated on the basis of a lattice approximation, in which the "segments" of the polymer can occupy the same kind of sites as the molecules of the solvent. Fowler and Rushbrooke gave a partial solution for the case of components occupying 1 and 2 sites, respectively. The more complete solution was furnished by Chang[8] and extended by Miller[9] to a treatment of molecules occupying 3 sites. The general lattice treatment for linear polymers occupying any number of sites was developed by Huggins and Flory and will be discussed later in this section.

Although the lattice site treatment for calculation of entropy of mixing is

[2] E. A. Guggenheim, *Trans. Faraday Soc.*, **33**, 151 (1937).

[3] E. Hückel, *Z. Elektrochem.*, **42**, 753 (1936).

[4] R. H. Fowler and G. S. Rushbrooke, *Trans. Faraday Soc.*, **33**, 1272 (1937).

[5] K. H. Meyer and R. Luhdemann, *Helv. Chim. Acta*, **18**, 307 (1935).

[6] C. G. Boissonnas, *Helv. Chim. Acta*, **20**, 768 (1937).

[7] K. H. Meyer, *Z. physik. Chem.*, **B44**, 383 (1939).

[8] Chang, *Proc. Cambridge Phil. Soc.*, **35**, 265 (1939).

[9] A. R. Miller, *Proc. Cambridge Phil. Soc.*, **38**, 109 (1942); **39**, 54 (1943).

rigorous for solid solutions, it is less satisfactory for liquid solutions. Methods for calculating the entropy of solution without recourse to the lattice approximation were made by Zimm,[10] Hildebrand,[11] and Huggins.[12] The treatments of Huggins and Zimm have the advantage of mathematical rigor but are quite complex. The discussion of Hildebrand (which is similar to an earlier discussion by Meyer and Mark[13]) is relatively easy to follow and shall be presented below as the free volume theory of entropy of solutions.

3. Free Volume Theory of Entropy of Dilution

Boltzmann's equation (VIII.12) can be used to derive the entropy change during isothermal expansion of an ideal gas in a very simple fashion. The thermodynamic probability W at constant temperature of an idealized point molecule in a volume V is proportional to the volume:

$$W = cV \qquad (VIII.17)$$

The probability of N noninteracting point molecules in the volume V is the product of the probabilities of each.

$$W = (cV)^n \qquad (VIII.18)$$

The entropy according to equation (VIII.12) is:

$$S = Nk \ln V + Nk \ln c$$
$$= nR \ln V + nR \ln c \qquad (VIII.19)$$

where $n = N/N_{av.}$ = number of moles in volume V.
The entropy of isothermal expansion from V_1 to V_2 is:

$$S_2 - S_1 = nR \ln (V_2/V_1) \qquad (VIII.20)$$

If we wish to take into account the finite size of the gas molecules, then the probability of a single gas molecule in a volume V is:

$$W = c(V - nb) \qquad (VIII.21)$$

where b is the excluded volume per mole due to the finite size of the other gas molecules in the volume V_1 and n is the number of moles of molecules present. The excluded volume per mole, b, is closely related to the geometric volume of one mole of the gas molecules.

[10] B. H. Zimm, J. Chem. Phys., **14**, 164 (1946).
[11] J. H. Hildebrand, J. Chem. Phys., **15**, 225 (1947).
[12] M. L. Huggins, J. Phys. & Colloid Chem., **52**, 248 (1948).
[13] K. H. Meyer and H. Mark, Ber., **61**, 1947 (1928).

The entropy of isothermal expansion of n moles of gas from V_1 to V_2 will, in this case, be:

$$S_2 - S_1 = nR \ln (V_2 - nb)/(V_1 - nb) \qquad \text{(VIII.22)}$$

The entropy change when n moles are transferred from state 1 to state 2 may be taken as:

$$\Delta S = nR \ln \frac{\text{free volume in state 2}}{\text{free volume in state 1}} \qquad \text{(VIII.23)}$$

Equation (VIII.23) can be applied to solutions of gases or liquids in the following manner: suppose that n_0 and n_p moles of solvent and solute, respectively, are transferred from the pure state, where they occupy molar volumes V_0 and V_p to a solution of volume V and composition $n_0 + n_p$. Further, let the excluded volumes per mole of the solvent and the solute molecule be b_0 and b_p. The entropy of the internal degrees of freedom of the molecules will be assumed to be the same in the pure state and in solution, so that the change in entropy will be purely configurational change. In the case of the solvent molecules, n_0 moles are transferred from the pure solvent state where they have a free volume $n_0(V_0 - b_0)$ to the solution where the free volume is $V - n_0 b_0 - n_p b_p$. For the solute molecules, n_p moles are transferred from the pure solute where they have a free volume $n_p(V_p - b_p)$ to the solution where the free volume is $V - n_0 b_0 - n_p b_p$. From equation (VIII.23), the entropy of mixing will be:

$$\Delta S_{mix} = n_0 R \ln \frac{V - n_0 b_0 - n_p b_p}{n_0(V_0 - b_0)} + n_p R \ln \frac{V - n_0 b_0 - n_p b_p}{n_p(V_p - b_p)} \qquad \text{(VIII.24)}$$

If we are dealing with liquid solutions and the volume of the solution is additive, then $V = n_0 V_0 + n_p V_p$. Also, it is reasonable to assume that the free volumes are proportional to the molar volumes. With these approximations, and by differentiating (VIII.24) with respect to n_0 at constant n_p, we obtain:

$$\overline{\Delta S_0} = - R \ln \phi_0 - R\phi_p \left(1 - \frac{1}{x}\right) \qquad \text{(VIII.25)}$$

where $\phi_0 = n_0 V_0/V$ and $\phi_p = n_p V_p/V$ are the volume fractions of solvent and solute, respectively, and x is the ratio of molar volumes V_p/V_0.

Zimm[14] and Huggins[15] have calculated the entropies of dilution for the

[14] B. H. Zimm, J. Chem. Phys., 14, 164 (1946).
[15] M. L. Huggins, J. Phys. & Colloid Chem., 52, 248 (1948).

case of mixing spheres of unequal size and for the case of solutions of long rigid rods.

For the solutions of spherical molecules of unequal size:

$$\frac{\overline{\Delta S_0}}{R} = \frac{\phi_p}{x} + \frac{4}{x}\,\phi_p^2 + \frac{10}{x}\,\phi_p^3 + \cdots \qquad \text{(VIII.26)}$$

where x is the ratio of the volumes of the solute molecules to solvent molecules.

Since for dilute solutions $\phi_p/x = x_p$ and the higher powers of ϕ_p can be neglected, such solutions behave as nearly "ideal" dilute solutions. (x_p is the mole fraction of polymer.)

For solutions of cylindrical rodlike molecules which are large both in length and in cross section compared with the close-packed spherical solvent molecules:

$$\frac{\overline{\Delta S_0}}{R} = \frac{\phi_p}{x} + \frac{2\sqrt{2}}{\pi}\left(\frac{r_0}{r_p}\right)^3 \phi_p^2 + \cdots \qquad \text{(VIII.27)}$$

where x is the ratio of volume of solute to solvent molecule, r_0 is the radius of the spherical solvent molecules, and r_p is the cross-sectional radius of the rodlike solute molecules.

4. Lattice Model for Entropy of Dilution of Flexible Linear Macromolecules

The free volume treatment given in the last section would appear to be most strictly applicable to the gaseous state. The lattice model treatment given for ideal solutions is, as previously mentioned, conceptually most applicable to solid solutions. It is therefore of interest to see whether a lattice site treatment for flexible linear molecules will lead to the same results as the free volume method.

The application of a lattice site treatment to account for the abnormal entropy of mixing of flexible linear macromolecules was first suggested by Meyer.[16] He stated that the configurational entropy could be calculated from the lattice site model shown below, in which "segments" of the flexible polymer molecules are assumed to be interchangeable with solvent molecules. The coordination number, Z, of the lattice is defined as the number of sites surrounding any given site (see Fig. VIII-3).

[16] K. H. Meyer, Z. physik. Chem., **B44**, 383 (1939).

Flory[17] and Huggins[18] successfully carried out the calculations for this model arriving at nearly identical formulas for the configurational entropy and entropy of dilution. If the segments of the long chain molecules were severed from one another the number of configurations would be given by:

$$W = (N_0 + xN_p)!/N_0!(xN_p)!$$

where N_0 is the number of polymer molecules, and x is the number of segments per molecule. In the actual case, where the segments are tied to

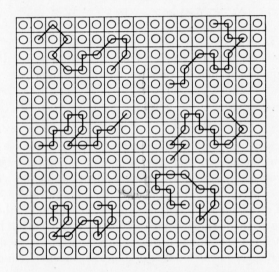

Fig. VIII-3.   The Meyer lattice model.

one another, there clearly are fewer possible configurations. On the other hand the number of configurations is larger than:

$$W = (N_0 + N_p)!/N_0!N_p!$$

which would be the case if the polymer molecules as a whole were interchangeable with the segments. A segment in the interior of a chain molecule has $Z - 1$ sites to choose from if the rest of the lattice were otherwise

[17] P. J. Flory, *J. Chem. Phys.*, **9**, 660 (1941); **10**, 51 (1942); **13**, 453 (1945); **11**, 425 (1944).

[18] M. L. Huggins, *J. Chem. Phys.*, **9**, 440 (1941); *Ann. N. Y. Acad. Sci.*, **44**, 431 (1943); *J. Phys. Chem.*, **46**, 151 (1942); *J. Am. Chem. Soc.*, **64**, 1712 (1942); *Ind. Eng. Chem.*, **35**, 216 (1943).

empty, whereas if it were unattached to the rest of the chain it could occupy any site in the entire lattice. A fundamental assumption necessary for the counting is that, if the lattice is already partly occupied, the local density of unoccupied sites available to a bound segment is equal to the over-all density of unoccupied sites in the entire lattice. The number of configurations obtained using this assumption is:

$$W = \frac{(N_0 + xN_p)!}{N_0!N_p!} \left(\frac{Z}{N_0 + xN_p}\right)^{N_p} \left(\frac{Z-1}{N_0 + xN_p}\right)^{(x-2)N_p}$$

$$\cong \frac{(N_0 + xN_p)!}{N_0!N_p!} \left(\frac{Z-1}{N_0 + xN_p}\right)^{(x-1)N_p} \tag{VIII.28}$$

If we consider a solution of N_0 solvent molecules and a distribution in sizes of polymer molecules in which we have N_x x-mers:

$$W = \frac{(N_0 + \Sigma xN_x)!}{N_0!\Pi N_x!} \left(\frac{Z-1}{N_0 + \Sigma xN_x}\right)^{\Sigma(x-1)N_x} \tag{VIII.29}$$

This treatment was somewhat amended by Huggins[19] to account for the interference of the already laid down segments of a polymer molecule with the configurational possibilities of subsequent segments. The effect of intermolecular interactions in producing nonrandom mixing in the cases where a heat of mixing is present was treated by several authors.[20-22]

All of these methods agree very closely as to the final result for entropy of dilution, which can be obtained from equation (VIII.28) by differentiating $k \ln W$ with respect to the number of moles of solvent. An expression involving volume fraction results:

$$\overline{\Delta S_0} = -R \left[\ln (1 - \phi_p) + \phi_p \left(1 - \frac{1}{x}\right) + \text{correction terms}\right] \tag{VIII.30}$$

where ϕ_p is the volume fraction of the solute and x the ratio of molar volume of polymer to solvent. The various theories differ only in the correction terms. If the correction terms are neglected and if x is large, then, except in dilute solutions, the term involving ϕ_p/x is completely negligible and the entropy of dilution has an extremely simple form which is independent of the nature of the solvent or solute and is identical with equation (VIII.27)

[19] M. L. Huggins, *Ann. N. Y. Acad. Sci.*, **44**, 431 (1943).
[20] W. J. C. Orr, *Trans. Faraday Soc.*, **40**, 206, 320 (1944).
[21] T. Alfrey, Jr., and P. M. Doty, *J. Chem. Phys.*, **13**, 77 (1945).
[22] E. A. Guggenheim, *Proc. Roy. Soc.*, **A183**, 203, 213 (1944).

derived by the free volume theory. The correction terms account for the shape and structure of the polymer. For linear flexible polymer molecules the entropy of dilution calculated by Huggins on the basis of the lattice model (Fig. VIII-3) is:

$$\overline{\Delta S_0} = -R\left[\ln(1-\phi_p) + \left(1-\frac{1}{x}\right)\phi_p + \frac{1}{Z'}\phi_p^2 + \text{higher terms}\right]$$

(VIII.31)

where Z' is approximately equal to the coordination number of the lattice (*i.e.*, the number of lattice sites surrounding a given lattice site). For dilute solutions where expansion of the logarithm is justified:

$$\overline{\Delta S_0} \cong R\left[\frac{\phi_p}{x} + \left(\frac{1}{2} - \frac{1}{Z'}\right)\phi_p^2\right]$$

(VIII.32)

An important modification of the lattice site theory was made by Flory[23] to account for discrepancy between theory and experiment in the range of very dilute solutions. The fundamental assumption of the lattice site treatment is that the local density of polymer segments in the neighborhood of a given segment of the polymer molecule is the same as the over-all density of polymer segments in the lattice. This is a fairly reasonable approximation in moderately concentrated solutions. However, in very dilute solutions a random distribution is no longer an apt description of the situation because each polymer occupies a given number of sites in a localized region of the lattice, and between these regions are regions completely filled by solvent. In the region occupied by the polymer molecules, the concentration of solute segments depends on the swelling volume of each polymer molecule; in the regions between the solute molecules the concentration of solute segments is zero.

Using this model, a new counting method was used to derive the entropy of dilution in very dilute solutions in terms of the "swelling volume." The swelling volume was defined as the effective volume of the loosely coiled chain in solution and includes the volume of the polymer plus entrapped solvent. The swelling factor is defined as the ratio of swelling volume to the volume per chain of the unswollen polymer. In terms of this new statistical calculation, the slope of the osmotic pressure curve π/c plotted against c is:

$$\frac{4s}{x} f(x/s)$$

[23] P. J. Flory, *J. Chem. Phys.*, **13**, 453 (1945).

where x is the number of segments per polymer molecule, s is the swelling factor and $f(x/s)$ is a calculated function.[23]

The validity of this theoretical approach is reinforced by *a priori* calculation of the swelling factor from a completely different physical measurement.   The intrinsic viscosity (in deciliters per gram) of the polymer solutions may be expressed as:

$$[\eta] = 0.025 \ sv \qquad\qquad (VIII.33)$$

where v is the specific volume of the unswollen polymer.   Using values of s obtained in this manner in the formula for the slope of the osmotic pressure curve, good agreement with experiment was obtained.

C. HEAT OF DILUTION

The heat of dilution for simple liquids has been given theoretical treatment by van Laar,[24] Scatchard,[25] and Hildebrand.[26]   According to the latter author the heat of dilution can be written as:

$$\overline{\Delta H_0} = BV_0\phi_p^2 = B'\phi_p^2 \qquad\qquad (VIII.34)$$

where V_0 is the molar volume of the solvent, ϕ_p is the volume fraction of solute, and B is defined as:

$$B = K \ (\sqrt{E_0/V_0} - \sqrt{E_p/V_p})^2 \qquad\qquad (VIII.35)$$

where E_0 and E_p are the molar energies of vaporization for solvent and solute.   The quantities E_0/V_0 and E_p/V_p are the latent energies of evaporation per unit volume for solvent and solute, respectively.*   The quantity K is a constant that is unity in the case of simple molecules, but turns out to be different from unity for polymer solutions.

Formula (VIII.34) always gives a positive value for the heat of dilution, *i.e.*, the heat of solution is always endothermic and tends to oppose the process of solution.   The reason for this is the basis on which (VIII.34) is derived.   In the molecular derivation it is assumed that the binding forces between the molecules solvent-solvent, solvent-solute, and solute-solute are similar in nature.   The solvent-solute interaction energy is therefore taken as the geometric mean of the solvent-solvent, solute-solute interac-

---

[24] J. J. van Laar, *Z. physik. Chem.*, **72**, 723 (1910).

[25] G. Scatchard, *Chem. Revs.*, **8**, 321 (1931); *Trans. Faraday Soc.*, **33**, 160 (1937).

[26] J. H. Hildebrand, *J. Am. Chem. Soc.*, **38**, 1452 (1916); *Solubility of Nonelectrolytes*, 2nd edition, Reinhold, New York, 1936.

* Sometimes called cohesive energy density or c.e.d.

tion energy. This treatment obviously neglects the possibility of specific interaction forces between solvent and solute.

Inasmuch as B approaches zero when the molar cohesive energies of solvent and solute become identical, equation (VIII.34) expresses the organic chemists' rule that "like dissolves like"; in this case the criterion for "like" is the comparative values of the cohesive energy densities.

Table VIII-1 gives the values of the square roots of the cohesive energy densities for a wide variety of liquids. In the case of polymers, it is obviously impossible to obtain values for the energies of vaporization because most polymers pyrolyze before they vaporize. However, approximate values can be obtained by considering the cohesive energy densities for a homologous series. For example, the cohesive energy densities of the paraffins C_nH_{2n+2} increase with chain length and tend to a limiting value of around 60 cal./cc. as n becomes large.

The cohesive energy densities of polymers are best obtained by direct experiment. It is clear that the swelling of a cross-linked polymer in a

TABLE VIII-1

VALUES OF $\sqrt{E_0/V_0}$ FOR VARIOUS SOLVENTS[a,b]

Solvent	$\sqrt{E_0/V_0}$, (cal./cc.)$^{1/2}$	Solvent	$\sqrt{E_0/V_0}$, (cal./cc.)$^{1/2}$
Linear dimethyl siloxanes (2 to 11 Si atoms)	5.90–4.97	Ethyl bromide	8.95
Aliphatic fluorocarbons	5.5–6.2	Benzene	9.15
Aromatic fluorocarbons	7.5–8.2	Styrene	9.20
Neopentane	6.3	Ethyl mercaptan	9.25
n-Pentane	7.00	Chloroform	9.3
n-Hexane	7.40	Dimethyl sulfide	9.4
1-Hexene	7.4	Methyl bromide	9.65
Diethyl ether	7.5	1,4-Dioxane	9.95
1,3-Butadiene	7.6	Acetone	10.0
n-Octane	7.6	Methyl formate	10.1
Diisobutylene	7.7	Methylamine	11.2
Cyclohexane	8.2	n-Butanol	11.4
p-Cymene	8.1	Isopropyl alcohol	11.5
Furan	8.2	n-Propyl alcohol	11.9
Cyclopentane	8.7	Acetonitrile	12.1
p-Xylene	8.78	Ethyl alcohol	12.7
Decalin (cis)	8.8	Methyl alcohol	14.3
Toluene	8.93	Water	23.4

[a] R. L. Scott, *Thesis*. Princeton University, 1945.
[b] G. Gee., *Trans. Inst. Rubber Ind.*, **18**, 266 (1943).

variety of solvents will show a swelling maximum at the point where co-hesive energy density of solvent and polymer are identical. Gee[27] used this method to obtain the cohesive energy density of a variety of synthetic

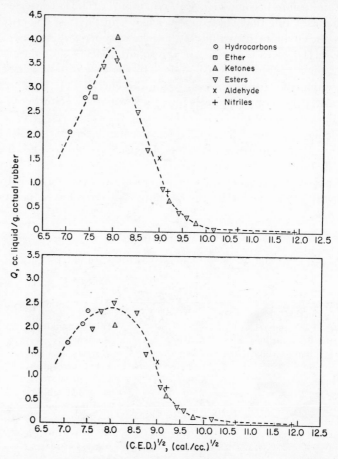

Fig. VIII-4.   Swelling of natural rubber in various solvents: at top, pure gum; at bottom, tire tread.

rubbers.   A typical example is shown in Figure VIII-4.   Values of the square roots of the cohesive energy densities for various polymers are given in Table VIII-2.

[27] G. Gee, "Thermodynamics of Rubber Solutions and Gels," in *Advances in Colloid Science*, Vol. II.   Interscience, New York, 1946.

TABLE VIII-2

SQUARE ROOT OF COHESIVE ENERGY DENSITY FOR POLYMERS

Polymer	$\sqrt{E_p/V_p}$	Polymer	$\sqrt{E_p/V_p}$
Polyisobutylene	8.05[a]	Butadiene-vinylpyridine 75–25	9.35[a]
Polyisoprene (natural rubber)	8.35[a]	Butadiene-acrylonitrile 75–25	9.5[a]
Polybutadiene (emulsion)	8.40[a]	Butadiene-acrylonitrile	9.6[a]
Polybutadiene (sodium)	8.60[a]	Natural rubber	7.92[b]
Butadiene-styrene copolymers		Butadiene-styrene 75–25	8.09[b]
85% butadiene, 15% styrene	8.50[a]	Neoprene G.N.	8.18[b]
75% butadiene, 25% styrene	8.55[a]	Thiokol F.A.	9.38[b]
60% butadiene, 40% styrene	8.67[a]	Butadiene-acrylonitrile 75–25	9.38[b]
Polystyrene	9.1[a]	Polyethylene	7.87[c]
Neoprene G.N.	9.2[a]	Styrene-divinylbenzene	8.50[d]
		Polyvinyl chloride	9.48[e]

[a] R. L. Scott, *Thesis*. Princeton University, 1945.
[b] G. Gee, *Trans. Inst. Rubber Ind.*, **18**, 266 (1943).
[c] R. B. Richards, *Trans. Faraday Soc.*, **42**, 20 (1946).
[d] R. F. Boyer and R. S. Spencer, in *High Polymer Physics*, Paper 5, Part III, Remsen Press, New York, 1948.
[e] P. Doty and H. S. Zable, *J. Polymer Sci.*, **1**, 90 (1946).

If the expressions for entropy of dilution, equation (VIII.18), and heat of solution (VIII.34) are combined, the free energy of dilution for solutions of long chain flexible molecules is:

$$\frac{\overline{\Delta F_0}}{RT} = \ln a_0 = \ln (1 - \phi_p) + \left(1 - \frac{1}{x}\right) \phi_p + \mu \phi_p^2 \quad \text{(VIII.36)}$$

or for dilute solutions:

$$\frac{\overline{\Delta F_0}}{RT} = \ln a_0 = -\frac{\phi_p}{x} + (\mu - {}^1\!/_2) \phi_p^2 \quad \text{(VIII.37)}$$

where:

$$\mu = \frac{1}{Z'} + \frac{B'}{RT} \quad \text{(VIII.38)}$$

D. COMPARISON OF THEORETICAL AND EXPERIMENTAL FREE ENERGIES OF DILUTION

The criterion for the validity of the theories of polymer solutions is to see whether the equations (VIII.36)–(VIII.38) will fit experimental data at a single temperature over the entire concentration range with a single value of μ. Conversely, these theoretical equations have been used extensively to interpret experimental results on osmotic pressure, vapor pressure lowering, and freezing point depression. In most cases the concentration is expressed in terms of c, $i.e.$, grams of polymer per cubic centimeter of solution, rather than in terms of volume fraction.

The Huggins-Flory equation (VIII.37) for the free energy of dilution of dilute polymer solutions when expressed in terms of c, becomes:

$$\frac{\overline{\Delta F_0}}{RT} = \ln a_0 = -\frac{V_0}{M_p} c + \frac{(\mu - \frac{1}{2})c^2}{d_p^2} \quad (VIII.39)$$

where d_p is the density of the solute and is equal to M_p/V_p.

From equations (VIII.39) and (VIII.6)–(VIII.8), one obtains for dilute solutions of high polymers:

$$\ln \frac{p}{p_0} = -\frac{V_0}{M_p} c + \frac{(\mu - \frac{1}{2})c^2}{d_p^2} \quad (VIII.40)$$

$$\pi = \frac{RT}{M_p} c + \frac{RT}{V_0 d_p^2} (\frac{1}{2} - \mu)c^2 \quad (VIII.41)$$

$$\theta = -\frac{RT_f^2}{L_f} V_0 \left[\frac{c}{M_p} + \frac{(\frac{1}{2} - \mu)c^2}{V_0^2 d_p^2} \right] \quad (VIII.42)$$

As an example of the way in which these equations are used, in the case of osmotic pressure measurements a plot of π/c against c is made, and in

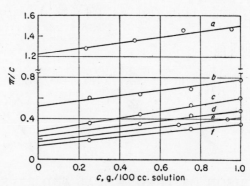

Fig. VIII-5. Osmotic pressure curves of refractionated polystyrene in butanone at 27°C.[28]

the range of reasonably dilute solutions these curves give straight lines (see Fig. VIII-5). The intercept of such a line is RT/M_p and can be used to calculate the molecular weight; the slope can be used to calculate the interaction constants μ. Values of μ obtained for various polymer-solvent

[28] A. I. Goldberg, W. P. Hohenstein, and H. Mark, $J.\ Polymer\ Sci.$, 2, 503 (1947).

systems are tabulated in Table VIII-3. A polymer will be completely miscible with a liquid if $\Delta \bar{F}_0$ is negative at all concentrations. The greater the negative value of $\Delta \bar{F}_0$, the farther the binary system is from phase separation, and in more customary language, the greater is the solvent power. Inasmuch as $\Delta \bar{F}_0$ depends only on the molecular weight of the polymer and on the interaction constant μ, the latter provides a measure of the solvent power of a given liquid for a polymer. As the value of μ increases from negative values through zero to 0.55, the solvent action becomes progressively poorer, until at a μ value of approximately 0.55 separation into two phases occurs.

TABLE VIII-3

VALUES FOR μ FOR VARIOUS POLYMER-SOLVENT SYSTEMS

Components	μ	Temp., °C.	Components	μ	Temp., °C.
Cellulose acetate–tetrachloroethane	−1.8	24.4[a]	Polyvinyl chloride–butyl acetate	0.40	53[c]
Cellulose nitrate-acetone	0.19	20[a]	Polyvinyl chloride-butyl acetate	0.41	76[c]
Cellulose nitrate-acetone	0.26	22[a]	Polyvinyl chloride-acetone	0.63	27[c]
Cellulose nitrate-acetone	0.30	27[a]	Polyvinyl chloride-acetone	0.60	53[c]
Cellulose nitrate-cyclohexanone	0.15	25[a]	Polyvinyl chloride-benzene	0.77	76[c]
Gutta percha-benzene	0.52	25[a]	Polyvinyl chloride-dioctyl ether	2.6	53[c]
Gutta percha-carbon tetrachloride	0.28	27[a]	Polyvinyl chloride-dioctyl ether	2.8	76[c]
Polydichlorostyrene-butanone	0.50	27[a]	Rubber-benzene	0.44	25[a]
Polyisobutylene-benzene	0.50	27[b]	Rubber-benzene-10% methanol	0.26	25[a]
Polyisobutylene-cyclohexane	0.44	27[b]	Rubber-benzene-15% methanol	0.50	25[a]
Polystyrene-benzene	0.20	25[a]	Rubber-carbon disulfide	0.49	25[a]
Polystyrene-butanone	0.48	5[a]	Rubber-carbon tetrachloride	0.28	15–20[a]
Polystyrene-ethyl laurate	0.47	25[a]	Rubber-chloroform	0.37	15–20[a]
Polystyrene-isoamyl laurate	0.91	25[a]	Rubber-cumene	0.38	15–20[a]
Polystyrene-toluene	0.44	27[a]	Rubber-cyclohexane	0.33	6[a]
Polyvinyl acetate-acetone	0.44	27[c]	Rubber-ether	0.51	15–20[a]
Polyvinyl chloride-trioctyl phosphate	−0.76	53[c]	Rubber-light petroleum	0.43	25[a]
Polyvinyl chloride-trioctyl phosphate	−0.65	76[c]	Rubber-tetrachloroethane	0.36	15–20[a]
Polyvinyl chloride-dibutyl phthalate	−0.04	53[c]	Rubber-toluene	0.43	27[a]
Polyvinyl chloride-dibutyl phthalate	−0.01	76[c]			

[a] M. L. Huggins, *Ann. N. Y. Acad. Sci.*, **44**, 431 (1943).
[b] P. J. Flory, *J. Am. Chem. Soc.*, **65**, 372 (1943).
[c] P. M. Doty and H. S. Zable, *J. Polymer Sci.*, **1**, 90 (1946).

The only polymer-solvent system that was investigated over the entire concentration range is the system rubber-benzene studied by Gee and Treloar.[29]   In this system the value of μ remained remarkably constant over almost the entire concentration range.   The disturbing fact revealed by this data is that the theory fits experiment least well in the range of quite dilute solution.

The heat of dilution is obtainable from the temperature dependence of the free energy of dilution from equation (VIII.5).   Gee and Treloar have measured the heats of dilution for the system rubber-benzene by studying the temperature dependence of osmotic pressure and vapor pressure. They find that $\overline{\Delta H_0}/\phi_p^2$ varies from 250 cal./mole in concentrated solution to 50 cal./mole at infinite dilution.

A simple way of obtaining the contribution of heat of dilution is from the equation:

$$\mu = \frac{1}{Z'} + \frac{B'}{RT} \tag{VIII.43}$$

If a plot of μ against $1/T$ is made, a straight line should be obtained whose slope is B'/R and whose intercept is $1/Z'$.   The slope therefore provides a direct measure of the heat of dilution from equation (VIII.34).   This method has been employed by Doty and Zable and also by Spencer and Boyer.[30]

The results of all these studies can be summarized as follows:

(1) μ is not strictly a constant but tends to increase with increasing concentration.   This is most serious in the range of very dilute solutions where a rigorous theory would be very desirable for the purpose of calculating molecular weights from experimental data.

(2) Both $1/Z'$ and B' in equation (VIII.43) are more rapidly varying functions of concentrations than is μ.   Apparently the equation (VIII.39) for free energy of dilution is fairly accurate through a fortuitous cancellation of errors in the heat and entropy expressions.

(3) The values of Z' that are calculated from application of equation (VIII.43) are generally much lower than is physically reasonable, especially in cases where the heat of dilution is small.   In other words, the value of μ in dilute athermal solutions is higher than the theory would predict.

Stated in another way, the slopes of the π/c vs. c curves for polymer-solvent systems, where there is no heat of solution, are smaller than would

[29] G. Gee and L. R. G. Treloar, *Trans. Faraday Soc.*, **38**, 147 (1942).

[30] P. M. Doty and H. S. Zable, *J. Polymer Sci.*, **1**, 90 (1946).   R. F. Boyer and R. S. Spencer, in *High Polymer Physics*, Paper 5, part III, Remsen Press, New York, 1948.

be predicted by the original Flory-Huggins theory. Flory's newer theory for the very dilute solution, which was discussed in section C, appears to overcome this theoretical difficulty.

In spite of these shortcomings of the theory of polymer solutions, a large body of experimental fact has been systematized by the theoretical framework presented here. We must conclude that it is best to regard the μ value as a semiempirical "constant" whose application to polymer-liquid systems aids in correlating and predicting the results of thermodynamic measurements.

E. SOLUBILITY OF MACROMOLECULES

Empirical observations have indicated that a given liquid will be a solvent for a polymer if it resembles the structural units of the polymer (e.g., toluene is a good solvent for polystyrene) or, more generally, if the cohesive energy densities of solvent and polymer are nearly equal. In certain cases, specific interactions appear to exist between the solvent and certain groups of the polymer (e.g., phosphate plasticizers and polyvinyl chloride, cuprammonium and cellulose). Linear amorphous polymers dissolve more readily than crystalline polymers. For example, silk extracted from the glands of the silkworm before extrusion and crystallization is water-soluble. Also, polyethylene has to be heated to a temperature at which much of its crystallites melt before it will dissolve. Flexible linear macromolecules such as starch are more soluble than rigid molecules such as cellulose. Very rigid polymers show little solubility. Polytetrafluoroethylene, which is very crystalline and, in addition, has very rigid molecules, is not soluble in any known solvent except molten sodium, which attacks it chemically.

The molecular weight of the solvent also plays a role in determining solubility. It is only rarely that two polymers are mutually soluble. Even when the chemical structures of the two polymers are quite similar, as in the case of polyethylene and polyisobutylene, high temperatures are necessary to achieve compatibility.

When a polymer of homogeneous molecular weight is insoluble in a given liquid, two phases form. A certain amount of solvent (which may be considerable) is present at equilibrium in the polymer-rich phase, but the solvent is nearly pure liquid.

Solubility can be treated theoretically in terms of the same theories that were developed for colligative properties.[31-33] As is to be expected,

[31] P. J. Flory, J. Chem. Phys., 12, 425 (1944).

[32] G. Gee, Trans. Faraday Soc., 38, 276 (1942).

[33] R. L. Scott and M. Magat, J. Chem. Phys., 13, 172, 178 (1945).

the interaction constant μ plays a fundamental role. If the free energy of dilution for a fractionated polymer of fixed molecular weight is plotted against volume fraction, for small values of μ the free energy will always be

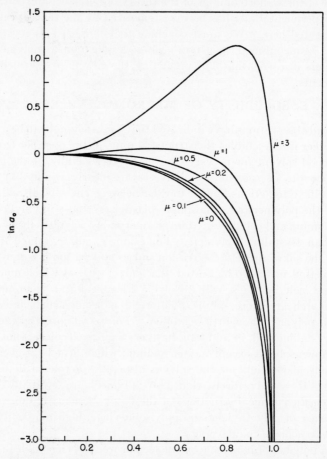

Fig. VIII-6. Logarithmic activity of solvent *vs.* volume fraction of very high molecular weight solute for various values of μ.

decreasing. Above a certain critical value of μ the curves and S shapes indicate separation into two phases, and hence insolubility. The critical value of μ is:

$$\mu_c = \frac{1}{2}\left[1 + \left(\frac{V_0}{V_p}\right)^{1/2}\right]^2 = \frac{1}{2}\left[1 + \left(\frac{1}{x}\right)^{1/2}\right]^2 \qquad \text{(VIII.44)}$$

where $x = V_p/V_0$ is the ratio of molar volume of solute to that of solvent and is proportional to the degree of polymerization of the polymer.

Graphs of $\overline{\Delta F_0}/RT$ vs. volume fraction for various values of μ are shown in Figure VIII-6.

The volume fraction of polymer dissolved in solvent at the critical point is given by:

$$\phi_p = 1/(1 + \sqrt{x}) \qquad (VIII.45)$$

The critical solution temperature above which the two phases disappear is given by:

$$T_c = \frac{2B'x}{R(1 + \sqrt{x})^2} \qquad (VIII.46)$$

In order to discuss the solubility of a polymer containing a distribution of molecular weights it is necessary to develop equations for the partial molar free energies for each component of different molecular weight.[31,33] The critical conditions for complete miscibility (equations VIII.44 to VIII.46) remain unaltered except that x is replaced by its number average value $\bar{x}_n$. The solubility is determined from the condition that the partial molar free energy of each component must be the same in both phases.

The theory of solubility is at present only partially developed because of severe mathematical difficulties.

The following expression for the ratio of concentration of polymer of molecular weight M_i in the solvent and polymer phases has been obtained empirically and theoretically:

$$\ln \frac{\phi_i'}{\phi_i''} = aM_i \qquad (VIII.47)$$

where ϕ_i' is the volume fraction of molecular weight M_i in the polymer phase, ϕ_i'' is the volume fraction of the polymer of molecular weight M_i in the solvent phase, and a is a constant depending on the interaction constant and also on the distribution of molecular weights in the system. Schulz[34] developed this equation and applied it to the case of a mixture of two liquids. If one of the liquids is a solvent and the other a nonsolvent, it follows that the proportion γ of the nonsolvent in the critical mixture that will just dissolve a polymer of molecular weight M is given by:

$$\gamma = A + B/M \qquad (VIII.48)$$

where A and B are constants.

[34] G. V. Schulz, Z. physik. Chem., A179, 321 (1937).

F. FRACTIONATION OF POLYMER SOLUTIONS

Inasmuch as most natural polymers and all synthetic polymers are heterogeneous in molecular weight, methods for separating the various molecular weight fractions are of great importance. In a recent review article on the subject,[35] Cragg and Hammerschlag listed various methods for fractionation (see the accompanying table). In addition to these methods, Debye has recently suggested the use of thermal diffusion as a means of fractionation of high polymers.[36]

Method	Principle on which separation is based
I. Solubility Methods	
1. Fractional precipitation...............	Solubility decreases with molecular weight
(a) by addition of precipitant	
(b) by cooling	
2. Fractional solution	
(a) solvent of varying composition	
(b) varying temperature	
3. Distribution between two immiscible solvents..........................	Distribution coefficient depends on molecular weight
II. Rate of Solution Method (diffusion into a single solvent)........................	Smaller molecules diffuse faster
III. Ultracentrifuge...........................	Sedimentation velocity increases with molecular weight
IV. Chromatographic Adsorption................	Smaller molecules are adsorbed preferentially
V. Ultrafiltration through Graded Membranes.....	Sieving action
VI. Molecular Distillation.....................	Larger molecules are less volatile

For linear high polymers, fractionation methods depending upon solubility have so far proved most practicable and are by far the most widely used. Of the various solubility methods, fractional precipitation is most popular. On the other hand, ultracentrifugation has been quite successfully used for the fractionation of globular proteins. Molecular distillation is of value for fractionation of low molecular weight polymers or to remove the very low fractions from high polymers. The other methods are as yet not widely used.

The theory of fractionation by solubility methods is, of course, an application of the theory of solubility and has been only partially developed. However, certain principles of effective fractionation appear to be borne out by theory and experiment. These have been summarized by Cragg and Hammerschlag:

[35] L. H. Cragg and H. Hammerschlag, *Chem. Revs.*, **39**, 79 (1946).

[36] P. Debye and P. P. Debye, in *High Polymer Physics*. Remsen Press, New York, 1948.

"Fractionation is never completely efficient; the fractions obtained are never completely homogeneous with respect to molecular weight, although more so than the original material. Refractionation improves the uniformity of the fractions, but only up to a certain point; there is no further significant improvement after the third fractionation. Better results are obtained by suitably recombining a small number of fractions, if only a few are required, than by separating out the few larger fractions directly. The efficiency of a fractionation is greater the more dilute the supernatant solution and it is greater in the lower than in the high molecular weight range."

The conclusion that fractionations are most efficient in dilute solutions has been questioned. In practice, most fractionations are carried out

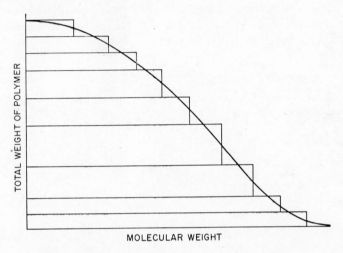

Fig. VIII-7. Integral weight distribution curve.

from solutions in which the initial concentration of the total polymer is about 1%.

The method of fractional precipitation can be outlined as follows: The polymer is brought into solution and successive amounts of nonsolvent are added to cause precipitation. After each addition of nonsolvent the two phases are separated by decantation and the amount of polymer in the polymer-rich phase determined by evaporation of solvent; the polymer is then redissolved and a molecular weight measurement made. More nonsolvent is added, the two phases separated by decantation, and the same process repeated.

In this way an integral weight distribution curve shown in Figure VIII-7 can be obtained by merely plotting the weight of each fraction as a function of molecular weight, adding the weight of each fraction to the weight of the preceding fraction. The smooth line drawn through Figure VIII-7 is the integral weight distribution curve. Any point of the curve gives the total weight of polymer molecules whose molecular weight exceeds the value M of the abscissa. The differential weight distribution curve can be obtained by taking the negative slope of the integral weight distribution curve as a function of molecular weight (Fig. VIII-8). This curve gives the weight of polymer having a given molecular weight as a function of molecular weight. It is, when normalized to unity, identifiable with W_n discussed in Chapters XI and XII.

The number distribution curve may be obtained by dividing each point on the differential weight distribution curve by the molecular weight

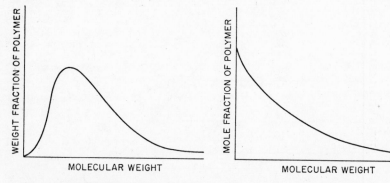

Fig. VIII-8.   Differential weight distribution curve.

Fig. VIII-9.   Differential number distribution curve.

(Fig. VIII-9). This gives the number of moles of polymer having a given molecular weight as a function of molecular weight. When normalized to unity it is identifiable with the mole fraction distribution curve.

Strictly speaking, these distribution curves are not really continuous curves but are functions defined only at certain discrete values of the molecular weight corresponding to the integral values of the degree of polymerization. The weight fraction distribution $W(M_i)$ may in certain cases be defined only for a set of discrete values of M_i, i.e., $M_i = iM_0$, where $i = 1, 2, 3, 4, \ldots$. On the other hand, to obtain a continuous function, one may say that the weight fraction of polymer having molecular weights between M and $M + dM$ is given by $W(M)dM$. In this case the curve described by $W(M)$ as a function of M is known as the weight fraction distribution curve. Similarly, the mole fraction distribution $X(M_i)$

may be defined for only discrete values of M_i, in which case $X(M_i)$ is the mole fraction of polymer molecules having a molecular weight M_i. Or we may define the continuous function $X(M)$, where $X(M)dM$ is the mole fraction of molecules in the distribution whose molecular weight lies between M and $M + dM$.

The success of a fractionation depends primarily on the choice of solvent and precipitant. In Table VIII-4 a few systems that have been used are indicated. More complete data are given elsewhere.[37]

TABLE VIII-4

POLYMER-SOLVENT-PRECIPITANT SYSTEMS FOR FRACTIONATION

Polymer	Solvent	Precipitant
Cellulose	Sodium hydroxide	Water-acetone
Cellulose	0.5 M cupriethylene-diamine	H_2SO_4 (1 N)
Cellulose	Sodium hydroxide	Sodium sulfate
Cellulose acetate	Acetone	Water
Gelatin	Water	Alcohol
Polystyrene	Benzene	Ethanol
Polystyrene	Benzene	Acetone
Polystyrene	Chloroform	Methanol
Polystyrene	Methyl ethyl ketone	Methanol
Polyisobutylene	Benzene	Acetone
Polymethyl methacrylate	Benzene	Cyclohexane
Rubber	Benzene or toluene	Alcohol or acetone
Buna S	Benzene	Methanol

Fractionation by cooling instead of adding precipitant has also been accomplished, in particular by Midgley and associates working with natural rubber. Bloomfield and Farmer carried through a very careful study of the fractional solution of natural rubber using mixtures of petroleum ether (solvent) and acetone (nonsolvent)—25% petroleum ether for the first fraction, 50% petroleum ether for the second fraction and suitable mixtures for higher fractions. Care was taken to prevent oxidative degradation of the rubber during this process.

Whereas in fractional solution methods, equilibrium should be maintained throughout, in diffusion methods fractions are separated before equilibrium is established. In this method the polymer is placed in contact with a solvent, the supernatant liquid is removed after a definite time interval and replaced with fresh solvent, etc. The method depends on the

[37] L. H. Cragg and H. Hammerschlag, *Chem. Revs.*, **39**, 79 (1946).

difference in rate of diffusion and solution of long-chain molecules compared with shorter ones. A fair amount of work has been done using this method for fractionation of natural rubber. Gee has questioned whether fractional extraction by a single solvent can be made quantitatively reproducible.

G. MOLECULAR WEIGHT AVERAGES

In many cases when dealing with polymeric materials the process of fractionation is too time-consuming for practical purposes and so instead one measures molecular weight *averages*. Since most molecular weight determinations are made in dilute solution, the process of measuring an average molecular weight consists in measuring the weight concentration of the polydisperse polymer, and then measuring a physical property such as turbidity, osmotic pressure, viscosity, etc. If one then calculates a molecular weight from the observed physical property and the total weight concentration of polymer, the calculated molecular weight will be some sort of molecular weight average which depends on the physical method used.

Two types of molecular weight averages are particularly important: the number average molecular weight and the weight average molecular weight. In calculating the number average molecular weight, the molecular weight of each species is weighted by the mole fraction of this particular species which occurs in the polydisperse system. Mathematically speaking, the number average molecular weight $\bar{M}_n$ is defined as:

$$\bar{M}_n = \sum_i X_i M_i = \frac{\sum N_i M_i}{\sum N_i} \qquad \text{(VIII.49)}$$

where X_i is the mole fraction of species i, M_i the molecular weight of species i, N_i the number of moles of species i, and the summation extends over all the species. For a continuous distribution:

$$\bar{M}_n = \int MX(M)dM \qquad \text{(VIII.50)}$$

The number average molecular weight is clearly equal to the total weight of polymer divided by the total number of moles of polymer molecules.

In calculating the weight average molecular weight, the molecular weight of each species is weighted by the weight fraction of this particular species which occurs in the polydisperse system, so that:

$$\bar{M}_w = \sum_i W_i M_i = \frac{\sum N_i M_i^2}{\sum N_i M_i} \qquad \text{(VIII.51)}$$

where W_i is the weight fraction of species i, and N_i and M_i have the same definition as before. The weight average for a continuous distribution is defined by:

$$\bar{M}_w = \int MW(M)dM \qquad \text{(VIII.52)}$$

To indicate the types of molecular weight averages obtained by various physical measurements, let us suppose that a certain property P_i of a solution containing a monodisperse solution was related to the molecular weight M_i and to the weight concentration c_i by the formula:

$$P_i = KM_i^a c_i \qquad \text{(VIII.53)}$$

For a polydisperse system, the physical property measured is:

$$P = \sum P_i = \sum KM_i^a c_i \qquad \text{(VIII.54)}$$

The average molecular weight that one would measure using this physical property in a polydisperse system is:

$$\bar{M}_p = \left[\frac{P}{K\sum c_i}\right]^{1/a} = \left[\frac{\sum c_i M_i^a}{\sum c_i}\right]^{1/a} \qquad \text{(VIII.55)}$$

Inasmuch as the weight concentration c_i is proportional to $N_i M_i$, where N_i is the number of moles of species i, and M_i the molecular weight of species i, equation (VIII.55) can be rewritten as:

$$\bar{M}_p = \left[\frac{\sum N_i M_i^{a+1}}{\sum N_i M_i}\right]^{1/a} \qquad \text{(VIII.56)}$$

In the case of turbidity measurements, $a = 1$, so that the average molecular weight is a weight average molecular weight; for osmotic pressure or freezing point depression measurements, $a = -1$, so that these colligative properties measure a number average molecular weight. For the case of viscosity measurements of linear macromolecules, a often lies between 0.5 and 1.0, so that the viscosity average molecular weight lies somewhere between the number average and the weight average.[38]

H. SWELLING OF POLYMERS

The swelling of polymeric materials by liquids is a common property of all polymers. However, two cases are of particular importance: the swelling of three-dimensional polymers, such as cross-linked rubbers,

[38] P. J. Flory, *J. Am. Chem. Soc.*, **65**, 372 (1943).

polystyrene cross-linked with divinyl benzene, or wool; and the swelling of crystalline polymers, such as cellulose.

The swelling of cross-linked rubbers proceeds rapidly at first and then more slowly, with no completely well-defined limiting value. Scott[39] showed that it was possible to divide the process of swelling into two fairly definite processes, an initial rapid swelling followed by a secondary swelling which he termed the increment and which proceeds at an approximately constant rate. If the swelling is carried out *in vacuo*, no swelling increment is observed and a true swelling equilibrium is reached. This verifies the correctness of Scott's hypothesis that a primary chemical bond rupture is the cause of the swelling increment.

Gee[40,41] studied the swelling of vulcanized rubbers in a wide variety of solvents. By plotting the imbibition ϕ (cubic centimeters of liquid per cubic centimeter of swollen rubber) as a function of the cohesive energy density (c.e.d.) of the solvents, he found that these curves look approximately like Gaussian error curves (Fig. VIII-4) and that a maximum swelling was attained at a given value of the c.e.d. This value was taken to be the value of the c.e.d. of the rubber. The difference of extent of swelling of the rubber in various liquids was presumed due to the heat of mixing, which is taken to be zero at the point of maximum swelling. Gee[40,41] and particularly Salomon[42] emphasized the importance of specific groups in determining the amount of swelling.

Frenkel[43] postulated that the limited swelling of vulcanized rubbers should be treated as an equilibrium between the osmotic forces of the solvent tending to penetrate the three-dimensional structure and the elastic reaction of the stretched rubber which is due to entropy forces discussed in Chapter X. Flory and Rehner[44] developed an expression for limited swelling in terms of the Flory-Huggins theory of polymer solutions and the statistical theory of rubber elasticity:

$$\ln(1 - \phi_p) + \phi_p + \mu\phi_p^2 + \rho_p V_0 \phi_p^{1/3}/M_c = 0 \qquad \text{(VIII.57)}$$

where ϕ_p is the volume fraction of polymer in the swollen phase, V_0 the molar volume of the solvent, μ the interaction constant discussed previ-

[39] J. R. Scott, *Trans. Inst. Rubber Ind.*, **5**, 95 (1929).

[40] G. Gee, *Trans. Inst. Rubber Ind.*, **18**, 266 (1943).

[41] G. Gee, *Trans. Faraday Soc.*, **18**, 418 (1942).

[42] G. Salomon and G. J. van Amerongen, *J. Polymer Sci.*, **2**, 355 (1947); G. Salomon, *ibid.*, **3**, 173, 776 (1948).

[43] J. Frenkel, *Acta Physicochim. U. R. S. S.*, **9**, 235 (1938).

[44] P. J. Flory and J. Rehner, Jr., *J. Chem. Phys.*, **11**, 521 (1943). Compare P. J. Flory, *ibid.*, **18**, 108 (1950).

ously in this chapter, ρ_p the polymer density, and M_c the molecular weight between cross links in the rubber.

Scott and Magat[45] have applied these equations to a wide variety of synthetic rubbers in a wide variety of solvents. Doty[46] applied equation (VIII.57) as a means of obtaining μ values for plasticizers of polyvinyl chloride.

The swelling of partially crystalline substances such as cellulose are less well understood. A wide variety of swelling isotherms for cellulose in water have been given. Among the most recent theories is one by White and Eyring,[47] in which the Brunauer-Emmett-Teller method for adsorption is combined with the statistical theory of swelling.

[45] R. L. Scott and M. Magat, *J. Polymer Sci.*, **4**, 555 (1949).
[46] P. M. Doty and H. S. Zable, *J. Polymer Sci.*, **1**, 90 (1946).
[47] H. White and H. Eyring, *J. Textile Research*, **17**, 523 (1947).

IX. KINEMATICS OF LIQUIDS AND SOLUTIONS: VISCOSITY, DIFFUSION, AND ULTRACENTRIFUGATION

A. VISCOSITY OF SIMPLE LIQUIDS AND SOLUTIONS

One of the most important properties of the liquid state is the ability to flow; the study of viscosity, which is a measure of resistance to flow, has been of interest in research and industry. In industry the peculiar high viscosity of solutions of high polymers has played an important role in the fashioning of films, filaments, and varnished articles of every kind, and it may be said that in many cases viscosity may constitute one of the most essential criteria of quality for the solutions used industrially. For this reason, many standard technical methods have been devised for measurement of viscosity.[1]

The phenomenon of high viscosity of polymer solutions already aroused scientific interest nearly forty years ago.[2-6] The recent importance of viscosity measurements as a means of determining molecular weights of high polymers was initiated by Staudinger in his book *Die hochmolekularen organischen Verbindungen*.

The coefficient of viscosity which measures resistance to flow, is defined by Newton's equation relating shearing stress to rate of shear:

$$f = \eta \frac{ds}{dt} \qquad \text{(IX.1)}$$

where f is the shearing stress, η the coefficient of viscosity, and ds/dt the

[1] See E. C. Bingham, *Fluidity and Plasticity*, McGraw-Hill, New York, 1922. E. Hatschek, *The Viscosity of Liquids*, London, 1928. G. Barr, *Viscosimetry*, London, 1931. *First and Second Reports on Viscosity and Elasticity*, North-Holland, Amsterdam, 1935 and 1938.

[2] E. Berl, *Z. ges. Schiess- u. Sprengstoffw.*, **5**, 82 (1910).

[3] W. Biltz, *Z. physik. Chem.*, **73**, 481 (1910); **83**, 625, 683 (1913); **91**, 705 (1916).

[4] J. Duclaux, *Compt. rend.*, **152**, 1590 (1911).

[5] W. Ostwald, *Kolloid Z.*, **24**, 7 (1919); **43**, 190 (1927); **49**, 60 (1929).

[6] O. Sackur, *Z. physik. Chem.*, **70**, 477 (1910).

rate of shear. Liquids that obey equation (IX.1) are termed Newtonian liquids, and almost all simple liquids are of this kind, provided the rate of shear is not too high.

Viscometers, which are instruments designed to measure viscosity of liquids, are of three general types. Capillary viscometers are instruments in which the rate of flow of a liquid through a capillary tube is measured. The viscosity is given by the formula:

$$\eta = \frac{\pi a^4 P}{8l(dV/dt)} \tag{IX.2}$$

where a is the radius of the capillary, l is the length of the capillary, P is the driving pressure (dynes/cm.^{2}), and dV/dt is the rate of efflux (cubic centimeters per second).

Recent work on polymer solutions has shown two capillary instruments to be very suitable—the Ostwald-Fenski and the Ubbelholde. For accurate viscosity determinations it is necessary that the length of the capillary be long compared with its bore if equation (IX.2) is utilized. For precise work, kinetic energy corrections must be taken into account. This is usually done by employing the equation:

$$\eta = A\rho t + \frac{B\rho}{t} \tag{IX.3}$$

where ρ is the density of the liquid, t the time of flow, and A and B are constants for a given capillary instrument that can be obtained by a calibration with two standard liquids.

A second type of viscometer is the rotating cylinder or Couette type. The torque required to maintain a constant angular velocity between two concentric cylinders separated by the liquid in question is measured. The viscosity is given by the formula:

$$\eta = \frac{T\delta}{2\pi a^3 l\omega} \tag{IX.4}$$

where T is the torque, l is the length of the cylinder, ω is the angular velocity, a the radius of the inner cylinder, and δ the clearance between cylinders.

Falling ball viscometers in which the rate of fall of a ball through a liquid is measured, have also been utilized. In this case, when a constant velocity of fall is attained, the frictional force given by Stokes' law must balance the force of gravity. Under these conditions:

$$\eta = \frac{2}{9} \frac{gr^2(\rho_b - \rho_0)}{u} \tag{IX.5}$$

where g is the acceleration of gravity, r the radius of the ball, $\rho_b - \rho_0$ the difference of densities of ball and liquid, and u the limiting velocity.

Viscosities of simple liquids decrease with increasing temperature and volume and increase with increasing pressure. At constant pressure the logarithm of viscosity varies nearly linearly with the reciprocal of absolute temperature. At constant temperature, the logarithm of viscosity varies nearly linearly with pressure. Perhaps most significant of all, the viscosity at constant volume is nearly constant over wide ranges of temperature and pressure (Batchinski's rule).

Many attempts have been made to interpret the viscosity of liquids in terms of the molecular structure of the liquid state. Two general approaches have been used, one which emphasizes the similarity between liquid and gas, and another which emphasizes the strong intermolecular forces and dense packing in a liquid and its consequent similarity to the solid. For gases, the kinetic theory satisfactorily explains the observed viscosity as due to a transfer of momentum by collisions between planes of molecules moving with different velocities. This theoretical approach was extended to the case of liquids by van der Waals' and Andrade. On the other hand, Frenkel,[7] Eyring,[8] Barrer,[9] and other authors have regarded flow in liquids as a process in which the molecules moved from one equilibrium position to the next by a process requiring the surmounting of an energy barrier. Eyring derives the following relation for viscosity:

$$\eta = \frac{h}{V} e^{\Delta F_{visc.}/RT} \tag{IX.6}$$

where V is the volume of the flowing unit, and $\Delta F_{visc.}$ is the free energy of activation for viscous flow, and h is Planck's constant.

For many liquids, excepting metals, the free energy of activation for viscous flow turns out to be the heat of vaporization divided by 2.45. Eyring states that most of the free energy of activation for viscous flow is essential to create a "hole" in the liquid for the molecule to move into, the size of these holes being smaller than the size of the molecules. The fact that the "empty space" of the liquid is of fundamental importance in determining viscosity is shown by the following empirical equation:[10]

$$\frac{1}{\eta} = \Phi = \text{const.} \ (V - V_s') \tag{IX.7}$$

[7] I. Frenkel, *Kinetic Theory of Liquids*, Oxford Univ. Press, London, 1946.

[8] H. Eyring, *J. Chem. Phys.*, **4**, 283 (1936).

[9] R. Barrer *Trans. Faraday Soc.*, **39**, 48, 59, 237 (1943).

[10] A. Batschinski, *Z. physik. Chem.*, **84**, 643 (1913).

where Φ, the fluidity (reciprocal of viscosity), is taken as proportional to the volume of the liquid minus a constant volume V_s', which is found to be slightly larger than the volume of the solid.

The following theoretical formulas have also been proposed for the viscosity of liquids:

Van der Waals':

$$\eta = 0.355 \; n^2 d^4 m \sqrt{\frac{2kT}{m}} \; \frac{v}{v-b} \exp\left(-\epsilon/kT\right) \qquad (IX.8)$$

where n, d, m = concentration, diameter, and mass of the molecules, respectively; ϵ = energy difference between the average energy of a molecule and the energy at the moment of collision; v = volume; and b = covolume or excluded volume.

Andrade's formula for viscosity:

$$\eta = 1.33 m v n^{1/3} \qquad (IX.9)$$

where ν, the characteristic frequency, is obtained at the melting point by Lindemann's formula:

$$\nu = const. \left[\frac{T_s}{M V_s^{2/3}}\right]^{1/2} \qquad (IX.10)$$

where T_s = melting temperature; M = molecular weight; V_s = molar volume. At melting point, inserting (IX.10) into (IX.9) we obtain:

Andrade's[11] viscosity formula at melting point:

$$\eta = 5.1 \times 10^{-4} M^{1/2} T_s^{1/2} V_s^{-2/3} \qquad (IX.11)$$

Herzog and Kudar's[12] formula for viscosity:

$$\eta = 7.67 \times 10^{-5} \frac{T_s^{1/2} v_s^{1/3}}{M^{1/6}(v-b)} \qquad (IX.12)$$

where v_s = specific volume at the melting point. Many other viscosity formulas of equal merit have been proposed by Frenkel,[13] Born and Green,[14] and others.

The theory of liquid viscosity is in a relatively incomplete state, although the theories developed up to the present shed much light on the problem. A unification of the "transfer of momentum" theories and "activation" theories are much to be desired as is also a more complete understanding of the fact that equations (IX.6) and (IX.7) are simultaneously good approximation laws for variation of viscosity with temperature.

[11] E. N. daC. Andrade, *Phil. Mag.*, **17**, 497 (1934).
[12] Herzog and Kudar, *Z. Physik*, **80**, 217 (1933); **83**, 28 (1933).
[13] I. Frenkel, *Kinetic Theory of Liquids*, Oxford Univ. Press, London, 1946.
[14] M. Born and H. Green, *Proc. Roy. Soc.*, **A 190**, 455 (1947).

These questions will be finally resolved only when the theory of the liquid state is further advanced.

For simple liquid mixtures, various proposals have been made to obtain an expression for the viscosity of the mixture in terms of the viscosities of the liquid components. Eyring, Roseveare, and Powell[15] state that the best law seems to be the following proposed by Kendall:[16]

$$\ln \eta_{mix.} = x_1 \ln n_1 + x_2 \ln n_2 \qquad (IX.13)$$

where $\eta_{mix.}$ is the viscosity of the mixture, and x_1, η_1, x_2, and η_2 are the mole fraction and viscosities of the liquid components 1 and 2, respectively. This law amounts to an averaging of the free energy of activation for viscous flow. This seems reasonable in terms of the activation-hole model for liquid flow.

In the field of colloidal and polymer solutions an entirely different type of viscosity law for the solutions is required. In these cases the contribution of the colloidal or polymer molecules to the solution viscosity have a geometric and hydrodynamic origin.

Because of this, one of the most characteristic features of high polymer chain molecules is the abnormally high viscosity of their solutions. Because of the essential simplicity of viscosity measurements, it is the most widely used of all physical chemical methods for the study and characterization of high polymers.

B. EINSTEIN'S LAW FOR VISCOSITY OF COLLOIDAL SUSPENSIONS

For very dilute suspensions of rigid spherical particles that are wet by the solvent and are large compared to the discontinuities of the solvent but small compared to the dimensions of the instrument used for measuring viscosity, Einstein[17] showed that the viscosity η of the suspension relative to that of the solvent η_0 is a linear function of the volume fraction ϕ and is independent of the particle size, as is shown in the following equation:

$$\eta/\eta_0 = \eta_r = 1 + 2.5\phi \qquad \text{or} \qquad \eta_r - 1 = \eta_{sp} = 2.5\phi \qquad (IX.14)$$

where η_{sp} is the so-called specific viscosity and η_r the relative viscosity.

In the field of the viscosity of colloidal suspensions it was necessary to extend the results of Einstein to account for the case of other nonspherical shapes (such as rods, plates) and also to extend the results to higher con-

[15] H. Eyring, W. E. Roseveare, and R. Powell, *Ind. Eng. Chem.*, **33**, 430 (1941).

[16] Kendall, *Medd. Vetenskapsakad. Nobelinst.*, **2**, 25 (1913).

[17] A. Einstein, *Ann. Physik*, **19**, 289 (1906); **34**, 591 (1911).

centrations. Guth, Gold, and Simha[18] derived the following expression ex
tending Einstein's equation to more concentrated solutions:*

$$\eta = \eta_0[1 + 2.5\phi + 14.1\phi^2 + \ldots] \qquad\qquad (IX.15)$$

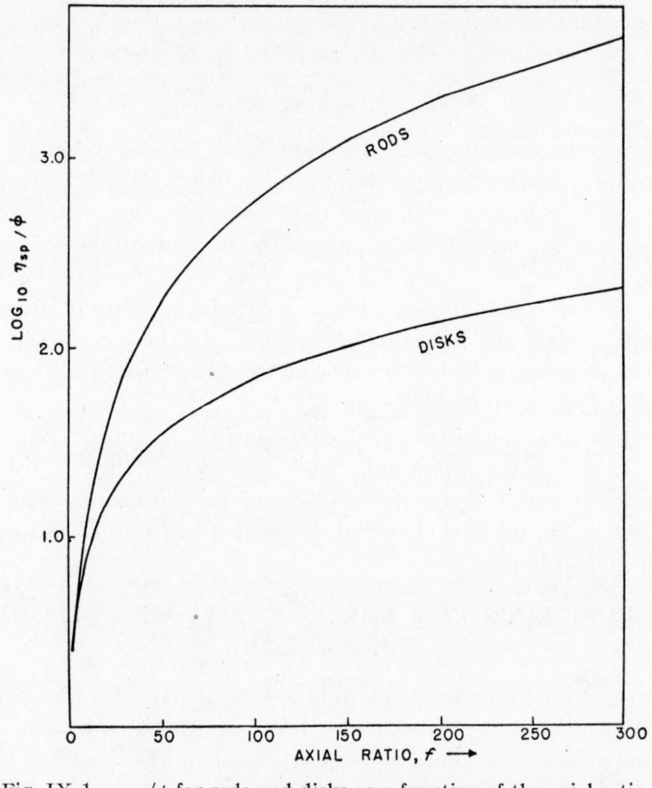

Fig. IX-1. η_{sp}/ϕ for rods and disks as a function of the axial ratio.

the results of the Einstein calculation have been variously tested and con
firmed. Bancelin and Sven Oden working with spherical sols of gamboge
and sulfur, and Eirich[19] working with glass spheres and fungi spore verified
the validity of equation (IX.14) for dilute solutions and the approximate
validity of equation (IX.15) for more concentrated solutions.

[18] E. Guth and R. Simha, *Kolloid Z.*, **74**, 266 (1936). O. Gold, *Dissertation*, Vienna
1937.

[19] F. Eirich, *Kolloid Z.*, **74**, 276 (1936); **81**, 7 (1937).

* A recent paper by V. Vand (*J. Phys. & Colloid Chem.*, **52**, 277, 1948) derives the
formula:

$$\eta = \eta_0(1 + 2.5\phi + 7.349\phi^2 + \ldots)$$

Jeffery[20] was the first to work on the problem of extending Einstein's hydrodynamic treatment to nonspherical particles and succeeded in solving the problem for ellipsoids. The problem is complicated by the fact that the answers are different for strong and weak Brownian motion.

For nonspherical particles, subject to strong Brownian movement Simha[21] obtained the relationships (IX.16) and (IX.17) in terms of the axial ratio f for large values of f. The functional relations between axial ratio and η_{sp}/ϕ for rods and disks are shown graphically in Figure IX-1.

For rods:

$$\frac{\eta_{sp}}{\phi} = \frac{f^2}{15(\ln 2f - {}^3\!/_2)} + \frac{f^2}{5(\ln 2f - {}^1\!/_2)} + \frac{14}{15} \qquad \text{(IX.16)}$$

For disks:

$$\frac{\eta_{sp}}{\phi} = \frac{16}{15} \frac{f}{\tan^{-1} f} \qquad \text{(IX.17)}$$

The first of these equations has been shown to be in good agreement with experimental measurements on rodlike particles of known axial ratio. A survey of equations for viscosity of colloidal solutions is given in Table IX-1.

In the case of solutions of high polymer *molecules* (as opposed to colloidal suspension such as sulfur sols and gold sols) it proved very useful to use the concepts of the Einstein equation, in particular to define an intrinsic viscosity by means of the following equation:

$$[\eta] = \left[\frac{\eta_{sp}}{c}\right]_{c \to 0} \qquad \text{(IX.18)}$$

where c is the concentration of the solution. Or alternatively:

$$[\eta] = \left(\frac{\ln \eta_r}{c}\right)_{c \to 0} \qquad \text{(IX.19)}$$

Inasmuch as intrinsic viscosities are at present almost universally calculated with the concentration units expressed as grams per 100 cc. of solution in the United States, it is clear that a solution that obeys the Einstein equation will have an intrinsic viscosity of $0.025\,v$, where v is the specific volume of the solute. The intrinsic viscosities of typical macromolecules, such as chemical cellulose, natural rubber, and polystyrene, are of the order of mag-

---

[20] G. B. Jeffery, *Proc. Roy. Soc. London*, **A102**, 163 (1923).

[21] R. Simha, *J. Phys. Chem.*, **44**, 25 (1940).

TABLE IX-1.   EXPRESSIONS FOR SPECIFIC VISCOSITY OF SOLUTIONS AND SUSPENSIONS[a]

Type of suspension or solution	At extreme dilution		At moderate concentrations
	With complete Brownian movement	Without the influence of Brownian movement	Without Brownian movement
Rigid spheres	Einstein, Simha $2.5\,c$		Gold, Guth and Simha $2.5\,c + 14.1\,c^2$
Liquid (soft) spheres	Taylor $r.c$; with r varying from 2.5 down to 1.		—
Rigid rod-like particles — minimum value	Guth, Huggins, Jeffery $2.0\,c$	Jeffery $2.0\,c$	—
Rigid rod-like particles — maximum value	Huggins, Kuhn $\left(2.5 + \dfrac{f^2}{16}\right)c$ Simha $\left[\dfrac{f^2}{15(\ln 2f - \frac{3}{2})} + \dfrac{f^2}{5(\ln 2f - \frac{1}{2})} + \dfrac{14}{15}\right]c$ Eisenschitz $\dfrac{f^2}{15 \ln 2f - \frac{4.5}{2}}\cdot c$	Jeffery $\left[\dfrac{f}{2\ln 2f - 3} + 2\right]c$ Eisenschitz $\dfrac{1.15\,f}{11 \ln 2f}\cdot c$	Gold and Guth $\left[\dfrac{f}{2\ln 2f - 3} + 2\right]c + \dfrac{kf^3}{(2\ln 2f - 3)^2}\cdot c^2$
Rigid discs — minimum value	Guth $\dfrac{5}{12}\dfrac{f}{\tan^{-1}f}\cdot c$ $\dfrac{16}{15}\dfrac{f}{\tan^{-1}f}\cdot c$	Jeffery $2.06\,c$	—
Rigid discs — maximum value	Guth, Jeffery $\left[\dfrac{4f}{3\tan^{-1}f}\right]^2\cdot c$	Jeffery $\dfrac{4f}{3\tan^{-1}f}\cdot c$	

nitude of one hundred times greater. Obviously, chainlike macromolecules in solution have much more space-filling power than the compact particles of, for example, a gold sol. In addition, the intrinsic viscosities of colloidal sols or of compactly folded spherical molecules, such as the globular proteins that obey Einstein's equation, are independent of the molecular weight or size of the dissolved particles, whereas the intrinsic viscosities of randomly coiled or linearly rigid macromolecules depend markedly on the molecular weight.

Expressed in the customary units (concentration in terms of grams per 100 cc.) the intrinsic viscosity divided by 0.025 is the "hydrodynamic specific volume" of the polymer molecules at infinite dilution. It is therefore to be expected that the intrinsic viscosity will be a measure of the size and shape of the molecule in solution. It is found that *intrinsic* viscosity is not *very* temperature sensitive, particularly when compared to the high temperature dependence of viscosity for liquids. To the extent that the temperature will affect the shape of the molecule in solution, the intrinsic viscosity will change. For example, if at higher temperatures the molecules can overcome their hindering intramolecular potentials and become more or less coiled, then the intrinsic viscosity should change with temperature.

The effect of solvent on the intrinsic viscosity of macromolecules can also be interpreted in terms of the shape of the dissolved solute molecules. In athermal solvents (no heat of mixing) the polymer molecule will assume approximately the same shape that they would have in free space. In poor solvents, the molecules (if flexible) should tend to curl up and the intrinsic viscosity should therefore decrease. Such an effect was observed by Alfrey, Bartovics, and Mark,[22] who showed that the intrinsic viscosity of a polymer solution kept decreasing as nonsolvent was added, until the precipitation point was reached.

It has recently been proposed that the concentration units for c be expressed in grams of solute per cubic centimeter of solution. In these units, the intrinsic viscosity would be one hundred times greater than in the practical units described above, and the intrinsic viscosity divided by 2.5 could be considered the "hydrodynamic volume" of the solute in cubic centimeters per gram.

The concentration units in which c is expressed for determination of intrinsic viscosities have been expressed in various ways in the literature. Staudinger used "base-molar" (*Grundmolar*) concentrations, for which the concentration was expressed in terms of the molar weight of the repeating

[22] T. Alfrey, A. Bartovics, and H. Mark, *J. Am. Chem. Soc.*, **64**, 1557 (1942).

segment of the polymer per liter of solution. For example, in the case of normal paraffins, unit concentration is taken to be 14 grams of paraffin per liter of solution. Meyer and co-workers have used weight per cent of the solute as the unit of concentration. It would obviously be desirable to standardize the use of concentration units, and the present tendency is to use grams per 100 cc. as a practical unit and grams per cc. as a theoretical unit.

C. STAUDINGER'S LAW FOR VISCOSITY OF MACROMOLECULAR SOLUTIONS

Staudinger was among the first to emphasize the importance of viscosity measurements for the determination of molecular weights of high polymer molecules. He postulated that the intrinsic viscosity of a polymer solution was proportional to its molecular weight:

$$[\eta] = KM \tag{IX.20}$$

where K is a constant for a homologous series of polymers of a given molecular structure. In order to evaluate this constant for various polymers, Staudinger obtained absolute molecular weights by cryoscopic and osmotic pressure measurements.

Inasmuch as viscosity measurements are so simple as to be very suitable for routine laboratory and industrial purposes, rather intensive research was initiated to verify or disprove the findings of Staudinger. Also, a rather active controversy started over the theoretical interpretation of the significance of Staudinger's law. Staudinger himself believed that his viscosity law applied to all linear macromolecules and that the linear relation between molecular weight and intrinsic viscosity implied that the molecules were rigid rods in solution. On the other hand, Meyer, Mark, Kuhn, and other workers insisted that many linear macromolecules adopted a randomly kinked configuration in solution. Recent developments in the interpretation of light scattering from polymer solutions and in the hydrodynamic theory of intrinsic viscosity of solutions of chain molecules appear to have resolved this controversy, as discussed in sections D and E.

The experimental work on the verification of Staudinger's law showed that, whereas in certain cases, particularly for fairly low molecular weight polymers, Staudinger's equation fitted the experimental data, in other cases certain modifications of this equation had to be made.

Some very interesting early work designed to test Staudinger's equation was carried out with homologous series of polymers of increasing molecular weight, as for example a series of n-paraffins.[23-25] A table (IX-2) of intrinsic viscosities and the calculated Staudinger constants for some normal paraffins are given from the data of Meyer and van der Wyk. (These authors used solutions of weight concentration 0.886% in CCl_4, and calculated their intrinsic viscosities using weight per cent as concentration units. We have recalculated their Staudinger constants using grams per 100 cc. as the concentration units. (A weight per cent of 0.886 of paraffin in CCl_4 is very closely equal to 1.4 grams per 100 cc. of CCl_4.)

TABLE IX-2

Hydrocarbon	M	$\eta_{sp}{}^a \times 10^4$	$K \times 10^5$
$C_{17}H_{36}$	240.3	190 $\pm$ 5	5.7
$C_{18}H_{38}$	254.3	208 $\pm$ 5	5.9
$C_{19}H_{46}$	268.3	227 $\pm$ 5	6.1
$C_{22}H_{46}$	310.3	289 $\pm$ 4	6.7
$C_{26}H_{54}$	366.4	373 $\pm$ 4	7.3
$C_{30}H_{62}$	422.5	449 $\pm$ 4	7.6
$C_{34}H_{70}$	478.5	520 $\pm$ 4	7.8

^{a} Weight concentration = 0.886%.

Two empirical equations deserve special mention:[26-29]

$$[\eta] = KM + a \qquad (IX.21)$$

$$[\eta] = KM^a \qquad (IX.22)$$

The second of these relations in particular was found to apply to many polymers over quite wide ranges of molecular weight. The constant a appearing in this equation will be shown to have as theoretical lower and upper limits the values of 0.5 and 2.0. Experiments showed that the values of a actually obtained did indeed have this range of values. A value of approximately 0.66 was very often found for linear flexible molecules. In

[23] H. Staudinger and R. Nodzu, Ber., 63, 721 (1930). H. Staudinger and E. Ochiai, Z. physik. Chem., A158, 51 (1931). H. Staudinger and F. Staiger, Ber., 68, 707 (1935).
[24] K. Meyer and van der Wyk, Helv. Chim. Acta, 18, 1067 (1935); J. chim. phys., 32, 549 (1935); Kolloid Z., 76, 278 (1936); Ber., 69, 545 (1936); Helv. Chim. Acta, 19, 218 (1936).
[25] G. W. Nederbragt, and J. W. M. Boelhouwer, Physica, 13, 305, (1947).
[26] R. Fordyce and H. Hibbert, J. Am. Chem. Soc., 61, 1905, 1910, 1912 (1939).
[27] H. Mark, Der Feste Körper, Hirzel, Leipzig, 1938, p. 103.
[28] R. Houwink, J. prakt. Chem., 155, 241 (1940).
[29] P. J. Flory, J. Am. Chem. Soc., 65, 372 (1943).

TABLE IX-3. INTRINSIC VISCOSITY–MOLECULAR WEIGHT RELATIONSHIP FOR SEVERAL POLYMERS

Polymer	Solvent	Temp., °C.	Mol. wt. range	$K \times 10^4$	a	Ref.
Amylose*	Ethylenediamine	25	8,000–96,000	0.157	1.25	1
Cellulose acetate	Acetone	25	11,000–130,000	0.19	1.03	2
Cellulose acetate-butyrate	Acetone	25	12,000–210,000	1.37	0.83	3
Cellulose acetate-butyrate	Acetic acid	25	12,000–210,000	1.46	0.83	3
Cellulose acetate-butyrate	Pyridine	25	12,000–210,000	1.33	0.83	3
Cellulose nitrate	Acetone	27	15,000–400,000	0.38	1.0	4
Nylon*	90% formic acid	25	5,000–25,000	11.0	0.72	4
Poly-ε-aminocaprolactam*	40% H_2SO_4	—	400–5,000	23.9	0.51	5
Polyvinyl acetate	Acetone	20	43,000–640,000	2.76	0.66	6
Polystyrene*	Benzene	30	10,000–600,000	1.7	0.72	7
Polystyrene (prepared at 60° C.)	Toluene	30	550,000–2,050,000	1.6	0.69	8
Polymethyl methacrylate	Chloroform	20	56,000–980,000	0.49	0.82	9
Polydimethylsiloxane	Toluene	25	2,500–150,000	2.00	0.66	10
Polyisobutylene	Benzene, cyclohexane	20	5,600–1,300,000	3.60	0.64	11
Natural rubber	Toluene	25	40,000–1,500,000	5.02	0.667	12
GR-S	Toluene	30	25,000–920,000	5.4	0.66	13
GR-S	Toluene	30	25,000–500,000	5.25	0.667	14
Polybutadiene (Na-polymerized)	Toluene	25	60,000–800,000	11.0	0.62	15
Neoprene	Toluene	25	40,000–1,500,000	5.0	0.615	15
Buna N	Toluene	25	25,000–380,000	4.9	0.64	15
Buna N	Acetone	25	25,000–100,000	5.0	0.64	15
Buna N	Chloroform	25	25,000–100,000	5.4	0.68	15
Buna N	Benzene	25	25,000–100,000	1.3	0.55	15

* Measurements made on unfractionated samples. Number-average molecular weight was used in equation (IX.22).

1. J. F. Foster and R. M. Hixon, J. Am. Chem. Soc., 66, 557 (1944).
2. A. M. Sookne and M. Harris, Ind. Eng. Chem., 37, 475 (1945).
3. J. W. Tamblyn, D. R. Morey and R. H. Wagner, Ind. Eng. Chem., 37, 573 (1945).
4. E. Husemann and G. V. Schulz, Z. physik. Chem., B52, 1 (1942). M. L. Huggins, Ind. Eng. Chem., 35, 980 (1943).
5. G. B. Taylor, J. Am. Chem. Soc., 69, 633 (1947).
6. H. Matthes, J. prakt. Chem., 162, 245 (1943).
7. H. Staudinger and H. Warth, J. prakt. Chem., 155, 261 (1940).
8. R. A. Gregg and F. R. Mayo, J. Am. Chem. Soc., 70, 2373 (1948).
9. T. Alfrey, A. Bartovics and H. Mark, J. Am. Chem. Soc., 65, 2319 (1943).
10. J. H. Baxendale, S. Bywater and M. G. Evans, J. Polymer Sci., 1, 237 (1946).
11. A. J. Barry, J. Applied Phys., 17, 1020 (1946).
12. P. J. Flory, J. Am. Chem. Soc., 65, 372 (1943).
13. W. C. Carter, R. L. Scott and M. Magat, J. Am. Chem. Soc., 68, 1480 (1946).
14. D. M. French and R. H. Ewart, Anal. Chem., 19, 165 (1947).
15. R. L. Scott, W. C. Carter and M. Magat, J. Am. Chem. Soc., 71, 220 (1949).

Table IX-3 is presented the constants K and a that have been used for relating viscosity to molecular weight according to equation (IX.22).

D. THEORY OF VISCOSITY FOR THE FREE-DRAINING LINEAR MOLECULE

Kuhn[30] was the first to obtain a hydrodynamic solution to the problem of the viscosity of dumbell molecules and linearly rigid "pearl necklace" molecules in solution. Huggins[31] extended Kuhn's method[30] to treat the case of the randomly coiled molecule and was the first to derive Staudinger's law. Hermans,[32] Kuhn,[33] and Kramers[34] have also solved this problem, and Debye[35] has recently published a very succinct presentation of these treatments which we shall follow below.

The model of the molecule used in these theories is to assume that the molecule consists of a number, $N + 1$, of atomic groups connected to each other by rigid links, the consecutive links making a definite angle with each other (for example, the tetrahedral angle for carbon-carbon links) but able nevertheless to rotate freely around each other around this fixed bond angle. It is assumed that each of these groups is acted upon by a frictional force fv if it is moving relative to a solvent with a velocity v. It is assumed also that there is no interaction between the atomic groups due to their disturbance of the flow lines of the solvent, *i.e.*, we consider the case of the free-draining molecule.

Let us assume that we have a solvent between two parallel plates, the lower one stationary and the upper one moving relative to the lower one with a constant velocity. The velocity distribution of the flowing liquid is therefore as portrayed in Figure IX-2. Let us consider that the lower plane is the xy plane and that a flow gradient α is established so that the velocity of the liquid in the x direction at any point will be:

$$V = \alpha z \qquad (IX.23)$$

A polymer molecule suspended in this liquid will move due to the frictional forces acting on the atomic groups. Inasmuch as there are no external forces acting on the molecule, the center of gravity will move with

[30] W. Kuhn, *Z. physik. Chem.*, **A161**, 1 (1932); *Kolloid Z.*, **62**, 269 (1932).

[31] M. L. Huggins, *J. Phys. Chem.*, **42**, 911 (1938); **43**, 439 (1939); *Applied Phys.*, **10**, 700 (1939).

[32] J. J. Hermans, *Physica*, **10**, 777 (1943).

[33] W. Kuhn and H. Kuhn, *Helv. Chim. Acta*, **26**, 1324 (1943).

[34] H. A. Kramers, *J. Chem. Phys.*, **14**, 415 (1946).

[35] P. Debye, *J. Chem. Phys.*, **14**, 636 (1946).

the velocity of the solvent at the position where the center of gravity of the molecule is momentarily located.

If we consider that each of the atomic groups are momentarily moving with the velocity of the center of gravity (as though the molecule were instantaneously made rigid) then there is a relative velocity between the flowing solvent and the atomic groups. The relative velocity of the liquid with respect to the velocity of the center of gravity of the molecule is shown in Figure IX-3.

Since the frictional force acting on each group is equal to the friction constant, f, times the relative velocity of the solvent with respect to the

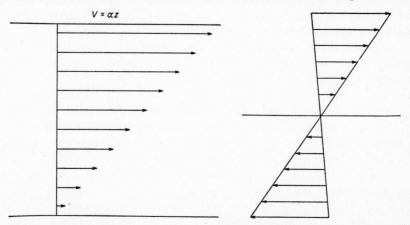

Fig. IX-2. Velocity distribution in flowing liquid.

Fig. IX-3. Relative velocity distribution
in flowing liquid with respect to center
of gravity of one of the solute molecules.

atomic groups, it is obvious from Figure IX-3 that the frictional forces will tend to rotate the molecule as a whole around the y axis through the center of gravity. The angular velocity ω of this rotation must be such that the average moment of force around the center of gravity is zero. It can easily be shown that:

$$\omega = \alpha/2 \qquad (IX.24)$$

where α is the shear gradient.

The frictional energy losses associated with the rotation of the molecule will appear in the form of an enhanced solution viscosity.

If n is the number of molecules per cubic centimeter, the energy losses per second per cubic centimeter due to the rotation of the polymer molecules becomes:

$$W' = \frac{nf\alpha^2}{6} Av \left\langle \sum r^2 \right\rangle \qquad \text{(IX.25)}$$

where f is the friction factor and $Av \left\langle \sum r^2 \right\rangle$ is the average value of the sum of squares of the distance of each atomic group to the center of gravity of the molecule. This extra energy loss due to rotation is equivalent to an increase in the macroscopic viscosity of the medium from η to η'. In a medium of viscosity η the total energy loss per second and per cubic centimeter in a velocity distribution given by equation (IX.23) is equal to:

$$W = \eta\alpha^2 \qquad \text{(IX.26)}$$

inasmuch as α is the rate of shear and η is the shearing stress.

Because of the presence of the polymer molecules and their rotation in the solvent, the medium acts as if its viscosity was increased from η to η' and the energy loss due to the rotation of the polymer molecules is:

$$W' = (\eta' - \eta)\alpha^2 \qquad \text{(IX.27)}$$

Equations (IX.25) and (IX.27) represent the same thing, so that:

$$\eta' - \eta = {}^1/_6 nf Av \left\langle \sum r^2 \right\rangle \qquad \text{(IX.28)}$$

In order to complete the calculation of intrinsic viscosity it is necessary to know the average square of the distance of each of the $N + 1$ groups of the molecule to the center of gravity. If the groups of the molecule are labelled from zero to N, then the average square of the distance from the ν group to the center of gravity in a randomly coiled molecule is:

$$Av \left\langle r_\nu^2 \right\rangle = \frac{1 + p}{1 - p} Na^2 \left[\frac{1}{3} - \frac{\nu}{N} \left(1 - \frac{\nu}{N} \right) \right] \qquad \text{(IX.29)}$$

where a is the length of a link and p is the cosine of the angle between consecutive links ($^1/_3$ for C—C bonds).

The summation appearing in equation (IX.28) can be approximated by an integral, giving:

$$Av \left\langle \sum_0^N r_\nu^2 \right\rangle = \frac{1}{6} \frac{1 + p}{1 - p} N^2 a^2 \qquad \text{(IX.30)}$$

Equation (IX.28) therefore becomes:

$$\eta' - \eta = \frac{1}{36} nf \frac{1 + p}{1 - p} N^2 a^2 \qquad \text{(IX.31)}$$

In order to obtain the value for specific viscosity, we divide $\eta' - \eta$ by η to give:

$$\eta_{sp} = \frac{1}{36} \frac{nf}{\eta} \frac{1+p}{1-p} N^2 a^2 \qquad \text{(IX.32)}$$

The intrinsic viscosity in the ordinary units (deciliters per gram) may be obtained by dividing η_{sp} by the concentration in grams per 100 cc., which is $100\ nNm$, where m is the mass of one group. This gives:

$$[\eta] = \frac{1}{3600} \frac{f/\eta}{m} \frac{1+p}{1-p} Na^2 = \frac{1}{3600} \frac{f/\eta}{m} R_0^2 \qquad \text{(IX.33)}$$

This verifies Staudinger's empirical rule that the intrinsic viscosity is proportional to the molecular weight (or to the number of chain atoms N along the polymer chain). In order to further simplify this expression it is necessary to express the frictional factor f in simpler terms. This can be done by assuming that Stokes' law holds on a molecular scale, and thereby representing each group by an effective atomic sphere of radius ρ. According to Stokes' law, $f = 6\pi\eta\rho$, which when substituted in equation (IX.33) gives:

$$[\eta] = \frac{\pi}{600} \frac{\rho R_0^2}{m} \qquad \text{(IX.34)}$$

where R_0^2 is the mean square distance between chain ends.

It is possible to calculate the intrinsic viscosity of rigid rods by this same method. Starting with equation (IX.28) we shall calculate the average square of the distance from each of the $N + 1$ groups of the molecule to the center of gravity. For a rigid rod the center of gravity is the center atom, and the mean square distance of each atom from the center of gravity is a constant, so that no averaging is necessary:

$$Av \left\langle \sum r_n^2 \right\rangle = 2 \sum_{n=1}^{N/2} r_n^2 = \frac{a^2 N(N+1)(2N+1)}{6} \qquad \text{(IX.35)}$$

Proceeding just as before, we obtain the following formulas for the intrinsic viscosities of rigid rods:

$$[\eta] = \frac{\pi}{1200} \frac{\rho}{m} a^2(N+1)(2N+1) \cong \frac{\pi}{600} \frac{\rho}{m} N^2 a^2 \qquad \text{(IX.36)}$$

$$[\eta] \cong \frac{\pi}{600} \frac{\rho R^2}{m} \qquad \text{(IX.37)}$$

where R is the end-to-end length of the rigid rod.

From these expressions it is clear that the intrinsic viscosity of a rigid rod is proportional to the square of its molecular weight (number of chain atoms along the polymer chain). Also, expressed in terms of the distance between the first and last chain atoms, the formulas for intrinsic viscosity of a random coil and of a rigid rod are the same for the free-draining model.

The free-draining model for intrinsic viscosity of long chain molecules has been given very exact treatment by Kramers,[36] who also considered the intrinsic viscosities of branched molecules of various shapes. These results have been applied by Nederbragt and Boelhouwer[37] to the calculation of the viscosities of aliphatic hydrocarbons of various shapes.

E. INTRINSIC VISCOSITIES OF CHAIN MOLECULES ACCOUNTING FOR HAMPERED FLOW OF SOLVENT THROUGH THE MOLECULE

A chain molecule in solution adopts a more or less randomly kinked shape. Inside of this random coil we have solvent molecules as well as segments of the polymer chains. The solvent outside the molecular coil is free to move unhampered. The solvent within the coil is more or less entrapped, particularly if the density of polymer segments within the coil is high.

Fikentscher and Mark[38] and Kuhn[39] considered that such a swollen molecule must itself act like an Einstein sphere in its effect on increasing the viscosity of the solution. The intrinsic viscosity for a simple molecular model of this kind is:

$$[\eta] = 0.025sv \tag{IX.38}$$

where v is the specific volume of the polymer and s is the swelling factor of the chain molecule in solution. The swelling factor is the ratio of the effective volume of the particle in solution (including trapped or bound solvent) divided by the actual molecular volume. As can be seen from the above equation we can expect that good solvents such as would cause a large swelling of the cross-linked polymer of similar structure will tend to enhance the intrinsic viscosity.

The swelling factor, s, has been estimated in various ways. For a compactly folded molecule the swelling volume is unity (or may be somewhat

[36] H. A. Kramers, *J. Chem. Phys.*, **14**, 415 (1946).
[37] G. W. Nederbragt and J. W. M. Boelhouwer, *Physica*, **13**, 305 (1947).
[38] H. Fikentscher and H. Mark, *Kolloid Z.*, **49**, 185 (1929).
[39] W. Kuhn *Kolloid Z.*, **68**, 2 (1934).

higher due to solvation). For a randomly coiled molecule, the volume of the solvent that is within the molecular coil is proportional to the three-halves power of the molecular weight (or to three-halves power of the number of links in the chain). Inasmuch as the volume of the chain itself is proportional to the molecular weight, the swelling factor, s, is proportional to the square root of the molecular weight.

An equivalent expression for the intrinsic viscosity is:

$$[\eta] = 0.025 \ \Omega/M \tag{IX.39}$$

where Ω is the effective volume of the molecule in solution and M is the mass of the molecule. Kuhn[39] pointed out that the molecular volume of a randomly coiled molecule (including entrapped solvent) should be proportional to the volume of a sphere whose radius was equal to the root mean square distance between the ends of the molecule:

$$\Omega \sim \frac{4}{3} \pi R_0^3 \sim M^{3/2} \tag{IX.40}$$

$$[\eta] \sim M^{1/2}$$

A combination of the free-draining model theory and the entrapped solvent (equivalent Einstein sphere) model was apparently first envisaged by Kuhn and Kuhn.[40] They postulated that the flow lines of the solvent penetrated in part through the molecule, but that the solvent in the interior of the molecule exhibited hampered flow. Solving the hydrodynamic equations of flow partly with the aid of models, they arrived at the following formula for intrinsic viscosity (deciliters per gram).[41]

$$[\eta] = \frac{bR_0^2}{4800M} \frac{N}{-0.05 + 0.12 \log_{10}(R_0^2/L_0 d) + 0.037 L_0/R_0} \tag{IX.41}$$

where L_0 is the maximum end-to-end length of the molecule, N, the number of links, $b = L_0/N$, R_0 the root mean square end-to-end length, d is the thickness of the chain, and M is the mass of the molecule. For large values of N, equation (IX.41) reduces to:

$$[\eta] = 0.0057 \ R_0^3/M \tag{IX.42}$$

which gives an intrinsic viscosity proportional to the square root of the

[40] W. Kuhn and H. Kuhn, *Helv. Chim. Acta*, **26**, 1394 (1943).

[41] W. Kuhn and H. Kuhn, *Helv. Chim. Acta*, **30**, 1233 (1947); *J. Chem. Phys.*, **16**, 838 (1948).

molecular weight. For small values of N, Kuhn showed that formula (IX.41) reduces to Staudinger's law.

A combination of the theories of the intrinsic viscosity for free-draining molecules and the entrapped solvent model was given by Debye,[42] who proposes that the free-flowing solvent penetrates the swollen spherical coil to a certain calculable extent. For low molecular weights the extent of penetration is complete, so the free-draining model is applicable and the intrinsic viscosity is proportional to the molecular weight; for high molecular weights the depth of penetration of the free-flowing solvent into the molecule is small; most of the solvent in the interior of the molecule is trapped and the intrinsic viscosity approaches a square root dependence on molecular weight as in equation (IX.40).

The polymer molecule is assumed to extend, on the average, over a spherical volume of radius R_s, and the density ν of the atomic groups is assumed to be constant. If the total number of atomic groups is N, we have:

$$\frac{4}{3}\pi\nu R_s^3 = N \tag{IX.43}$$

The other important parameter that defines the hydrodynamic properties of the molecule is the length L, which determines the depth into the molecular sphere through which a disturbance of the solvent on the outside can penetrate. This quantity is defined by the equation:

$$\frac{1}{L^2} = \frac{\nu f}{\eta_0} \tag{IX.44}$$

where f is the frictional factor, and η_0 the viscosity of the solvent. Or:

$$L = \left(\frac{\pi}{3}\frac{\eta_0}{f}\right)^{1/2} \frac{R_s^{3/2}}{N^{1/2}} \tag{IX.45}$$

The intrinsic viscosity turns out to be a universal function of R_s/L, the ratio of the radius of the molecular sphere and the length, L, determining the amount of shielding:

$$[\eta] = \frac{\Omega_s}{M}\,\phi(R_s/L) \tag{IX.46}$$

where:

$$\phi(x) = 0.025[1 + (3/x^2) - (3/x)\coth x]/[1 + (10/x^2)\{1 + (3/x^2) -$$
$$(3/x)\coth x\}]$$

[42] P. Debye and A. M. Bueche, *J. Chem. Phys.*, 16, 573 (1948).

and where $\Omega_s = {}^4/_3\pi R_s^3$ is the volume of the sphere occupied by the polymer molecule and M is the mass of polymer molecule.

For small values of R_s/L we approach the behavior of a free draining molecule. The limiting form of ϕ in this case is (if we express $[\eta]$ in deciliters per gram):

$$\phi(R_s/L) = \frac{1}{1000}\left(\frac{R_s}{L}\right)^2 + \cdots \qquad \text{(IX.47)}$$

So that:

$$[\eta] = \frac{1}{1000}\frac{f}{\eta}\frac{R_s^2}{m} \qquad \text{(IX.48)}$$

where m is the mass of a single atomic group. Comparing this formula with the one previously derived, it is seen that according to this theory the effective hydrodynamic radius R_s of the molecular sphere is related to the mean square end-to-end length by the formula:

$$R_s^2 = {}^5/_{18}R_0^2 \qquad \text{(IX.49)}$$

For the other limiting case, where R_s/L is large (i.e., the depth of penetration of the freely flowing solvent into the molecular sphere is small):

$$\phi(R_s/L) = 0.025\left[1 - \frac{3L}{R_s} + \cdots\right] \qquad \text{(IX.50)}$$

which in the limit gives an intrinsic viscosity formula:

$$\eta = 0.025\frac{\Omega_s}{M} = \frac{0.015R_0^3}{M} \qquad \text{(IX.51)}$$

where $\Omega_s = {}^4/_3\pi R_s^3$ is the volume of the molecular sphere, M is the mass of the molecule. Equation (IX.51) is, of course, merely Einstein's equation.

By inspection of equation (IX.45), and remembering that for a coiling molecule $R_s \sim N^{1/2}$, it is clear that the ratio of R_s/L will be small for small values of N (or for low molecular weights), whereas R_s/L will be large for large values of N (or large molecular weights). In other words, for a relatively low degree of polymerization the intrinsic viscosity will be proportional to the molecular weight, and Staudinger's law will apply. For very high molecular weights, the intrinsic viscosity will be proportional to the square root of molecular weight. Debye has shown that for intermediate molecular weights the theoretical form for $\phi(R_s/L)$ gives approximate agreement with the law:

$$[\eta] = KM^a \qquad \text{(IX.52)}$$

where a is between 0.5 and 1.0.

Brinkman[43] has simultaneously derived similar results concerning the viscosity of long chain molecules. He treats the molecule as a cluster of segments through which the solvent can flow, but which act to disturb the flow lines of the solvent.

The description of the flow through the porous molecular mass is in terms of a modification of Darcy's equation for flow through porous media. The flow is described by means of a permeability constant h of the molecular cluster and the solvent viscosity η_0. Assuming that the radius of the cluster is proportional to the square root of the number of links, N, according to the laws of the random chain, Brinkman obtains:

$$[\eta] = 0.025 \, svf_2(N) \qquad \text{(IX.53)}$$

where s is the swelling factor (proportional to $N^{1/2}$), and $f_2(N)$ is a complicated function of the number of links in the chain. Brinkman finds that according to his formula the intrinsic viscosity is approximately given by:

$$[\eta] = KM^{0.71} \qquad \text{(IX.54)}$$

This result is in agreement with many empirically observed molecular weight–viscosity relationships.

Kirkwood and Riseman[44] have also developed a hydrodynamic theory for the intrinsic viscosity of chain molecules, which apparently starts from fewer physical assumptions than the theories previously mentioned. Their final result is:

$$[\eta] = \frac{1}{3600} \frac{f/\eta_0}{m} R_0^2 F(x) \qquad \text{(IX.55)}$$

where f is the frictional coefficient, η_0 the viscosity of the solvent, m the mass per atomic group, and R_0^2 is the mean square distance between ends of the polymer chain. Also:

$$x = fN^{1/2}/\sqrt{6\pi^3} \, \eta_0 b \qquad \text{(IX.56)}$$

where b is defined by $R_0^2 = Nb^2$ and:

$$F(x) = \frac{6}{\pi^2} \sum_{k=1}^{\infty} \frac{1}{k^2(1 + x/\sqrt{k})} \qquad \text{(IX.57)}$$

[43] H. C. Brinkman, *Proc. Amsterdam. Acad.*, **50**, No. 6 (1947); *Applied Scientific Research*, **A1**, 27 (1947).

[44] J. G. Kirkwood and J. Riseman, *J. Chem. Phys.*, **16**, 565 (1948).

The formula of Kirkwood and Riseman also reduces to Staudinger's law for small values of N and to the square root dependence on chain length for large values of N. Values of $F(x)$ are tabulated in the article by Kirkwood and Riseman. The limiting value of $[\eta]$ for large values of the chain length N is:

$$[\eta] = 0.0060 \frac{R_0^3}{M} \tag{IX.58}$$

For small values of N the value of $F(x)$ is unity: in this case equation (IX.55) reduces to the Staudinger-Huggins-Debye value of $[\eta]$ for the free draining model (see equation IX.33). Debye and Bueche have shown that formula (IX.55) agrees fairly closely with (IX.46).

F. EFFECT OF CONCENTRATION ON VISCOSITY OF MACROMOLECULAR SOLUTIONS

The intrinsic viscosity of polymer solutions has been defined in two ways —both of which should give the same result. The definition used in the previous section has been:

$$[\eta] = \left[\frac{\eta_{sp}}{c} \right]_{\lim c \to 0} \tag{IX.59}$$

The other definition suggested by Kraemer[45] is:

$$[\eta] = \left[\frac{\ln \eta_{rel}}{c} \right]_{\lim c \to 0} \tag{IX.60}$$

Both of these expressions have been used in the practical evaluation of the intrinsic viscosities of polymer solutions.

Equation (IX.60) is identical with (IX.59) because, as the concentration approaches zero, η_{rel} approaches unity, so that:

$$\ln \eta_{rel} = \ln[1 + (\eta_{rel} - 1)] \cong \eta_{sp} \tag{IX.61}$$

For practical purposes the utilization of (IX.59) or (IX.60) depends on whether in the region of very dilute solutions a plot of η_{sp}/c vs. c or a plot of $\ln \eta_{rel}/c$ vs. c will be more nearly linear and have a small slope and thus make for easier extrapolation to infinite dilution.

This question leads naturally into the problem of the viscosity of concentrated solutions of high polymers. This problem is a very complicated

[45] E. O. Kraemer, *Ind. Eng. Chem.*, **30**, 1200 (1938).

one from both the theoretical and experimental point of view because in fairly concentrated solutions one encounters non-Newtonian flow and combined elastoviscous behavior.

A great variety of empirical relationships have been proposed to express the relationship between viscosity and concentration. A few of these will be enumerated below:

Arrhenius[46]

$$\ln \eta_{rel} = kc \qquad\qquad (IX.62)$$

Houwink,[47] Bungenberg de Jong, Kruyt, and Lens[48]

$$\ln \eta_{rel} = ac + bc^2 \qquad\qquad (IX.63)$$

Fikentscher and Mark[49]

$$\eta_{sp} = k \frac{bc}{1 - bc} \qquad\qquad (IX.64)$$

Bredée and de Booys[50]

$$\eta_{sp} = Ac + Bc^2 + Cc^3 \qquad\qquad (IX.65)$$

Huggins[51] has recently shown that most of the proposed relationships may be approximated by:

$$\eta_{sp}/c = [\eta] + k'[\eta]^2 c \qquad\qquad (IX.66)$$

This equation is of the same form as an earlier one given by Guth.[52] In this equation k' is a constant depending on the solute-solvent system and on the temperature, but is independent of molecular weight. Spencer and Boyer[53] have shown that the effect of heterogeneity of molecular weight is to increase the value of k'.

Spencer and Williams[54] state that a recent equation proposed by Martin:[55]

[46] S. Arrhenius, Z. physik. Chem., 1, 285 (1887).

[47] R. Houwink, Kolloid Z., 79, 138 (1937).

[48] H. G. Bungenberg de Jong, H. R. Kruyt, and W. Lens, Kolloid-Beihefte, 36, 429 (1932).

[49] H. Fikentscher and H. Mark, Kolloid Z., 49, 135 (1930).

[50] H. L. Bredée and J. de Booys, Kolloid Z., 79, 31, 43 (1937).

[51] M. L. Huggins, J. Am. Chem. Soc., 64, 2716 (1942).

[52] E. Guth, Kolloid Z., 74, 147 (1936); 75, 15 (1936).

[53] R. S. Spencer and R. F. Boyer, Polymer Bull., 1, 129 (1945).

[54] R. S. Spencer and J. L. Williams, J. Colloid Sci., 2, 117 (1947).

[55] A. F. Martin, ACS Meeting, Memphis, April 20–24, 1942.

$$\eta_{sp}/c = [\eta] \exp k' [\eta]c \qquad\qquad (IX.67)$$

appears to fit experimental data up to polymer concentrations of 5% and beyond.

G. VISCOSITY OF POLYELECTROLYTE SOLUTIONS

Polyelectrolytes are long chain molecules in which ions are attached to the chain structure. Such, for example, would be polyacrylic acid and its

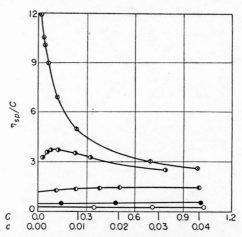

Fig. IX-4.   Viscosity curve for poly-N-n-butyl-4-vinylpyridonium bromide: ⊗, water; ◑, 0.001082 N KBr; ◐, 0.01029 N KBr; ●, 0.1003 N KBr; and O, 1.086 N KBr.[57] Top abcissa, C = grams polyelectrolyte per 100 cc. solution. Bottom abcissa, c = equivalents of bromide per liter exclusive of added potassium bromide.

sodium salts. The viscosity behavior of weak polyacids and their sodium salts was first studied by Staudinger.[56]

The viscosity behavior of strong polyelectrolytes has been the subject of a series of researches by Fuoss and collaborators.[57] Polyvinylpyridine offers an opportunity to prepare a polymer which can be converted readily into a strong polyelectrolyte by addition of alkyl halides or hydrogen chloride. We then have the interesting situation in which every other carbon atom of

[56] H. Staudinger, *Die hochmolecularen, organischen Verbindungen.* Springer, Berlin, 1932.

[57] R. M. Fuoss and U. P. Strauss, *J. Polymer Sci.*, **3**, 246, 602 (1948). R. M. Fuoss, *ibid.*, **3**, 603 (1948).

the chain carries, for example, an alkyl pyridonium group. These ionic groups are thus constrained to remain near each other regardless of the concentration of the solution.

The viscosity curves η_{sp}/c vs. c of polyelectrolytes in water are strongly concave upward, in contrast to the behavior of linear polymers as shown in Figure IX.4. With high concentrations of added simple electrolytes, the η_{sp}/c vs. c plots of polyelectrolytes begin to resemble those of ordinary linear polymers. Oster, Fuoss, and Strauss[58] have suggested that part of the ionic atmosphere of the polyion is carried along with it as a portion of the moving hydrodynamic unit. Therefore, if intrinsic viscosity is a measure of the volume of the polyion, we have:

$$[\eta] = A[R + B/\kappa]^3 \qquad\qquad (IX.68)$$

where A and B are constants, R is the Kuhn radius of the polyion, and κ is the reciprocal Debye-Hückel radius of the ionic atmosphere. Inasmuch as κ is proportional to the square root of the ionic strength, a plot of the cube root of the intrinsic viscosity *versus* the inverse square root of the ionic strength gives a straight line.

An empirical function that fits the data for viscosity of polyelectrolyte solutions is:

$$\frac{\eta_{sp}}{c} = \frac{A}{1 + Bc^{1/2}} + D \qquad\qquad (IX.69)$$

The quantity $A + D$ is the limit approached at zero concentration and is the analog of the intrinsic viscosity of ordinary polymers, which depends on the molecular weight of the polymer. The quantity $Bc^{1/2}$, on the other hand, depends on the electrostatic interactions between polyions and dissociated counterions and hence is a function of the dielectric constant of the solvent.

The mean square distance between chain ends for polyelectrolytes as a function of the electrolyte concentration has been computed by Hermans and Overbeek[58] and by Kuhn.[58] Theoretical expressions for the intrinsic viscosity were also obtained by these authors.

The work on the fundamental physical properties of synthetic polyelectrolytes promises to be of great importance in understanding the complicated behavior of biologically important polyelectrolytes such as proteins.

---

[58] R. M. Fuoss and U. P. Strauss, *J. Polymer Sci.*, **3**, 602 (1948). See also J. J. Hermans and Th. G. Overbeek, *Bull. soc. chim. Belg.*, **57**, 154 (1948), and W. Kuhn, *ibid.*, **57**, 421 (1948).

H. ANOMALOUS FLOW OF LIQUIDS

According to the Hagen-Poiseuille law, the volume of a liquid, V, which flows through a capillary of radius a and length l in time t is given by the expression:

$$V = \frac{\pi}{8\eta} \frac{\Delta P}{l} t a^4 \qquad (IX.70)$$

The amount is thus proportional to the product of the pressure difference and the time of flow. Small pressure differences give, for equal cross sections, long periods of flow; large pressure differences give correspondingly shorter periods. In many liquids (e.g., glycerin and lactic acid) and in numerous solutions (e.g., cane sugar in water), this proportionality between the total amount of liquid flowing through the viscometer and the product $\Delta P t$ is in fact well satisfied over large pressure ranges. Frequently, however, we come across exceptional deviations; for example, in lubricating oils and particularly in solutions of high polymers.

Considering the Hagen-Poiseuille formula we find that departures from the behavior expected from Newton's law can be represented if we substitute for the Newtonian equation relating shearing stress f and rate of shear ds/dt:

$$f = \eta \frac{ds}{dt} \qquad (IX.71)$$

a more general expression which would satisfy experimental facts. Rabinowitsch,[59] Reiner,[60] Weissenberg,[61] Bingham,[62] Eyring,[63] Scott-Blair,[64] and others[65] have contributed to our understanding of the anomalous behavior of viscous liquids. Two types of departure from the normal behavior of a viscous liquid have been observed experimentally and discussed theoretically.

(a) The solution or liquid resembles a solid in having properties of elasticity and rigidity as well as flow properties. The subject of combined viscoelastic behavior will be treated more fully in Chapter X. In par-

[59] B. Rabinowitsch, *Z. physik. Chem.*, **A145**, 1 (1929).

[60] M. Reiner, *Kolloid Z.*, **50**, 199 (1930). *J. Rheol.*, **2**, 337 (1931).

[61] K. Weissenberg, *Kolloid Z.*, **46**, 277 (1928).

[62] E. C. Bingham, *Fluidity and Plasticity*. McGraw-Hill, New York, 1922.

[63] H. Eyring, *J. Chem. Phys.*, **4**, 283 (1936).

[64] G. W. Scott-Blair, *A Survey of General and Applied Rheology*. Pitman, London, 1945.

[65] W. J. Lyons, *J. Chem. Phys.*, **13**, 43 (1945).

ticular, certain systems, such as sols of Al_2O_3, Fe_2O_3, CeO_2, V_2O_5, benzopurpurin, etc., manifest a phenomenon of a yield point which shall be discussed briefly below (equation IX.80).

(b) To express the hydrodynamics of solutions of high polymers it appears necessary to employ instead of the Newtonian expression (equation IX.71) a more general relationship between rate of shear and shearing stress:

$$ds/dt = F(f) \qquad (IX.72)$$

For a wide variety of systems, Bingham[66] found that the observed flow behavior could be described by the equation:

$$f - f_0 = \eta \frac{ds}{dt} \qquad (IX.73)$$

In materials obeying equation (IX.73), f_0 performs the function of a yield point for the liquid exhibiting anomalous flow behavior. Below a shear stress of f_0 the liquid apparently stores up elastic energy and no flow is observed. Only when the shearing stress exceeds the yield point will a velocity gradient and true flow be produced in the material.

Szegvari[67] has shown that the behavior of many inorganic sols (e.g., V_2O_5, Al_2O_5, CeO_2, and Fe_2O_5) and also some dyestuff suspensions can be described by the simple equation (IX.73).

On the other hand, high polymer solutions, even when they exhibit only small elastic effects, will exhibit viscous effects that reduce to Newton's equation for very low shearing stresses but deviate considerably at higher shearing stresses. Reiner,[68] in connection with measurements of Herschel and Bulkly[69] on benzene solutions of rubber, has proposed a law of the form:

$$ds/dt = af + bf^2 - cf^3 \qquad (IX.74)$$

A more general empirical law would of course be a power series expansion:

$$ds/dt = af + bf^2 + cf^3 + df^4 + \ldots \qquad (IX.75)$$

A molecular theory of non-Newtonian flow was developed by Eyring[70]

[66] E. C. Bingham, *Fluidity and Plasticity*, McGraw-Hill, New York, 1922.
[67] A. Szegvari, *Z. physik. Chem.*, **A145**, 1 (1929).
[68] M. Reiner, *Kolloid Z.*, **39**, 80 (1926); **50**, 199 (1930); *J. Rheol.*, **1**, 14 (1929).
[69] W. H. Herschel and R. Bulkley, *Kolloid Z.*, **39**, 291 (1926).
[70] H. Eyring, *J. Chem. Phys.*, **4**, 283 (1936).

based on the concept that a stress gradient within a condensed phase aids the molecules in surmounting the activation energy barriers between equilibrium positions. The relation between rate of shear and shearing stress obtained by this theory is:

$$ds/dt = A \sinh Bf \qquad (\text{IX.76})$$

where A and B are expressible in terms of molecular constants. Application of equation (IX.76) usually results in good agreement with experimental data, but the observed variation of B with experimental conditions has not been definitely explained.[71-73]

I. FREE DIFFUSION OF DISSOLVED PARTICLES

If a soluble substance is placed in a liquid in such a way that it initially occupies only a part of the volume, it will eventually disperse itself uniformly throughout the entire space occupied by the liquid. This phenomenon, which acts independently of gravitation and depends only on the random thermal collisions, is called free diffusion. The fundamental definition of the diffusion constant comes from Fick's law:

$$Q = -D(dc/dx) \qquad (\text{IX.77})$$

where Q is the diffusion current, which is the net amount of material that passes a plane of unit area in unit time, dc/dx is the concentration gradient, and D is the diffusion constant. Fick's law holds only under conditions of high dilution, and in concentrated solutions D may be a function of concentration and concentration gradient.

The importance of measurement of diffusion constant arises in part from the fact that it provides a means of estimating the size of particles in solution.

Einstein[74] showed that the diffusion constant for suspended or dissolved particles could be calculated by the principles of molecular dynamics. He obtained the equation:

$$D = RT/N_{Av.}F \qquad (\text{IX.78})$$

where F is the frictional force acting on a particle that is moving with unit

[71] A. Tobolsky, R. E. Powell, and H. Eyring, in *The Chemistry of Large Molecules.* (Frontiers in Chemistry, Vol. I), Interscience, New York, 1943, pp. 129–190.

[72] J. H. Greenblatt and D. Fensom, *Ind. Eng. Chem.*, **39**, 1037 (1947).

[73] R. S. Spencer and R. E. Dillon, *J. Colloid Sci.*, **3**, 163 (1948).

[74] A. Einstein, *Ann. Physik*, **77**, 549 (1905).

velocity. For a spherical particle, the friction coefficient, F, is given by Stokes' law:

$$F = 6\pi\eta r \qquad (IX.79)$$

where η is the viscosity of the solvent and r is the radius of the spherical particle. By substitution of (IX.79) in (IX.78) we obtain the expression for the diffusion constant of spherical particles:

$$D = \frac{RT}{N_{Av.}} \frac{1}{6\pi\eta r} \qquad (IX.80)$$

The diffusion coefficient has the dimensions of square centimeters per second. By inserting the absolute values of R and $N_{Av.}$ in equation (IX.80) and by assuming a temperature of 300°K. and a viscosity of 0.01 poise (H_2O at 20°) we obtain the very simple relation:

$$Dr \sim 2 \times 10^{-13}$$

The calculation of the diffusion constant of spherical particles arose from a consideration of the phenomenon of Brownian movement. If particles having dimensions of the order of magnitude of 1 μ or less are placed in a liquid, an irregular swarming known as Brownian movement occurs. Einstein postulated that the motion of the suspended particles was acquired by transfer of momentum during collisions with the molecules of the liquid. In other words, the average kinetic energy of translation of the suspended particles in the liquid is given by the equipartition principle:

$$E = \frac{3}{2} \frac{RT}{N_{Av.}} \qquad (IX.81)$$

A particle subject to Brownian movement will pursue a completely random course, but with an average kinetic energy of translation given by equation (IX.81). If at time $t = 0$ the particle started out in the plane $x = 0$, then the probability dW that at a time t the particle will be in a plane between x and $x + dx$ is:

$$dW = \frac{1}{\sqrt{\pi D t}} \exp\left(-x^2/4Dt\right)dx \qquad (IX.82)$$

From equation (IX.82), the mean square displacement $\overline{x^2}$ in the x direction in a time interval t is given by the equation:

$$\overline{x^2} = 2Dt = \frac{2RT}{N_{Av.}F} t \qquad (IX.83)$$

or for spherical particles:

$$\overline{x^2} = \frac{RT}{N_{Av.}} \frac{t}{3\pi\eta r} \qquad \text{(IX.84)}$$

Perrin[75] and coworkers carried out numerous experiments with suspensions of gamboge and mastic in order to test the validity of equation (IX.84). The disperse systems were separated by fractional centrifuging into systems of particles having fairly uniform sizes between 0.2 μ and 12 μ and were therefore visible in an ordinary microscope. Inasmuch as their Brownian motion could be observed under the microscope, and the radius calculated by other methods, it was possible to apply equation (IX.84) to determine experimentally Avogadro's number. A few of Perrin's results are given in Table IX-4.

TABLE IX-4

PERRIN'S DETERMINATION OF AVOGADRO'S NUMBER BY MEASURING
DISPLACEMENTS OF GAMBOGE PARTICLES

Radius, μ	T	Viscosity	t, sec.	R.m.s. displacement, μ	$N_{Av.}$ $\times 10^{-23}$ (calc.)
0.212	290	0.011	30	7.09	6.5
0.212	290	0.011	60	10.65	5.8
0.212	290	0.011	90	11.31	7.7

Given a large number of particles, in a very dilute suspension, each one of them moves independently under the influence of the thermal impacts of the molecules of the liquid. The particles travel around in the containing vessel, each according to the probability distribution (IX.82). Eventually, each one of them will have occupied all the volume elements of the liquid, remaining, on the average, equally long in each. If the observed particles were at first confined in a given space, they will disperse in the course of time and finally spread uniformly through the whole volume at their disposal.

The measurement of diffusion coefficients has been summarized by Ul mann,[76] Lehner and Smith,[77] Valkó,[78] and Geddes.[79] Absolute measure

[75] J. Perrin, *Kolloid-Beihefte*, **1**, 221 (1910).

[76] M. Ulmann, *Molekulgrossenbestimmung hochpolymer Naturstoffe.* Steinkopff Dresden, 1936, pp. 80 ff.

[77] S. Lehner and J. E. Smith, *Colloid Symposium Monograph*, **13**, 65 (1936).

[78] E. Valkó, *Die kolloidchemischen Grundlagen der Textilchemie.* Berlin, 1937.

[79] A. L. Geddes, in A. Weissberger, ed., *Physical Methods of Organic Chemistry*, Par I. 2nd ed., Interscience, 1949.

ments of diffusivity involve the principle that diffusion takes place through a continuous medium, the diffusing material at the beginning of the experiment being distributed homogeneously on one side of a sharp initial interface. In an idealized experimental setup, a solution containing the particles whose diffusion is the subject of investigation is placed in a tube and separated from the pure solvent by a partition. The partition must then be rapidly removed without causing turbulence. The concentration changes at various points along the tube are noted, and from these data the

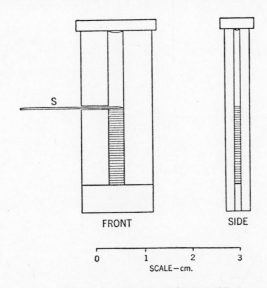

Fig. IX-5. The Fürth-Nistler diffusion cell.

diffusion coefficient is calculated. Such an experimental setup was devised by Nistler[80] and improved by Lamm[81] (Fig. IX-5).

Diffusion coefficients can also be calculated during observations with the ultracentrifuge by observing the spreading of the sedimentation meniscus as discussed in the next section.

If the mass of a nonspherical particle is known, measurement of the diffusion coefficient can be used to obtain an estimation of the shape of the particle. The molecular friction coefficient is defined as:

$$F = RT/N_{Av}.D \qquad (IX.85)$$

[80] A. Nistler, *Kolloidchem.-Beihefte*, **28**, 296 (1929).
[81] O. Lamm, *Arkiv Kemi, Mineral. Geol.*, **B17**, No. 13 (1943).

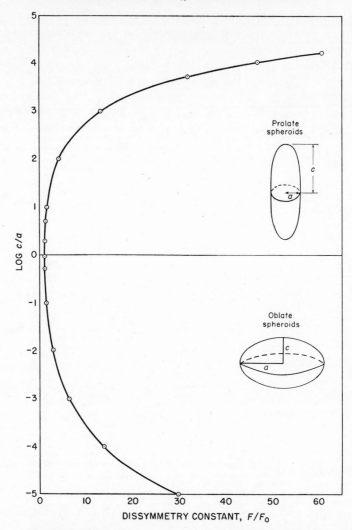

Fig. IX-6.   Dissymmetry constant as a function of axial ratio.

The friction coefficient, F_0, of a sphere of equal mass m and density ρ can be calculated by the formula:

$$F_0 = 6\pi\eta r \qquad (IX.86)$$

where:

$$^4/_3\pi r^3 = m/\rho$$

The ratio of F/F_0 is known as the dissymmetry constant. Perrin[82] and Herzog and coworkers[83] have given formulas for the dissymmetry coefficients in terms of the axial ratios which are plotted in Figure IX-6.

Mehl, Oncley, and Simha[84] have compared the results of diffusion measurements and viscosity measurements (using formula IX.16) in obtaining the axial ratio of various protein molecules (Table IX-5).

TABLE IX-5

COMPARISON OF AXIS RATIOS f AS DETERMINED BY DIFFUSION AND VISCOSITY

Protein	f calc. from Diffusion Experiments	Viscosity Measurements
Egg albumin	3.8	5.0
Serum albumin	5.0	5.6
Hemoglobin	3.7	4.6
Amadin	5.4	6.0
Octopus hemocyanin	7.2	7.3
Gliadin	10.9	10.5
Homarus hemocyanin	5.2	5.5
Helix pomatia hemocyanin	4.8	5.5
Serum globulin	7.6	7.3
Thyroglobulin	7.8	7.(
Lactglobulin	5.2	5.1
Pepsin	2.5	4.(

The diffusion constants for linear macromolecules are less fully elucidated. Simha[85] has shown that if the intrinsic viscosity–molecular weight relation is expressible by the formula:

$$[\eta] = KM^a \qquad (IX.87)$$

then the diffusion constant will have the formula:

$$D = K'M^{-(1/3+0.27a)} \qquad (IX.88)$$

Kuhn and Kuhn[86] have discussed the diffusion constants of linear randomly coiled macromolecules in terms of the free-draining model, the complete immobilization model, and the hampered flow model as discussed in our sections on viscosity. They showed that:

[82] E. Perrin, *J. Phys. Radium*, **7**, 1 (1936).
[83] R. O. Herzog, R. Illig, and H. Kudar, *Z. physik. Chem.*, **A167**, 329 (1933).
[84] J. W. Mehl, J. L. Oncley, and R. Simha, *Science*, **92**, 132 (1940).
[85] R. Simha, *J. Chem. Phys.*, **13**, 188 (1945).
[86] W. Kuhn and H. Kuhn, *Helv. Chim. Acta*, **26**, 1394 (1943).

$$D \sim M^{-1} \qquad \text{(free draining model)}$$
$$D \sim M^{-0.5} \qquad \text{(complete immobilization)}$$

Debye and Bueche[87] have given a theory for the diffusion constant and friction constant of dissolved macromolecules. If a polymer molecule is dragged through a liquid with a velocity v, a force Fv will have to be applied. The friction constant, F, for the entire macromolecule should be contrasted to the friction constant, f, for the atomic spheres. The diffusion constant, D, follows from Einstein's relation:

$$D = RT/N_{Av}.F \qquad \text{(IX.89)}$$

For the friction constant, F, Debye and Bueche find:

$$F = 6\pi\eta R_s \psi(\sigma) \qquad \text{(IX.90)}$$

$$\sigma = R_s/L$$

$$\psi(\sigma) = \frac{1 - (1/\sigma) \tanh \sigma}{1 + (^3/_2\sigma^2)[1 - (^1/\sigma) \tanh \sigma]} \qquad \text{(IX.91)}$$

where the symbols have the same meaning as in section E, namely, R_s is the radius of the equivalent sphere, and L is the shielding length defined by equations (IX.43), (IX.45) and (IX.49). For low shielding (low degrees of polymerization):

$$F = Nf \qquad \text{(IX.92)}$$

For high degrees of shielding (large degrees of polymerization):

$$F = 6\pi\eta R_s \qquad \text{(IX.93)}$$

Kirkwood and Riseman have also obtained expressions for the friction constant, F, of a dissolved linear macromolecule.

$$F = (Nf)/[1 + Nf/(3\pi/128)^{1/2}6\pi\eta_0 R_0] \qquad \text{(IX.94)}$$

where f is the friction constant for the atomic groups, N the degree of polymerization, η_0 the viscosity of the solvent, and R_0 the root mean square end-to-end length of the molecule. The diffusion constant may of course be obtained from Einstein's relation (equation IX.89).

J. APPLICATION OF HIGH CENTRIFUGAL FIELDS

Ultracentrifugal methods provide a powerful tool for investigation of solutions and suspensions. Svedberg[88] was the first to use high-speed cen-

[87] P. Debye and A. M. Bueche, *J. Chem. Phys.*, 16, 573 (1948).

[88] T. Svedberg, *Chem. Revs.*, 20, 81 (1937). T. Svedberg and K. O. Pedersen, *The Ultracentrifuge*, Clarendon Press, London, 1940.

trifuges for the analysis of colloidal systems and has brought the method to a high state of perfection. The original apparatus has been simplified by various workers.[89-94]

Under suitable conditions, ultracentrifugation provides a means of measuring molecular weight or particle size in solution, and, if the material is not uniform in particle size, the degree of nonuniformity may be defined. Information regarding the aggregation, state of solvation, and size and shape of the particles may also be inferred from ultracentrifuge data. The technique also permits the fractionation by purely mechanical means of mixed macromolecules from the fluids in which they are found. This procedure has been particularly useful in connection with biological fluids, as in the fractionation of various proteins from human and animal blood.

The evaluation of the molecular properties is made possible by measuring: (a) the sedimentation equilibrium; (b) the sedimentation rate; and (c) the coefficient of diffusion.

Two types of ultracentrifugation instruments are generally useful, one for sedimentation equilibrium measurements in which a centrifugal acceleration not larger than $15,000g$ is sufficient, and the other for sedimentation rates in which a ten- to twentyfold greater centrifugal acceleration is required.

The rate of sedimentation is determined by observing the rate of movement of a boundary which separates the solution from the pure solvent. In the majority of cases the color of the solution, its absorption in the ultraviolet, or its refractive index is the means by which the moving boundary is followed.

The centrifugation may be continued until the concentration as a function of the distance from the axis of rotation no longer changes, so that a balance is set up between the centrifuging forces and the thermal diffusion.

Observations with the ultracentrifuge permit the calculation of the true coefficient of diffusion. If the particles are sufficiently small the sedimentation boundary will spread because of diffusion, and from this spreading the coefficient of diffusion can be calculated.

1. Sedimentation Equilibrium

The analysis of sedimentation equilibrium is based on the following thermodynamic equation, which applies when the concentration of each inde-

[89] M. Schlesinger, *Kolloid Z.*, **67**, 135 (1934).
[90] W. J. Elford, *Brit. J. Exptl. Path.*, **17**, 399, 422 (1936).
[91] E. Henriot and E. Huguenard, *J. Phys. Radium*, **8**, 433 (1927).
[92] J. W. McBain, *J. Am. Chem. Soc.*, **57**, 780, 2631 (1935); **59**, 2489 (1937).
[93] J. W. Beams, *Rev. Sci. Instruments*, **6**, 299 (1935).
[94] J. Biscoe, E. G. Pickels, and R. W. G. Wyckoff, *Rev. Sci. Instruments*, **7**, 246 (1936).

pendently variable component of the solution becomes an unchanging function of the distance from the axis of rotation:

$$RT\, d \ln a_i - M_i(1 - v_{xi}\rho_x)\omega^2 x\, dx \qquad \text{(IX.95)}$$

where a_i is the activity of component i with molecular weight M_i and partial specific volume v_{xi}, and ρ_x is the density of the solution at a distance x from the axis of rotation of the rotor revolving with an angular velocity ω.

In order to make possible calculations of the molecular weight from sedimentation equilibrium data, it is necessary to work in sufficiently dilute solutions such that the activity is proportional to the concentration. Under these conditions, equation (IX.95) can be integrated giving:

$$M = \frac{2RT \ln (c/c_0)}{(1 - v\rho)\omega^2(x^2 - x_0^2)} \qquad \text{(IX.96)}$$

where c is the concentration at the distance x from the center of rotation and c_0 is the concentration at a reference point in the solution x_0 centimeters from the rotor center. The concentration may be determined by optical methods such as light absorption. If the molecular weight of the substance in solution or suspension is uniform, than a plot of $\ln c$ vs. x^2 should give a straight line, from whose slope the molecular weight of the dissolved substance may be determined by equation (IX.96).

If the material in solution or suspension is polydisperse with regard to molecular weight, then the $\ln c$ vs. x^2 line is curved in such a way that the slope is greater at the smaller values of x. Methods for obtaining various molecular weight averages from the experimental data have been given by Kraemer.[95]

2. Sedimentation Velocity Methods

In a sufficiently high-speed centrifuge, a dissolved macromolecular material of uniform molecular weight will sediment with a more or less sharp boundary, depending on the amount of thermal diffusion. The rate at which the mean position of the boundary moves depends on the rate of centrifugation and can be determined experimentally. Svedberg defined the "sedimentation constant" s by the equation:

$$s = \frac{dx/dt}{\omega^2 x} = \frac{\ln (x_2/x_1)}{\omega^2(t_2 - t_1)} \qquad \text{(IX.97)}$$

[95] E. O. Kraemer, in Svedberg and Pedersen, *The Ultracentrifuge*. Clarendon Press, London, 1940, pp. 342–353.

where dx/dt is the instantaneous rate of sedimentation at point x, and x_2 and x_1 are the distances of the mean points of the boundary from the center of rotation at times t_2 and t_1. The quantity s has the dimensions of time, and it has been agreed to designate 10^{-13} second—when used to measure sedimentation constants—as one Svedberg unit.

The fundamental equation for calculation of molecular weights from sedimentation rate data is obtained by setting the centrifugal acceleration times the buoyancy-corrected mass of the particle equal to its velocity times the frictional coefficient:

$$\frac{M}{N_{Av.}} (1 - v\rho)\omega^2 x = F \frac{dx}{dt} \qquad \text{(IX.98)}$$

$$M = \frac{N_{Av.}Fs}{1 - v\rho} \qquad \text{(IX.99)}$$

The frictional coefficient is related to the diffusion constant through equation (IX.85). Hence:

$$M = \frac{sRT}{(1 - v\rho)D} \qquad \text{(IX.100)}$$

The diffusion coefficient can be obtained from a separate experiment according to the various devices given in the references to section I. Under suitable conditions, particularly in monodisperse systems, the diffusion coefficient can be obtained from ultracentrifugation data by measuring the rate of spread of the sedimentation boundary. The following equation has been used by Svedberg:

$$\frac{dn}{dz} = \frac{n_1 - n_0}{2\sqrt{\pi D t}} \exp\left(-z^2/4Dt\right) \qquad \text{(IX.101)}$$

where n_1 = refractive index of the solution; n_0 = refractive index of the pure solvent; dn/dz = change of refractive index in the region of the meniscus; and z = distance of the point of measurement from the position of maximum concentration.

In the case which we often encounter—a polydisperse system—the sedimentation boundary is no longer sharp even in the absence of diffusion. In the case of a continuous distribution of molecular weights the boundary between solution and pure solvent is vague, and from its shape at different times one can draw deductions concerning the distribution curves of the particles in the solution. In the case of polydisperse systems, which exhibit only a few and relatively widely differing particle sizes, the individual com-

ponents may be separated deliberately under certain conditions by centrifuging; two or more relatively sharp boundaries are then visible.

If the molecular weight is known from other measurements, (e.g., osmotic pressure data), then equation (IX.99) can be used to obtain the frictional coefficient of the sedimenting particle in terms of the experimentally
measurable sedimentation constant:

$$F = \frac{M(1 - v\rho)}{N_{Av}s} \qquad (IX.102)$$

It is assumed that the frictional coefficient involved in sedimentation is
the same as the frictional coefficient involved in free diffusion studies.
Frictional ratios can then be computed as the actual frictional coefficient
obtained from equation (IX.102) (or from diffusion experiments) divided
by $6\pi\eta r_e$, where η is the viscosity of the solution and r_e is the radius of a
spherical particle with the same mass and density as the particle in question.   The frictional ratio, as discussed in section I, can be used to estimate
particle shapes.

3. Some Results Obtained by the Ultracentrifuge

Although some interesting and important work has been done with linear
macromolecules[96,97] the complication of the field is still very great.   Most

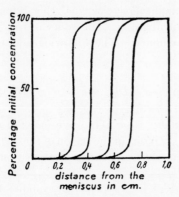

Fig. IX-7. The boundary between solution of sedimenting hemocyanine and pure
solvent, recorded photometrically at four
different positions.

of the very important work with the ultracentrifuge has been accomplished
in the field of globular proteins. As a result of extensive investigations
Svedberg claimed that, for globular proteins having a frictional ratio of

[96] R. Signer and H. Gross, Helv. Chim. Acta., 17, 726 (1934).
[97] E. O. Kraemer and W. H. Lansing, J. Am. Chem. Soc., 55, 4319 (1933).

less than 1.5, the molecular weights appear to be an integral multiple of 17,500, which may indicate a certain basic regularity in arrangement of amino acid groupings. A final decision of this controversial "rule" awaits further experimental evidence.

As an example of the type of data obtained with the ultracentrifuge, Figure IX-7 (Svedberg), shows the photometric registration of the meniscus during four exposures of sedimenting hemocyanine from *Helix pomatia* at pH 5.5 in a centrifugal field of 45,000 g. The separate exposures were made at five minute intervals; the lower part of the cell was filled with solution, the upper with the pure solvent (water). It is immediately evident from

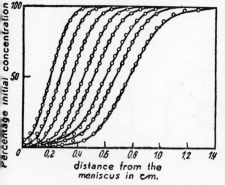

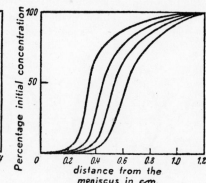

Fig. IX-8. Photometric curves of sedimenting lactalbumin.

Fig. IX-9. Photometric curves of sedimenting tobacco mosaic virus.

the curves that the sedimentation process was very rapid and complete; after about twenty minutes all the protein had been forced to the bottom and the supernatant liquid was quite clear. Further, the meniscus was very sharp, indicating large particles and a uniform degree of dispersion. This case is ideally suited to the application of the velocity and equilibrium method and indicates a monodisperse system with $M = 6,740,000$.

In this connection, the centrifuging of the proteins of tobacco mosaic virus, as well as of α-lactalbumin, may be cited as examples of a hetero-disperse system involving large particles and a homodisperse system involving much smaller ones. For the latter, especially, very intense fields are required for centrifuging, and the apparently vague boundary is to be attributed to the influence of diffusion. Figure IX-8 represents the curves obtained directly by a sedimentation measurement on α-lactalbumin at an acceleration of 310,000 g. Here, there was a period of forty minutes between successive determinations; the value of M was 17,000. The full lines are those obtained experimentally; the points are calculated on the assumption that a homodisperse suspension of the molecular weight indicated above broadens the meniscus by diffusion. It is evident that there is very marked agreement between the points calculated and the curves obtained experimentally. Figure IX-9 relates to tobacco mosaic virus and indicates a high molecular dispersion of heterogeneous character.

K. FLOW BIREFRINGENCE OF LIQUIDS AND SOLUTIONS

Many liquids and solutions which are normally isotropic become doubly refracting when subject to shearing stress. The effect is seen most clearly when the liquid or solution to be studied is placed in the annular space between two concentric cylinders. If the liquid is viewed between crossed

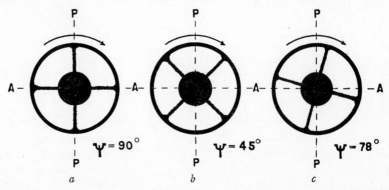

Fig. IX-10. The cross of isocline as it appears in solutions of (a) ovoglobulin, (b) low molecular weight polystyrene, (c) myosin.[98]

nicol prisms or crossed polaroids, it is dark while the liquid is at rest. If one cylinder is now rotated with respect to the other, the liquid flowing in the annular space now appears bright when viewed through crossed nicols, except for a dark 4 armed cross, each arm being 90° from its neighbors. This is known as the "cross of isocline." The position of this cross with respect to the planes of vibration PP and AA, of the light transmitted by the polarizer and analyzer, respectively, is one of the important quantities to be measured in a flow birefringence experiment. The larger of the two angles between the cross of isocline and the planes PP and AA is known as the "angle of isocline," Ψ[98] (see Fig. IX-10).

[98] An excellent review article on streaming birefringence is that of J. T. Edsall, in E. O. Kraemer, ed., *Advances in Colloid Science*, Vol. I. Interscience, New York, 1942. Chapter IX.

The stream lines of the liquid moving between the rotating cylinders are perpendicular to the radii drawn from the center of the inner cylinder. The four arms of the cross of isocline appear in those regions in which the optic axis of the flowing liquid is parallel (or perpendicular) to PP or AA. (The optic axis of any substance is the direction in the substance through which light rays pass without being doubly refracted.)

The angle between the optic axis and the stream lines—the "extinction angle," ψ—is always between $0°$ and $45°$. The extinction angle is the complement of the experimentally measured angle of isocline ($\Psi + \psi = 90°$).

The magnitude of the double refraction is defined as the difference in refractive index between light vibrating parallel to the optic axis and light vibrating perpendicular to the optic axis. The extinction angle and the magnitude of the double refraction as a function of the velocity gradient are the experimental quantities from which the investigator infers the shape of the dissolved particles.

In pure liquids the extinction angle is always $45°$, and the double refraction, $n_e - n_0$, is a linear function of the velocity gradient. In colloidal solutions the extinction angle approaches $45°$ at low velocity gradients, but as the velocity gradient increases the optic axis may approach parallelism with the stream lines.

The theoretical treatment of streaming birefringence presents numerous difficulties. Boeder[99] has considered the problem for the case of thin rods confined to move in a plane. The motion of the rods is defined by a single parameter—the angle ϕ that the rods make with the flow lines.

Let $\rho(\phi)$ define the distribution function, which describes the number of particles whose axes lie between ϕ and $\phi + d\phi$. The tendency of the particles to attain an isotropic distribution due to Brownian motion in the absence of external forces is described by an analog of Fick's law:

$$\frac{dn}{dt} = -\theta \frac{\partial \rho}{\partial \phi} \qquad \text{(IX.103)}$$

where dn is the net number of molecules whose orientation shifts in the time dt across the angle ϕ from lower to higher values, and θ is the so-called rotary diffusion constant.

In the case in which a shearing flow gradient is present the spatial distribution function, $\rho(\phi)$, is determined by the competition between the orienting effect of the flow lines and the disorienting tendencies of the Brownian movement. This competition can be expressed in terms of the parameter

[99] P. Boeder, Z. Physik, 75, 258 (1932).

α, which is equal to the velocity gradient, G, divided by the rotary diffusion constant, θ.

The results of Boeder are a set of theoretical curves for the extinction angle and the double refraction as a function of α. By comparing experimental curves for extinction angle and the double refraction as a function of the measured velocity gradient with Boeder's theoretical curves, a value of the rotary diffusion constant can be obtained.

The rotary diffusion constants obtainable from streaming birefringence data can be related to the sizes and shapes of the dissolved particles. For example, the rotary diffusion constant for spherical particles is related to the radius, r, of the particles and the viscosity, η, of the medium by a formula of Einstein:

$$\theta = \frac{RT}{N_{Av.}} \frac{1}{8\pi\eta r^3} \tag{IX.104}$$

This formula was verified by J. Perrin[100] by direct microscopic observations of spherical colloidal mastic particles which had small colored impurities on their surface, which enabled their rotary motion to be observed.

For nonspherical particles in three-dimensional flow, the solutions can no longer be expressed in terms of a single rotary diffusion constant but rather in terms of a rotary diffusion tensor. The three-dimensional orientation problem has been treated by Peterlin and Stuart.[101] The rotary diffusion constants for ellipsoids of revolution were evaluated by Gans[102] and Perrin.[103]

Experimental studies of flow birefringence have been carried out on several elongated protein molecules, such as rabbit myosin,[104] tobacco mosaic virus[105] (pH 6.8), and fibrinogen,[106] giving lengths of 11,600, 7200, and 1800 Å., respectively. Experimental studies of linear macromolecules have also been carried out,[107,108] but theoretical complications of interpretation are still considerable.

[100] J. Perrin, *Compt. rend.*, **149**, 549 (1909).
[101] A. Peterlin and H. A. Stuart, *Z. Physik*, **112**, 1, 129 (1939).
[102] R. Gans, *Ann. Physik*, **86**, 628 (1928).
[103] F. Perrin, *J. Phys. Radium*, **5**, 497 (1934).
[104] A. I. V. Muralt and J. T. Edsall, *J. Biol. Chem.*, **89**, 315, 351 (1930).
[105] J. W. Mehl, *Cold Spring Harbor Symposia Quant. Biol.*, **6**, 218 (1938).
[106] G. Boehm and R. Signer, *Klin. Wochschr.*, **11**, 599 (1932).
[107] R. Signer and H. Gross, *Z. physik. Chem.*, **A165**, 161 (1933).
[108] A. J. de Rosset, *J. Chem. Phys.*, **9**, 766 (1941).

X. MECHANICAL BEHAVIOR OF HIGH POLYMERS

The physical properties of high polymers are by far their most important attribute from the point of view of their practical utilization. Natural and synthetic polymers are used as lubricating oils, adhesives, waxes, surface coatings, films, rubbers, plastics, papers, and textiles, and in all these cases some physical characteristics of the substance such as viscosity or elasticity are of paramount importance. An understanding of the relationship between the physical properties and molecular structure of polymers is essential to the polymer scientist who desires to synthesize new materials or to modify and process existing polymers.

Perhaps the most striking physical characteristic of polymers compared to the solid state of low molecular compounds is the property of high elasticity. Whereas metals and other structural materials can be elastically deformed for only a fraction of a percent, rubberlike polymers are capable of reversible elastic extensions of several hundred percent. Other important attributes of certain polymers are their plastic flow and delayed elasticity. These phenomena all have a direct interpretation in terms of the structural characteristics of polymers.

A. CONCEPTS OF STRESS AND STRAIN

When matter is subjected to certain geometrical constraints, *e.g.*, when it is confined to a fixed volume, it responds by exerting forces on the bodies imposing the restraints. Or, stated alternatively, when a fixed portion of matter is subjected to external forces under conditions such that inertial motion of the body as a whole is prevented, it responds by a change of shape or dimension. The change in geometrical state of the body is described as the *strain;* the balanced system of forces in the interior of the body is known as the *stress*.

There are three particularly elementary types of strain for isotropic materials for which the stress is simply related to the external forces: simple tension, simple shear, and uniform (hydrostatic) compression. These are illustrated in Figure X-1.

321

The shear strain is defined as the tangent of the angle of shear (for sufficiently low shears, $\tan \gamma = \gamma$); the tensile strain is defined as $\Delta l/l$, where Δl is the increase in length. For uniform (hydrostatic) compressions the strain is defined as $\Delta V/V$, where ΔV is the volume decrease. The strains discussed in this section will be restricted to very small values.

The stresses in a strained substance are defined by calculating the force per unit area exerted by the molecules on one side of a small planar slit upon the molecules on the other side in the limit as the area of the slit ap-

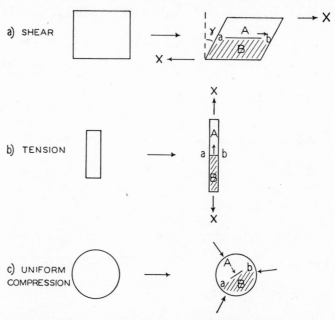

Fig. X-1. Simple shear (a), simple tension (b), and uniform hydrostatic compression (c).

proaches zero. In Figure X-1 we consider the forces exerted by the molecules on side A upon the molecules on side B across the slit ab. At each point of the body such a slit ab may be oriented in an infinite number of directions. Each direction is defined by the normal to the slit, the direction of the normal being taken from side B to side A in Figure X-1. Even at a given point in the body the stress varies with the direction of the normal. The relation existing between the stress vectors and the corresponding normal vectors is best described by tensor calculus.

For simple shear, the stress associated with the slit ab (Fig. X-1) is perpendicular to the normal to *ab*.   For simple tension the stress is in the direction of the normal to *ab* (Fig. X-1).   For hydrostatic compression, the stress is always in the direction opposite to the normal to the slit *ab*, independent of the direction of *ab*.   In these three cases the stresses defined as above are equal to the force per unit area on the surfaces of the body on which they are applied.

The classical theory of elasticity treats ideally elastic solids for which, according to the famous dictum of Hooke, the stress is proportional to the strain.   In the most general case of a nonisotropic body there are six components of stress and six components of strain.   Hooke's law can then be expressed in terms of six linear equations relating each of the components of stress with each of the six components of strain.   For isotropic bodies, on the other hand, these relations are very considerably simplified.   The elastic behavior in these cases can be described in terms of a shear modulus G, a Young's modulus E, a compression or bulk modulus B and the Poisson ratio σ, only two of which are independent.   The Poisson ratio is defined as the ratio between the relative lateral contraction and the relative longitudinal extension in a stretched elastic body.   For substances that do not change in volume upon stretching, the Poisson ratio is equal to 0.5.

The Hooke's law relations for the isotropic elastic solid are:

$$f_\gamma = G\gamma = Gs_\gamma \qquad (\text{X.1})$$

$$f_l = E \ \Delta l/l = Es_l \qquad (\text{X.2})$$

$$f_p = B \ \Delta V/V = Bs_p \qquad (\text{X.3})$$

where f_γ, f_l and f_p refer to the shear stress, tensile stress, and pressure, respectively, and s_γ, s_l and s_p refer to the corresponding strains.   In the subsequent discussion we shall often find it convenient to omit the subscripts when writing the strains and stresses, since in most cases it will be obvious which components are under consideration.

The bulk modulus, Young's modulus and shear modulus are related through the Poisson ratio by the following equations:

$$E = 2(1 + \sigma)G \qquad (\text{X.4})$$

$$B = E/3(1 - 2\sigma) \qquad (\text{X.5})$$

As contrasted to elastic solids, ideal fluids such as liquids or gases will not support fixed shearing strains or tensile strains.   In other words these substances will show no resistance to infinitely slow changes of shape.   They will, however, respond in elastic fashion to changes of volume.   Also, if changes of shape are imposed with a finite velocity, shearing stresses will develop which are proportional to the rate of shear in accordance with Newton's viscosity law:

$$f = \eta \frac{ds}{dt}$$ (X.6)

where η is the coefficient of viscosity.

B. STATISTICAL THERMODYNAMIC TREATMENT OF ELASTIC BEHAVIOR

The thermodynamic equation relating to changes in the state of a body subject only to isotropic expansion and compression is:

$$dE = T\, dS - p\, dV$$ (X.7)

The pressure can thus be considered to consist of an internal energy and an entropy contribution as follows:

$$p = T\, (\partial S/\partial V)_T - (\partial E/\partial V)_T$$ (X.8)

The internal energy contribution to the pressure $(\partial E/\partial V)_T$ is often called the internal pressure. It can be evaluated from the following equation (known as the thermodynamic equation of state):

$$(\partial E/\partial V)_T = T(\partial p/\partial T)_V - p$$ (X.9)

If the pressure at constant volume varies proportionally with the absolute temperature, as in the case of ideal gases, then it is clear from equation (X.9) that the internal pressure is zero. This is equivalent to stating that the pressure of an ideal gas arises only from the entropy term in equation (X.8), that is:

$$p = T(\partial S/\partial V)_T$$ (X.10)

for an ideal gas.

The entropy S and thermodynamic probability W are related by the Boltzmann equation:

$$S = k \ln W$$ (X.11)

For a perfect gas consisting of N particles in a volume V the independent probability of each particle is proportional to the volume. For N independent particles:

$$W = (cV)^N$$ (X.12)

where c is a function of temperature only.

Combining equations (X.10), (X.11), and (X.12) one arrives at the equation of state for ideal gases:

$$p = NkT/V \qquad (X.13)$$

For substances which are subject only to simple tension the thermodynamic equation relating to changes in state is:

$$dE = T\,dS + Z\,dl \qquad (X.14)$$

where Z is the tensile force and l is the length. The tensile force may be regarded as arising from an energy and an entropy contribution.

$$Z = (\partial E/\partial l)_T - T(\partial S/\partial l)_T \qquad (X.15)$$

The internal energy contribution to the tensile force may be evaluated by the equation:

$$(\partial E/\partial l)_T = Z - T(\partial Z/\partial T)_l \qquad (X.16)$$

An extremely significant fact is that solid bodies can be classified into two distinct categories on the basis of equation (X.16). On the one extreme we have crystalline solids with a Young's modulus in the neighborhood of 10^{11} to 10^{12} dyne/cm.^{2} and a very small ultimate elongation. If these materials are extended to a constant length and the temperature is lowered maintaining the same length, there is a continual large rise in stress. This indicates from equation (X.16) that $(\partial E/\partial l)_T$, the energy contribution to the stress, is large and positive. On the other hand we have typical natural and synthetic rubbers with a Young's modulus in the neighborhood of 10^6 to 10^7 dyne/cm.^{2} and a reversible elasticity up to several hundred percent elongation. If these materials are extended to a fixed length within a range of moderately high extensions and the temperature is then lowered maintaining the length constant, the force will fall *proportionally with the absolute temperature*. From equation (X.16) it is clear that in this case the energy contribution to the stress is zero. The retractive force in stretched rubber therefore arises from the decrease in the entropy of the system upon stretching. In molecular terms, this means that the flexible rubber chains have fewer configurations in the stretched state than in the unstretched state. These facts were first elucidated by Meyer,[1] Guth and Mark,[2] and Kuhn[3] and are the basis of the modern theories of rubber elasticity.

[1] K. H. Meyer, G. von Susich, and E. Valkó, *Kolloid Z.*, **59**, 208 (1932).
[2] E. Guth and H. Mark, *Monatsh.*, **65**, 93 (1934).
[3] W. Kuhn, *Kolloid Z.*, **68**, 2 (1934).

Another consequence of the fact that the stress at fixed length is propor tional to the absolute temperature in rubberlike substances is that th temperature will increase in rapid (adiabatic) stretching [*i.e.*, $(\partial T/\partial l)$ is positive]. This is analogous to the rise in temperature during the adia batic compression of ideal gases.

To show how energy and entropy elasticity can be correlated wit molecular properties, we shall discuss two highly idealized models. Firs consider a one-dimensional linear array of $N + 1$ atoms vibrating aroun positions of equilibrium with a lattice distance equal to a_0. For small dis placements of an atom from its equilibrium position we shall assume tha the restoring force is proportional to its displacement from equilibrium:

The equilibrium length, l_0, of the lattice is clearly:

$$l_0 = Na_0$$

If the system is subjected to a homogeneous extension so that the lattic distance is now a, the new length is:

$$l = Na$$

The potential energy, E, of the strained lattice is given by

$$E = \tfrac{1}{2}Nk(a - a_0)^2 \qquad \text{(X.17}$$

where k is the force constant between the atoms. The tensile force on th strained lattice is given by:

$$Z = dE/dl = k(a - a_0) = ka_0(l - l_0)/l_0 \qquad \text{(X.18}$$

For an *idealized* fiber consisting of parallel chains, each one of which be haved in the fashion discussed above, the Young's modulus would be:

$$E = ka_0/A = 4\pi^2 \nu^2 m a_0/A \qquad \text{(X.19}$$

where A is the effective area of each chain (*i.e.*, $1/A$ is the number of chain per unit cross section). The force constant k is related to the vibratio frequency ν and mass m by $k = 4\pi^2 \nu^2 m$.

On the other hand, let us consider a linear one-dimensional chain com posed of N links hinged to one another in such a way that each link ca point either in the positive or in the negative direction. Such a chain ca be represented diagrammatically as follows:

$$+ + - - - + - + - - + -$$

This model is a one-dimensional representation of a flexible rubbe chain. If the length of each link is a_0, and the number of positive components is x, the end-to-end length l of the chain is:

$$l = a_0 |2x - N|$$ (X.20)

For a perfectly flexible chain each possible configuration is assumed to have the same energy. For different end-to-end lengths the energy of the system is therefore the same. However, the number of configurations consistent with a given end-to-end length varies, being a maximum when the end-to-end length is zero. This means the entropy decreases as the end-to-end length increases, which can only be balanced by a force Z on the system equal to:

$$Z = -T(\partial S/\partial l)_T$$ (X.21)

The entropy as a function of length can be calculated by the Boltzmann equation relating entropy to configurational probability P:

$$S = k \ln W$$ (X.22)

The total number of configurations W for a system having x positive components and $N - x$ negative components is:

$$W = N!/[x!(N - x)!]$$ (X.23)

From equations (X.20)–(X.23) one can derive the equation of state:[4]

$$l/Na_0 = \tanh (Za_0/kT)$$ (X.24)

$$Z \sim (kT/Na_0^2)l \quad \text{(for small end-to-end lengths)}$$ (X.25)

Equation (X.25) can be derived by using Stirling's approximation in equation (X.23). It shows that for this system (involving only entropy changes) the force at constant length is proportional to the absolute temperature.

In the above model we may assign an energy ϵ each time successive segments are pointed in opposite directions (*i.e.*, each time a positive component is followed by a negative component or *vice versa*). If ϵ is negative the chains will tend to fold at low temperatures, whereas if ϵ is positive the chains will tend to extend at low temperatures. The equation of state for this one-dimensional model is:[5,6]

---

[4] E. Guth and H. Mark, *Monatsh.*, **65**, 93 (1934). E. Guth and H. James, *J. Chem. Phys.*, **11**, 455 (1943).

[5] E. Guth and H. James, Communication at January 1949 meeting of the American Physical Society at Columbia University.

[6] A. V. Tobolsky and K. W. Scott, included in *Doctoral Thesis* of K. W. Scott, Princeton University, 1949.

$$\sinh\left(Za_0/kT\right) = [t/(1 - t^2)^{1/2}] \exp\left(\epsilon/kT\right) \qquad (X.26)$$

$$t = l/Na_0$$

C. KINETIC THEORY OF ELASTICITY

A true "rubbery" state of matter can be achieved whenever sufficiently flexible linear amorphous polymers are linked together by chemical cross bonds. The amount of cross linkage must be sufficient to tie the original molecules together into a gel structure, but must not be too extensive, so that there is a sufficient length of flexible molecular chain between the cross links. A macroscopic sample of vulcanized rubber may indeed be regarded as a single gigantic network molecule. The portions of the network structure between contiguous cross links are referred to as *network chains*.

Kuhn[7] was the first to give a statistical theory for rubber networks which extended the theory of Guth and Mark[4] for linear chains. This treatment was later amended by Treloar[8] and presents a satisfactory and simple approach to the problem. It is assumed that the distance between the fixed points (cross links) of a network chain is given by the probability distribution function $p(xyz)$ for the random chain:

$$p(xyz) \ dx \ dy \ dz = (b^3/\pi^{3/2}) \exp\left(-b^2(x^2 + y^2 + z^2)\right) dx \ dy \ dz \quad (X.27)$$

Kuhn thereupon introduced the concept of entropy of a single chain by introducing Boltzmann's relation:

$$s(xyz) = k \ln p(xyz) = c_1 - kb^2(x^2 + y^2 + z^2) \qquad (X.28)$$

Before stretching, the radius vectors joining the ends of the network chains are spherically distributed in space. It is assumed that for N_0 network chains, the distribution function $D_0(xyz)$ describing the orientations and magnitudes of these vectors is:

$$D_0(xyz)dx \ dy \ dz = N_0 p(xyz)dx \ dy \ dz \qquad (X.29)$$

The configurational entropy S_0 of the sample of N_0 network chains before stretching is:

$$S_0 = \int_{-\infty}^{\infty}\int_{-\infty}^{\infty}\int_{-\infty}^{\infty} s(xyz) \ D_0(xyz)dx \ dy \ dz \qquad (X.30)$$

If the sample is stretched in the x direction so that its length changes from l_0 to l, and if it is assumed that the volume of the sample remains constant and that the separations of chain ends are changed in the same

---

[7] W. Kuhn, *Kolloid Z.*, **68**, 2 (1934).

[8] L. R. G. Treloar, *Trans. Faraday Soc.*, **40**, 59 (1944).

ratio as the macroscopic dimensions of the sample, the new distribution function $D'(xyz)dx\,dy\,dz$ describing the distance between chain ends is:

$$D'(xyz)dx\,dy\,dz = (N_0b^3/\pi^{3/2})\exp\left(-b^2(x^2/\alpha^2 + \alpha y^2 + \alpha z^2)\right)dx\,dy\,dz$$

$$(\text{X.31})$$

where $\alpha = l/l_0$.

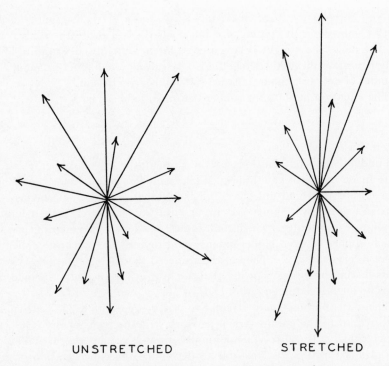

UNSTRETCHED STRETCHED

Fig. X-2. Change in the distribution function of the network chains on stretching.

In other words the distribution function changes from a spherical symmetry to ellipsoidal symmetry (see Fig. X-2). The entropy S' in the strained state is given by:

$$S' = \int\int\int s(xyz)D'(xyz)dx\,dy\,dz \qquad (\text{X.32})$$

From equations (X.27)–(X.32) it follows that:

$$S' - S_0 = -\tfrac{1}{2}N_0k(\alpha^2 + 2/\alpha - 3) \qquad (\text{X.33})$$

The equation of state is derived from the thermodynamic equation:

$$Z = -T(\partial S/\partial l)_T = -(T/l_0)(\partial S/\partial \alpha)_T \qquad (X.34)$$

where Z is the tensile force.

Combining equations (X.33) and (X.34) we arrive at the fundamental equation of rubber elasticity:

$$f = NkT[\alpha - (1/\alpha^2)] = (\rho RT/M_c)[\alpha - (1/\alpha^2)] \qquad (X.35)$$

where f is the stress *based on original cross section*, N is the number of network chains per unit volume of rubber, ρ is the density of the rubber, and M_c the molecular weight between cross links. For initially infinite linear polymer molecules linked together at tetrafunctional juncture points the number of network chains is twice the number of cross links.

The equation of state for rubber deformed in shear is:

$$f = NkT\,\gamma \qquad (X.36)$$

where γ is the shear strain.

Fundamental contributions to the present theory of rubber elasticity were made by Guth and James,[9] Wall,[10] and Flory and Rehner.[11] Equation (X.35) will hold until very high deformations (*e.g.*, 300 percent extension), until crystallinity sets in, or until the chains reach their limit of ultimate extensibility. Guth and James developed an equation of state which applies to even higher extensions, provided there is no complicating effect of crystallinity. They also considered the effect of various types of cross-linking processes showing that a constant "front factor" should perhaps be introduced in equation (X.35).

The most thoroughgoing attempt to verify equation (X.35), particularly with regard to the parameters of network structure, was made by Flory.[12] By vulcanizing Butyl polymer of known initial molecular weight and known initial unsaturation, he was able to determine the concentration of cross linkages and the concentration of effective network chains in his vulcanizates. The equation Flory proposed to account for the finite size of the unvulcanized polymer is:

$$f = (g\rho RT/M_c)[1 - (2M_c/M)][\alpha - (1/\alpha^2)] \qquad (X.37)$$

where M_c is the molecular weight between cross linkages and M the molec-

[9] E. Guth and H. James, *J. Chem. Phys.*, **11**, 455 (1943).

[10] F. T. Wall, *J. Chem. Phys.*, **10**, 132, 485 (1942); **11**, 527 (1943).

[11] P. J. Flory and J. Rehner, *J. Chem. Phys.*, **11**, 512 (1943).

[12] P. J. Flory, *Chem. Revs.*, **35**, 51 (1944). P. J. Flory, N. Rabjohn, and M. C. Shaffer, *J. Polymer Sci.*, **4**, 225 (1949).

ılar weight of the primary molecules. M_c is equal to 1 divided by twice the number of moles of cross links per gram rubber. The factor g (which turned out to be approximately three) was essentially introduced to obtain conformity between theory and experimental values of the stress at $x = 3$. It was suggested that this factor might possibly arise from entanglements of the chain molecules between the network juncture points, which would themselves act as effective cross links.

The birefringence of rubbers subject to tensile stresses was treated by Kuhn[13] and by Treloar[14] on the assumption that the optical anisotropy arises from the same long range configurational changes that cause the entropy decrease treated above. These authors show that for moderate extensions:

$$\frac{\text{stress}}{\text{temperature} \times \text{birefringence}} = \text{constant} \qquad (\text{X}.38)$$

where the constant is related to the optical properties of the segments of the rubber chain. Equation (X.38) can be used as another criterion for rubberlike behavior.

D. CLASSICAL THEORY OF VISCOELASTIC BEHAVIOR

Many substances such as dough, pitch, and tar obviously combine elastic and viscous behavior, *i.e.*, they respond elastically to rapid deformations but will flow if subjected to a steady application of stress. Viscoelastic behavior is in fact characteristic of all substances, but is most especially found in polymers. Attempts to develop a theory of viscoelastic behavior date back to the two renowned physicists, Maxwell and Boltzmann, and the history of this subject is interestingly reviewed by Leaderman[15] and by Alfrey.[16]

The simplest type of viscoelastic behavior was postulated by Maxwell to obey the equation:

$$ds/dt = (1/E)(df/dt) + (1/\tau E)f \qquad (\text{X}.39)$$

where s is a component of strain (*e.g.*, simple tensile strain), f is a component of stress (*e.g.*, tensile stress), E is the elastic modulus, and τ is the so-called relaxation time of the system.

[13] W. Kuhn, *J. Polymer Sci.*, **1**, 380 (1946).

[14] L. R. G. Treloar, *Trans. Faraday Soc.*, **43**, 277, 289 (1947).

[15] H. Leaderman, *Elastic and Creep Properties of Filamentous Materials*. The Textile Foundation, 1943.

[16] T. Alfrey, *Mechanical Behavior of High Polymers*. Interscience, New York, 1948.

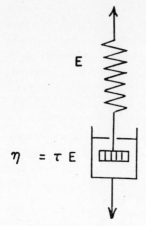

E

$\eta = \tau E$

Fig. X-3. The Maxwell model.

A mechanical model that behaves in the manner defined by equation (X.39) is a spring and dashpot coupled in series, if the elastic constant of the spring is taken as E and the damping constant or viscosity of the dash-pot is taken as τE. This mechanical system is known as the Maxwell model (Fig. X-3).

If a substance that obeys equation (X.39) is rapidly extended to a fixed strain s_0 and maintained at that strain, the stress will decay according to the law:

$$f = s_0 E \exp(-t/\tau) \qquad (X.40)$$

Certain substances exist whose relaxation behavior approximates equation (X.40). In

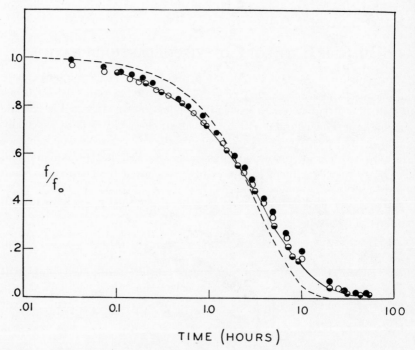

TIME (HOURS)

Fig. X-4. Relaxation of stress in polysulfide rubber H-11 at various elongations, and plot of exp $(-t/\tau)$ at 60°C.: ●, 10% extension; ○, 30% extension; ◖, 50% extension; - - -, exp $(-t/\tau)$ with $\tau = 3$ hrs.

Figure X-4 is shown the *fractional* decay of stress in a typical polysulfide rubber plotted against logarithmic time.   On the same plot is shown the decay function $\exp(-t/\tau)$ with $\tau = 3.0$ hours.   Maxwellian decay of stress when plotted against logarithmic time always shows the same type of behavior as that exhibited in Figure X-4, namely, the major portion of the decay of stress occurs over two cycles of logarithmic time.   In fact the effect of a change in the relaxation time is merely to cause a horizontal displacement of the decay curve along the logarithmic time axis.

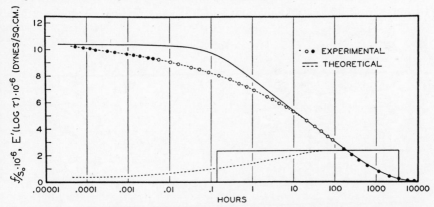

Fig. X-5. Composite relaxation of stress curve at 30°C. for an unfractionated polyisobutylene polymer of viscosity-average molecular weight 6,600,000. Experimental points obtained at 30° are shown as open circles. Solid black circles are extrapolated values calculated by suitable translation along the logarithmic time axis of data obtained at other temperatures. Solid lines indicate box distribution of relaxation times and associated relaxation curve obtained by the graphic method described in the text (see Fig. X-11). Dashed lines indicate actual relaxation curve and relaxation time distribution, which undoubtedly will extend to even shorter times.

Most substances when maintained at constant extension (and constant temperature) do not show a decay of stress that obeys equation (X.39). Instead they generally show a decay of stress that extends over many cycles of logarithmic time. A relatively typical case is given in Figure X-5, where the circled points are experimental data for relaxation of stress in polyisobutylene plotted as f/s_0 vs. log t.

To describe this more general behavior, an extension of the Maxwell theory is required. This can be accomplished by generalizing the Maxwell theory to the consideration of a *distribution* of relaxation times.   The mechanical model that corresponds to the generalized Maxwell theory consists of a parallel arrangement of Maxwell elements (Fig. X-6).

The mathematical formulation of this theory is:

$$ds/dt = [1/E(\tau)][df(\tau)/dt] + [1/\tau E(\tau)]f(\tau) \qquad (X.41)$$

$$f = \int_0^\infty f(\tau)\,d\tau$$

where s is the observed strain, f the observed stress, and $E(\tau)\,d\tau$ the contribution to the modulus of the Maxwell elements whose relaxation times lie between τ and $\tau + d\tau$. The quantities $f(\tau)$ are the partial stresses associated with the relaxation time, τ. Equation (X.41) is of course a continuous set of differential equations which is valid for every value of τ and

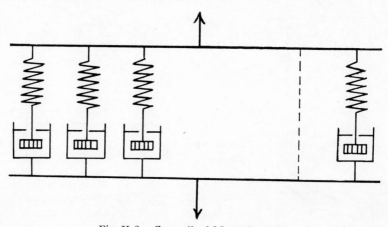

Fig. X-6.   Generalized Maxwell model.

the solution of these equations depends on the knowledge of the distribution function $E(\tau)$, which is called the distribution of relaxation times.

If a substance obeying equations (X.41) is rapidly extended to a fixed strain, s_0, and maintained at that constant strain, the decay of stress with time will be given by:

$$f(t) = s_0 \int_0^\infty E(\tau)e^{-t/\tau}\,d\tau \qquad (X.42)$$

Wiechert proposed the use of a Gaussian distribution of relaxation times to generalize the simple Maxwell theory. Another distribution of relaxation times, used by Becker[17] to describe hysteresis in ferromagnetic behavior, and also discussed by Kuhn and coworkers,[18] in reference to vibrational properties of polymers is:

[17] R. Becker and W. Doring, *Ferromagnetismus*. Springer, Berlin, 1939, page 254.

[18] W. Kuhn, O. Kunzle, and A. Preissmann, *Helv. Chim. Acta*, **30**, 307, 464, 839 (1947).

$$E(\tau) = E_0/\tau \qquad \tau_l < \tau < \tau_m$$

$$E(\tau) = 0 \qquad \tau < \tau_l; \quad \tau > \tau_m \qquad \text{(X.43)}$$

This distribution was applied by Andrews et al.[19] to decay of stress in poly-isobutylene, and the comparison of theory and experiment is shown in Figure X-5. The value of E_0 is very easily calculated from the observed relaxation data. In the region where the relaxation curve is linear when plotted against logarithmic time, E_0 is equal to the negative slope of this straight line divided by 2.303:

$$- (d/d \log t)(f/s_0) = 2.303 \ E_0 \qquad \text{(X.44)}$$

If we are dealing with a system whose largest relaxation time is finite, the stress in a sample maintained at constant extension will approach zero asymptotically after a sufficiently long time. Also, if such a system is subjected to a constant stress f_0, after a sufficiently long time the rate of strain will become constant and will be given by the equation:

$$ds/dt = f_0/ \int_{\tau_l}^{\tau_m} \tau E(\tau) \ d\tau \qquad \text{(X.45)}$$

The over-all viscosity $\bar{\eta}$ of such a system in the case of shear strain is, by comparison with Newton's equation (X.6):

$$\bar{\eta} = \int_{\tau_l}^{\tau_m} \tau G(\tau) \ dt \qquad \text{(X.46)}$$

where we have written $G(\tau)$ rather than $E(\tau)$ to emphasize that here we are dealing with simple shear experiments.

For the distribution of relaxation times given by equation (X.43), the over-all viscosity $\bar{\eta}$ is:

$$\bar{\eta} = G_0(\tau_m - \tau_l) \qquad \text{(X.47)}$$

The generalized Maxwell equations expressed by (X.41) are sufficient to describe the most general type of *linear* viscoelastic behavior.[20] With these equations it is theoretically possible to describe the results of all mechanical experiments such as creep under constant stress, forced and free vibration studies, etc.[21-24] In general, however, the description of

[19] R. D. Andrews, N. Hofman-Bang, and A. V. Tobolsky, *J. Polymer Sci.*, **3**, 669 (1948).

[20] For a complete and general discussion and definition of linear viscoelastic behavior, see T. Alfrey, *Mechanical Behavior of High Polymers*. Interscience, New York, 1948.

[21] R. Simha, *J. Applied Phys.*, **13**, 201 (1942).

[22] B. Gross, *ibid.*, **18**, 212 (1947).

[23] T. Alfrey and P. Doty, *ibid.*, **16**, 700 (1945).

[24] R. Sips, *J. Polymer Sci.*, **5**, 69 (1950).

creep in terms of the generalized Maxwell model and in terms of equations (X.41) is quite difficult. The simplest mechanical model that manifests the phenomena of creep and creep recovery is the so-called Voigt model illustrated in Figure X-7.

The differential equation corresponding to the Voigt model is:

$$f = (1/J)s + (\tau/J)(ds/dt) \tag{X.48}$$

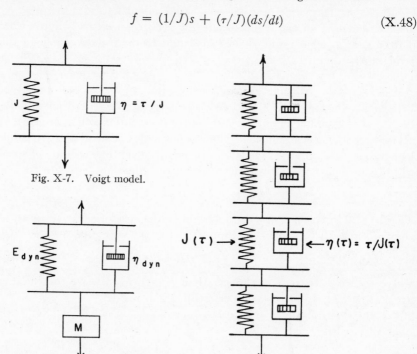

Fig. X-7.   Voigt model.

Fig. X-9.   Voigt model representing vibrational properties.

Fig. X-8.   Generalized Voigt model.

where J is the elastic compliance (*i.e.*, the reciprocal of the modulus) and τ in this case is generally called the retardation time. Creep under constant stress f_0 in this case is given by:

$$s = f_0 J(1 - e^{-t/\tau}) \tag{X.49}$$

No substance has been found as yet that shows the creep behavior predicted by equation (X.49). To treat real creep data, recourse must be had to a generalized Voigt model shown in Figure X-8 in which we deal with a distribution of retardation times.

Mathematically, the generalized Voigt model is formulated as:

$$f = [1/J(\tau)][s(\tau)] + [\tau/J(\tau)][ds(\tau)/dt]$$ (X.50)

$$s = \int_0^\infty s(\tau)\, d\tau$$

For creep under constant stress f_0 we have:

$$s = f_0 \int J(\tau)(1 - e^{-t/\tau})d\tau$$ (X.51)

The mechanical properties of polymers subject to forced or free vibrations of a given frequency are of very considerable interest. In this case the dynamic properties of the polymer at a given frequency are generally represented by an equivalent Voigt model (see Fig. X-9), in which the spring constant $E_{dyn.}$ and the viscosity of the dashpot $\eta_{dyn.}$ are functions of the frequency.

The reason why $E_{dyn.}$ and $\eta_{dyn.}$ are functions of the frequency is that, in reality, the mechanical behavior of the polymer should be described, for example, by a generalized Maxwell model. In terms of the distribution function of the generalized Maxwell model, $E_{dyn.}$ and $\eta_{dyn.}$ are given by:

$$E_{dyn.}(\omega) = \int [\omega^2\tau^2 E(\tau)/(1 + \omega^2\tau^2)]d\tau$$

$$\omega\eta_{dyn.}(\omega) = \int [\omega\tau E(\tau)/(1 + \omega^2\tau^2)]d\tau$$ (X.52)

where ω is the angular frequency of the vibration.

It has been observed that for many polymeric materials the product of the dynamic viscosity and the angular frequency is approximately constant.

Kuhn[25] has discussed this problem in cases where the creep curve of a material can be represented by the equation:

$$s/f_0 = (a + \ln t)/b$$ (X.53)

Kuhn showed that in these cases in a suitable frequency range:

$$\omega\eta_{dyn.} = \pi b/2a^2$$ (X.54)

By use of the distribution function (X.43) Tobolsky and Dunell showed that the correlation between stress relaxation and dynamic properties is remarkably simple, and mathematically even more direct than the correlation between creep data (expressible by equation X.53) and dynamic properties.[26] If the stress relaxation curve f/s_0 is linear when plotted against logarithmic time, the data can be expressed in terms of the distribution function (X.43), where τ_l and τ_m are, respectively, smaller and greater

[25] W. Kuhn, O. Kunzle, and A. Preissmann, *Helv. Chim. Acta*, **30**, 307, 464, 839 (1947).

[26] B. A. Dunell and A. V. Tobolsky, *J. Chem. Phys.*, **17**, 1001 (1949).

than the smallest and largest recorded times. For dynamic experiments in which $1/\tau_m < \omega < 1/\tau_l$, the following very simple relationship exists:

$$\omega\eta_{dyn.} = \pi E_0/2 \qquad (X.55)$$

where $2.303\ E_0$, as mentioned before, is the negative slope of the relaxation curve plotted in the form of f/s_0 vs. $\log t$.

TABLE X-1

CALCULATION OF DYNAMIC LOSSES FROM STRESS RELAXATION DATA

Material	Temp., °C.	$\eta\omega$, dynes/cm.^{2} Calculated	Observed
Hevea (gum stock)	40	0.026×10^6	0.24×10^6
	100	0.045	0.13
Hevea (tread stock^a)	40	0.48	2.5
	100	0.55	1.1
GR-S (gum)	40	0.11	0.85
	100	0.11	0.42
GR-S (tread)	40	1.1	7.8
	100	0.40	3.0
Butaprene (gum)	40	0.17	1.7
	100	0.25	0.70
Butaprene (tread)	40	0.42	4.1
	100	0.40	1.5
Neoprene (gum)	40	0.33	0.85
	100	0.33	0.68
Neoprene (tread)	40	0.82	3.9
	100	0.86	2.0
Nylon	20	0.8×10^9	3.8×10^9
Viscose rayon	20	1.4×10^9	4.8×10^9
Acetate rayon	20	1.2×10^9	1.5×10^9
Feather keratin	20	0.70×10^9	1.5×10^9
Raw silk	20	2.3×10^9	3.8×10^9
Polyethylene	20	0.18×10^9	0.82×10^9

^{a} The tread stocks are vulcanizates into which 50% by weight of carbon black has been incorporated.

This relation was applied to stress relaxation data and dynamic data for rubbers and fibers[27-29] and the predicted values of $\omega\eta_{dyn.}$ were compared with the observed values as shown in Table X-1.[30] In order of magnitude,

[27] A. V. Tobolsky, I. B. Prettyman, and J. H. Dillon, *J. Applied Phys.*, **15**, 309 (1944).
[28] J. H. Dillon, I. B. Prettyman, and G. L. Hall, *ibid.*, **15**, 309 (1944).
[29] B. A. Dunell, *Doctoral Thesis.* Princeton University, 1949.
[30] B. A. Dunell and A. V. Tobolsky, *J. Chem. Phys.*, **17**, 1001 (1949).

agreement exists between the theoretical values obtained from equation (X.55) and the observed values of $\omega\eta_{dyn.}$, but the theoretical values are generally smaller.

E. LINEAR AMORPHOUS POLYMERS

Synthetic linear polymers can be prepared in degrees of polymerization ranging from two to several tens of thousands. In this range their properties vary from those of ordinary liquids, through the viscous liquid stage, and on to the rubbery or the solid plastic stage. In this section we shall discuss only polymers under conditions such that in the unstretched state they show no indication of crystalline scattering in their x-ray diagrams. Also, we shall first restrict ourselves to the higher temperature ranges in which the polymers behave in a "rubbery" rather than a "glassy" fashion. At the end of this section we shall briefly discuss the "glassy" state.

The most characteristic property of linear amorphous polymers in the lower molecular weight range is their viscosity. Studies by Flory[31] of the viscosity of linear polyesters at temperatures above their melting points gave rise to the following relationship:

$$\eta = A e^{BZ_w^{1/2}} e^{\Delta H\ddagger/RT} \qquad (X.56)$$

In the above equation A and B are constants, Z_w is the weight average chain length and $\Delta H\ddagger$ is the heat of activation of viscous flow (which in this case is approximately 8 kcal./mole). Since the heat of activation for viscous flow is independent of molecular weight for chains that contain more than approximately thirty chain atoms, it was suggested[31,32] that the molecular flow must occur by "segmental motion" in which portions of the chains make unitary jumps relatively independently of each other. The effect of chain length would appear to be largely of geometric origin, arising from the obvious fact that the kinetic segments are tied to one another except at the ends of the molecule, and that for flow to occur there must be a certain amount of "cooperation" of the segmental motion.

Studies of the viscosities of a homologous series of polydimethylsiloxanes gave results very similar to those for the molten polyesters.[33] Equation (X.56) was found to apply with somewhat different values of the constants A and B, and number average chain length was used rather than weight average. On the other hand, studies of viscosity as a function of molecular

[31] P. J. Flory, *J. Am. Chem. Soc.*, **62**, 1057 (1940).

[32] W. J. Kauzmann and H. Eyring, *J. Am. Chem. Soc.*, **62**, 3113 (1940).

[33] A. J. Barry, *J. Applied Phys.*, **17**, 1020 (1946).

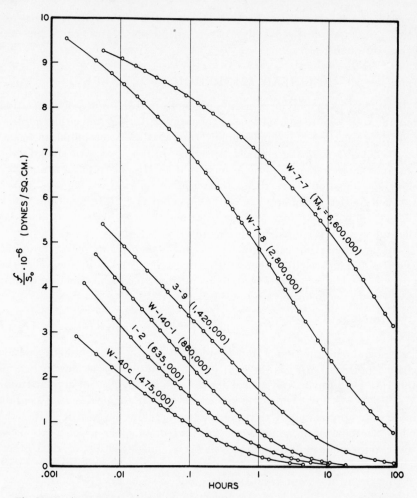

Fig. X-10. Experimental curves for relaxation of stress at constant extension for a series of unfractionated polyisobutylene polymers of different viscosity average molecular weights measured at 30°C.

weight[34] and temperature[34,35] in a series of homologous polyisobutylenes indicate that equation (X.56) does not generally apply over a wide range of molecular weight. Instead, the viscosity can be expressed more generally by the formula:

$$\eta = f(Z)e^{\Delta H\ddagger/RT} \qquad (X.57)$$

[34] T. G. Fox, Jr., and P. J. Flory, *J. Am. Chem. Soc.*, **70**, 2384 (1948).
[35] J. D. Ferry and G. S. Parks, *Physics*, **6**, 356 (1935).

where $f(Z)$ is a function of the chain length which continually increases with Z in a relatively complicated way. For sufficiently large values of Z, the heat of activation for viscous flow is independent of the chain length. Though $\Delta H\ddagger$ is fairly constant over a wide temperature range it begins to increase markedly in the lower temperature ranges.

Although the mechanical behavior of linear amorphous polymers is adequately expressed by a viscosity coefficient in the range of very low molecular weight, for higher chain lengths the elastic properties as well as

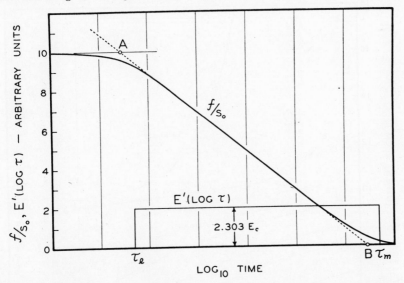

Fig. X-11. Relaxation of stress curve f/s_0, and distribution function E' (log τ), for system characterized by a Becker-Kuhn distribution of relaxation times. Intersection points of characteristic straight line with maximum and zero stress axes are indicated as A and B. τ_l and τ_m are the minimum and maximum relaxation times of the system.

the viscous behavior of these substances must be considered to describe adequately their mechanical behavior. In fact, for sufficiently high molecular weights and in a certain temperature range polyisobutylene behaves almost as an ideally elastic rubber, as will be discussed below.

The viscoelastic properties of high molecular weight polyisobutylene as a function of temperature and molecular weight have been studied by the method of stress relaxation at constant extension.[36] The stress relaxation curves at 30°C. plotted in the form f/s_0 vs. log time for unfractionated polyisobutylenes of a wide range of viscosity average molecular weights

[36] R. D. Andrews, N. Hofman-Bang, and A. V. Tobolsky, *J. Polymer Sci.*, **3**, 669 (1948).

are shown in Figure X-10.   As noted in section D of this chapter, these decay curves can be described approximately in terms of the distribution function:

$$E(\tau) \, d\tau = (E_0/\tau) \, d\tau \qquad \tau_l < \tau < \tau_m$$
$$E(\tau) = 0 \qquad \tau < \tau_l; \quad \tau > \tau_m \qquad (\text{X.58})$$

The constants of this distribution function can easily be related to the experimentally observed relaxation function (f/s_0 $vs.$ $\log t$).   2.303 E_0 is the

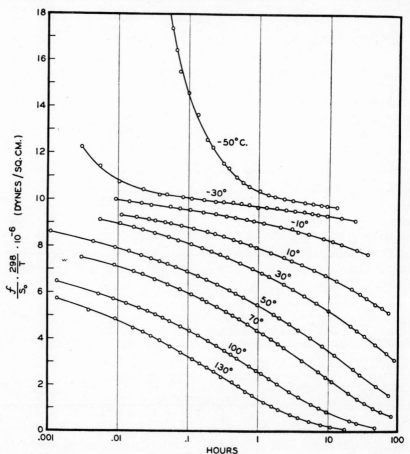

Fig. X-12.   Relaxation of stress for unfractionated polyisobutylene of viscosity-average molecular weight 6,600,000 at a series of temperatures.   Stress is plotted in the form of limiting Hooke's law modulus for small strains "reduced" to 25°C. so as to correct for the kinetic theory effect.

negative slope of the relaxation curve in the range in which it is linear in log time; τ_m is approximately 1.78 times the intercept of the extrapolated straight line portion of the curve on the log time axis, and τ_l is approximately 1.78 times the time at which the extrapolated straight line portion of the relaxation curve attains the "zero time" value of the stress. These relationships are demonstrated in Figure X-11. In the lower molecular weight range the measurements could not be made rapidly enough to obtain the portion of the relaxation curve that corresponds to the approach to the zero time value, and so τ_l could not be defined.

The data obtained for polyisobutylene indicate that, for the fractionated polymers in the "rubbery" range, $E_0 = 1.06 \times 10^6$ dynes/cm.^{2} and is independent of temperature and molecular weight, whereas, for the unfractionated polymers, $E_0 = 0.72 \times 10^6$ dynes/cm.^{2}. Furthermore, in the molecular weight range between 500,000 and 6,000,000, τ_m obeys the equation:

$$\tau_m = 4.5 \times 10^{-26} M^{3.30} e^{14,000/RT} \qquad (X.59)$$

The experimental relaxation curves at various temperatures for a very high molecular weight polyisobutylene are shown in Figure X-12.[37] These are of particular interest because they show that at $-30°$C. one can truly say that an equilibrium stress is attained by this non-cross-linked linear polymer.

If the distribution function (X.58) is truly applicable to this stress relaxation data, the viscosity measured by a shear creep experiment should be, according to equation X.47 (and if $\tau_l \ll \tau_m$):

$$\eta = (E_0/3)\tau_m \qquad (X.60)$$

where the factor 3 is introduced to change from tension to shear, assuming a Poisson ratio of 0.5. The comparison between viscosities calculated in this way and the viscosity data of Fox and Flory[38] is shown in Table X-2.

The stress in a strained sample of polyisobutylene at temperatures above $-30°$C. must arise from an entropy elasticity. This was demonstrated by experimental studies of birefringence during stress decay at constant length.[39] In all cases the relationship:

[37] R. D. Andrews, F. H. Holmes, and A. V. Tobolsky, *J. Polymer Sci.*, *in preparation.*
[38] T. G. Fox, Jr., and P. J. Flory, *J. Am. Chem. Soc.*, **70**, 2384 (1948).
[39] R. S. Stein, *Doctoral Thesis.* Princeton University, 1948. Similar results for unvulcanized natural rubber were found by R. S. Stein and A. V. Tobolsky, *Textile Research J.*, **43**, 302 (1948).

$$\frac{\text{stress}}{\text{temperature} \times \text{birefringence}} = \text{constant} \tag{X.61}$$

was shown to hold even during relaxation in accordance with the predictions of the statistical theories of rubber elasticity and birefringence.

The experimental results appear to indicate that when high molecular weight polyisobutylene is stretched, some portions of the chain structure (perhaps chain entanglements) act as fixed points and that, at least instantaneously, the conditions of the kinetic theory of elasticity are valid. The molecular weight M_c between fixed points as calculated from equation

TABLE X-2

CALCULATION OF BULK VISCOSITY FROM STRESS RELAXATION DATA

T, °C.[a]	M_v[a]	η (poises) (observed[a])	η (poises) calc. for fractions from Eq. (X.60)[b]
−9	80,000	2.58×10^8	0.93×10^8
8	660,000	1.97×10^{10}	2.0×10^{10}
28	660,000	2.04×10^9	3.7×10^9
38	221,000	5.37×10^7	4.7×10^7
78.5	80,000	1.38×10^5	1.2×10^5
112	783,000	2.95×10^7	4.0×10^7
115	1,400,000	2.19×10^8	2.3×10^8
160	660,000	2.95×10^6	3.0×10^6
190	80,000	2.09×10^3	0.98×10^3
217	56,500	330	135
217	115,000	3.39×10^3	1.4×10^3
217	660,000	7.6×10^5	4.5×10^5

[a] Data of Fox and Flory on polyisobutylene fractions.
[b] From a forthcoming paper by R. D. Andrews and A. V. Tobolsky.

(X.35) is 8000 as compared to a value for M_c of approximately 6600 for a soft vulcanized Butyl rubber. In the case of the stretched linear polymer, however, there is a progressive diffusion of the molecular chains back to the original unstrained configurations because of the absence of restraining permanent cross linkages. The diffusion process consists of a segmental flow of the linear polymers, with an activation energy for the segmental "jump" of about 14 kcal. The complicated internal rotations that are possible during this diffusion give rise to a distribution of relaxation times whose upper limit depends on the molecular weight of the molecules. The effect of temperature is merely to displace the entire spectrum of relaxation times by a fixed amount along the log time axis, so that the activation energy of each relaxation time must be the same.

At sufficiently low temperatures all amorphous polymers, linear or cross linked, enter into a state which might be termed the glassy state, which is characterized by the fact that in a relatively narrow temperature range the

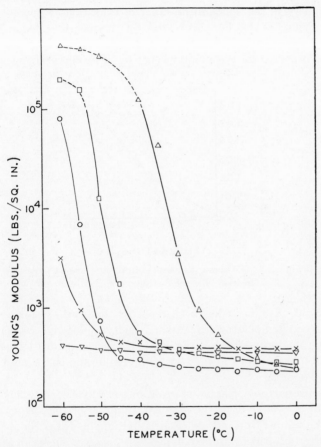

Fig. X-13. Young's modulus *vs.* temperature for various rubber vulcanizates (deflection measured 10 seconds after application of load): O, natural rubber; ∇, polybutadiene; ×, butadiene-styrene 85/15; □, butadiene-styrene 75/25; △, butadiene-styrene 60/40. (After J. W. Liska.)

"instantaneous" modulus of the material may increase by several hundredfold. In this region of transition all properties such as the modulus and the specific volume are, however, very time dependent. Figure X-13 shows a plot of Young's modulus *vs.* temperature in the transition region for several types of rubbers. In this case the modulus was determined by measuring deflection 10 seconds after application of load.

If rapid measurements of specific volume as a function of temperature are made through the transition region, the curves generally show an abrupt change of slope in the temperature range of transition; a good example is shown in Figure X-14. For this reason this temperature region has been called the "apparent second order transition." A table of transition temperatures measured at the point where the V–T curve changes slope is

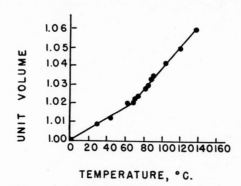

Fig. X-14. Volume *vs.* temperature at "second order transition" for polymethyl methacrylate.[40]

given in Table X-3.[41] It has been reported that if the volume measurements at each temperature are carried out very slowly, so that a true equilibrium is obtained, the apparently abrupt change of slope shown in Figure X-14 disappears and the true V–T equilibrium curve has a continuous change of slope.

The transition to a "glassy" state from the rubbery state has been attributed to a freezing-in of the segmental motion of the long-chain polymers. The temperature at which such freezing-in will occur depends on the structural properties of the polymer, the cohesive energy density being an important factor. Typical rubbers with low glass transition temperatures have low cohesive energy densities. On the other hand, plastics such as polystyrene and polymethyl methacrylate are in their glassy state at room temperature and have relatively high glass transition temperatures as well as high cohesive energy densities. Other structural variables such

[40] H. A. Robinson, R. Ruggy, and E. Slantz, *J. Applied Phys.*, **15**, 343 (1944).

[41] R. F. Boyer and R. S. Spencer, in *Advances in Colloid Science*, Vol. II. Interscience, New York, 1946, page 1.

as chain flexibility, steric effects, and internal plasticization of the chain by side groups also have important influences.

The viscoelastic properties of substances in their glassy state have not been investigated extensively. Stress relaxation curves of polyisobutylene in a range of temperatures approaching the glassy state are shown in Figure X-15.[42] Studies of stress relaxation in polyisobutylenes of different molecular weights and of Butyl rubber indicated that at sufficiently low temperatures the viscoelastic properties are independent of molecular weight and are also practically independent of the presence of cross linkages. The

TABLE X-3

"SECOND-ORDER TRANSITION TEMPERATURES" FOR VARIOUS HIGH POLYMERS

Material	T_m, °C.	Material	T_m, °C.
Polyisobutylene	−74	Polyvinyl chloride	75
Natural rubber	−73	Polyvinylidene chloride	−17
GR-S rubber	−61	Polyacrylic acid	80–95
Hycar OR rubber	−23	Polymethyl acrylate	3
Cellulose nitrate, F-2	52.6	Polymethyl methacrylate	57–68
Cellulose acetate, B-96	68.6	Polyvinyl ethyl ether	−10
Cellulose acetobutyrate, AA-5	49.9	Polyvinyl isobutyl ether	−10
Cellulose acetopropionate, CP-1	38.8	Polystyrene	81
		Polyindene	85
Ethyl cellulose	43	Polyvinyl carbazole	84
Polyvinyl acetate	28	Polyvinyl pyrrolidine	54
Polyvinyl alcohol	85	Glyptal	83–87
		Nylon	47
Polyvinyl partial butyral	50.1	Ebonite	80–85

stress decay curves at low temperatures are of quite different shape from the curves obtained at high temperatures and the apparent activation energy of stress relaxation is very much higher in the glassy state than in the rubbery state.

These results indicate that the instantaneous "modulus" of polymers stretched in their glassy state arises from a shift in short range interatomic distances rather than from the long range configurational changes that occur when these same substances are stretched in their "rubbery" state above the glass transition temperature. The force resisting stretching in the glassy state should probably be regarded as arising from a change in internal energy rather than from a change of entropy. Relaxation of stress is very rapid in the region of transition because only small range atomic movements are required to release distortion. Also, the change of viscoelastic properties with temperature here is not easily described as due to a simple translation of the relaxation time spectrum along the log time axis.

[42] G. M. Brown and A. V. Tobolsky, *J. Polymer Sci.*, *in press*.

An indication that the mechanism of stretching is completely different in the glassy state from that in the rubbery state is obtained by simultaneous measurements of stress and birefringence. The ratio, which is a con-

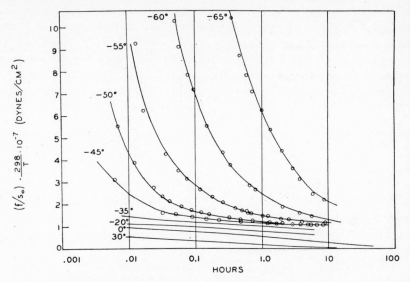

Fig. X-15.   Relaxation of stress at low temperatures for unfractionated polyisobutylene of viscosity-average molecular weight 1,240,000.

stant in the rubbery range of temperature, changes very markedly in the region of the glass transition, there occasionally being a reversal of the sign of this quantity at the transition temperature.[43]

F. CHEMORHEOLOGY

At sufficiently elevated temperatures polymeric materials are subject to chemical reactions that affect their structural properties. The structural changes are reflected in the viscoelastic behavior of these substances. For example, thin strips of natural rubber will show rapid creep under constant load in air at 130°C. because of oxidative scission of the polymeric chains, but the creep can be retarded almost completely if the experiments are carried out *in vacuo* at the same temperature.*

[43] R. S. Stein and A. V. Tobolsky, *Textile Research J.*, 18, 302 (1948).   R. S. Stein, S. Krimm, and A. V. Tobolsky, *ibid.*, 19, 8 (1949).

* The effect of oxygen on stress relaxation and creep was reported by M. Mooney, W. E. Wolstenholme, and D. S. Villars, *J. Applied Phys.*, 15, 324 (1944);   A. V. Tobolsky, I. B. Prettyman, and J. H. Dillon, *ibid.*, 15, 380 (1944);   W. C. Schneider and M. Magat, *Doctoral Thesis* of W. C. Schneider, Princeton University, 1945.

Viscoelastic behavior induced by chemical reaction will be termed "chemorheology." This phenomenon is not readily observed in linear polymers, inasmuch as molecular flow by diffusion is generally much more rapid than relaxation or flow caused by chemical reaction. However, in "infinite" three-dimensional polymers that have no alternate mechanism for flow, the rheological behavior at sufficiently high temperatures is almost always determined by chemical reactions.

The simplest chemorheological behavior is manifested by the polysulfide rubbers[44,45] whose basic structures before vulcanization are:

$$. \ . \ . \ RS_xRS_xRS_xRT$$

where R is a hydrocarbon residue, S_x refers to monosulfide, disulfide, trisulfide, and tetrasulfide linkages that occur statistically distributed along the chains, and T is the terminal linkage (generally an SH or SNa linkage).

In the polysulfide rubbers there is a continuous metathetical interchange of bonds of the following kinds (trisulfide and tetrasulfide linkages are also involved in these interchanges):

$$\begin{array}{c} R-S-S-R \\ + \\ R'-S-S-R' \end{array} \xrightarrow{\text{[cat]}} \begin{array}{c} R-S \quad S-R \\ | + | \\ R'-S \quad S-R' \end{array}$$

$$\begin{array}{c} R-S-S-R \\ + \\ R'-S-H \end{array} \xrightarrow{\text{[cat]}} \begin{array}{c} R-S \quad S-R \\ | + | \\ R'-S \quad H \end{array}$$

$$\begin{array}{c} R-S-S-R \\ + \\ R'-S-Na \end{array} \longrightarrow \begin{array}{c} R-S \quad S-R \\ | + | \\ R'-S \quad Na \end{array}$$

The exchanges may be catalyzed by traces of catalyst left over from the polymerization or the vulcanization. Such interchanges between bonds of adjacent network chains or between a network chain and a terminal group do not affect the over-all structure of the rubber or the physical properties measured by short term experiments. If the rubber were always maintained in an unstressed condition there would be no simple physical means of inferring that these exchanges were occurring. However, if the rubber is stretched to a constant length and maintained at that length, these interchanges will allow the network structure to come to equilibrium with its new strained condition, and so there will occur a relaxation of stress to zero. The situation is analogous (on a different scale of time) to what occurs in liquid flow. It is not immediately obvious that the molecules in a beaker of water are continually exchanging places. This becomes much

[44] M. D. Stern and A. V. Tobolsky, *J. Chem. Phys.*, **14**, 93 (1946).
[45] M. Mochulsky and A. V. Tobolsky, *Ind. Eng. Chem.*, **40**, 2155 (1948).

more apparent if the water is poured into a new shape of container. Just as the water poured from one container to another is identical in its properties, so too is stretched polysulfide rubber which has been allowed to decay to zero stress identical with the original material except for shape.

When the rubber is stretched to a fixed relative length α, the stress at zero time is proportional to the concentration, N, of network chains originally present. If the rubber is maintained at the relative length α, at time t only $N(t)$ of these chains will not have been affected by the metathetical interchanges. We shall assume that at time t the relative stress $f(t)/f(0)$ is equal to $N(t)/N(0)$. The equation defining $N(t)$ is:

$$-[1/N(t)][dN(t)/dt] = n_1 c_2 k' \qquad \text{(X.62)}$$

Where n_1 is the number of linkages along each network chain available for interchange (*e.g.*, the total number of disulfide, trisulfide, and tetrasulfide linkages), c_2 is the concentration of linkages from other chains that take part in the interchange reaction (*e.g.*, the concentration of mercaptan or mercaptide terminals or of some undetermined catalyst), and k' is the specific rate of reaction.

Integration of equation (X.62) gives:

$$f(t)/f(0) = N(t)/N(0) = \exp(-kt) \qquad \text{(X.63)}$$

where $k = n_1 c_2 k'$.

Decay of stress at constant extension in polysulfide rubbers was shown to obey equation (X.63).[44] (See Figure X-4.) The temperature dependence of k follows the Arrhenius equation with an activation energy of approximately 24 kcal./mole. The absolute value of k differs very widely from one type of polysulfide rubber to another and probably depends largely upon the unknown concentration c_2. In this connection it was shown that allowing mercaptans or molecular sulfur to diffuse into the structures caused a tremendous increase in the absolute value of k.[46]

At sufficiently low strains the polysulfide rubbers behave approximately like Maxwell bodies in that they obey equation (X.39). At higher strains, even though the stress decay at constant extension is Maxwellian [*i.e.*, equation (X.63) is obeyed], new viscoelastic equations had to be developed to account for the nonlinearity of the kinetic theory stress-strain law.[47] For example, the creep behavior at high strains deviated markedly from the linear creep predicted by the Maxwell equation (X.39).[48]

[46] M. Mochulsky and A. V. Tobolsky, *Rubber Chem. Tech.*, **22**, 712 (1949).
[47] M. S. Green and A. V. Tobolsky, *J. Chem. Phys.*, **14**, 80 (1946).
[48] P. J. Blatz and A. V. Tobolsky, *J. Chem. Phys.*, **14**, 113 (1946).

Another somewhat more complicated type of chemorheological behavior is common to all rubbers having a hydrocarbon chain backbone. These rubbers are subject to attack by molecular oxygen as are all other organic substances. Among other effects, oxygen produces scission of the network chains as well as cross linking (oxidative vulcanization), both reactions

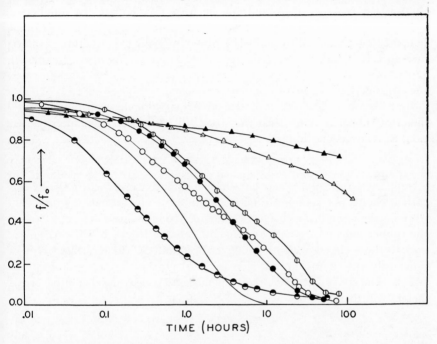

Fig. X-16. Decay of stress for various vulcanized rubbers at 130°C. Data obtained at 50% extension and plotted in the form $f(t)/f(0)$ vs. log time. ◖, neoprene; — natural rubber; O, butyl; ●, buna-N; ◑, buna-S; △, polyester rubber; ▲, polyethylacrylate rubber.

occurring simultaneously. These reactions occur at all temperatures but are quite rapid above 100°C. Inasmuch as the relative rates of these reactions are different in different types of rubber, certain rubbers such as Butyl will tend to soften in air at elevated temperatures, while others such as GR-S tend to harden under the same conditions.

When hydrocarbon rubbers such as natural rubber, GR-S, and neoprene are maintained at constant extension at elevated temperatures, the oxygen of the air causes cross linking and scission at exactly the same rates as if the rubber were unstretched. A fundamental assumption has been that to a first approximation the cross-linking reactions that are occurring do not affect the stress in the stretched sample, but form network structures that are in equilibrium with respect to the strained length of the sample.[49,50] If this be so, then the decay of stress at elevated temperatures occurring in cross-linked rubbers maintained at constant length is a direct measure of the scission reaction alone and can be used to calculate the number of cleavages.[51]   The large differences in rate of stress relaxation at elevated temperatures exhibited by rubbers of different chemical structure is shown in Figure X-16, where relative stress at constant extension vs. log time at 130°C. is shown for several types of rubber vulcanizates.   In all these cases the stress decay is caused by oxidative scission.

If at zero time the number of "effective" network chains per cubic centimeter of rubber is $N(0)$, then the stress $f(0)$ (based on original cross section) at relative length α is:

$$f(0) = N(0)kT[\alpha - (1/\alpha^2)] \qquad (\text{X.64})$$

Suppose that at time t there have been q oxidative cleavages of the hydrocarbon chains per cubic centimeter of rubber. The number $N(q)$ of network chains per cubic centimeter still effective in maintaining the stress in the rubber vulcanizate held at constant relative length α will correspond only to those chains which have never been cut. Cleavages that occur in previously cut chains do not decrease $N(q)$ nor do they cause a decay of stress. The stress f at time t (corresponding to q cleavages per cubic centimeter) will therefore be:

$$f = N(q)kT[\alpha - (1/\alpha^2)] \qquad (\text{X.65})$$

The relation between $N(q)$ and q can be obtained from the equation:

$$-[dN(q)]/[dq] = [N(q)]/[N(0)] \qquad (\text{X.66})$$

which upon integration gives:

$$q = -N(0) \ln (N(q)/N(0)) = -N(0) \ln (f/f(0)) \qquad (\text{X.67})$$

Since $N(0)$ can be determined from equation (X.64) by measuring $f(0)$ and α, and $f/f(0)$ is merely the relative stress decay obtained directly from the stress relaxation curve, the number of cuts per cubic centimeter of rubber can be determined as a function of time. This value of q can be compared to the number of oxygen molecules absorbed per cubic centimeter of

[49] A. V. Tobolsky, I. B. Prettyman, and J. H. Dillon, J. Applied Phys., 15, 380 (1944).
[50] A. V. Tobolsky and R. D. Andrews, J. Chem. Phys., 13, 3 (1945).
[51] A. V. Tobolsky, D. Metz, and R. B. Mesrobian, J. A. C. S., 72, 1942 (1950).

rubber up to that time, which can be measured in a separate apparatus. Experimentally, it turns out that at high temperatures approximately one molecule of oxygen is absorbed per cut, whereas at lower temperatures many molecules of oxygen are absorbed per cut.[52]

If the number of cleavages per cubic centimeter is a linear function of the time, *i.e.*:

$$q = \hat{c}t \tag{X.68}$$

Then from equation (X.67) and (X.68) one obtains:

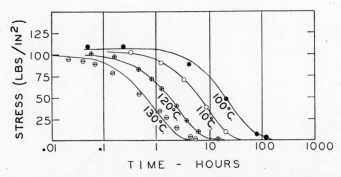

Fig. X-17. Decay of stress caused by oxidative scission in a vulcanized natural rubber at several temperatures. Samples maintained at 50% extension. Solid curves correspond to the equation $f = f_0 \exp(-kt)$.

$$f/f(0) = \exp(-ct/N(0)) = \exp(-kt) \tag{X.69}$$

In other words, if the number of cuts per cubic centimeter is a linear function of time, the decay of stress at constant extension follows the Maxwellian decay law. This type of stress decay was found to apply to vulcanized natural rubber at high temperatures as shown in Figure X-17.

The place of "chemorheology" in the viscoelastic behavior of vulcanized rubber is best shown in Figure X-18, where stress relaxation data for vulcanized natural rubber over a wide range of temperatures is presented. Around room temperature, very slight stress relaxation is evidenced, and the substance behaves in a nearly ideally elastic fashion. At low temperatures, the rubber in the "glassy" state has an initially high value of the "modulus," but after a time the stress decays to the value determined by the primary three-dimensional network. At high temperatures the decay to zero stress signifies that the primary bonds of the network are being cut.

[52] A. V. Tobolsky, D. Metz, and R. B. Mesrobian, *J. A. C. S,* **72,** 1942 (1950).

The *net* effect of the cross linking and scission reactions can be measured by allowing the rubber to remain in an unstrained condition at elevated temperatures and then occasionally making rapid measurements of the "modulus" (*i.e.*, the stress required to attain a fixed elongation). During the long intervals between the occasional measurements of the "modulus," the rubber is maintained in the unstrained condition. To distinguish experiments of this type from the measurements of stress decay at constant extension (where the rubber is continuously maintained at fixed length), the former have been termed "intermittent" and the latter "continuous."

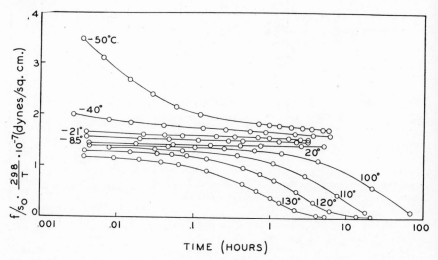

Fig. X-18.   Decay of stress at constant extension in a vulcanized natural rubber over a wide temperature range.

If the cross-linking reaction is faster than the scission reaction, the stress measured in the "intermittent" experiment will increase with time; if the converse is true then the stress measured in these experiments will decrease with time. Curves for relative decay of stress at constant extension and "intermittent" measurements of the relative modulus are shown in Figure X-19. At any given time, the quantity U shown in this figure measures the fraction of the original network chains as yet uncut by oxygen, whereas the quantity X measures the relative concentration of new network chains formed by cross linking compared to the original concentration of network chains.

If rubber samples are maintained at constant extension at temperatures at which their properties are governed by "chemorheological" behavior, they will exhibit a "permanent set" or irrecoverable deformation when released from their strained position. The reason for this permanent set is twofold: in the first place, the original network structure that is under strain is being destroyed gradually by scission, so that the retractive force that tends to restore the sample to its original length is continually decreasing; second, new network structure is being formed by cross linking

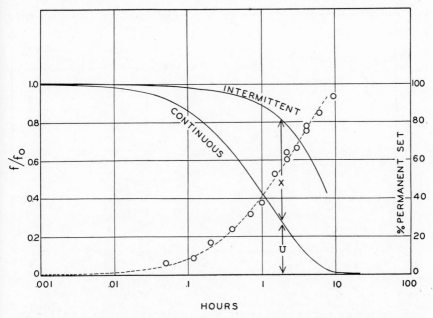

Fig. X-19.   Relaxation and permanent set in a natural rubber vulcanizate at 130°C.: - - -, theoretical permanent set curve; O, experimental permanent set values.

which is in equilibrium with the strained condition of the sample and which therefore resists any change from the strained length of the sample. When the sample is released it will return to a length at which these two opposing forces balance each other.

These two opposing forces can be related to the quantities U and X.[53] If l_u is the unstretched length of the rubber, l_x is the length at which the rubber is maintained in the stretched condition, and $l(t)$ is the length to which the rubber returns on being released at time t, the permanent set can be calculated from the equation:

[53] R. D. Andrews, E. E. Hanson, and A. V. Tobolsky, *J. Applied Phys.*, **17**, 352 (1946).

$$\frac{l(t) - l_u}{l_x - l_u} = \left\{\left[\frac{C_1}{(U/X)C_2 + 1} + 1\right]^{1/3} - 1\right\} C_3 \qquad (X.70)$$

$$C_1 = \left(\frac{l_x}{l_u}\right)^3 - 1 \qquad C_2 = \left(\frac{l_x}{l_u}\right)^2 \qquad C_3 = \frac{1}{(l_x/l_u) - 1}$$

Experimental results on permanent set gave good agreement with the theoretical equation (X.70). In Figure X-19 experimental values of per-

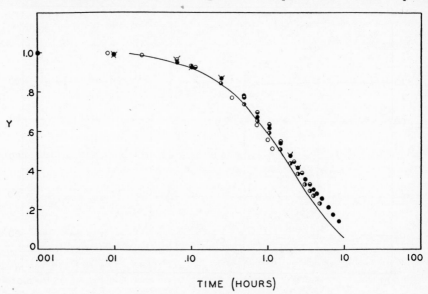

TIME (HOURS)

Fig. X-20. Creep in vulcanized natural rubber at 120°C. The creep data are plotted in the form Y vs. log t where:

$$Y = [l_i/l_u - (l_u/l_i)^2]/[l(t)/l_u - (l_u/l(t))^2]$$

●, $l_i/l_u = 1.1$.　◑, $l_i/l_u = 1.2$.　◓, $l_i/l_u = 1.4$.
○, $l_i/l_u = 2$.　—, stress relaxation plotted as $f(t)/f(0)$.

manent set are shown for vulcanized natural rubber maintained at 50% extension at 130°C. The theoretical curve is calculated from the U and X values obtained from the "intermittent" and "continuous" curves.

Creep under constant load in the chemorheological temperature range can also be related to the stress relaxation curve in the case that the *cross-linking reaction is slow compared to scission*.[54,55] If l_u is the unstretched

[54] A. V. Tobolsky and R. D. Andrews, *J. Chem. Phys.*, **13**, 3 (1945).
[55] R. D. Andrews, R. B. Mesrobian, and A. V. Tobolsky, *A. S. M. E. Transactions*, **67**, 569 (1945).

length of the rubber, l_i is the length attained immediately after the application of the load, and $l(t)$ the length at time t, one can derive:

$$\frac{(l_i/l_u) - (l_u/l_i)^2}{(l(t)/l_u) - (l_u/l(t))^2} = U \tag{X.71}$$

where $U = f(t)/f(0)$ is the relative stress at time t obtained from the stress relaxation curve. Figure X-20 shows comparison of creep curves plotted as:

$$[(l_i/l_u) - (l_u/l_i)^2]/[l(t)/l_u - (l_u/l(t))^2] \text{ vs. log time}$$

with stress relaxation data plotted in the form $f(t)/f(0)$ vs. log time for vulcanized natural rubber at 120°C.

The chemorheological behavior of keratin is even more complex than that of vulcanized rubbers. Keratin is also a three-dimensional polymer, the cross links being disulfide linkages from the cystine residues of the polypeptide chains. These cross links can be severed and reconstituted by numerous chemical agents as was shown by Speakman,[56,57] Astbury,[58] Harris,[59] and Lundgren.[60] Under suitable conditions, therefore, keratin from feathers, etc. can be dissolved and respun into synthetic fibers. Wool fibers can be treated with reagents that first break the disulfide linkage (without solubilizing the wool) and afterward the disulfide linkages can be replaced by linkages that are more stable to chemical and biological attack. Permanent waves in human hair are achieved by first chemically rupturing the cystine linkages and then reconstituting the linkages after the hair has been "set." A complete physicochemical description of the viscoelastic and chemorheological behavior of keratin, however, is still remote.

G. CRYSTALLINITY

The x-ray scattering from amorphous polymers such as unstretched natural rubber is essentially similar to the scattering from liquids—namely, diffuse halos are obtained. In 1925, Katz made the fundamental discovery that if natural rubber is stretched to 400% extension or higher, sharp peaks characteristic of the scattering of crystalline substances become

[56] J. B. Speakman, *Proc. Roy. Soc., London*, **B103,** 377 (1928).

[57] J. B. Speakman and S. Y. Shah, *J. Soc. Dyers Colourists*, **57,** 108 (1941).

[58] W. T. Astbury, *Fundamentals of Fibre Structure.* Oxford Univ. Press, London, 1933.

[59] M. Harris, L. R. Mizell, and L. Fourt, *Ind. Eng. Chem.*, **34,** 833 (1942).

[60] H. P. Lundgren, A. M. Stein, V. M. Koorn, and R. A. O'Connell, *J. Phys. & Colloid Chem.*, **52,** 180 (1948).

evident.[61] Many natural polymers such as cellulose, silk, wool, and un-
denatured proteins show definite evidence of crystallinity in the unstretched
state. The natural fibers all show orientation of the crystallites even in the
unstretched state. Many synthetic polymers such as polythene are also
crystalline, and can be prepared with oriented or unoriented crystallites.

In general, symmetrical chain structure such as found in vinylidene
polymers of the vinylidene chloride type give rise to crystalline polymers.
Vinyl polymers, which have *dl*-isomerism, are crystalline only if the side
group is relatively small.

The structure of crystalline polymers is generally regarded to be as pic-
tured in Figure X-21. A single molecule may go completely through a

Fig. X-21. The structure of polymers: (a) amorphous, (b) crystalline, (c)
oriented crystalline.[16]

crystallite, emerge in an amorphous area, and enter another crystallite (if
the molecule is long and the crystallites are short!). The detailed structure of polycrystalline polymers must be defined in terms of: (*1*) unit cell
of the crystallites; (*2*) dimensions of the crystallites; (*3*) orientation of the
crystallites; and (*4*) total percent of crystalline material.

The x-ray method is still the best method for obtaining this kind of information, though in certain instances, such as cellulose, percent crystallinity has been determined by the accessibility of various reagents. The
specific volumes of the crystalline and amorphous regions are different, and
this has been the most widely used tool in studying rates of crystallization
and extents of crystallization once the densities of these two phases have

[61] J. R. Katz, *Naturwiss.*, **13**, 410 (1925).

been established.[62,63]   For example, the density of amorphous rubber at −10°C. is 0.93 and the density of the crystallites at that temperature is 0.97.[64]

The effects of crystallinity on mechanical properties are: (1) tremendous increase of tensile strength and impact strength; (2) increase in modulus; and (3) decrease in dimensional stability because of melting of crystallites.

All natural and synthetic textile fibers are crystalline and oriented, since high tensile strength and fairly high modulus are so necessary in this case. Crystalline plastics such as polythene have tremendous impact strength compared to amorphous, glassy plastics such as polystyrene.

In oriented crystalline polymers the total percentage of crystalline material is a monotonically decreasing function of the temperature and above a critical temperature T_m all the crystallites are melted out. When portions of the long chains come together to form a crystallite, there is a decrease in the entropy (randomness) of the system and also a decrease of the internal energy equivalent to the heat of crystallization. The equation for the fraction $1 - \lambda$ of the polymer involved in crystallites as a function of the temperature and elongation is:[65]

$$1 - \lambda = 1 - \{[\tfrac{3}{2} - \varphi(\alpha)]/[\tfrac{3}{2} - \theta]\}^{1/2}$$

$$\varphi(\alpha) = (6/\pi)^{1/2} \, \alpha/n^{1/2} - (\alpha^2/2 + 1/\alpha)/n$$

$$\theta = s_f/k - h_f/kT \qquad\qquad (X.72)$$

where α is the relative length l/l_0, n is the number of freely rotating segments per polymer chain, h_f is the heat of fusion per segment of the polymer, s_f the entropy of fusion per segment, k is Boltzmann's constant, and T the absolute temperature.

The effect of crystallites on the modulus is rather complex and depends both on the total amount of crystalline material and on the number of crystallites per unit volume. If the amount of crystalline material is relatively small and if the crystallites are small in size, they may be considered to act in much the same way as chemical cross links. If this type of polycrystalline material is stretched, the force resisting stretching arises mainly from the decrease of configurational entropy in the amorphous regions. The crystallites retard molecular diffusion almost as effectively as chemical

[62] N. Bekkedahl, J. Research Natl. Bur. Standards, 13, 411 (1934).

[63] L. A. Wood, in Advances in Colloid Science, Vol. II. Interscience, New York, 1946, page 57.

[64] W. H. Smith and N. P. Hanna, J. Research Natl. Bur. Standards, 27, 229 (1941).

[65] P. J. Flory, J. Chem. Phys., 15, 397, 684 (1947).

cross links, so that relaxation of stress at constant extension is relatively slow. On the other hand, as the temperature is raised, some of the crystallites will melt out completely, so that the concentration of "cross links" becomes smaller with increasing temperature and the modulus of the material is therefore lowered as the temperature is raised.

Some of these facts are illustrated in Figure X-22, where curves of stress at constant extension *vs.* log time are shown for an *N*-substituted polyamide over a range of temperatures below its melting point.[66] It is clear

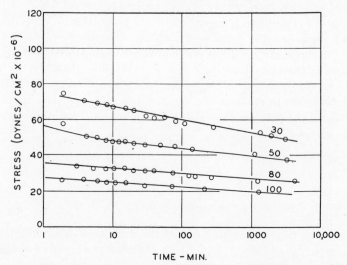

TIME - MIN.

Fig. X-22. Relaxation of stress for a partially *N*-substituted polyamide maintained at 50% extension at various temperatures. These results are typical for many polycrystalline polymers.

from this figure that the fractional decay of stress does not increase with increasing temperature. The main effect of temperature appears to be a decrease in the modulus of the material, which is accounted for by the decreasing amount of crystallites and of crystalline material as the temperature is raised. The change of the viscoelastic behavior with temperature cannot be accounted for by a simple displacement of the relaxation time distribution function along the log time axis. The area under the curve of the distribution function as well as its position and possibly its shape must be changing with temperature.

[66] R. S. Stein and A. V. Tobolsky, *J. Textile Research*, **18**, 201, 302 (1948).

Relaxation of stress at constant extension is in fact caused by a completely different mechanism than is true in amorphous polymers. It often arises from a slow growth of new crystalline material or from the orientation of already existing crystallites. This is most readily shown by the fact that the birefringence will often increase at constant extension, whereas the stress decreases.[66,67] Under certain conditions the growth of oriented crystallites in a stretched polymer will cause a spontaneous increase in length of the sample over and above the length to which it was originally stretched.

A "permanent" orientation of crystalline polymers can be achieved if the polymer is stretched at high temperature and then cooled while the polymer is maintained in its stretched state. The orientation will disappear and the polymer will shrink along the axis of orientation if it is heated above the temperature at which it was originally stretched and oriented.

This phenomenon is more readily understood if we examine the nature of the stress–temperature curves at constant extension. If we stretch the material to a fixed length at temperature T, and then lower the temperature, the stress will decrease even more rapidly than proportionally to absolute temperature (provided that the degree of crystallinity is not too high!). This decrease of stress as the temperature is lowered in excess of the kinetic theory prediction arises from the fact that new oriented crystalline material keeps forming, largely growing around the already formed crystallites. If the temperature is raised—but *not allowed to exceed the original temperature* T, at which the sample was stretched—the stress–temperature curve is reversible. In fact a thermodynamic treatment has been given which relates the slope of the reversible stress–temperature curve to the percentage of crystalline material formed.[68]

$$f = NkT\{[\alpha - (1/\alpha^2)] - (6n/\pi)^{1/2}(1 - \lambda)\}/\lambda \qquad (X.73)$$

where N is the number of network chains per cubic centimeter, n is the number of freely rotating segments per chain, and $1 - \lambda$ is the fractiona degree of crystallization calculable from equation (X.72).

If the sample is maintained at constant length and the temperature is raised above the temperature T_1, at which it was first stretched, to a higher temperature T_2, there is an *irreversible* decrease in stress. When the temperature is lowered from T_2 (while still maintaining constant strain) a *new* re-

[67] P. A. Thiessen and W. Wittstadt, *Rubber Chem. Technol.*, **12**, 736 (1939).
[68] P. J. Flory, *J. Chem. Phys.*, **15**, 397 (1947)

versible stress–temperature curve is obtained provided that temperature T_2 is not exceeded.* These relationships are shown in Figure X-23.[66]

The irreversible decrease of stress when the material is brought from T_1 to T_2 is probably caused by the complete melting of certain crystallites which at temperatures T_1 and below were acting as effective cross links. When the temperature at T_2 is lowered to T_1, the same total amount

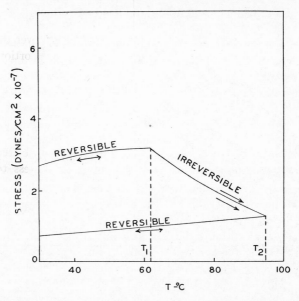

Fig. X-23.   Reversible and irreversible stress–temperature curves for a partially N-substituted polyamide maintained at 100% extension.

of crystalline material is reformed, but it enters the structure in equilibrium with respect to the stretched length of the sample,[66] just as cross links formed while the sample is strained do not contribute to the stress at that value of the strain.   Possibly, though not necessarily, the new crystalline material formed as the temperature is lowered from T_2 to T_1 enters mainly around the crystallites that remained unmelted at T_2.

* The analogous reversible-irreversible lengthening and shortening of crystalline polymers under load when subject to temperature cycles of the type described above was first reported by Leaderman for the case of nylon: H. Leaderman, *Elastic and Creep Properties of Filamentous Materials and Other High Polymers*, The Textile Foundation, Washington, D.C.   A qualitative interpretation of this data was given by T. Alfrey, *Mechanical Behavior of High Polymers*, Interscience, New York, 1948, page 412.

In materials such as natural rubber which are amorphous in the unstretched condition but which form crystallites on stretching, the appearance of these crystallites has a profound effect on physical properties. In the first place the tensile strength of the material is enormously increased, which explains why noncrystallizing synthetic rubbers have to be heavily reinforced with carbon black to attain tensile strengths approaching that of nonreinforced natural rubber. Second, the stress–strain curve changes very markedly, the "modulus" of the material becoming much higher at the elongations at which the crystallites are forming. Even though the crystallites enter the structure at equilibrium with respect to the strain at which they are formed, they act as effective cross links in resisting any further increase of the strain.

In very highly crystalline polymers it is probable that the change of internal energy on stretching due to short range relative motion of the atomic groups is more significant than the change in configurational entropy of the amorphous regions. This would account for the very high value of the modulus of certain well-oriented textile fibers (10^{10} dynes/cm.^{2} or greater). The properties of oriented fibers naturally show a dependence upon the direction in which they are measured.

Inasmuch as very high stresses are involved in the stretching of textile fibers, it is possible that the unit process of flow is non-Newtonian. A generalization of Eyring's molecular theory of viscous flow to the case of viscoelastic behavior leads to nonlinear equations which can be integrated.[69] The theory of nonlinear viscoelastic behavior has been developed extensively and applied to the properties of textile fibers by Eyring, Halsey, and coworkers.[70]

[69] A. V. Tobolsky and H. Eyring, *J. Chem. Phys.*, **11**, 125 (1943).

[70] H. Eyring and G. Halsey, in H. A. Robinson, ed., *High Polymer Physics*. Remsen Press, New York, 1948, pages 61–116.

XI. STEP REACTION POLYMERIZATION

Although the first synthetic high polymers were probably prepared
rly in the 19th century, and synthetic high polymers were made for com-
ercial exploitation early in this century, it was only during the latter part
f the 1920's and the early 1930's that the fundamental scientific principles
nderlying the formation of synthetic high polymers were clearly eluci-
ated. Although many scientific workers must share the credit for this
evelopment, Wallace H. Carothers,[1] whose work inspired the development
f nylon, was the first to clearly and dramatically emphasize the all-im-
ortant concept of functionality that underlies the science of synthetic high
olymers.

When ethyl alcohol and acetic acid are condensed to form ethyl acetate,
: is the hydroxyl group on the alcohol and the carboxyl group on the acid
hat are the important groups in each molecule that take part in the reac-
ion. These are called the *functional groups*, and ethyl alcohol and acetic
cid each have one functional group per molecule and are therefore termed
ionofunctional molecules.

On the other hand, consider what happens when ethylene glycol and
dipic acid are allowed to condense. Each of these molecules has *two*
unctional groups, one on each end. The end-to-end condensation of car-
ooxyl and hydroxyl groups leads to linear polyesters of high molecular
veight. Introduction of polyfunctional molecules such as glycerol (func-
ionality 3) or pentaerithrytol (functionality 4) will obviously lead to
ranched polymers and networks. Some typical examples of polyconden-
ations are listed in Table XI-1.

Carothers also clearly distinguished between polycondensations (such
s the formation of polyesters and polyamides) and addition polymeriza-
.ions (vinyl and diene polymerizations). For our purposes it will be best
.o classify these groups as *step reaction polymerizations* and *chain reaction
polymerizations*.

[1] H. Mark and G. S. Whitby, eds., *Collected Papers of Wallace Hume Carothers on
High Polymeric Substances.* Interscience, New York, 1940.

TABLE XI-1

SOME EXAMPLES OF POLYCONDENSATION POLYMERS

Type	Examples

Polyesters	$HO(CH_2)_yCOOH \longrightarrow HO-[(CH_2)_yCO-O]_x-H + H_2O$
	$HO(CH_2)_yOH + HOOC(CH_2)_2COOH \longrightarrow HO-[(CH_2)_yOCO-(CH_2)_2CO-O]_x-H + H_2O$
	$HOOC(CH_2)_4COOH + CH_2OH$
	     $\mid$—CHOH
	     $\mid$—CH$_2$OH $\longrightarrow$ Three-dimensional polymer

Polyamides	$NH_2(CH_2)_5COOH \longrightarrow H-[NH(CH_2)_5CO-]_x-OH$ $NH_2(CH_2)_6NH_2 + HOOC(CH_2)_4COOH \longrightarrow H-[NH(CH_2)_6NHCO-(CH_2)_4CO-]_x-OH + H_2O$
Polysulfides	$ClCH_2CH_2Cl + Na_2S_y \longrightarrow Cl[CH_2CH_2S_y]_xNa + NaCl$ $(y = 1, 2, 3, 4)$
Poly-α-amino acids (proteins)	$NH_2CHR'COOH + NH_2CHR''COOH \longrightarrow H-[NHCHR'CONHCHR''CO-]_x-OH + H_2O$
Polyglucose anhydrides (cellulose, starch)	$[C_6H_{12}O_6] \longrightarrow \{[C_6H_{10}O_4]-O-[C_6H_{10}O_4]\}_x + H_2O$
Phenolaldehyde	

$+ CH_2O \longrightarrow$ Three-dimensional structures

Type	Examples
Polysiloxanes	$\begin{array}{c} R \\ HO-Si-OH \\ R \end{array}$ $\longrightarrow$ $HO\left[\begin{array}{c} R \\ Si-O \\ R \end{array}\right]_x H$
	$\begin{array}{c} R \\ HO-Si-OH + HO-Si-OH \\ R \end{array}$ $\begin{array}{c} R \\ R \\ OH \end{array}$ $\longrightarrow$ Three-dimensional structures
Polyoxymethylenes	$CH_2CH_2 \longrightarrow [-CH_2CH_2OCH_2CH_2O-]_x$ $\diagdown O \diagup$
Polypeptides	$\begin{array}{c} NH \\ CHR\ C=O \\ \diagdown O \diagup \\ C=O \end{array}$ $\longrightarrow$ $\left[\begin{array}{c} O \\ \| \\ -NHCHRC- \end{array}\right]_x + CO_2$
Urea-formaldehyde	$NH_2-CO-NH_2 + CH_2O \longrightarrow$ Three-dimensional polymers of complex partly doubtful structure
Melamine-formaldehyde	$\begin{array}{c} NH_2 \\ C \\ N \quad CNH_2 \\ H_2NC \quad N \\ N \end{array}$ $+ CH_2O \longrightarrow$ Three-dimensional polymers of complex partly doubtful structure

A. STEP REACTION POLYMERIZATIONS AND FUNCTIONALIT

By step reaction polymerizations we shall mean polymerizations for whi each individual step in the reaction proceeds at the same specific rat The large majority of polycondensations and the opening of ring compoun to give long chain molecules seem to obey this kinetic law to first appro mation.[2]

The equality of the specific rate of each step must, of course, be inte preted somewhat broadly. In the case where glycerol is used as one of th monomers in a polyesterification, the secondary hydroxyl group reacts a different specific rate than the primary hydroxyl groups, but *all* primar hydroxyl groups react with the same specific rate, and *all* secondary h droxyl groups react at another, but identical, specific rate. Furthermor the condensations to form dimer and trimer appear to have somewhat di ferent specific rates than the condensations to form higher aggregate Finally the specific rates may possibly be altered as the viscosity of th medium changes with continued polymerization.

Carothers[3] was the first to give a mathematical relation between the e tent of reaction and the average degree of polymerization for polycondens tion reactions.

Let f = functionality of the monomer, N_0 = number of monomers a the start of the reaction, and N = number of molecules at the end of th reaction. We shall define the extent of reaction, p, as the number of th functions that have been used to form linkages divided by the origina number of functions. If we neglect the possibility of intramolecular con densations, then, each time a linkage is formed, we reduce the number o molecules by one. The total number of linkages that must have forme when the number of molecules has been reduced from N_0 to N is therefor $N_0 - N$. Inasmuch as two functional groups are lost whenever a linkag is formed, one obtains:

$$p = \text{extent of reaction} = \text{fraction of functional groups lost} =$$

$$2(N_0 - N)/N_0 f$$

$$p = 2N_0/N_0 f - 2N/N_0 f$$

[2] An excellent review article on polycondensation is that of P. J. Flory, *Chem. Revs.* **39**, 137 (1946), and in R. E. Burk and O. Grummitt, eds., *High Molecular Weight Or ganic Compounds*, Interscience, New York, 1949, pages 211–282.

[3] W. H. Carothers, *Trans. Faraday Soc.*, **32**, 39 (1936).

ut since the number average degree of polymerization $\bar{P}_n$ is clearly the
tal number of monomeric residues of the system divided by the total
umber of independent molecules, $\bar{P}_n = N_0/N$. Our equation therefore
comes:

$$p = (2/f) - (2/\bar{P}_nf) \qquad \bar{P}_n = 1/(1 - fp/2) \qquad \text{(XI.1)}$$

It is clear from equation (XI.1) that when $p = 2/f$ the number average
egree of polymerization becomes infinite. A clarification and interpreta-
on of this will be discussed in Section H.

Equation (XI.1) can be used for mixtures of molecules of different func-
onalities, provided the number average functionality is used. For ex-
mple, when two moles of glycerol are condensed with three moles of suc-
nic acid, there are six functional groups from each three molecules of suc-
nic acid. There are, therefore, on the average, $12/5 = 2.4$ functions per
olecule, and this is the number average functionality that must be used
equation (XI.1). For example, when the reaction between two moles
f glycerol and three moles of succinic acid is half complete, then according
o the equation the number average degree of polymerization is 2.5.

Dimethyldichlorosilane will, upon exposure to water, hydrolyze to the
nstable dimethyldihydroxysilane, which immediately condenses to form a
olymer (see Table XI.1). If, in the fractional separation of dimethyl-
ichlorosilane there remains one mole percent of trimethylchlorosilane,
hen upon exposure to water and *complete* condensation the polymerization
egree is only 200. This can be seen by substituting $f = 1.99$ and $p = 1$
n equation (XI.1). The monofunctional material acts as a controller or
tabilizer of molecular weight.

If two bifunctional molecules are condensed together (*e.g.*, hexamethyl-
nediamine and adipic acid), the molecular weight will be greatly lowered
f one of the two components is present in stoichiometric excess (compare
he discussion in Section I).

B. STATISTICS OF BIFUNCTIONAL CONDENSATIONS

If we consider the condensation of bifunctional monomers in which each
unctional group is as reactive as any other, no matter what the size of the
nolecule it is attached to, then it is clear that at any extent of reaction, p,
ve have a distribution of polymers of various degrees of polymerization.[4]
following the argument of Flory,[5] we choose a monomer unit at random
rom the system and ask for the probability, W_n, that it is a part of a mole-

[4] W. Chalmers, *J. Am. Chem. Soc.*, **56**, 912 (1934).

[5] P. J. Flory, *J. Am. Chem. Soc.*, **58**, 1877 (1936).

cule consisting of n such units (an n-mer). In a linear n-mer there mu be $(n - 1)$ linkages and two unreacted end groups. The probability a linkage in random condensation of the type under discussion must equal to p, the extent of reaction as defined in the section above, where the probability of an unreacted end group is $(1 - p)$. Also, the selecte monomer unit could be in any one of n possible positions along the chai The desired probability is therefore:[5-7]

$$W_n = np^{n-1}(1 - p)^2 \qquad \text{(XI.2}$$

W_n is also the weight fraction of the original monomer bound into n-me provided we neglect the weight of the water or other fragments split o during condensation.

If the original number of monomers is N_0, then the number of n-mer N_n, is given by:

$$N_n = N_0 W_n/n = N_0 p^{n-1}(1 - p)^2 \qquad \text{(XI.3}$$

The total number of molecules N is given by:

$$N = \sum_{n=1}^{\infty} N_n = N_0(1 - p) \qquad \text{(XI.4}$$

The mole fraction, X_n, of n-mers is:

$$X_n = N_n/N = p^{n-1}(1 - p) \qquad \text{(XI.5}$$

The number average degree of polymerization is defined by:

$$\bar{P}_n = \sum_{n=1}^{\infty} nX_n = N_0/N = 1/(1 - p) \qquad \text{(XI.6}$$

The weight average degree of polymerization is:

$$\bar{P}_w = \sum_{n=1}^{\infty} nW_n = (1 + p)/(1 - p) \qquad \text{(XI.7}$$

For high degrees of conversion (p nearly unity) the weight average i nearly double the number average.

Equations (XI.2) and (XI.5) define the differential weight distributio curve and the differential number distribution curve of the so-called ran dom distribution. Plots of these distributions are shown for various value

[6] W. Kuhn, *Ber.*, **63**, 1503 (1930), gives the same formula for the treatment of random degradation of high polymers.

[7] G. V. Schulz, *Z. physik. Chem.*, **B30**, 379 (1935), gives the same formula for siz distribution formed during polymerization of vinyl monomers.

p in Figures XI-1 and XI-2.   It is clear that for all values of p there is
ore monomer than dimer, more dimer than trimer, etc.   However, the
·tal weight of the various species passes through a maximum depending
ı the extent of reaction, p.   The maximum of the differential weight dis-
·ibution curve occurs at a degree of polymerization equal to $-1/\ln p$.
 It is clear from equation (XI.6) that in order to get a high degree of
ɔlymerization it is necessary to get very complete reaction of the functional
·oups.   For example, to get a number average degree of polymerization
ᴵ 100 it is necessary to have 99% of the functional groups reacted.   In
ıe case of polyesterifications, for example, this requires that the water of

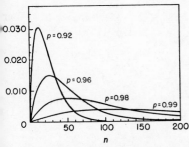

ig. XI-1.   Weight fraction distribution
curve for random polycondensation.

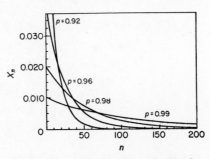

Fig. XI-2.   Mole fraction distribution
curve for random polycondensation.

ʒaction be very thoroughly removed during reaction to prevent back-
ʒaction.   It also means that monofunctional impurities must be kept down
ɔ a minimum and that exactly equivalent amounts of glycol and dibasic
cid must be used.

C. RING VERSUS CHAIN FORMATION

 In the preceding section it was assumed that no intramolecular condensa-
ɩon can take place, that is, that hydroxy acids will always condense in thᶜ
ɔllowing way:

$$HORCOOH \longrightarrow H-[OR\overset{\displaystyle O}{\overset{\|}{C}}]_x-OH$$

 However, depending on the number of carbon atoms in the group R of
ꞙORCOOH and upon reaction conditions, there is a competing tendency
ɔ form ring compounds.   For example, γ-hydroxybutyric acid does not

form a polyester on heating but instead forms the cyclic butyrolacto
which does not polymerize on hydrolysis:

$$HOCH_2CH_2CH_2COOH \longrightarrow \begin{matrix} H_2C & O \\ | & \diagdown C{=}O \\ H_2C & CH_2 \end{matrix} \quad + \quad H_2O$$

δ-Hydroxyvaleric acid forms a lactone which, on the addition of sma
amounts of water or acid, polymerizes to the polyester:

$$HOCH_2CH_2CH_2CH_2COOH \longrightarrow \begin{matrix} H_2C & O \\ | & \diagdown C{=}O \\ H_2C & CH_2 \\ & C \\ & H_2 \end{matrix} \xrightarrow{[H_2O]} H \left[-O(CH_2)_4\overset{O}{\overset{\|}{C}}- \right]_x OH$$

α-Hydroxy acids such as lactic acid condense to give both the dimeric cyc
ester (a lactide) and a linear polymer:

$$\underset{CH_3}{HO-CH-COOH} \longrightarrow \begin{matrix} & O \\ & \| \\ CH_3CH & C \\ & O \\ O & HCCH_3 \\ & C \\ & O \end{matrix}$$

$$\underset{CH_3}{HO-CH-COOH} \longrightarrow H-\left[OCH(CH_3)CO - \right]_x OH$$

Carothers and co-workers[8] studied systematically the ease of ring forma
tion in hydroxy acids, dibasic acids, and amino acids and arrived at th
following conclusions:

(1) Three- or four-membered rings form only with great difficulty. When forme
they tend to open up to give the linear polymer under rather mild conditions. The

[8] J. W. Hill and W. H. Carothers, *J. Am. Chem. Soc.*, **57**, 925, 5026 (1935). E. V
Spanagel and W. H. Carothers, *ibid.*, **57**, 929 (1935). W. H. Carothers, G. L. Doroug
and F. J. Van Natta, *ibid.*, **55**, 5023 (1933). See also review by P. J. Flory, *Chem. Rev*
39, 137 (1946), and in R. E. Burk and O. Grummitt, eds., *High Molecular Weight Organ*
Compounds, Interscience, New York, 1949, pp. 211–282.

acts are explained by the great strains imposed on the valence angles in making three-
or four-membered rings.

(2) γ-Hydroxy acids condense exclusively to form lactones, γ-amino acids give the
lactams, and succinic acid gives the anhydride. These five-membered rings are formed
very easily and do not open up to give the linear polymer. These facts are explained by
the virtually strainless configuration of the valence angles in five-membered rings:

$$
\begin{array}{ccc}
\overset{\displaystyle O}{\overset{\|}{C}} & \overset{\displaystyle O}{\overset{\|}{C}} & \overset{\displaystyle O}{\overset{\|}{C}} \\
H_2C \diagup \diagdown O & H_2C \diagup \diagdown NH & H_2C \diagup \diagdown O \\
| \quad\quad | & | \quad\quad | & | \quad\quad | \\
H_2C - CH_2 & H_2C - CH_2 & H_2C - C=O
\end{array}
$$

(3) Many six-membered rings (e.g., the cyclic esters) show a remarkable ease of conversion to the linear polymer. Similarly the polymers can be easily converted to the
rings by vacuum distillation. The remarkable ease of this transformation is unexplained.
Seven-membered units either yield polymer exclusively or if cyclic monomer is formed
it is convertible to linear polymers.

(4) Rings with eight to twelve atoms are formed from bifunctional condensations with
difficulty even in dilution or in vacuum at high temperatures in the presence of a cata-
yst. Both statistical improbability and internal repulsions from the hydrogen atoms
crowded in the ring are suggested as the reasons for the difficulty of formation of rings of
this size.

(5) Rings of large size—above 15 atoms—can be formed with somewhat greater ease.
Though statistically it is improbable that intramolecular condensation will be favored
to intermolecular condensation, the repulsion of hydrogen atoms in the rings no longer
exists.

Although under ordinary conditions of bifunctional condensations, linear
polymers are very much favored over macro rings, the macro rings can be
formed either by polymerization in very dilute solutions or by vacuum distillation of polymer at high temperatures in the presence of a catalyst.

The conclusions, which represent an over-all picture with regard to cyclic
esters, lactams, anhydrides, formals, and carbonates do not necessarily
hold true for other ring systems. For example, the cyclic siloxanes and
cyclic disulfides show a different pattern of behavior with respect to size.
Rings of large size appear to form with great ease in the case of the dimethyl
siloxanes.[9] Furthermore, at least one five-membered ring, tetrahydrofuran,
has recently been polymerized[10] using a mixture of aluminum chloride and
stannic chloride as the catalyst.

Table XI-2 gives a partial list of some polymerizable ring compounds.

[9] Eugene R. Rochow, *Introduction to the Chemistry of the Silicones*. Wiley, New
York, 1946.
[10] H. Meerwein, *Angew. Chem.*, **A59**, 168 (1947).

TABLE XI-2

SOME EXAMPLES OF POLYMERIZABLE RING COMPOUNDS

Compound	Structural formula
Ethylene oxide	CH_2—CH_2 bridged by O
Ethylenimine	CH_2—CH_2 bridged by NH
Tetramethylene formal	CH_2 bridging O—$(CH_2)_4$—O
Pentamethylene formal	CH_2 bridging O—$(CH_2)_5$—O
Triethylene glycol formal	O——CH_2——O / $(CH_2)_2$—O—$(CH_2)_2$—O—$(CH_2)_2$
Adipic anhydride	O bridging CO—$(CH_2)_4$—CO
Dimeric suberic anhydride	CO—$(CH_2)_6$—CO / O O / CO—$(CH_2)_6$—CO
Dimeric sebacic anhydride	CO—$(CH_2)_8$—CO / O O / CO—$(CH_2)_8$—CO
δ-Valerolactone	O—$(CH_2)_4$—CO (ring)
Ethylene oxalate	O—CH_2—CH_2—O—CO—CO (ring)
Glycolide	O bridging CH_2—CO—O—CH_2—CO
Lactide	O bridging $CH(CH_3)$—CO—O—$CH(CH_3)$—CO

TABLE XI-2 *(continued)*

Compound	Structural formula
Octamethylene carbonate*	┌────O────┐ (CH₂)₈—O—CO
Dimeric tetramethylene carbonate*	CO—O—(CH₂)₄—O | | O—(CH₂)₄—O—CO
Decamethylene oxalate*	┌──────O──────┐ (CH₂)₁₀—O—CO—CO
Decamethylene malonate*	┌────────O────────┐ (CH₂)₁₀—O—CO—CH₂—CO
Monomeric ethylene sebacate*	┌────────O────────┐ (CH₂)₂—O—CO—(CH₂)₈—CO
Dimeric ethylene sebacate*	CO—(CH₂)₈—CO—O—(CH₂)₂ | | O O | | (CH₂)₂—O — CO — (CH₂)₈—CO
ε-Caprolactone	┌─O─┐ (CH₂)₅—CO
ε-Caprolactam	┌─NH─┐ (CH₂)₅—CO
Hexamethylene adipamide	NH—(CH₂)₆—NH | | CO—(CH₂)₄—CO
Cyclic ethyl ether disulfide	┌──────────────┐ S—(CH₂)₂—O—(CH₂)₂—S
Cyclic ethyl formal disulfide	┌────────────────────┐ S—(CH₂)₂—O—CH₂—O—(CH₂)₂—S
Octamethyltetrasiloxane	O——Si(CH₃)₂——O——Si(CH₃)₂ | | Si(CH₃)₂—O—Si(CH₃)₂—O

* The polymerizability of these substances and many others of similar structure is inferred by Carothers. See *Collected Papers of Wallace Hume Carothers on High Polymeric Substances*, New York, 1940, pp. 215, 218.

D. KINETICS OF POLYCONDENSATIONS

The statistics of polycondensations indicate that the size distribution shows no discontinuity between monomer and polymer (as will be shown to be the case in chain reactions). The most logical and simplest method of following the course of the polymerization is to titrate the unreacted functional groups.* To a good first approximation the reactivity of a functional group can be considered independent of the size of the molecule to which it is attached. Bifunctional condensations can therefore be treated in much the same way as monofunctional condensations.[11,12]

In the uncatalyzed condensation of exactly equivalent amounts of diethylene glycol and adipic acid, the course of the condensation was followed by measuring by titration the fraction, p, of functional groups that at a given time, t, have been reacted.[11] It was found that plots of $1/(1 - p)^2$ versus time gave essentially straight lines. This corresponds to third-order kinetics.

$$-dC/dt = kC^3 \qquad \text{(XI.8)}$$

$$2kt = 1/C^2 - 1/C_0^2 \qquad \text{(XI.9)}$$

where C is the concentration of reacting groups, k is the velocity constant, and C_0 is the initial concentration.

If the volume shrinkage due to the escape of water is neglected, $C = C_0(1 - p)$, and:

$$2C_0^2 kt = [1/(1 - p)^2] - 1 \qquad \text{(XI.10)}$$

The third-order kinetics arise from the fact that the esterification is catalyzed by the unreacted carboxyl groups. An example of third-order polycondensation is shown in Figure XI-3.

In the particular case cited (diethylene glycol and adipic acid polymerized at 202°C.) equation (XI.10) was not obeyed till the degree of polymerization was 5, but was obeyed between D.P. = 5 and D.P. = 14.

The reaction order of the polycondensation can be reduced and the rate greatly accelerated by use of acid catalysts.[11,13] For example, p-toluenesulfonic acid (0.4 mole per cent) was used as a catalyst for the polyconden-

---

* If the monomer is easily separable from the dimer, trimer, and other condensates, the reaction may be followed by measuring the relative proportion of monomer and condensate. H. Dostal and R. Raff, Z. physik. Chem., **B32**, 117 (1936).

[11] P. J. Flory, J. Am. Chem. Soc., **61**, 3334 (1939).

[12] W. O. Baker, C. S. Fuller, and J. H. Heiss, J. Am. Chem. Soc., **63**, 2142 (1941).

[13] P. J. Flory, J. Am. Chem. Soc., **62**, 2261 (1940).

ation of equivalent amounts of diethylene glycol and adipic acid at 109°. The kinetic equation in this case is:

$$-dC/dt = k'C_{cat.}C^2 \qquad (XI.11)$$

$$C_0C_{cat.}k't = [1/(1-p)] - 1 \qquad (XI.12)$$

where $C_{cat.}$ represents the catalyst concentration. Equation (XI.12) describes the observed behavior satisfactorily after the initial portion of the esterification. The experimental data is shown in Figure XI-4.

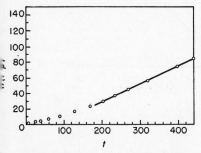

Fig. XI-3. Kinetics of uncatalyzed polycondensation: diethylene glycol-adipic acid at 166°C. (after P. J. Flory[11]). (*t* is in minutes)

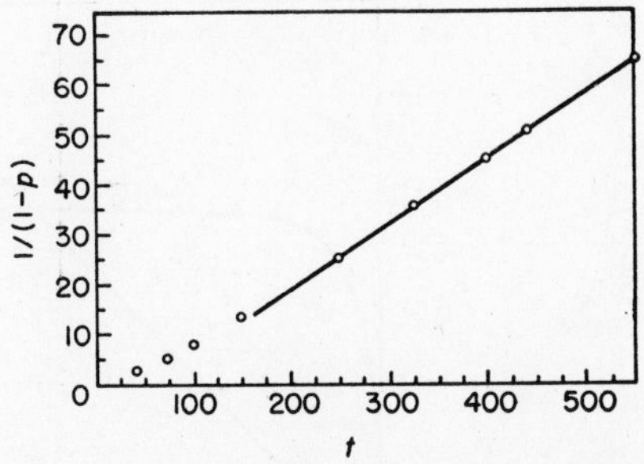

Fig. XI-4. Diethylene glycol-adipic acid at 109°C. with 0.4 mole per *p*-toluenesulfonic acid used as a catalyst. (*t* is in minutes)

Inasmuch as the number average degree of polymerization, $\bar{P}_n$, is equal to $1/(1-p)$, it is clear from equation (XI.10) that for third-order polycondensation kinetics:

$$\bar{P}_n = [\text{const.} \times (t+1)]^{1/2} \qquad (XI.13)$$

which, except for the very beginning of the reaction, indicates that the degree of polymerization for third-order polycondensations increases as the square root of the time of polymerization.

For second-order polycondensations, from (XI.12):

$$\bar{P}_n = \text{const.} \times (t+1) \qquad (XI.14)$$

which indicates that except for the beginning of the reaction the number average degree of polymerization is proportional to the time of polymerization.

Plots of $\bar{P}_n$ and p as a function of time for third-order polycondensation kinetics (uncatalyzed) and second-order polycondensation kinetics (catalyzed) are shown in Figure XI-5.

E. DETAILED KINETICS OF STEP REACTIONS: Type I =

$$m_i + m_j \longrightarrow m_{i+j}$$

The simplest instance of polycondensation that has been worked out in detail is the case where one single type of elementary reaction is involved and which takes place again and again under practically unchanged conditions and with unchanged specific rate. This process is between functional groups and is considered independent of the size of the molecule to

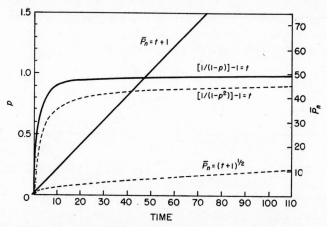

Fig. XI-5. Degree of polymerization and extent of reaction as functions of time for catalyzed and uncatalyzed polycondensations.

which the functional group belongs.[14]   To describe the system under consideration we consider the polycondensation of a bifunctional monomer (such as a long-chain aminocarboxylic acid), assume that the elementary reactions between functional groups are bimolecular, and introduce the following symbols:[15] N_0 = total number of moles of the monomer at the beginning of reaction; N_x = number of moles of x-mer at time t; $m_x = N_x/N_0$: and k_f = specific reaction rate constant for the condensation of two functional groups.

With these notations the differential equations of the polycondensation reaction are as follows:[15]

$$dm_1/dt = -2k_f m_1 \sum_{s=1}^{\infty} m_s \tag{XI.15}$$

[14] W. Chalmers, *J. Am. Chem. Soc.*, **56**, 913 (1934).

[15] H. Dostal and R. Raff, *Z. physik. Chem.*, **B32**, 117 (1936).

This equation describes the disappearance of the monomer, m_1, due to reaction (at either end) with itself and with chains of all possible lengths. To describe the net rate of formation of x-mer we have:

$$\frac{dm_x}{dt} = \frac{2k_f}{2} \sum_{s=1}^{s=x-1} m_s m_{x-s} - 2k_f m_x \sum_{s=1}^{s=\infty} m_s \qquad \text{(XI.16)}$$

The first term states that x-mers are formed by combination of two smaller molecules whose indices just add up to x. Division by two is necessary because each term in the summation is counted twice, once when $s < (x - s)$ and once when $s > (x - s)$. The second term accounts for the disappearance of x-mer by reaction with all the other molecules in the system. The solution of equations (XI.15) and (XI.16) is:

$$m_x = p^{x-1}(1 - p)^2 \qquad \text{(XI.17)}$$

$$p = k_f t/(1 + k_f t) \qquad \text{(XI.18)}$$

Equation (XI.17) obviously is the same size distribution (the so-called random size distribution) that we have already obtained by statistical methods.

In equation (XI.17) p obviously has the same meaning as in the previous sections, namely, the fraction of the functions lost. This can best be followed during the reaction by titration of end groups. The kinetics of the reaction can also be followed by determining the number of moles of monomer N_1 as a function of time. According to equation (XI.17) $N_1 = N_0 (1 - p)^2$, and so by determination of N_1, p can be determined and checked against equation (XI.18). Or, finally, the total amount of condensate from dimer up to the most highly condensed molecules can be measured. The weight fraction of these condensates will be $1 - (1 - p)^2$, and from this expression, too, p can be measured as a function of time, and compared with equation (XI.18). A further check upon the validity of the theory can be obtained by fractionation and comparison of the differential weight distribution with the expression:

$$W_n = np^{n-1}(1 - p)^2 \qquad \text{(XI.19)}$$

F. DETAILED KINETICS OF STEP REACTIONS: Type II =

$$m_j + m \longrightarrow m_{j+1}$$

Another type of polyreaction which can be characterized by a single rate constant is represented by successive addition of a certain monomer to a functional group. If one introduces a certain number of active nuclei or

functional groups in a system whose molecules can add to them, a polymer
is formed according to the scheme:

$$N_1 + M \longrightarrow N_2$$
$$N_2 + M \longrightarrow N_3$$
$$N_j + M \longrightarrow N_{j+1}$$

N_1 represents the active functional molecules that start the whole process. These can be originally put into the system in a certain constant
amount, or they can be formed slowly during the reaction. $N_2, N_3, N_4 \ldots$
are the species having one, two, or three monomer units, M, added to the
starting molecule. Dostal and Mark[16] and Flory[17] have developed the
kinetics for the above type of reaction, which differs from the polycondensations discussed in the previous section in that only monomer addition
takes place and that no addition of polymer to polymer occurs. This type
II polycondensation differs from the typical radical chain processes by the
fact that there is no termination or cessation involved in this present case.

The polymerization of ethylene oxide with glycols, amines, or acids as
initiators is a typical case of this type of polymerization; the initiating
functional group can be OH, NH_2, NH, SH, or COOH; the propagating
group is the OH group provided by the stepwise addition of the oxide.[17]

Let N_0 be the *initial* number of initiating molecules (*e.g.*, glycol molecules) and $N_1, N_2, N_3 \ldots$ be the number of these molecules having zero, one,
two, three, etc. added ethylene oxide molecules at time t. We shall assume
that the number of ethylene oxide molecules, M, is present in such large
excess that it is essentially unchanged during the course of the reaction.
Since we are only concerned either with the unreacted initiating molecules
or with initiating molecules to which ethylene oxide molecules have been
added, it is clear that $\Sigma N_x = N_0$.

$$dN_1/dt = -kN_1$$
$$dN_2/dt = kN_1 - kN_2 \qquad\qquad \text{(XI.20)}$$
$$\cdots\cdots\cdots\cdots\cdots$$
$$dN_x/dt = kN_{x-1} - kN_x$$

inasmuch as the species N_1 disappears by reacting with monomer whose
concentration is assumed to remain unity during the reaction, and x-mer
is formed by the reaction of $(x - 1)$-mer with monomer and disappears by
the reaction of x-mer with monomer.

[16] H. Dostal and H. Mark, *Z. physik. Chem.*, **B29**, 299 (1935); *Trans. Faraday Soc.*,
32, 54 (1936).

[17] P. J. Flory, *J. Am. Chem. Soc.*, **62**, 1561 (1940).

The solution of this set of equations is:[16,17]

$$\frac{N_x}{N_0} = \frac{e^{-kt}(kt)^{x-1}}{(x-1)!} \qquad x = 1,2,3, \ldots \qquad \text{(XI.21)}$$

which obeys the condition that:

$$\sum_1^\infty N_x = N_0$$

Assuming that the molecular weights of the initiating molecule (ethylene glycol) and the propagating molecule (ethylene oxide) are equal, or at least very similar, one gets the weight fraction distribution curve:

$$W_x = \frac{1}{1 + kt}\frac{e^{-kt}x(kt)^{x-1}}{(x-1)!} \qquad x = 1,2,3,4,\ldots \qquad \text{(XI.22)}$$

This distribution is considerably sharper than the random distribution derived for polycondensation products. Unfortunately, no experimental evidence exists to check this expression.

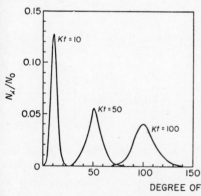

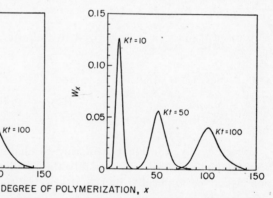

Fig. XI-6. Weight fraction distribution curve for type II polycondensation.

Fig. XI-7. Mole fraction distribution curve for type II polycondensation.

The number average and the weight average degrees of polymerization are given by the following expression:

$$\bar{P}_n = \sum_1^\infty x(N_x/N_0) = 1 + kt \qquad \text{(XI.23)}$$

$$\bar{P}_w = \sum_{x=1}^\infty xW_x = 1 + kt + kt/(1 + kt) \qquad \text{(XI.24)}$$

It is clear from equations (XI.23) and (XI.24) that with increasing time the ratio of the number and weight average degrees of polymerization approaches unity, indicating a very sharp distribution in molecular weights. Graphs of W_x and N_x/N_0 as functions of the degree of polymerization, x, for various values of kt are shown in Figures XI-6 and XI-7.

The general scheme of polymerization presented here should be applicable to the polymerization of many ring compounds to straight chain polymers. For example, ϵ-caprolactam can be polymerized by a trace of water, or catalytically by sodium metal (which first forms a lactam salt) :[18]

$$\overline{HN(CH_2)_5CO} + H_2O \longrightarrow H-[NH(CH_2)_5CO]_x-OH$$

Similarly, ring disulfides can be polymerized by sodium polysulfide, by mercaptides, or by ionic catalysts such as $FeCl_3$:[19, 20]

$$
\begin{array}{c}
O \\
H_2C \overset{\diagup\diagdown}{} CH_2 \\
| \qquad | \\
H_2C \qquad CH_2 \\
| \qquad | \\
S-S
\end{array}
+ NaSC_4H_9 \longrightarrow C_4H_9-(SCH_2CH_2OCH_2CH_2S)_x-Na
$$

Siloxane rings can be polymerized by sulfuric acid and other ionic catalysts :[21]

$$
\begin{array}{c}
Si(CH_3)_2-O-Si(CH_3)_2 \\
| \qquad\qquad | \\
O \qquad\qquad O \\
| \qquad\qquad | \\
Si(CH_3)_2 -O-Si(CH_3)_2
\end{array}
+ H_2SO_4 \longrightarrow HSO_4-
\begin{bmatrix}
CH_3 \\
| \\
Si-O \\
| \\
CH_3
\end{bmatrix}_x
-H
$$

Unfortunately, the kinetics of ring to chain transformations have not been studied in detail. Presumably the mechanism presented in this section would be applicable in the absence of competing reactions such as interchanges between the terminals of growing chain and the linkages of an already completed polymer. In many of these ring-chain formations it is reasonable to suppose that an active group at the end of the growing chain propagates the chain by interchanging with the functional linkage in the ring compound, *i.e.*, a mercaptide terminal in a growing polysulfide chain adds on a ring disulfide by a mercaptide disulfide interchange reac-

[18] W. E. Hanford and R. M. Joyce, *J. Polymer Sci.*, **3**, 167 (1948).
[19] F. O. Davis and E. M. Fettes, *J. Am. Chem. Soc.*, **70**, 2611 (1948).
[20] A. V. Tobolsky, F. Leonard, and G. P. Roeser, *J. Polymer Sci.*, **3**, 604 (1948).
[21] W. Patnode and D. F. Wilcock, *J. Am. Chem. Soc.*, **68**, 358 (1946).

tion. An interesting property of ring-to-chain transformations is that they occur with little change in volume.[20]

G. INTERCHANGE REACTIONS IN CONDENSATION POLYMERS

In condensation polymers the possibility of interchange reactions always exists. For example, in polyesters it has been shown that the hydroxyl terminal of a given chain can interchange with an ester linkage of another chain.[22] An example of interchange in low molecular weight esters would be:

$$CH_3O\overset{O}{\overset{\|}{C}}C_3H_7 + C_2H_5OH \longrightarrow C_2H_5O\overset{O}{\overset{\|}{C}}C_3H_7 + CH_3OH$$

In the case of polyamides there is considerable evidence for the occurrence of amino-amide interchanges analogous to the alcohol-ester interchange described above. Furthermore, it is likely that an amide-amide interchange can also occur.[23]

In the polysulfide polymers, ample evidence exists for the occurrence of interchange reactions.[24] In the ether and formal disulfide polymers, for example, catalyzed exchanges between mercaptan and mercaptide terminals and disulfide linkages occur with great ease even at room temperature:

$$RSSR + R_1SNa \longrightarrow RSSR_1 + RSNa$$

In the polysiloxanes, exchange reactions between Si—O linkages, catalyzed by ionic catalysts such as H_2SO_4, have also been demonstrated.[25,26]

In these interchanges between polymer molecules it is clear that there is no net change in the number of molecules before and after interchange, and so the number average molecular weight is unchanged. However, the distribution in molecular weights can be affected very considerably. For example, these interchanges were followed by studying the change in melt viscosity which depends on weight average molecular weight.[22]

The equilibrium size distribution[27,28] obtained by thermodynamic methods is:

[22] P. J. Flory, *J. Am. Chem. Soc.*, **64**, 2205 (1942).
[23] M. M. Brubaker, D. D. Coffman, and F. C. McGrew, U. S. Pat. 2,399,237 (1944).
[24] E. Fettes and F. Davis, Thiokol Corporation, *private communication.*
[25] W. Patnode and D. Wilcock, *J. Am. Chem. Soc.*, **68**, 358 (1946).
[26] D. W. Scott, *J. Am. Chem. Soc.*, **68**, 356, 2294 (1946).
[27] A. V. Tobolsky, *J. Chem. Phys.*, **12**, 402 (1944).
[28] P. J. Flory, *J. Chem. Phys.*, **12**, 425 (1944).

$$N_x = N_0 p^{x-1}(1 - p)^2$$

where p is defined by:

$$p/(1 - p)^2 = K$$

and K is an equilibrium constant. Interchange reactions between completed polymers can also be used to effect copolymerization.

H. STATISTICS OF POLYFUNCTIONAL CONDENSATIONS AND CONSTITUTION OF THREE-DIMENSIONAL CONDENSATION POLYMERS

When bifunctional molecules are condensed, they give linear polymeric molecules having two unreacted end groups. The weight fraction of n-mer was shown to be:

$$W_n = n p^{n-1}(1 - p)^2 \qquad (XI.25)$$

On the other hand, when polyfunctional monomers are condensed we get a much broader weight distribution curve. The reason is that the larger molecules have a large number of ends and therefore have better opportunity for growth. When a monomer of functionality, f, has condensed to form an n-mer, there have been formed $n - 1$ bonds (neglecting intramolecular linkage) and there are, therefore, $nf - 2(n - 1)$ unreacted end groups on each n-mer instead of just two as in the case of the linear polymer. In the case of polyfunctional monomers, the number of ways in which an n-mer can be hooked together is obviously vast. Furthermore, after a certain degree of reaction, a definite fraction of the polymeric material becomes "infinite" in size and is known as gel.[29,30] The physical properties of the gel fraction are quite distinct from those of the sol fraction. In contrast to the sol fraction, the gel is infusible (does not flow on heating) and is insoluble in solvents that do not destroy it chemically.[29-33]

Through the outstanding work of Flory[34] and of Stockmayer,[35] the ex-

[29] Bozza, *Giorn. chim. ind. applicata*, **14**, 400 (1932).
[30] W. H. Carothers, *Trans. Faraday Soc.*, **32**, 39 (1936).
[31] R. H. Kienle and A. G. Hovey, *J. Am. Chem. Soc.*, **51**, 518 (1929).
[32] R. H. Kienle and F. E. Petke, *J. Am. Chem. Soc.*, **62**, 1053 (1940); **63**, 481 (1941).
[33] H. Staudinger and Hener, *Ber.*, **67**, 1164 (1934).
[34] P. J. Flory, *J. Am. Chem. Soc.*, **63**, 3083, 3091, 3096 (1941); *Chem. Revs.*, **39**, 137 (1946), and in R. E. Burk and O. Grummitt, eds., *High Molecular Weight Organic Compounds*, Interscience, New York, 1949, pp. 211–282.
[35] W. Stockmayer, *J. Chem. Phys.*, **11**, 45 (1943); **12**, 125 (1944).

tremely complicated problem of size distribution, gel point, and sol–gel ratio in polyfunctional systems has been solved.

The size distribution in polymer arising from the condensation of a monomer of functionality, f, to an extent of reaction, p, is:

$$W_n = \frac{(fn - n)!\,f}{(n - 1)!\,(fn - 2n + 2)!}\, p^{n-1}(1 - p)^{fn - 2n + 2} \qquad (\text{XI.26})$$

the factor p^{n-1} arises from the fact that an n-mer has $n - 1$ linkages and the factor $(1 - p)^{fn - 2n + 2}$ comes from the $fn - 2n + 2$ unreacted end groups. The remaining factor arises from the structural isomerism of the complicated branched molecules. Figure XI-8 shows the theoretical weight

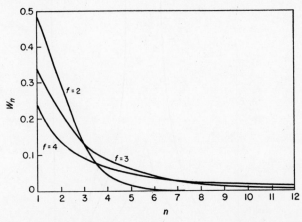

Fig. XI-8. Weight fraction distribution curve for bifunctional, trifunctional, and tetrafunctional polycondensations at $p = 0.3$.

distribution curves for bifunctional, trifunctional, and tetrafunctional condensing monomers when the extent of reaction p is equal to 0.3. As was stated previously, the molecules of higher functionality show a broader distribution of sizes because of their increased possibilities for growth in many directions.

The number average degree of polymerization has already been obtained (equation XI.1):

$$\bar{P}_n = \frac{1}{1 - fp/2} \qquad (\text{XI.27})$$

The weight average degree of polymerization is obtained by summation:

$$\bar{P}_w = \sum_{n=1}^{\infty} nW_n = \frac{1+p}{1-(f-1)p} \tag{XI.28}$$

It is clear that the weight average degree of polymerization becomes "infinite" before the number average molecular weight does. The critical ex-

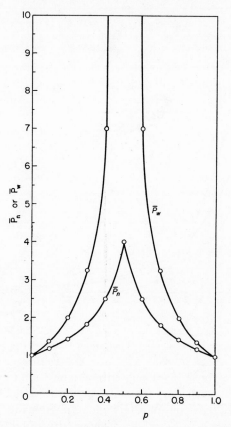

Fig. XI-9. Number average and weight average polymerization degrees as a function of extent of reaction for trifunctional condensation.

tent of reaction, p_c, at which the weight average molecular weight goes to infinity and which is identified as the gel point is

$$p_c = 1/(f-1) \tag{XI.29}$$

It is to be noted that at the gel point, where the weight average degree of polymerization is infinite, the number average degree of polymerization (measured by depression of freezing point, etc.) is quite small (*e.g.*, 3 in the tetrafunctional case and 4 in the trifunctional case). Figure XI-9 shows plots of the number average and weight average degrees of polymerization as a function of the extent of reaction for trifunctional condensation. In the case in which a mixture of molecules of different functionality is used, equations (XI.26), (XI.28), and (XI.29) still hold, provided that we use a weight average functionality, $\bar{f}_w$, and equation (XI.27) holds provided we use a number average functionality $\bar{f}_n$. These quantities are defined as follows:

$$\bar{f}_w = \sum f_i^2 N_i / \sum f_i N_i \tag{XI.30}$$

$$\bar{f}_n = f_i N_i / \sum N_i$$

where N_i is the number of monomers of functionality f_i being used in the condensation.

In a reaction between a polyfunctional monomer and bifunctional monomers such as:

$$\begin{array}{c} A \\ \diagdown \\ A + A - A + B - B \\ \diagup \\ A \end{array}$$

a somewhat different set of definitions prove useful. Instead of describing the molecules in terms of size, they are described in terms of the number of branch points (*i.e.*, polyfunctional units) the molecule contains, regardless of the length of chain between branch points. Instead of defining the problem in terms of p, the extent of reaction, a new quantity α is defined, where α is the probability that one leg of a branch unit leads via a chain of bifunctional units to another branch unit. The weight fraction of molecules composed of n' branch units is (provided that the proportion of branch units is small):

$$W_n' = 2 \frac{(fn' - n' + 1)!}{n'!(fn' - 2n' + 2)!} \alpha^{n'}(1 - \alpha)^{fn' - 2n' + 2} \tag{XI.31}$$

We can describe this distribution as a complexity distribution rather than a size distribution.

The calculation of α in terms of the stoichiometry and the extent of reaction is presented in the original papers.[36] The similarity between equations (XI.31) and (XI.26) is apparent.

The critical value of α at which the formation of infinite network becomes possible is:

$$\alpha_c = 1/(f - 1) \tag{XI.32}$$

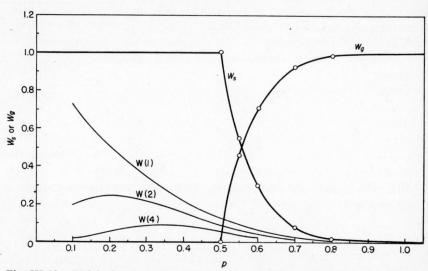

Fig. XI-10. Weight fraction of monomer, dimer, tetramer, sol, and gel as a function of extent of reaction in trifunctional polycondensation.

The percentage of gel has also been calculated from the distribution equation. In the simple, trifunctional case, where $p > p_c = 1/2$, the weight per cent of sol and gel, W_s and W_g, are:

$$W_s = \frac{(1 - p)^3}{p^3} \qquad W_g = 1 - \frac{(1 - p)^3}{p^3} \tag{XI.33}$$

From the complexity distribution function in polymers composed of long chains joined by trifunctional units it follows that when $\alpha > \alpha_c = \frac{1}{2}$:

$$W_s = \frac{(1 - \alpha)^2}{2} \qquad W_g = 1 - \frac{(1 - \alpha)^2}{2} \tag{XI.34}$$

Equations (XI.26) and (XI.31) are valid for the molecules of the sol

[36] P. J. Flory, *J. Am. Chem. Soc.*, **51**, 518 (1939).

fraction even beyond the point of gelation, provided that we include the gel fraction as part of the total weight in calculating weight fraction. At any extent of reaction p' (or α') beyond the critical point of gelation, the *relative* distribution in sizes or complexities between the sol molecules is identical to the *relative* size or complexity distribution at a complementary value of p (or α) before gelation. In the trifunctional case, the complementary value is $p = 1 - p'$ (or $\alpha = 1 - \alpha'$). At complementary values of p' and p, the expressions for the weight fraction $W_n(p')$ and $W_n(p)$ are related as follows:

$$W_n(p')/W_n(p) = W_s(p') \qquad n = 1,2,3,4 \ldots \qquad (XI.35)$$

where $W_s(p')$ is the weight fraction of the sol at the extent of reaction p', and is independent of n. Figure XI-10 shows the weight fraction of monomer, dimer, and tetramer and also the sol and gel fractions as a function of the extent of reaction for trifunctional polycondensations.

I. POLYMERIZATION OF NYLON

One of the classical developments of condensation polymerization has been the successful synthesis of fiber-forming polyamides, generically known as nylons, from diamines and dibasic acids. The development of nylon arose during the course of fundamental investigations of condensation polymers initiated by Carothers.[37] The early developments in this work were recently reviewed by Coffman, Berchet, Peterson, and Spanagel.[38]

The polyamides were selected as a suitable system from which textile fibers might be formed because of their analogous structure to wool and silk, and because they had strong intermolecular forces and a tendency to crystallize. The early exploratory work failed to give polymers suitable for spinning. A fundamental advance was made when it was realized that exact control of molecular weight was necessary, and that for this purpose utmost purity was required. For high molecular weights an exact equivalence of the acid and amide functions is necessary.

For the purpose of processing nylon it is desirable to achieve a degree of polymerization of 40 or higher and to ensure that the degree of polymerization and hence the melt viscosity does not change during the processing

[37] H. Mark and G. S. Whitby, eds., *Collected Papers of Wallace Hume Carothers on High Polymeric Substances*. Interscience, New York, 1940.
[38] D. D. Coffman, G. J. Berchet, W. R. Peterson, and E. W. Spanagel, *J. Polymer Sci.*, **2**, 3.6 (1947).

operation. For these reasons it is desirable to start with completely equivalent amounts of dibasic acid and diamine, add a known amount of monofunctional acid (e. g., lauric acid) or amine or an excess of one of the monomers to obtain the desired degree of polymerization, and then carry the reaction as far toward completion as possible. The added substances are known as stabilizers. By this procedure a predetermined degree of polymerization can be achieved, and, inasmuch as the molecules will not have any complementary amide-forming end groups, no further change in degree of polymerization will occur during processing.

To achieve a complete equivalence of dibasic acid and diamine, a salt of these reactants is first prepared. The number of moles of stabilizer required will equal the number of moles of diamine-dibasic acid salt divided by the average degree of polymerization required. This follows because, at complete reaction, the number of stabilizer molecules, S, is equal to the number, N, of polymer molecules. If $\bar{P}_n$ is the number-average degree of polymerization and N_0 the number of molecules of the diamine-dibasic acid salt, then:

$$S = N = N_0/\bar{P}_n \qquad (XI.36)$$

To obtain a polymer of a specified intrinsic viscosity (see Chapter IX) the following approximate formula can be used:

$$\frac{\text{moles stabilizer}}{\text{required}} = \frac{\text{mol. wt. of salt} \times \text{moles salt}}{16,000 \times [\eta]} \qquad (XI.37)$$

In the preparation of a salt of the diamine and dibasic acid, alcoholic solutions of the monomers are brought together and exact equivalence is attained by following the neutralization electrometrically. A white salt precipitates on cooling:

$$H_2N(CH_2)_6NH_2 + HOOC(CH_2)_4COOH \longrightarrow H_2N(CH_2)_6NH_3OOC(CH_2)_4COOH$$

The polymerization is carried out either by heating the salt under conditions that permit the removal of water or by heating the salt in an inert solvent such as cresol or xylenol.

In the first case the salt is charged into water together with stabilizer and heated in a sealed autoclave to prevent an escape by volatilization and subsequent deficiency of one of the components. The condensation is initially carried out at high temperatures (250–300°C.) and high pressures (250–275 p.s.i.) and in the absence of oxygen to prevent oxidative gelling. Condensation is forced to completion by removing the water originally added and that formed during condensation by heating at reduced pressures.

The melting points of polyamides, of course, vary with the structure of the monomers from which they were made. The polymer from hexa-methylenediamine and adipic acid has a melting point of about 250°C. It is soluble in formic acid, phenol, cresol, hot formamide, and cold concentrated hydrochloric acid. It is hydrolyzed slowly by strong mineral acids or alkalis. The polymers are crystalline and can be oriented. Continuous filaments are prepared by extruding the molten polyamide through narrow orifices and collecting the extruded filaments on a rotating bobbin. To obtain high tensile strength these filaments must be cold drawn (oriented) to about four times their original lengths.

J. SYNTHETIC POLYPEPTIDES

Inasmuch as naturally occurring proteins are known to be linear condensates of α-amino acids, it is of great interest to synthesize high molecular weight polypeptides to serve as protein analogs. Polypeptides of low molecular weight were prepared in the classical research of Emil Fischer, and the same step-by-step condensations were used to prepare low molecular copolymers of amino acids.[39] Frankel and Katchalski[40] reported synthesis of polypeptides of as many as 110 units by self-condensation of glycine methyl ester and alanine ethyl ester, and similar condensations of the sodium salts of amino acids were reported by Pacsu.[41]

The most promising method of obtaining high molecular polypeptides appears to have been discovered inadvertently by Leuchs and co-workers.[42] These workers isolated several N-carboxyamino acid anhydrides and observed a self-condensation. Among the N-carboxyamino acid anhydrides and their condensates that they described were:

N-Carboxyglycine anhydride   N-Carboxy-dl-phenylglycine anhydride

[39] E. Abderhalden and A. Foder, *Ber.*, **49**, 561 (1916).

[40] M. Frankel and E. Katchalski, *J. Am. Chem. Soc.*, **64**, 2264, 2271 (1942).

[41] E. Pacsu and E. J. Wilson, Jr., *J. Org. Chem.*, **7**, 117, 126 (1942).

[42] H. Leuchs, *Ber.*, **39**, 857 (1906). Leuchs and Manassi, *ibid.*, **40**, 3243 (1907). Leuchs and Geiger, *ibid.*, **41**, 1721 (1908). Curtius and Sieber, *ibid.*, **55**, 1543 (1922).

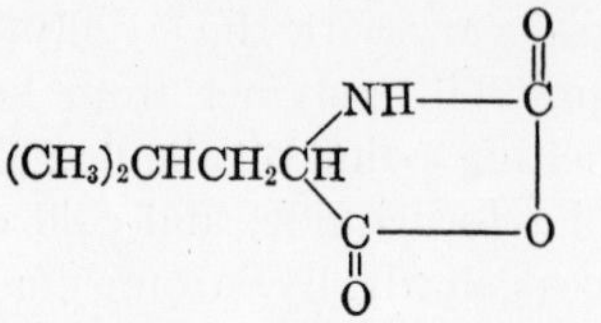

N-Carboxy-*l*-leucine anhydride 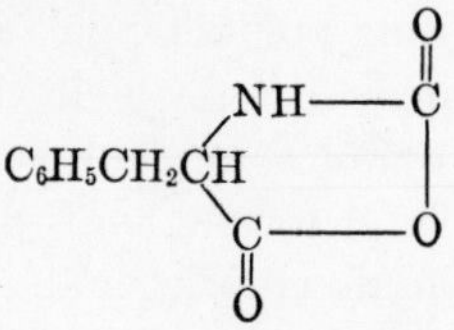   N-Carboxy-*dl*-phenylalanine anhydride

Leuchs and co-workers referred to the condensates of the above N-carboxy-amine acid anhydrides as glycine anhydride, phenylglycine anhydride, etc.

Wessely[43] appears to be the first to have suspected that these condensation products were polypeptides.

Meyer and Go[44] studied the condensation product of N-carboxyglycine anhydride and concluded that it was a high polymeric polypeptide of about 30 glycine residues. They compared its x-ray diagram with that of heptaglycylglycine and showed that the diagrams were very similar. They wrote the reaction as follows:

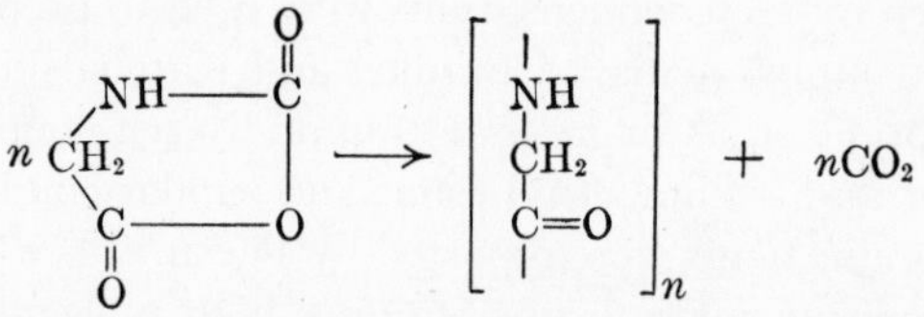

Woodward and Schramm[45] reported the preparation of very high molecular weight copolymers by the Leuchs synthesis, and emphasized the importance and generality of the method as a means of producing protein analogs of the general form:

I $HOOCCHR_1NH(COCHR_2NH)_nCOCH(R_{n+2})NH_2$

They write for the mechanism of the reaction:

$$H_2O + \overset{\text{II}}{\overline{CO-CH(R)-NH-CO-O}} \longrightarrow HOOC-CH(R)-NH-COOH$$

$$\xrightarrow{-CO_2} HOOC-CH(R)-NH_2 \xrightarrow{+\text{II}} HOOC-CH(R)-NH-COCHR-NH-$$

$$COOH \xrightarrow{-CO_2} HOOC-CH(R)-NH-COCHR-NH_2 \xrightarrow{+\text{II}} \text{etc.}$$

[43] Wessely *et al.*, *Z. physiol. Chem.*, **146**, 72 (1925); **154**, 91 (1926); **155**, 402 (1926); **170**, 38 (1927). Wessely *et al.*, *Monatsh.*, **48**, 1 (1927).

[44] K. H. Meyer and Y. Go, *Helv. Chim. Acta*, **17**, 1488 (1934). Y. Go and H. Tani, *Bull. Soc. Chem. Japan*, **14**, 510 (1939).

[45] R. B. Woodward and C. H. Schramm, *J. Am. Chem. Soc.*, **69**, 1551 (1947).

These authors carried out the condensation by dissolving N-carboxy-l-leucine anhydride and N-carboxy-dl-phenylalanine in reagent benzene. They claim that they obtained copolymers of structure I with $n > 10,000$, and that the degree of polymerization can be controlled by the amount of water dissolved in the benzene.

Katchalski, Grossfeld, and Frankel[46] have reported the formation of polylysine derivatives by the condensation of ϵ-carbobenzoxy-α-carboxyl-l-lysine anhydride.

$$n \begin{array}{c} \text{O} \\ \parallel \\ \text{C} \rule{2cm}{0.4pt} \text{O} \\ | \qquad\qquad | \\ \text{HN} \rule{0.3cm}{0.4pt} \text{CHR} \rule{0.3cm}{0.4pt} \text{C=O} \end{array} + \text{H}_2\text{O} \longrightarrow \text{H}_2\text{N} \rule{0.3cm}{0.4pt} \text{CHR} \rule{0.3cm}{0.4pt} \text{CO} \rule{0.3cm}{0.4pt} \left[\text{HN} \rule{0.3cm}{0.4pt} \text{CHR} \rule{0.3cm}{0.4pt} \text{CO} \right]_{n-1} \text{OH} + n\text{CO}_2$$

where $R = -(\text{CH}_2)_4-\text{NH}-\text{CO}-\text{O}-\text{CH}_2-\text{C}_6\text{H}_5$. These polylysine derivatives are water soluble and are split by the glycerol extract of pancreatin as well as by crystalline trypsin.

Hanby, Waley, and Watson[47] have also reported the synthesis of polyglutamic acid by the same method.

[46] E. Katchalski, I. Grossfeld, and M. Frankel, *J. Am. Chem. Soc.*, **69**, 2565 (1947); also **58**, 879 (1946).

[47] W. E. Hanby, S. G. Waley, and J. Watson, *Nature*, **61**, 132 (1948).

XII. CHAIN REACTION POLYMERIZATION

This type of polymerization is largely confined to so-called addition polymerization consisting in the union of many unsaturated molecules to form a large molecule in which the individual units are connected by single bonds:

$$CH_2{=}CXY \longrightarrow -CH_2CXY(CH_2CXY)_nCH_2CXY-$$

The units combining to form the polymer may be all the same, or they may be of two or more types. The most common types of monomers are the vinyl and diene monomers, which may be regarded as derivatives of ethylene and butadiene.

Among the vinyl monomers it is generally found that complete substitution of one of the carbon atoms will not hinder polymerization as in vinylidene chloride. But substitution of both ethylene carbon atoms, as in 1,2-dichloroethylene, generally gives a monomer that will not polymerize by itself but may enter into copolymerization. Certain monomers of the type $CF_2{=}CXY$ will also polymerize by themselves. For monosubstituted ethylenes it is found that certain groups such as COOH, Cl, and C≡N promote the polymerizing tendencies, whereas alkyl groups repress the polymerizing tendencies. A partial list of important vinyl monomers is shown in Table XII-1.

Vinyl monomers may be polymerized by purely thermal or photochemical polymerization, or may be polymerized by radical-producing catalysts, ionic catalysts, or by sodium. In all cases the evidence for a chain reaction mechanism is very strong. Briefly, the fact that the molecular weight of the polymer remains essentially constant during polymerization and the fact that traces of impurities have strong catalytic or inhibitory effects are among the most striking evidences of chain reaction mechanisms in these systems.

A. NATURE OF THE CARBON-CARBON DOUBLE BOND

The electronic structure of the carbon-carbon double bond has been elucidated by quantum mechanical treatment by the methods of atomic and molecular orbitals.

395

TABLE XII-1

PARTIAL LIST OF VINYL, VINYLIDENE, AND DIENE MONOMERS

Monomer	Structure	Monomer	Structure
Ethylene	$H_2C=CH_2$	Vinylnaphthalene	$H_2C=CH$
Styrene	$H_2C=CH$		
Vinyl chloride	$H_2C=CH-Cl$	Indene	
Vinyl acetate	$H_2C=CH-OCOCH_3$	Coumarone	
Acrylic acid	$H_2C=CH-COOH$		
Methyl acrylate	$H_2C=CH-COOCH_3$	Tetrafluoroethylene	$F_2C=CF_2$
Ethyl acrylate	$H_2C=CH-COOC_2H_5$	Trifluoromonochloroethylene	$F_2C=CFCl$
Acrylonitrile	$H_2C=CH-C{\equiv}N$	Vinylidene chloride	$H_2C=CCl-Cl$
4-Monochlorostyrene	$H_2C=CH$ $-Cl$	Methyacrylic acid	$H_2C=CCH_3-COOH$
		Methyl methacrylate	$H_2C=CCH_3-COOCH_3$

α-Methylstyrene $H_2C=CCH_3$ (phenyl)

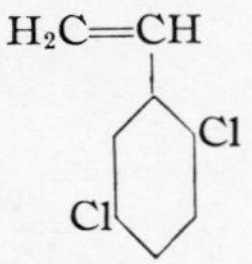

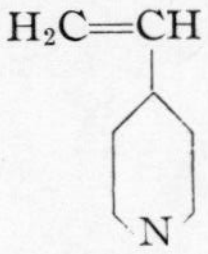

Isobutylene $H_2C=CCH_3$ / CH_3

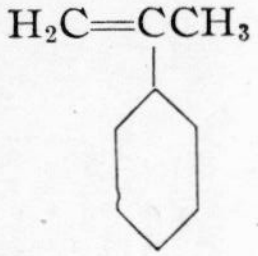

2-Nitropropene $H_2C=CCH_3$ / NO_2

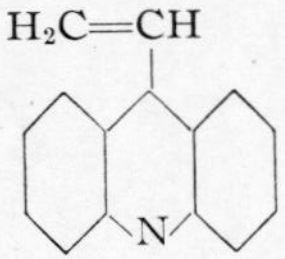

Butadiene $H_2C=CH-CH=CH_2$

Isoprene $H_2C=C(CH_3)-CH=CH_2$

2,3-Dimethylbutadiene $H_2C=C(CH_3)-C(CH_3)=CH_2$

Chloroprene $H_2C=C(Cl)-CH=CH_2$

2-Phenylbutadiene $H_2C=C\varphi-CH=CH_2$

Cyclopentadiene

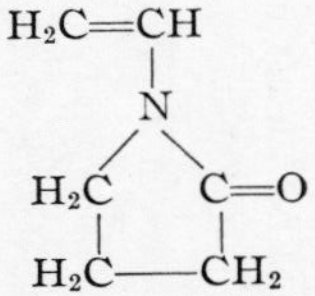

Vinylacetylene $H_2C=CH-C\equiv CH$

Acenaphthalene $HC=CH$ (ring)

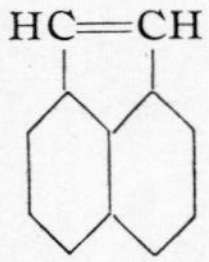

2,5-Dichlorostyrene $H_2C=CH$– (phenyl, Cl, Cl)

4-Vinylpyridine $H_2C=CH$– (pyridine, N)

Vinylcarbazole $H_2C=CH$– (carbazole, N)

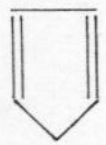

n-Butyl vinyl ketone $H_2C=CH-COC_4H_9$

Vinylpyrrolidone $H_2C=CH-N$ (ring, C=O, CH_2, H_2C, H_2C)

Using the language of the atomic orbital theory (method of directed valence bonds), it may be supposed that when a carbon atom takes part in double bond formation, one s and two p orbitals, $i.e.$, p_x and p_y, combine (hybridize) to form three trigonal orbitals that take part in bond formation with the orbitals (of opposite spin) from neighboring atoms. The direction of the bonds lies along the direction of maximum overlap of the orbital wave functions, and, for the case of trigonal orbitals (hybridized sp^2 orbitals), the bonds lie in the same plane (the xy plane) and make angles of 120° with each other. The fourth orbital (p_z) retains its p character unchanged and so the fourth bond is oriented along the z axis perpendicular to the plane containing the other three bonds. When two carbon atoms are joined by a double bond, one of the linkages is formed by the overlapping of one trigonal orbital from each atom, while the second linkage results from the pairing of the pure p_z orbitals. Normal single bonds, which are referred to as $\sigma\sigma$ bonds, have the maxima of the two orbitals involved in the bond lying in the same line, and this is the case of the first of the two linkages that comprise the double bond. In the second linkage, which involves the p_z orbital on each atom, the maxima of the orbitals lie parallel to each other. This type of bond is known as a $\pi\pi$ bond and is approximately thirty per cent weaker than the $\sigma\sigma$ bond. The occurrence of the $\pi\pi$ as well as the $\sigma\sigma$ linkage in the double bond explains the absence of free rotation in the bond. The two p_z orbitals of the $\pi\pi$ bond tend to overlap as much as possible in order to give maximum linkage strength, and this will occur only when these orbitals are parallel to each other and hence are in the same plane. Rotation out of this plane requires the surmounting of an energy barrier.

The electronic states of olefins, ethylene in particular, have been considered by Mulliken,[1] Hückel,[2] and Lennard-Jones[3] by the method of molecular orbitals. This theoretical treatment indicated that, while ten of the twelve electrons in ethylene are localized by pairs, taking up the positions between the carbon and hydrogen nuclei and between the two carbon nuclei as considered above, the remaining two electrons are distributed over the entire molecule. Thus they cannot be said to belong to any one carbon atom, for which reason they have been designated unsaturation electrons.

The energy states of these electrons are shown in Figure XII-1,[4] where

[1] R. S. Mulliken, $Rev.\ Mod.\ Phys.$, **14**, 265 (1942) and earlier work cited there.

[2] E. Hückel, $Z.\ Elektrochem.$, **43**, 752, 857 (1937) and earlier work cited there.

[3] J. E. Lennard-Jones and E. A. Coulson, $Trans.\ Faraday\ Soc.$, **35**, 811 (1939).

[4] H. M. Hulbert, R. A. Harman, A. V. Tobolsky, and H. Eyring, $Ann.\ N.\ Y.\ Acad.\ Sci.$, **44**, 371 (1943).

energy is plotted as a function of the angular rotation of one methylene group with respect to the other. In the lowest state, N, both electrons have antiparallel spins, so that ethylene is in a singlet state. When one of the electrons is promoted, two states are possible, a singlet state V in which the spins are paired and a triplet state T in which the spins are unpaired.

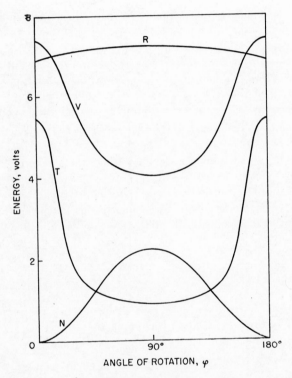

Fig. XII-1. The energy levels of ethylene: (N) normal singlet state; (T) excited triplet state; (V) excited singlet state; (R) the "Rydberg" state.

It has been postulated that the triplet state is a fairly low-lying state and that this activated "diradical" state plays a role in certain chemical reactions such as *cis-trans* isomerization.[5] In fact, *cis-trans* isomerizations have been considered to proceed by either a "triplet" mechanism in which

[5] J. L. Magee, W. Shand, and H. Eyring, *J. Am. Chem. Soc.*, **63**, 677 (1941).

the ethylene derivative is activated to the triplet state or by an ionic or polar mechanism in which the molecule remains in its normal state N but must surmount a high energy barrier when rotated 90° out of its plane.

Some evidence from interpretation of fluorescence data[6] indicates that the triplet state is often of much higher energy (70 kcal.) than the normal state and therefore not available for ordinary chemical reactions. Nevertheless, the existence of a low-lying triplet state would be an attractive hypothesis by which one could explain the apparently purely thermal polymerization of styrene and perhaps also the photochemical polymerization of vinyl monomers. The uncatalyzed thermal polymerization of styrene has been reproduced in various laboratories and a mechanism involving diradical formation as the initial step has been postulated but never completely proved.

In the large majority of cases, vinyl polymerizations are initiated by radical or ionic catalysts rather than by thermal or photochemical means. In the case of radical polymerizations the odd electron in a free radical that approaches the monomer molecule attracts the π electron of the double bond, which has a spin opposite to that of the electron in the free radical, eventually forming a normal electron pair bond with it; simultaneously, the electron with the same spin is repelled to the far end of the monomer, thus reconstituting a free radical. The steps may be indicated symbolically as follows:

$$R\uparrow + CH_2 {\overset{||}{}} CHX \longrightarrow \;\; \uparrow\downarrow CH_2CHX \uparrow \longrightarrow RCH_2CHX\cdot$$

When a positive ion such as a proton approaches the double bond it attracts both of the π electrons of the double bond to form a single covalent bond and leaves the remote carbon atom positively charged:

$$H^+ + CH_2 {\overset{\curvearrowleft}{}} CHX \longrightarrow H:CH_2CHX^+$$

Negatively charged ions have also been proposed as active intermediates in vinyl polymerization. In this case the approaching negative ion would repel the two π electrons of the double bond:

$$Y^- + CH_2 {\overset{}{}} CHX \longrightarrow Y:CH_2{-}CHX: \longrightarrow YCH_2CHX^-$$

[6] G. N. Lewis and M. Kasha, *J. Am. Chem. Soc.*, **66**, 2100 (1944).

B. RADICAL CHAIN POLYMERIZATION OF VINYL MONOMERS

The chain character of vinyl polymerization was recognized in a series of fundamental papers by Chalmers,[7] Staudinger,[8] Mark,[9] Flory,[10] Gee,[11] and Melville,[12] among others.* Many of the important principles of the chain reaction mechanisms in these polymerizations, both thermal and with benzoyl peroxide as catalyst, were clarified by Schulz[13] in a series of classical experimental papers on the polymerization of styrene. As in all kinetic studies of radical chain polymerization, two quantities were measured, the rate of conversion of monomer to polymer and the mean molecular weight of the polymer. Schulz found that during most of the polymerization the average molecular weight of the polymer formed was constant. Furthermore he found that the rate of conversion of monomer to polymer was proportional to the square root of the catalyst concentration and that the average molecular weight of the polymer formed was inversely proportional to the square root of the catalyst concentration.

These facts are consistent with the following mechanism:

$$\text{Cat} \xrightarrow{\ k_1\ } \text{R} \cdot \qquad\qquad \text{Initiation}$$

$$\text{R} \cdot + \text{M} \xrightarrow{\ k_2\ } \text{RM}_1^{\cdot}$$

$$\text{RM}_1^{\cdot} + \text{M} \xrightarrow{\ k_2\ } \text{RM}_2^{\cdot} \qquad\qquad \text{Growth} \qquad\qquad \text{(A)}$$

$$\text{......................}$$

$$\text{RM}_n^{\cdot} + \text{M} \xrightarrow{\ k_2\ } \text{RM}_{n+}^{\cdot}$$

$$\text{RM}_n^{\cdot} + \text{RM}_p^{\cdot} \xrightarrow{\ k_c\ } \text{RM}_{n+p}\text{R} \qquad\qquad \text{Termination}$$

$$\text{RM}^{\cdot} + \text{RM}_p^{\cdot} \xrightarrow{\ k_d\ } \text{RM}_n + \text{RM}_p$$

---

* The earliest paper which indicated that ethylene in the gas phase can be polymerized by free radicals was that of H. S. Taylor, *Proc. Am. Phil. Soc.*, **65**, 90 (1926).

[7] W. Chalmers, *Can. J. Research*, **7**, 113 (1932); *J. Am. Chem. Soc.*, **56**, 912 (1934).

[8] H. Staudinger and W. Frost, *Ber.*, **68**, 2351 (1935).

[9] H. Mark and R. Raff, *Z. physik. Chem.*, **B31**, 275 (1936).

[10] P. J. Flory, *J. Am. Chem. Soc.*, **59**, 241 (1937).

[11] G. Gee, *Trans. Faraday Soc.*, **31**, 969 (1935); **32**, 656, 666 (1936). A. C. Cuthbertson, G. Gee, and E. Rideal, *Proc. Roy. Soc. London*, **A170**, 300 (1939).

[12] H. Melville, *Proc. Roy. Soc. London*, **A163**, 511 (1937).

[13] G. V. Schulz and E. Husemann, *Z. physik. Chem.*, **B43**, 385 (1939); **B34**, 187 (1936). G. V. Schulz, A. Dinglinger, and E. Husemann, *ibid.*, **B39**, 246 (1938). G. V. Schulz, *Z. Elektrochem.*, **47**, 265 (1941).

TABLE XII-2

PARTIAL LIST OF FREE RADICAL PRODUCING CATALYSTS

Benzoyl peroxide	$C_6H_5COOCC_6H_5$ (with two C=O groups)
tert-Butyl hydroperoxide	$(CH_3)_3COOH$
Di-*tert*-butyl peroxide	$(CH_3)_3COOC(CH_3)_3$
Acetoyl peroxide	$CH_3COOCCH_3$ (with two C=O groups)
tert-Butyl perbenzoate	C6H5—COOC(CH3)3 (with C=O group)
Di-*tert*-butyl diperphthalate	benzene ring with two COOC(CH3)3 groups (each with C=O)
p-Bromobenzoyl peroxide	Br—C6H4—C(=O)—O—O—C(=O)—C6H4—Br
Cumene hydroperoxide	C6H5—C(CH3)2—COOH
Tetraphenylsuccinonitrile	$(C_6H_5)_2C—C—(C_6H_5)_2$ with CN groups on each central carbon
Aryldiazohydroxides	Ar—N=N—OH
Nitrosoacetanilide	C6H5—N(N=O)(COCH3)
Diazoaminobenzene	C6H5—N=N—NH—C6H5
2-Azobisisobutyronitrile	$(CH_3)_3C—N=N—C(CH_3)_3$ with CN groups on each carbon

where Cat represents the catalyst (benzoyl peroxide) and $R\cdot$ represents a radical ($\langle\!\!\!\bigcirc\!\!\!\rangle\cdot$ or $\langle\!\!\!\bigcirc\!\!\!\rangle COO\cdot$) resulting from the dismutation of the benzoyl peroxide. The growth of polymer starts by the addition of the radical to the double bond:

$$R\cdot + CH_2::CH\underset{X}{}\longrightarrow R:CH_2:\underset{X}{\overset{H}{C}}\cdot\xrightarrow{CH_2=CHX} RCH_2CHXCH_2CHX\cdot$$

and the ensuing radicals can then add to another monomeric bond in just the same way. The presence of catalyst fragments in polystyrene, polymethyl methacrylate and polyacrylonitrile has been substantiated, as has the validity of the above reaction scheme in other vinyl monomers.[14] Table XII-2 gives a partial list of some radical-producing catalysts.

The termination process occurs when two radicals add to one another or when they disproportionate according to the following mechanisms:

$$\text{\char`\~}CH_2CHX\cdot + \cdot CHXCH_2\text{\char`\~}\xrightarrow{\text{combination}}\text{\char`\~}CH_2CHXCHXCH_2\text{\char`\~}$$

$$\text{\char`\~}CH_2CHX\cdot + \cdot CHXCH_2\text{\char`\~}\xrightarrow{\text{disproportionation}}\text{\char`\~}CH_2CH_2X + CHX=CH\text{\char`\~}$$

The kinetic consequences of equations (A) can be deduced as follows: let $[c^*]$ be the total concentration of free radicals of all kinds, that is:

$$[c^*] = \sum (RM_n\cdot)$$

At the very beginning of the reaction $[c^*]$ keeps increasing as it forms from breakdown of the catalyst. The rate of disappearance of radicals in the termination step is proportional to the square of the concentration of radicals, and in a fairly short time† the rate of disappearance becomes equal to the rate of formation. At this point a steady state concentration of radicals is achieved, which can be determined by the equation:

$$k_1[\text{Cat}] = k_3[c^*]^2 \qquad\qquad\qquad (\text{XII.1})$$

$$[c^*] = (k_1/k_3)^{1/2}[\text{Cat}]^{1/2}$$

where $k_3 = k_c + k_d$.

Inasmuch as [Cat], the concentration of catalyst, generally does not change very much during the course of the polymerization, the steady

---

† Nozaki and Bartlett (*J. Am. Chem. Soc.*, **68**, 2377, 1946) have shown that in vinyl acetate polymerizations the steady state of radical concentration is reached before 2.3% of the monomer has polymerized.

[14] C. C. Price, *Ann. N. Y. Acad. Sci.*, **44**, 351 (1943).

state concentration is also constant throughout most of the reaction. The rate of conversion of monomer to polymer is given by:

$$-d[M]/dt = k_2[c^*][M] = k_2(k_1/k_3)^{1/2}[Cat]^{1/2}[M] \qquad (XII.2)$$

The kinetic chain length, ν, is given by:

$$\begin{aligned}\nu &= \text{velocity of growth/velocity of termination} \\ &= k_2[c^*][M]/k_3[c^*]^2 = k_2[M]/k_3[c^*] \\ &= k_2[M]/(k_1k_3)^{1/2}[Cat]^{1/2}\end{aligned} \qquad (XII.3)$$

Equation (XII.2) shows that the rate of polymerization is proportional to the square root of the catalyst concentration. Equation (XII.3) shows that the kinetic chain length, ν, is inversely proportional to the square root of the catalyst concentration. Inasmuch as the monomer concentration is fairly constant over a large part of the reaction, the kinetic chain length remains approximately constant during the reaction.

If the chain mechanism for the polymerization consists only in initiation, propagation, and termination, as discussed above, the kinetic chain length is equal to the number average degree of polymerization. Schulz, in fact, found that the degree of polymerization of polystyrene produced by benzoyl peroxide catalysis did indeed remain fairly constant throughout the polymerization and was inversely proportional to the square root of the catalyst concentration.

A complete discussion of the degree of polymerization obtained in vinyl polymerization cannot be achieved without introducing the concept of chain transfer to monomer and to other substances present in the system. In this basic elementary reaction, which will be more fully discussed in section C, a growing radical reacts with another molecule such as the monomer by abstracting an available atom such as a hydrogen atom. In this way the growing radical chain is terminated, but a new radical is produced from the monomer. This new radical adds monomer to start a new growing polymer chain.

$$RM_n^{\cdot} + M \xrightarrow{k_{TM}} RM_nH + M\cdot$$

$$M\cdot + M \xrightarrow{k_2} M_2^{\cdot} \longrightarrow \longrightarrow \longrightarrow M_n^{\cdot}$$

This elementary step, together with chain transfer to catalyst and chain transfer to polymer, must be considered in addition to those already presented in equations (A) for a complete discussion of the bulk polymerization of vinyl monomers. Chain transfer to monomer or to catalyst affects the number average degree of polymerization, $\bar{P}_n$. Chain transfer to polymer, which becomes more important as the fractional conversion of monomer to polymer increases, produces branched polymers but does not affect $\bar{P}_n$. On the other hand, the rate of polymerization as expressed by equation (XII.2) is unaffected by chain transfer, provided we assume that the term $k_1[\text{Cat}]$ refers specifically to the rate of spontaneous decomposition of catalyst into radicals. The over-all rate of catalyst decomposition will also include terms for induced decomposition of catalyst by radicals and for destruction of catalyst by radical transfer.

Most catalysts such as benzoyl peroxide, produce *monoradicals* such as $\varphi\text{COO}.$ in their initial cleavage. Furthermore, for many catalysts the chain transfer to catalyst is very small. In these cases of monoradical initiation and no chain transfer to catalyst the following relations can be derived:[15]

$$\frac{1}{\bar{P}_n} = \frac{k_{TM}}{k_2} + \frac{(k_c + k_d)^{1/2} k_1^{1/2} [\text{Cat}]^{1/2}}{2k_2[\text{M}]} \left[\frac{k_c + 2k_d}{k_c + k_d} \right]$$

$$\frac{1}{\bar{P}_n} = \frac{k_{TM}}{k_2} + \frac{(k_c + 2k_d)\,(-d[\text{M}]/dt)}{2k_2^2[\text{M}]^2}$$

Plots of $-d[\text{M}]/dt$ versus $[\text{Cat}]^{1/2}$, $1/\bar{P}_n$ versus $[\text{Cat}]^{1/2}$ and $1/\bar{P}_n$ versus $-d[\text{M}]/dt$ for styrene polymerization with suitable catalysts are shown in Figures XII-2a, b, and c, respectively, from the data of Johnson and Tobolsky.[15] These graphs are straight lines, as the theory predicts. The intercept in Figures XII-2b and 2c gives k_{TM}/k_2 directly. The relative values of k_c and k_d can be determined from the relation:

$$\frac{k_c}{2(k_c + k_d)} = \frac{k_1[\text{Cat}]/(-d[\text{M}]/dt) + (k_{TM}/k_2) - (1/\bar{P}_n)}{k_1[\text{Cat}]/(-d[\text{M}]/dt)}$$

provided that $k_1[\text{Cat}]$, the rate of spontaneous decomposition of catalyst into radicals, can be determined by independent measurements.

If the initiation step proceeds via a diradical, as has been often postulated for thermal and photoinitiated polymerizations, or as would probably be the case when cyclic peroxides are used as initiators, then it is clear that some of the growing polymer chains have *two* active ends. For diradical initiation it can be shown that:

$$\frac{1}{\bar{P}_n} = \frac{k_{TM}}{k_2} + \frac{k_d(-d[\text{M}]/dt)}{2k_2^2[\text{M}]^2} \qquad \textit{Diradical growth}$$

[15] D. H. Johnson and A. V. Tobolsky, paper presented at the fall 1947 meeting of the American Chemical Society, Atlantic City.

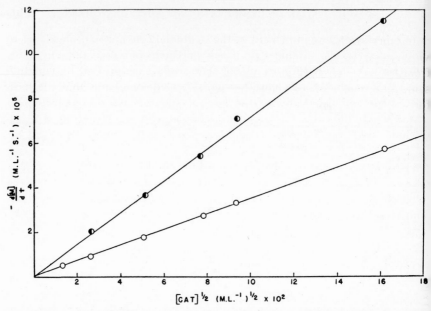

Fig. XII-2a. Rate of polymerization of styrene at 60°C. versus square root of catalyst concentration initiated by: (O) benzoyl peroxide; (◐) 2-azobisisobutyronitrile.

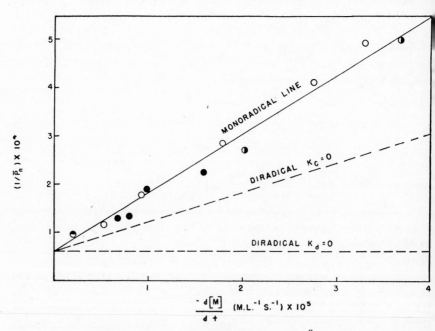

Fig. XII-2b. Reciprocal degree of polymerization versus rate of polymerization for styrene polymerized at 60°C.: (O) initiated by benzoyl peroxide; (◐) initiated by 2-azobisisobutyronitrile; (●) photoinitiated; (◓) thermally initiated.

In other words, a plot of $1/\bar{P}_n$ versus $-d[\mathrm{M}]/dt$ for a diradical-produced vinyl polymerization would have the same intercept but a different slope from the same plot for monoradical-produced polymerizations under the same conditions. This is shown in Figure XII-2b, where the diradical lines for the limiting conditions $k_c = 0$ and $k_d = 0$ are drawn as dotted lines.

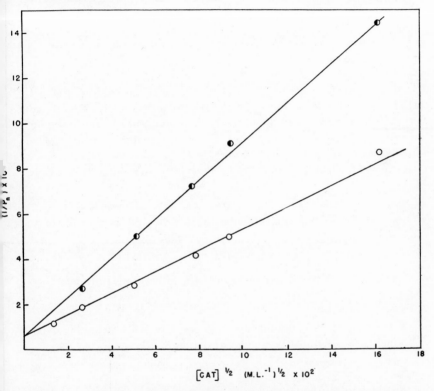

Fig. XII-2c. Reciprocal degree of polymerization versus square root of catalyst concentration for styrene polymerized at 60°C. initiated by: (O) benzoyl peroxide; (◖) 2-azobisisobutyronitrile.

It is interesting to observe that photopolymerizations of styrene at 60°C. at different intensities of illumination fall on the same line as defined by benzoyl peroxide and the other monoradical-producing catalysts rather than in the area defined by the two limiting diradical lines. It would therefore appear that photopolymerization of styrene at these wavelengths (around 3000 Å.) proceeds via monoradical initiation. The point for thermal polymerization shown in Figure XII-2b lies so near the intercept that it is hard to draw a conclusion as to whether this is a monoradical- or diradical-initiated polymerization.

A more complete treatment of the approach to the steady state of radical concentration can be given readily.[10,16] If we have a vinyl polymerization for which the rate of formation of radicals is given by V_1, then:

$$d[c^*]/dt = V_1 - k_3 [c^*]^2 \qquad (XII.4)$$

where $[c^*]$ is the concentration of radicals and k_3 is the specific rate of termination. Upon integration:

$$[c^*] = (V_1/k_3)^{1/2} \tanh t/\tau \qquad (XII.5)$$

where $\tau = (k_3 V_1)^{-1/2}$. For $t \gg \tau$, $[c^*]$ approaches its steady state value of $(V_1/k_3)^{1/2}$. τ is the mean life of the radicals and also the natural induction period of the polymerization, i.e., the time required to nearly reach the steady state concentration of radicals. It is clear that the steady state value of $[c^*]$, which we can call $[c^*]_\infty$, is related to τ and V_1 as follows:

$$[c^*]_\infty = V_1 \tau \qquad (XII.6)$$

The rate of polymerization when the steady state of radical concentration is reached is:

$$-d[M]/dt = k_2 [c^*][M] = k_2[M][V_1/k_3]^{1/2} \qquad (XII.7)$$

The half life of the monomer, τ_0 is of the order of magnitude:

$$\tau_0 = (k_3/V_1)^{1/2}/k_2 \qquad (XII.8)$$

If the steady state assumption is justified for all measurable extents of polymerization, τ_0 must be much larger than τ.

$$\tau_0/\tau = k_3/k_2 \gg 1 \qquad (XII.9)$$

The lifetime of the natural induction period:

$$\tau = (k_3 V_1)^{-1/2}$$

could be used to determine the absolute values of the rate constant k_3, since V_1, the rate of initiation, can be ascertained in photopolymerization or in benzoyl peroxide catalyzed polymerizations. So far, however, no one has succeeded in measuring the lifetime of the natural induction period.

Equations (A) postulate that the initiation step involves the decomposition of catalyst into radical fragments that add to the monomer and start

---

[16] W. H. Stockmayer, J. Chem. Phys., **12**, 143 (1944).

he polymerization. On the other hand, certain kinetic evidence indicated
hat monomer is involved in the initiation step as follows:[17,18]

$$\text{Cat} + \text{M} \xrightarrow{\;k_1''\;} \text{M}_1\cdot \tag{B}$$

This type of initiation would lead to a rate of polymerization proportional
o the $\frac{3}{2}$ power of the monomer.[17,18]

$$-d\text{M}/dt = k_2(k_1''/k_3)^{1/2}[\text{Cat}]^{1/2}[\text{M}]^{3/2} \tag{XII.10}$$

A more general equation that reverts to equation (XII.2) under certain
imiting conditions and to equation (XII.4) at the other limit is:[18,19]

$$-\frac{d[\text{M}]}{dt} = \text{Const} \times [\text{Cat}]^{1/2}[\text{M}]\left[\frac{K[\text{M}]}{1 + K[\text{M}]}\right]^{1/2} \tag{XII.11}$$

In order to explain an initiation step of type (B) and kinetic equations for
rate of consumption of monomer as equations (XII.11) and (XII.10) it was
first suggested that the peroxide catalyst forms a complex with monomer.[17-19] An interesting derivation of equation (XII.5) was given by
Matheson[20]; he described it as the "cage model" theory of peroxide-initiated
catalysis of vinyl polymerization. Whereas it is assumed that the peroxide
catalyst decomposes unimolecularly into radicals as in equations (A), the
radical pair thus produced is presumed to have the possibility of recombining before reacting with monomer. The competition between recombina-
tion and radical addition to monomer leads to the slightly enhanced rate of
peroxide decomposition in monomers as compared to other solvents.
   The reaction steps are assumed to be:

$$\varphi\overset{O}{\overset{\|}{C}}{-}O{-}O{-}\overset{O}{\overset{\|}{C}}\varphi \xrightarrow{\;k_1\;} 2\;\varphi\overset{O}{\overset{\|}{C}}{-}O\cdot$$

$$\varphi\overset{O}{\overset{\|}{C}}{-}O\cdot + \varphi\overset{O}{\overset{\|}{C}}{-}O\cdot \xrightarrow{\;k_r\;} \varphi\overset{O}{\overset{\|}{C}}{-}O{-}O{-}\overset{O}{\overset{\|}{C}}\varphi \quad \text{or} \quad \varphi\overset{O}{\overset{\|}{C}}O\varphi + CO_2 \tag{C}$$

$$\varphi\overset{O}{\overset{\|}{C}}{-}O\cdot + \text{M} \xrightarrow{\;k_i\;} \text{RM}_1\cdot$$

$$\text{RM}\cdot + \text{M} \xrightarrow{\;k_2\;} \text{RM}_2\cdot$$

[17] S. Medvedev and S. Kamenskaya, *Acta Physicochim. U. R. S. S.*, **13**, 565 (1940).
[18] H. Mark and D. Josefowitz, *Polymer Bull.*, **1**, 140 (1945).
[19] G. V. Schulz, A. Dinglinger, and E. Husemann, *Z. physik. Chem.*, **B39**, 246 (1938).
[20] M. S. Matheson, *J. Chem. Phys.*, **13**, 584 (1945).

. . . .

$$RM_n\cdot \ + \ M \ \xrightarrow{\ k_2\ } \ RM_{n+1}$$

$$RM_n\cdot \ + \ RM_p\cdot \ \xrightarrow{\ k_3\ } \ RM_{n+p}R$$

This set of equations (C) gives rise to the following rate expression:

$$-\frac{d[M]}{dt} = \frac{k_2}{k_3^{1/2}} \, [\text{Cat}]^{1/2}[M] \left[\frac{k_1(k_i/k_r)[M]}{1 + (k_i/k_r)[M]} \right]^{1/2}$$

In the case of the purely thermal polymerization of styrene, the rate of inititation (to form diradicals?) is believed to be second order.[21]

$$M \ + \ M \ \longrightarrow \ \text{diradical?} \qquad \text{rate of initiation} = k_1'[M]^2$$

In photochemical polymerization the rate of initiation is presumed to be proportional to the quanta of light absorbed per second:

$$M \ + \ h\nu \ \longrightarrow \ \text{radicals} \qquad \text{rate of initiation} = f(I)$$

C. EFFECT OF CHAIN TRANSFER ON DEGREE OF POLYMERIZATION

In an attempt to verify the kinetic equations of section B, Schulz[19,22] and Suess[23,24] carried out polymerizations of styrene in a series of solvents in order to be able to vary the initial concentration of monomer. They first assumed that the degree of polymerization was equal to the kinetic chain length. It was apparent from the experimental studies that, although the rate of conversion of monomer to polymer in various solvents could be explained by equations of the type developed in section B, there was an important effect of the solvent on the degree of polymerization not predicted by these equations. Flory[21] proposed that a chain transfer reaction of the following type was operative:

$$RM_n\cdot \ + \ SX \ \longrightarrow \ RM_nX \ + \ S\cdot$$

for example:

$$RM_n\cdot \ + \ CCl_4 \ \longrightarrow \ RM_nCl \ + \ CCl_3\cdot$$

[21] P. J. Flory, *J. Am. Chem. Soc.*, **59**, 241 (1937).
[22] G. V. Schulz and E. Husemann, *Z. physik. Chem.*, **B43**, 385 (1939).
[23] H. Suess, K. Pilch, and H. Rudorfer, *ibid.*, **A179**, 361 (1937).
[24] H. Suess and A. Springer, *ibid.*, **A179**, 81 (1937).

or:

$$RM_n\cdot + R^1SH \longrightarrow RM_nH + R^1S\cdot$$

In other words, a growing radical can abstract a neutral atom from another molecule (solvent, monomer, polymer, catalyst, or impurity).

In order that the reaction should not be slowed down by the presence of the solvent or other chain transfer agent it is necessary that the new radical $S\cdot$ (for example, $CCl_3\cdot$ or $RS\cdot$) should react quite rapidly with the monomer:

$$S\cdot + M \longrightarrow SM\cdot \rightarrow \rightarrow \rightarrow SM_n\cdot$$
$$CCl_3\cdot + M \longrightarrow Cl_3CM\cdot \rightarrow \rightarrow \rightarrow Cl_3CM_n\cdot$$

If chain transfer occurs to polymer molecules, the radicals left behind on the already completed chains will add monomer to form a branched molecule.

If we consider the possibility of chain transfer to the solvent as well as chain transfer to the monomer we can write for the number average degree of polymerization of the polymer chains:

$\bar{P}_n$ = velocity of propagation/velocity of termination + velocity of transfer to monomer + velocity of transfer to solvent

$$= \frac{k_2[c^*][M]}{k_3[c^*]^2 + k_T[c^*][S] + k_{TM}[c^*][M]}$$

$$= \frac{k_2M}{k_3[c^*] + k_T[S] + k_{TM}[M]}$$

Inserting the value of $[c^*]$ from equation (XII.1) and taking reciprocals, we obtain:

$$\frac{1}{\bar{P}_n} = \frac{(k_1k_3)^{1/2}[Cat]^{1/2}}{k_2} + \frac{k_{TM}}{k_2} + \frac{k_T[S]}{k_2[M]} \qquad (XII.12)$$

Plots of the reciprocal of the degree of polymerization against $[S]/[M]$ should therefore give straight lines whose intercept is:

$$(k_1k_3)^{1/2}[Cat]^{1/2}/k_2 + k_{TM}/k_2$$

and whose slope is k_T/k_2. If we are dealing with an uncatalyzed polymerization for which the initiation rate is bimolecular with respect to monomer (*i.e.*, $k_1'[M]^2$), we then get:

$$\frac{1}{\bar{P}_n} = \frac{(k_1'k_3)^{1/2} + k_{TM}}{k_2} + \frac{k_T[S]}{k_2[M]} \qquad (XII.13)$$

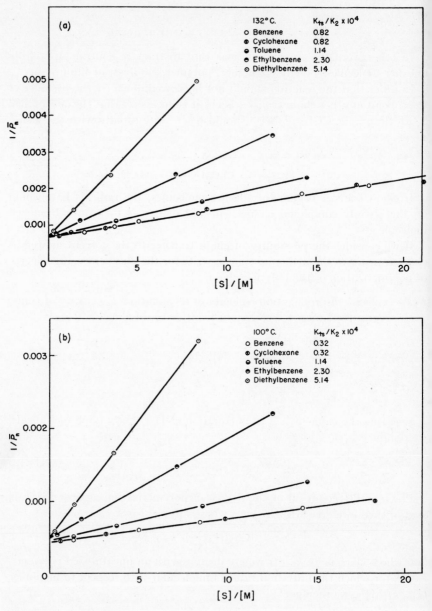

Fig. XII-3. Reciprocal degree of polymerization versus [S]/[M] for styrene poly-merized in various solvents at 132° (a) and at 100°C. (b).

Data on polymerization of styrene in various solvents[23,24] was interpreted in terms of equation (XII.13) by Mayo,[25] Harman, Hulburt, Tobolsky, and Eyring,[26] and Medvedev et al.[27] It is clear that $1/\bar{P}_n$ vs. [S]/[M] should give straight lines whose slope k_T/k_2 depends on the solvent and temperature as shown in Figure XII-3. The transfer constants k_T/k_2

TABLE XII-3

TRANSFER CONSTANTS OF HYDROCARBONS WITH STYRENE

Hydrocarbon	Transfer constant $\times 10^5$			$E_t - E_2{}^a$ kcal./mole	ln $A_t/A_2{}^a$
	60°	100°	132°		
Benzene...............	0.18	1.84	8.9	14.8	9.06
tert-Butylbenzene........	0.6	5.5	—	13.7	8.67
Toluene................	1.25	6.45	10.1	10.1	4.03
Ethylbenzene...........	6.7	16.2	29	5.5	−1.27
Isopropylbenzene........	8.2	20.0	—	5.5	−1.09
Diphenylmethane........	23	42	—	3.7	−2.76
Triphenylmethane.......	35	80	—	5.1	0.24
Fluorene...............	750	1240	—	3.1	0.19
Pentaphenylethane......	200,000	—	—	—	—
Cyclohexane............	0.24	1.6	8.7	13.4	7.21
n-Heptane..............	4.2	9.5	—	5.0	−2.44
Decalin................	4	—	—	—	—
Carbon tetrachloride.....	900	1810	3250	4.8	2.53

^{a} Calculated from the Arrhenius equation $C = Ae^{-E/RT}$, where $C = k_T/k_2$ is the transfer constant, E is the difference in activation energies for chain transfer and chain growth, $E_t - E_2$; and A, the frequency factor is the ratio A_t/A_2 for the two processes.

provide a means for estimating the relative reactivities of various solvents in the chain transfer reaction. From the change of slope with temperature one can calculate the difference in the activation energies for k_T and k_2, namely, $E_t - E_2$. The results obtained are very much in agreement with what is known about the attack on such molecules by chlorine and bromine in aliphatic substitution, and with the results of Taylor and Smith[28] on the attack of methyl radicals on various hydrocarbons in the gas phase. Among the aliphatic hydrocarbons, a tertiary hydrogen atom is most easily removed, and a primary hydrogen least easily. Benzyl hydrogen atoms

[25] F. R. Mayo, J. Am. Chem. Soc., 65, 2324 (1943).

[26] H. A. Hulburt, R. A. Harman, A. V. Tobolsky, and H. Eyring, Ann. N. Y. Acad. Sci., 44, 371 (1943).

[27] S. S. Medvedev, O. Koritskuya, and W. Alekseeva, J. Phys. Chem., U. S. S. R., 17, 391 (1943).

[28] H. S. Taylor and J. Smith, J. Chem. Phys., 7, 390 (1939); 8, 543 (1940).

(such as the α-hydrogen in toluene) and α-methylenic hydrogen atoms are very easily removed.

Mayo and Gregg[29] showed that equation (XII.13) holds for the thermal polymerization of styrene in carbon tetrachloride for solvent-to-monomer ratios between zero and two and four average degrees of polymerization from about 9000 to 50 (they used the molecular weight intrinsic viscosity relation:

$$\bar{M}_n = 184,000[\eta]^{1.277} \qquad (XII.14)$$

intrinsic viscosities being determined in benzene at 30°C.). These authors[30] also studied the activities of twelve solvents toward the growing styrene radical by using equation (XII.13). The results are summarized in Table XII-3. The remarkable activity of pentaphenyl ethane is particularly noteworthy, the transfer constant being approximately 2.0 at 60°C. The same high order of activity was also found for mercaptans.[31]

In the polymerization of synthetic rubber (butadiene-styrene copolymer, GR-S) it has been found that in order to produce a polymer of satisfactory plasticity (fairly low molecular weight) it is necessary to include a chain transfer agent such as dodecyl mercaptan in the polymerization formula. Mercaptans are extremely powerful chain transfer agents, the transfer constant being larger than unity,[31] and it is therefore necessary to use only slight amounts of mercaptan to control the molecular weight. Moreover, when the transfer constant is larger than unity the relative concentration of chain transfer agent to monomer becomes smaller during the course of the polymerization and molecular weight increases with conversion. The ideal chain transfer agent for control of molecular weight would be one for which the transfer constant is unity. Chain transfer agents such as mercaptans, which are used in small amounts to control molecular weight, are often called modifiers.

The distribution of molecular weights of the polymer being formed at a given moment during the course of a vinyl polymerization was first deduced by Schulz.[32] If the probability that a growing radical chain will add another monomer rather than terminate or transfer is denoted by p, then:

$$p = \text{velocity of growth/velocity of growth} +$$
$$\text{velocity of termination} + \text{velocity of transfer}$$

[29] R. A. Gregg and F. R. Mayo, *J. Am. Chem. Soc., in preparation.*
[30] R. A. Gregg and F. R. Mayo, *Discussion Faraday Soc.,* **2**, 328 (1947).
[31] W. V. Smith, *J. Am. Chem. Soc.,* **68**, 2059 (1946).
[32] G. V. Schulz, *Z. physik. Chem.,* **B30**, 379 (1935).

The probability, X_n, that the growing chain will have added exactly n monomer units before a termination or transfer is:

$$X_n = p^{n-1}(1 - p) \qquad \text{(XII.15)}$$

The probability that a chain has n units is of course equal to the mole fraction of n-mers. By comparison with equation (XI.4) it is clear that the distribution in sizes is of the same type as for linear condensation. Two differences must be borne in mind. First the distribution of molecular weights represented by equation (XII.15) above applies only to the polymer, *not* to the whole system including unreacted monomer, which is the case in polycondensations. Second, the value of p in the chain reaction case can be *very* nearly equal to unity if the growth step is very much faster than transfer plus termination, whereas in condensation polymerization p —the extent of reaction—is made to approach unity only with difficulty. For this reason, vinyl polymers can generally be prepared in a much higher range of degree of polymerization than condensation polymers. Furthermore, p need not change much during vinyl polymerizations if concentration of transfer agent does not change. Kinetic derivations of the distribution in molecular weights in vinyl polymerizations have given more exact expressions.[33-35]

When modifiers or regulators are used to control the molecular weight during a radical chain polymerization, it is of importance to know how the relative concentration of modifier and monomer are changing.[31] During the course of the polymerization of GR-S, it has been shown that the dodecyl mercaptan modifier enters the growing chains more rapidly than the monomer, so that toward the end of the reaction the mercaptan is largely depleted. This has of course led to several proposals for continuous addition of modifier during the course of the reaction.

The rate at which monomer disappears (equal to the rate at which it enters the polymer) is given by:

$$-d[M]/dt = k_2[M][c^*] \qquad \text{(XII.16)}$$

Where c^* is the total concentration of polymer radicals of all types.

The rate at which the modifier, S, is consumed is given by:

$$-d[S]/dt = k_T[S][c^*] \qquad \text{(XII.17)}$$

[33] H. A. Hulburt, R. A. Harman, A. V. Tobolsky, and H. Eyring, *Ann. N. Y. Acad. Sci.*, **44**, 371 (1943).

[34] G. Gee and H. W. Melville, *Trans. Faraday Soc.*, **40**, 240 (1944).

[35] E. F. Herrington and E. F. Robertson, *Trans. Faraday Soc.*, **38**, 490 (1942).

Dividing equation (XII.16) by equation (XII.17) we obtain:

$$d[M]/d[S] = k_2[M]/k_T[S] \qquad \text{(XII.18)}$$

The quantity $d[M]/d[S]$ is the relative rate at which monomer is consumed compared to the rate at which modifier is being consumed. It is also the relative rate at which monomer enters the chain compared to the rate at which chain transfer agents enter the chain. If the concentration is expressed on a molar basis $d[M]/d[S]$ is also the average degree of polymerization of the polymer being formed at the time when the concentration of monomer and modifier are [M] and [S], respectively.

If equation (XII.18) is integrated we obtain:

$$\ln \frac{[M]}{[M_0]} = \frac{k_2}{k_T} \ln \frac{[S]}{[S_0]} \qquad \text{(XII.19)}$$

Equation (XII.19) gives us the modifier concentration [S] when the monomer concentration is [M] and the initial concentrations of monomer and modifier are [M_0] and [S_0], respectively.

Inasmuch as the relative concentration of modifier to monomer changes during the course of the polymerization, the polymerization degree of the polymer formed also changes. If we assume that chain transfer to the modifier is the only important molecular weight controlling step, the values of $\bar{P}_n$ and $\bar{P}_w$ for the entire polymer formed up until a fractional degree of conversion x are given by:

$$\bar{P}_n = \frac{[M_0]}{[S_0]} \frac{x}{1 - (1 - x)^c} \qquad \bar{P}_w = \frac{2[M_0]}{c[S_0]} \frac{1 - (1 - x)^{2-c}}{(2 - c)x}$$

where $c = k_T/k_2$ is the chain transfer constant.[36]

D. INHIBITORS AND RETARDERS

An inhibitor or retarder of free radical catalyzed polymerizations must be a material that will react with a growing free radical and destroy its activity. Since most inhibitors are molecules rather than radical fragments the inhibitor must react with the growing radical to give a relatively inactive radical that will not add to monomer.

Price[37] has discussed the retardation of polymerization by aromatic nitro-compounds on this basis:

[36] A. V. Tobolsky, R. C. Fettes, and D. H. Johnson, *unpublished results.*
[37] C. C. Price, *Ann. N. Y. Acad. Sci.*, **44**, 351 (1943).

$$RM_n\cdot + \underset{NO_2}{\overset{Cl}{\bigcirc}}NO_2 \longrightarrow RM_n-\underset{NO_2}{\overset{H\ \ Cl}{\bigcirc}}-NO_2$$

$$\underset{NO_2}{\overset{R\ \ Cl}{RM_n-\bigcirc}}-NO_2 \qquad \underset{NO_2}{\overset{Cl}{RM_n\bigcirc}}-NO_2$$

One should observe that the substitution in the benzene ring occurs contrary to the ordinary directing effect of the substituents which are valid in polar or ionic reactions.

Aromatic nitro compounds not only act as retarders in the polymerization of styrene but fragments of these molecules are also found in polymer molecules prepared in their presence in the ratio of one fragment per polymer molecule.[37,38]

Hydroquinone is a powerful inhibitor of many free radical catalyzed polymerizations. Price suggests the following for this inhibitor action:

$$R\cdot + HO\bigcirc OH \longrightarrow RH + HO\bigcirc -O\cdot$$

$$R\cdot + HO\bigcirc O\cdot \longrightarrow RH + O=\bigcirc =O$$

$$R\cdot + O=\bigcirc =O \longrightarrow \left[O=\overset{H\ R\ H}{\bigcirc}=O\right] \longrightarrow HO\overset{R}{\bigcirc}-O\cdot$$

$$R\cdot + HO\overset{R}{\bigcirc}O\cdot \longrightarrow RH + O=\overset{R}{\bigcirc}=O$$

[38] S. G. Foord, *J. Chem. Soc.*, **1940**, 48.

In confirmation of the above mechanism, it has been pointed out that quinone is produced when methyl methacrylate is polymerized by benzoyl peroxide in the presence of hydroquinone.[39] Quinones are also known to be powerful inhibitors and to react with the radicals from acyl peroxides to give alkyl substituted quinones.

Cohen[40] showed that, during the inhibition by quinone of the peroxide-catalyzed polymerization of styrene, approximately one mole of quinone was consumed per mole of initiator during the induction period. According to Cohen, quinone acts as both an inhibitor and a retarder. An inhibitor characteristically gives an induction period in which absolutely no polymerization occurs. The induction period lasts until all inhibitor is consumed. A retarder slows down the rate of polymerization without producing an induction period. Melville and Watson[41] have recently presented a theoretical treatment of inhibition and retardation.

In Table XII-4 a list of some inhibitors and retarders of styrene polymerization is given in the approximate order of effectiveness under a fixed set of conditions.[42] It was also shown that these substances are good inhibitors for 3,4-dichlorostyrene and for 5-ethyl-2-vinylpyridine.

TABLE XII-4

SOME INHIBITORS OF STYRENE POLYMERIZATION (IN APPROXIMATE ORDER OF EFFECTIVENESS)

1.	Picric acid	7.	9,10-Phenanthroquinone
2.	Trinitrobenzene	8.	tert-Butylcatechol
3.	2,5-Dihydroxy-1,4-benzoquinone	9.	4-Amino-1-naphthol
4.	1,4-Naphthoquinone	10.	Hydroquinone
5.	1,4-Benzoquinone	11.	Phenyl-β-naphthylamine
6.	Chloranil	12.	Triphenyl phosphite

It has been found that oxygen will act as a fairly powerful inhibitor during the emulsion polymerization of styrene or in the photopolymerization of methyl methacrylate or styrene. The inhibition is apparently due to the addition of oxygen to radicals to form $ROO\cdot$, which is apparently somewhat inactive with regard to the addition to the double bond of the monomer. If polymerization is continued, however, polyperoxides may be formed which are essentially copolymers of oxygen and the monomer in question. These matters will be discussed further in section J.

[39] H. N. Alyea, J. J. Gartland, and H. R. Graham, *Ind. Eng. Chem.*, **34**, 458 (1942).
[40] S. G. Cohen, *J. Am. Chem. Soc.*, **69**, 1057 (1947).
[41] H. W. Melville and W. F. Watson, *Trans. Faraday Soc.*, **44**, 886 (1948).
[42] R. L. Frank and C. E. Adams, *J. Am. Chem. Soc.*, **68**, 908 (1946).

E. ABSOLUTE VELOCITY CONSTANTS FOR VINYL POLYMERIZATION

As we have seen in a previous section, it is generally accepted that four elementary types of reaction—initiation, propagation, transfer, and termination—are involved in addition polymerization. The usual kinetic measurements follow the rate of conversion of monomer to polymer and the molecular weight of the polymer produced. These measurements are insufficient to determine the absolute values of the four velocity constants involved.

Melville[43] in 1937 showed that the rotating sector method of Briers, Chapman, and Walters[44] can be used to measure the lifetime of growing polymer chains in photochemical reactions. If, in addition, the rate of chain initiation can be determined independently, then the absolute value for all four velocity constants can be determined. These methods were first applied by Melville[43] for the vapor phase polymerization of methyl methacrylate, and by Jones and Melville[45] for methyl acrylate vapor. These studies were then extended to the liquid phase polymerization of vinyl acetate by Bartlett and Swain[46,47] and Burnett and Melville.[48]

The theory of intermittent illumination which enables one to calculate the mean lifetime of the chain carriers of certain chain reactions was originated by Chapman, Briers, and Walters[44] and extended by various authors including Dickinson.[49]

It is assumed that the rate of initiation of radical chains is equal to $f(I)$, the intensity of absorbed radiation; i.e., every absorbed quantum starts a radical chain. The over-all rate, R, of the photochemical reaction varies as some power of $f(I)$ as follows:

$$R \propto [f(I)]^n \tag{XII.20}$$

For a photochemical polymerization, R represents the rate of conversion of monomer to polymer and $n = {}^1/_2$. By means of a rotating half sector one can obtain intermittent illumination for which the periods of light and dark are equal. Using sufficiently high sector speeds it is possible to make each individual period of light and dark very small compared to the life-

---

[43] H. Melville, *Proc. Roy. Soc.*, **A163**, 511 (1937).

[44] Briers, Chapman, and Walters, *J. Chem. Soc.*, **1926**, 562.

[45] T. T. Jones and H. W. Melville, *Proc. Roy. Soc.*, **A175**, 392 (1940).

[46] P. D. Bartlett and C. G. Swain, *J. Am. Chem. Soc.*, **67**, 2273 (1945).

[47] P. D. Bartlett and C. G. Swain, *J. Am. Chem. Soc.*, **68**, 2377, 2381 (1946).

[48] G. M. Burnett and H. W. Melville, *Nature*, **156**, 661 (1945).

[49] R. G. Dickinson, in Noyes and Leighton, eds., *Photochemistry of Gases*. Reinhold, New York, 1941, page 200.

time of the active radicals.   In this case the over-all effect of the interposition of the rotating half sector is to cut down the intensity of light absorbed by a factor of two.   Since the number of chains started per unit time is halved, the over-all rate will be given by:

$$R(\text{high sector speed}) \; \alpha \; [f(I)/2]^n \tag{XII.21}$$

For long equal periods of light and dark, the system is virtually illuminated for only half the time, so that:

$$R(\text{low sector speed}) \; \alpha \; {}^{1}\!/_{2}[f(I)]^n \tag{XII.22}$$

Therefore:

$$\frac{R(\text{high sector speed})}{R(\text{low sector speed})} = 2^{1-n} \tag{XII.23}$$

and if $n \equiv {}^{1}\!/_{2}$, as is true in photochemical polymerization:

$$\frac{R(\text{high sector speed})}{R(\text{low sector speed})} = \sqrt{2} = 1.414 \tag{XII.24}$$

By varying the periods of the intermittent illumination from very high sector speeds to very slow sector speeds the rate of the reaction will change from 0.707 times the rate of the reaction under steady illumination to 0.500 times this rate.   Theoretical curves have been derived which give the reaction rate as a function of τ/t, where τ is the lifetime of the chain carriers and t is the duration of the light interval during the periods of intermittent illumination.   By comparison of observed and theoretical curves the lifetime of the active species can be found.   For vinyl acetate, Melville and Burnett found that the lifetime of the active particle at 15.9°C. is 2.25×10^{-2} sec. when the intensity of absorbed radiation was 6.35×10^{-7} einstein per liter-sec.   Their data is reproduced in Figure XII-4.

If the total concentration of active radicals is denoted by $[c^*]$, the mean life of a radical is τ and the rate of formation of active radicals is $f(I)$ then:

$$[c^*] = f(I)\tau \tag{XII.25}$$

so that the concentration of active radicals can be determined if the rate of production of radicals and their mean life is known.

Melville assumes that for a photochemical polymerization:

$$\text{M} \xrightarrow{\;h\nu\;} P_1 \qquad\qquad \text{Initiation}$$

$$P_n + \text{M} \longrightarrow P_{n+1} \qquad\qquad \text{Propagation}$$

$$P_n + P_M \longrightarrow M_n + M_M \qquad \text{Termination}$$

$$\text{Kinetic chain length} = \frac{\text{velocity of polymerization}}{f(I)}$$

where M is a monomer molecule, P_n an active polymer of n units, and M_n the corresponding deactivated molecule. In photopolymerization of vinyl

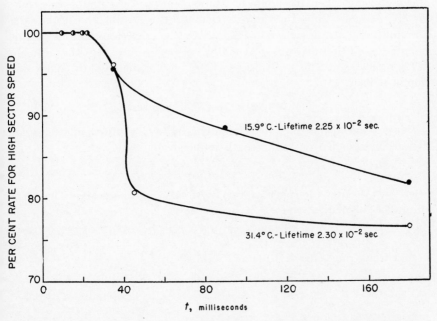

Fig. XII-4. Photopolymerization of vinyl acetate with rotating sector as a function of the period of illumination: rate expressed as a percentage of the rate at very high sector speeds.

acetate at 15.9°C. and 31.4°C. it was found[50] that the rate of polymerization was proportional to the square root of light intensity. By measuring the rate of polymerization (by volume change) and the degree of polymerization, it was found that every quantum of light produced one kinetic chain whose length was equal to the degree of polymerization (*i.e.*, no chain transfer occurred under these conditions). In order to get an independent check on the velocity of chain initiation, Burnett and Melville made use of benzoquinone as inhibitor. It appears that this inhibitor completely stops the reaction until it is completely used up, and the reaction from that point

[50] G. M. Burnett and H. W. Melville, *Proc. Roy. Soc., London,* **A189**, 456, 481 (1947).

proceeds exactly as in the absence of inhibitor. Moreover, one molecule of inhibitor appears to be consumed for each quantum of light absorbed. Melville and Burnett postulated that the light quanta are absorbed by the monomer to give diradicals, which immediately react with a benzoquinone molecule if such is present. The rate of disappearance of inhibitor under given conditions of illumination is taken to be equal to the rate $f(I)$ of starting chains when the inhibitor is absent or once the inhibitor is completely used up. From the value of $f(I)$ and τ it is possible to calculate the absolute concentration of radicals. At 15.9°C., under conditions of illumination such that $f(I)$ was 6.35×10^{-7} einstein per liter-sec., the mean life of the radicals was 2.25×10^{-2} sec. This gives for the absolute concentration of radicals:

$$[c^*] = 1.42 \times 10^{-8} \text{ mole per liter}$$

If it is assumed that the rate constants k_2 and k_3 for growth and termination are independent of chain length at the steady state:

$$d[c^*]/dt = f(I) - k_3[c^*]^2 = 0 \qquad (XII.26)$$

where $[c^*]$ denotes the concentration of all the active radicals. The overall rate of polymerization is given by:

$$-d[M]/dt = k_2[M][c^*] \qquad (XII.27)$$

so that from equations (XII.21) and (XII.22):

$$k_2 = \frac{-d[M]/dt}{[M][c^*]} \qquad (XII.28)$$

$$k_3 = f[I]/[c^*]^2 \qquad (XII.29)$$

where:

$$[c^*] = f(I)\tau$$

These equations allow a calculation of the propagation and termination specific rate constants in terms of the velocity of chain initiation, the overall rate of polymerization, and the lifetime of the active radicals.

Whereas Melville obtained the rate of chain initiation by measuring quanta absorbed per second, and also by the inhibitor method, Bartlett and Swain obtained the rate of chain initiation in photopolymerization by studying as a comparison the benzoyl peroxide catalyzed polymerization of vinyl acetate. The over-all rate of decomposition of benzoyl peroxide in any solvent is the sum of a spontaneous decomposition into radicals plus a decomposition induced by radicals. However, these two rates can be

TABLE XII-5

ABSOLUTE VALUES OF THE SPECIFIC RATE CONSTANTS FOR VINYL
POLYMERIZATIONS

Catalyst	Rate of initiation $= V_1 = k_1$ [Cat]		Ref.
	k_1 (sec.$^{-1}$)	Conditions	
Benzoyl peroxide	4.35×10^{-6}	60 °C. in styrene	a
	2.18×10^{-6}	45 °C. in ethyl acetate and in vinyl acetate	b
	$7.8 \ \times 10^{-8}$	25 °C. in vinyl acetate	c
	$5.3 \ \times 10^{13} e^{(-28300/RT)}$	vinyl acetate	c
2-Azobisiso-butyronitrile	3.06×10^{-4}	80 °C. in xylene	d
	3.04×10^{-4}	80 °C. in glacial acetic acid	d
	3.68×10^{-4}	80 °C. in N-dimethyl aniline	d
	$7.34 \times 10^{15} e^{(-31300/RT)}$	xylene; approximately true for all solvents	d
Di-*tert*-butyl peroxide	$3.2 \ \times 10^{-5}$	125 °C. in cumene	e
	$3.4 \ \times 10^{-5}$	125 °C. in tri-n-butyl amine	e
	$2.2 \ \times 10^{-5}$	125 °C. vapor phase	e
	31.2×10^{-5}	145 °C. in cumene	e
	23.0×10^{-5}	145 °C. vapor phase	e
	$6.4 \ \times 10^{16} e^{(-39100/RT)}$	all conditions	e

SPECIFIC RATE CONSTANTS FOR GROWTH AND TERMINATION

Monomer	k_2 (liter/mole-sec.)	k_3 (liter/mole-sec.)	Temp. (°C.)	Ref.
Styrene	6.91	1.83×10^6	0	f
	18.7	2.79×10^6	25	f
	$1.02 \times 10^6 e^{(-6500/RT)}$	$3.07 \times 10^8 e^{(-2300/RT)}$		f
Methyl metha-crylate	1.43	1.22×10^7	30	g
	3.67	1.87×10^7	60	g
	$5.13 \times 10^6 e^{(-6310/RT)}$	$1.36 \times 10^9 e^{(-2840/RT)}$		g
Vinyl acetate	325	$2.7 \ \times 10^7$	0	h
	690	$4.5 \ \times 10^7$	15.9	h
	1012	5.88×10^7	25	h
	2640	11.68×10^7	50	h
	3700	14.8×10^7	60	h
	$2.43 \times 10^8 e^{(-7320/RT)}$	$4.16 \times 10^{11} e^{(-5240/RT)}$		h
Butyl acrylate	13	$1.8 \ \times 10^4$	25	i
	14.5	$1.8 \ \times 10^4$	35	i
	$4.4 \times 10^4 e^{(-2000/RT)}$	$1.8 \ \times 10^4$		i

(*a*) K. Nozaki and P. D. Bartlett, *J. Am. Chem. Soc.*, **68**, 1686 (1946).
(*b*) K. Nozaki and P. D. Bartlett, *ibid.*, **68**, 2377 (1946).
(*c*) C. G. Swain and P. D. Bartlett, *ibid.*, **68**, 2381 (1946).
(*d*) F. M. Lewis and M. S. Matheson, *ibid.*, **71**, 747 (1949).
(*e*) J. H. Raley, F. F. Rust, and W. E. Vaughan, *ibid.*, **70**, 1336 (1948).
(*f*) C. H. Bamford and M. J. S. Dewar, *Proc. Roy. Soc. London*, **A192**, 309 (1948).
(*g*) M. S. Matheson, E. E. Auer, E. B. Bevilacqua, and E. J. Hart, *J. Am. Chem. Soc.*, **71**, 497 (1949).
(*h*) M. S. Matheson, E. E. Auer, E. B. Bevilacqua, and E. J. Hart, *ibid.*, **71**, 2610 (1949).
(*i*) H. W. Melville and A. F. Bickel, *Trans. Faraday Soc.*, **45**, 1049 (1949).

isolated and measured separately by suitable analysis of the data. It is assumed that the rate of chain initiation, V_1, in polymerization is equal to the rate of formation of radicals by the *spontaneous* first-order cleavage of the peroxide, which we have called $k_1[\text{Cat}]$. This assumes 100% efficiency of *each of the two* radicals from the catalyst in starting polymer chains. Since $k_1[\text{Cat}]$ has been determined for benzoyl peroxide in vinyl acetate, the rate of chain initiation is known for any catalyst concentration, and hence for any desired over-all rate of polymerization. Bartlett and Swain further assumed that the rate of chain initiation in a photopolymerization is the same as occurs in a benzoyl peroxide initiated polymerization of the same over-all rate, that is:

$$V_1 = k_1[\text{Cat}] = f(I)$$

Bamford and Dewar[51] studied the absolute velocity constants in styrene. Whereas Melville and Burnett postulated diradicals in photopolymerization of vinyl acetate, Bamford and Dewar considered in greater detail the fate of the diradicals and their conversion via chain transfer to monoradicals and inactive polymer. These authors found that chain transfer plays an important role in styrene polymerization at 0° and 25°C. Their experimental technique is the so-called viscosity method.

A photochemical polymerization of styrene is started and then the light is turned off. Even though the steady state concentration of radicals falls off with extreme rapidity, the slight postpolymerization in the absence of light can be detected because of the sensitivity of the measurement of solution viscosity.

A collection of some absolute values of the specific rate constants in certain vinyl polymerizations is given in Table XII-5.

F. COPOLYMERIZATION

Copolymerization of vinyl monomers (and of vinyl and diene monomers) is of great interest because it provides a means of producing synthetic polymers of a very wide variety of physical and chemical properties. Copolymerization is studied chiefly by determination of the over-all composition of the copolymer as a function of the initial ratio of monomer concentrations and of conversion. It is only in special cases that the composition of the copolymer is identical with the composition of the initial monomer charge. The relative rates at which monomers polymerize by themselves provides no adequate indication of the rates at which the monomers will

---

[51] C. H. Bamford and M. J. S. Dewar, *Proc. Roy. Soc., London*, **A192**, 309 (1938).

enter a copolymer.   In fact certain 1,2 disubstituted vinyl compounds which do not polymerize by themselves under known circumstances will copolymerize readily with other vinyl compounds.

Processes that affect only the initiation and termination processes do not affect copolymer composition.   For example, variation of the type of peroxide catalyst or catalyst concentration, or the presence of inhibitors or chain transfer agents do not affect the copolymer compositions.   These facts indicate that the growth reactions are the controlling factors in determining copolymer structure.

However, it should be pointed out that if an ionic catalyst rather than a radical catalyst is used, the entire nature of the copolymerization process for a given pair of monomers may well be changed.   In other words the competition between monomers for growing chains is changed completely if the growing chain is an ion rather than a radical.   The absolute concentration of radicals or the particular radical that started the polymerization seem to have no influence in radical copolymerization.

Early attempts to develop theories of copolymerization were made by Norrish and Brookman[52] and by Wall.[53]   Recent theoretical developments reported by Mayo, Lewis, Walling, and co-workers,[54] Alfrey, Goldfinger, and co-workers,[55] and Wall[56] appear to correlate most of the known facts about copolymerization.

Consider two vinyl monomers, M_1 and M_2, that are being copolymerized, and let the growing polymer molecules terminated by an active M_1 radical be denoted by $M_1 \cdot$ and the growing polymer molecules terminated by an active M_2 radical by $M_2 \cdot$.   Then four propagation constants govern the growth of active polymer chains:[57]

Rate

$$M_1 \cdot + M_1 \xrightarrow{k_{11}} M_1 \cdot \qquad k_{11}[M_1 \cdot][M_1]$$

$$M_1 \cdot + M_2 \xrightarrow{k_{12}} M_2 \cdot \qquad k_{12}[M_1 \cdot][M_2]$$

$$M_2 \cdot + M_2 \xrightarrow{k_{22}} M_2 \cdot \qquad k_{22}[M_2 \cdot][M_2]$$

$$M_2 \cdot + M_1 \xrightarrow{k_{21}} M_1 \cdot \qquad k_{21}[M_2 \cdot][M_1]$$

In a steady state of copolymerization the concentration of $[M_1 \cdot]$ must be

[52] R. G. W. Norrish and E. F. Brookman, *Proc. Roy. Soc.*, **A171**, 147 (1939).

[53] F. T. Wall, *J. Am. Chem. Soc.*, **63**, 1862 (1941).

[54] F. R. Mayo and F. M. Lewis, *J. Am. Chem. Soc.*, **66**, 1594 (1946).

[55] T. Alfrey and G. Goldfinger, *J. Chem. Phys.*, **12**, 205 (1944).

[56] F. T. Wall, *J. Am. Chem. Soc.*, **66**, 2050 (1944).

[57] T. Alfrey, F. R. Mayo, and F. T. Wall, *J. Polymer Sci.*, **1**, 581 (1946).

equal to the concentration of $[M_2\cdot]$. This means that the rate at which $[M_1\cdot]$ is being transformed to $[M_2\cdot]$ must equal the rate at which $[M_2\cdot]$ is being transformed to $M_1\cdot$.

$$k_{12}[M_1\cdot][M_2] = k_{21}[M_2\cdot][M_1]$$

We can therefore obtain the ratio of $M_2\cdot$ to $M_1\cdot$ even though we cannot obtain the absolute concentration of either:

$$[M_2\cdot]/[M_1\cdot] = k_{12}[M_2]/k_{21}[M_1] \qquad (XII.30)$$

The rate of consumption of monomer M_1, which is equal to its rate of appearance in the polymer, is given by:

$$-d[M_1]/dt = k_{11}[M_1\cdot][M_1] + k_{21}[M_2\cdot][M_1] = [M_1\cdot]\{k_{11}[M_1] + k_{21}[M_2]\} \qquad (XII.31)$$

The rate of consumption of monomer M_2, which is also equal to the rate with which it enters the polymer, is:

$$-d[M_2]/dt = k_{12}[M_1\cdot][M_2] + k_{12}[M_2\cdot][M_2]$$

$$= [M_1\cdot]\left\{k_{12}[M_2] + \frac{k_{11}k_{12}}{k_{21}}\frac{[M_2\cdot]}{[M_1]}\right\} \qquad (XII.32)$$

The ratio of the rate of consumption of monomer M_1 to the rate of consumption of monomer M_2 will be denoted by $d[M_1]/d[M_2]$ and is obtained by dividing equation (XII.32) into equation (XII.31):

$$\frac{d[M_1]}{d[M_2]} = \frac{[M_1]}{[M_2]}\frac{k_{21}}{k_{12}}\frac{k_{12}[M_2] + k_{11}[M_1]}{k_{22}[M_2] + k_{21}[M_1]} \qquad (XII.33)$$

If one introduces the quantities r_1 and r_2, where:

$$r_1 = k_{11}/k_{12} \qquad r_2 = k_{22}/k_{21} \qquad (XII.34)$$

$$\frac{d[M_1]}{d[M_2]} = \frac{[M_1]}{[M_2]}\frac{r_1[M_1] + [M_2]}{[M_1] + r_2[M_2]} \qquad (XII.35)$$

The quantities r_1 and r_2 are known as monomer reactivity ratios. A monomer reactivity ratio greater than 1 shows a tendency for the growing radical to add its own kind, whereas a monomer reactivity ratio less than 1 indicates a preference of the radical for the other monomer. Graphs of equation (XII.35) for various values of r_1 and r_2 are shown in Figure XII-5.

The rate at which monomers instantaneously enter the copolymer is also an expression for the composition of the copolymer being instantaneously

formed.   The detailed structure of the copolymer as well as its over-all
composition has also been worked out.[58]

It is clear from equation (XII.35) that it is only under special conditions

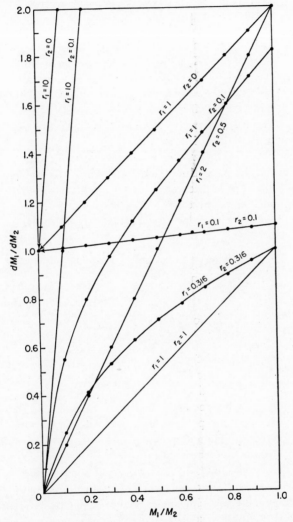

Fig. XII-5. The copolymerization equation: copolymer composition versus monomer composition for various values of r_1 and r_2.

[58] T. Alfrey and G. Goldfinger, *J. Chem. Phys.*, **12**, 205 (1944).

that the composition of the copolymer being formed is the same as the ratio of monomers present in the polymerizing bulk phase. This obtains only if:

$$\frac{r_1[M_1] + [M_2]}{[M_1] + r_2[M_2]} = 1 \qquad (XII.36)$$

For certain values of r_1 and r_2 it is possible to select a ratio of $[M_1]$ to $[M_2]$ such that equation (XII.36) is satisfied at the beginning of the reaction. Under these conditions the ratio of the monomer concentrations and the composition of copolymer remain constant throughout the course of the copolymerization. If r_1 and r_2 are both unity, the composition of the copolymer and the monomer ratio remain constant throughout the copolymerization regardless of the initial charge.

In the general case, the ratio of monomer concentrations and the copolymer composition changes throughout the course of the polymerization. The equations have been integrated by Mayo and Lewis.[59] Values of r_1 and r_2 can be obtained from these integrated equations by a graphical method, which is probably the most precise method in use for evaluating copolymerization data.

$$\log \frac{[M_2]}{[M_2]_0} = \frac{r_2}{1 - r_2} \log \frac{[M_2]_0[M_1]}{[M_1]_0[M_2]} -$$

$$\frac{1 - r_1 r_2}{(1 - r_1)(1 - r_2)} \log \frac{(r_1 - 1)([M_1]/[M_2]) - r_2 + 1}{(r_1 - 1)([M_1]_0/[M_2]_0) - r_2 + 1} \qquad (XII.37)$$

where $[M_1]_0$ and $[M_2]_0$ are the initial concentrations of M_1 and M_2.

Values of r_1 and r_2 can also be obtained directly from equation (XII.35) by carrying out the copolymerization only to a point where the concentration of the monomers is changed only slightly. In practice, this means that one should carry out the polymerizations to no further than five or ten per cent conversion. The composition of the copolymer $d[M_1]/d[M_2]$ is obtained for various monomer concentration ratios, and values of r_1 and r_2 to give the best fit to equation (XII.35) are determined.

The composition of the copolymer is obtained by chlorine analysis if one of the monomers is a chlorine-tagged monomer, or by carbon hydrogen ratios, etc. Simplifying experimental conditions are obtained when either M_1 or M_2 is in large excess:

[59] F. R. Mayo and F. M. Lewis, J. Am. Chem. Soc., 66, 1594 (1944).

M_1 *in excess*:

$$d/[M_1]/d[M_2] = r_1[M_1]/[M_2]$$

M_2 *in excess*:

$$d[M_1]/d[M_2] = [M_1]/r_2[M_2]$$

In determining a great variety of monomer reactivity ratios, it was pointed out that there are two extreme types of copolymerization,[60] the ideal and the alternating types. In the ideal type of copolymerization, r_1r_2 equals unity,[61] so that the relative reactivities of the two monomers are the same for both radical types, and random copolymers are formed. If the two monomers are nearly equal in reactivity, then both r_1 and r_2 will be close to unity, and the composition of the copolymer instantaneously formed will approximate the composition of the feed. If the monomers are of widely differing reactivities, the more active one will enter the copolymer very much faster until practically consumed.

In the alternating type of copolymerization a 1:1 copolymer is formed. Both monomer reactivity ratios are essentially zero and their product, r_1, r_2, is, of course, also zero. In this type of copolymerization, a monomer can add only to the opposite type of monomer.

No cases have yet been found where $r_1r_2 \gg 1$, *i.e.*, no instances of "side by side" polymerizations have been found nor have copolymers been formed in which a long sequence of M_1 units is followed by a long sequence of M_2 units. In other words, no cases have been found in which both monomers of a copolymerizing system definitely prefer to add to their own type of radical rather than to the radical of the other monomer.

Several explanations have been offered for the alternating tendency in copolymerization.[62-65] If one of the monomers (M_2) is a 1,1 disubstituted ethylene that cannot polymerize by itself, it is reasonable to suppose that for steric reasons M_2 will not be able to add to $M_2\cdot$, so that r_2 is very close to zero, and hence r_1r_2 is close to zero. Perhaps steric effects also play some role in 1,1 disubstituted ethylenes. For systems like styrene–maleic anhydride, where complex formation can occur between the monomers, it is

[60] F. B. Mayo, F. M. Lewis, and W. F. Hulse, *J. Am. Chem. Soc.*, **67**, 1701 (1945).
[61] F. T. Wall, *J. Am. Chem. Soc.*, **66**, 2050 (1944).
[62] F. B. Mayo, F. M. Lewis, and W. F. Hulse, *J. Am. Chem. Soc.*, **67**, 1701 (1945).
[63] C. C. Price, *J. Polymer Sci.*, **1**, 83 (1946).
[64] T. Alfrey and C. C. Price, *J. Polymer Sci.*, **2**, 101 (1947).
[65] F. R. Mayo, F. M. Lewis, and C. Walling, *J. Am. Chem. Soc.*, **70**, 1529 (1948).

TABLE XII-6

PRODUCTS OF MONOMER REACTIVITY RATIOS IN COPOLYMERIZATIONS AT 60°C.

	Vinyl acetate	Butadiene	Styrene	Allyl acetate	Vinyl chloride	Methyl methacrylate	Vinylidene chloride	Methyl acrylate	Methyl vinyl ketone	β-Chloroethyl acrylate	Methacrylonitrile	Acrylonitrile	Diethyl fumarate
Vinyl acetate													
Butadiene													
Styrene		1.08											
Allyl acetate	0.3		0.34										
Vinyl chloride	0.39		0.26										
Methyl methacrylate	<0.3		0.16										
Vinylidene chloride	<0.1		0.14			0.61							
Methyl acrylate			0.10										
Methyl vinyl ketone													
β-Chloroethyl acrylate			0.054	<0.3	—		—	0.8					
Methacrylonitrile			0.05		—	0.43							
Acrylonitrile	0.25		0.02		.07	0.24	0.34						
Diethyl fumarate	0.004		0.02		.06	—	0.56	—	1.1				

TABLE XII-7

RELATIVE REACTIVITIES OF MONOMERS WITH VARIOUS RADICALS AT 60°C.

Radical	Vinyl acetate	Styrene	Allyl acetate	Vinyl chloride	Methyl methacrylate	Vinylidene chloride	Methyl acrylate	β-Chloroethyl acrylate	Acrylonitrile	Diethyl fumarate
α-Vinylpyridine	—	1.82	—	—	2.54	—	—	—	25	14
o-Chlorostyrene	—	1.78	—	—	2.0	—	—	—	5.5	—
Styrene	>50	1.00	>50	50	2.2	12	5.5	1.0	1.6	—
Methyl methacrylate	70	1.9	>50	—	1.00	4.0	—	—	—	—
Methyl vinyl ketone	—	3.5	—	—	—	—	—	—	—	—
Methacrylonitrile	—	3.3	—	—	1.5	—	—	—	—	—
Acrylonitrile	16	2.5	—	50	0.75	2.7	1.1	—	1.00	—
β-Chloroethyl acrylate	10	1.9	>50	—	—	—	1.00	1.00	—	—
Methyl acrylate	>30	1.34	—	—	0.40	1.0	1.00	1.1	1.1	22
Vinylidene chloride	8	0.54	—	3.2	0.13	1.00	1.0	—	—	—
Methallyl chloride	—	0.05	—	3.2	0.1	0.9	—	0.25	—	—
Methallyl acetate	4.3	0.014	—	—	0.08	0.42	—	—	—	—
Vinyl chloride	1.00	0.06	—	1.00	0.05	0.31	0.2	—	0.30	—
Vinyl acetate	—	0.02	2.2	0.62	—	0.28	0.11	—	0.25	2.3
Isobutylene	0.33	—	—	0.49	—	0.65	—	—	—	0.3
Vinyl ethyl ether	—	0.01	—	—	0.02	0.31	0.3	—	0.2	—
Allyl chloride	1.7	0.03	—	—	0.02	0.22	0.2	—	0.18	—
Allyl acetate	>50	0.011	1.00	0.86	0.043	0.15	0.4	0.18	—	—
Maleic anhydride	90	—	>130	—	—	0.11	—	—	0.17	—
Diethyl fumarate	6	3.3	—	8.3	—	0.08	—	—	0.12	1.00
Diethyl maleate	1.5	0.15	—	1.3	0.05	0.08	—	—	0.08	—
Trichloroethylene	1.0	0.06	—	—	0.01	—	0.03	—	0.015	—
trans-Dichloroethylene	0.16	0.03	—	—	—	—	—	—	—	—
cis-Dichloroethylene	0.15	0.005	—	—	—	—	0.005	—	0.007	—
Tetrachloroethylene	—	0.005	—	—	—	—	—	—	—	—

TABLE XII-8[67a]

SOME RELATIVE MONOMER REACTIVITY FACTORS[a]

Monomer 1	e	Q	Monomer 2
α-Methylstyrene	−1.2	0.70	Methyl methacrylate
	−1.1	0.55	Acrylonitrile
	−0.8	0.50	Methacrylonitrile
p-Dimethylaminostyrene	−1.2	1.35	Styrene
	−1.55	1.66	Methyl methacrylate
Isobutylene	−1.1	0.2	Vinyl chloride
p-Methoxystyrene	−1.0	1.0	Styrene
	−1.1	1.22	Methyl methacrylate
	−1.1	1.23	p-Chlorostyrene
p-Methylstyrene	−0.9	1.05	Methyl methacrylate
	−0.9	0.92	p-Chlorostyrene
m-Methylstyrene	−0.8	0.95	Methyl methacrylate
α-Vinylthiophene	−0.8	3.0	Styrene
Butadiene	−0.8	1.33	Styrene
p-Chlorostyrene	−0.3	0.88	Styrene
	−0.6	1.20	Methyl methacrylate
p-Iodostyrene	−0.3	1.08	Styrene
	−0.6	1.28	Methyl methacrylate
m-Chlorostyrene	−0.2	0.96	Styrene
	−0.5	1.05	Methyl methacrylate
o-Chlorostyrene	−0.5	1.41	Styrene
	−0.2	1.15	Methyl methacrylate
p-Bromostyrene	−0.2	0.88	Styrene
	−0.5	1.27	Methyl methacrylate
m-Bromostyrene	−0.1	0.98	Styrene
	−0.4	1.20	Methyl methacrylate
α-Vinylpyridine	−0.1	1.07	Styrene
	−0.6	1.09	Methyl methacrylate
Vinyl acetate	−0.1	0.022	Vinylidene chloride
	−0.3	0.028	Methyl acrylate
	−0.4	0.026	Methyl methacrylate
	−0.3	0.047	Allyl chloride
	−0.5	0.010	Vinyl chloride
	−0.8	0.015	Vinyl chloride
	−0.9	0.022	Vinylidene chloride
Vinyl bromide	0.1	0.1	Vinyl acetate

Table continued

TABLE XII-8 *(concluded)*

Vinyl chloride	0.2	0.024	Styrene
	0.0	0.035	Methyl acrylate
	0.4	0.074	Methyl methacrylate
p-Cyanostyrene	0.3	1.61	Styrene
	−0.7?	2.26?	Methyl methacrylate
p-Nitrostyrene	0.4	1.86	Styrene
	0.4	1.06	*p*-Chlorostyrene
2,5-Dichlorostyrene	0.4	1.67	Methyl methacrylate
Methyl methacrylate	0.4	0.74	Styrene
Vinylidene chloride	0.6	0.2	Styrene
Allyl chloride	0.6	0.052	Vinylidene chloride
Methyl acrylate	0.6	0.42	Styrene
Methyl vinyl ketone	0.7	1.0	Styrene
β-Chloroethyl acrylate	0.9	0.46	Styrene
Methacrylonitrile	1.0	1.0	Styrene
	0.9	1.15	Styrene
	0.9	1.06	Vinyl acetate
	1.3	1.5	Methyl methacrylate
Acrylonitrile	0.9	0.68	Methyl vinyl ketone
	0.9	0.37	Vinyl acetate
	1.0	0.67	Vinyl acetate
	1.2	0.44	Styrene
	1.3	0.37	Vinyl chloride
	1.6	0.9	Vinylidene chloride
	1.6	0.75	Vinyl chloride
Diethyl fumarate	1.2	0.77	Styrene
	1.4	0.028	Vinylidene chloride
	1.9	0.28	Vinyl chloride

[a] Styrene: $e = -0.8$. $Q = 1.0$.

likely that strong interaction is also possible between radical and monomer. In these cases, complex formation results from the possibility of transfer of a single electron from one monomer to the other, and the same thing may happen between radical and monomer.[66,67] In many cases it appears to be necessary to consider special resonance forms related to those involved in molecular complex formation to obtain satisfactory interpretation of the alternating effect in copolymerization.[67] In addition to these special struc-

[66] P. D. Bartlett and K. Nozaki, *J. Am. Chem. Soc.*, **68**, 1495 (1946).

[67] C. Walling, E. R. Briggs, K. B. Wolfstirn, and F. R. Mayo, *J. Am. Chem. Soc.*, **70**, 1537 (1948).

[67a] C. C. Price, *J. Polymer, Sci.*, **3**, 772 (1948).

tural features, there appears to be a general effect of substituents in both the radical and monomer which may withdraw or supply electrons from the site of the reaction, resulting in effective charges on the doubly bound carbon atoms in the monomer or on the trivalent carbon atom in the radical.[63] The alternation in copolymerization would therefore result from the attraction of a negative double bond and a positive radical or *vice versa*. It is further presumed that the charge effect of a substituent is the same on the radical as on the monomer.[64]

The larger the difference in polarity or in donor acceptor properties of two monomers the greater will be the alternation tendency. In Table XII-6 (after Mayo, Lewis, and Walling) the monomers are arranged up to down and left to right in order of their increasing tendency to alternate with styrene. This order is therefore also the approximate increasing order of the tendency of their substituents to accept electrons from the double bonds (the poorest electron acceptors or the best electron donors being placed at the head of the columns and to the left of the rows). The figures in the table are the product of the monomer reactivity ratios in all the cases where these are known. It is clear that the product $r_1 r_2$ is theoretically equal to unity in the diagonal running from upper left to lower right, inasmuch as this diagonal refers to the polymerization of the monomers with themselves. The further away from this main diagonal the greater the difference in electron-accepting properties of the monomers, and, theoretically, therefore, the smaller the product $r_1 r_2$ should be. Table XII-6 shows that this is indeed the case, there being a general decrease of $r_1 r_2$ in each vertical column from top to bottom, and a general increase of $r_1 r_2$ in each horizontal row from left to right.

In addition to the alternating tendency there is a general order of reactivity of monomers to all types of radicals.[59,62] Monomers with conjugated vinyl, phenyl, carbonyl, nitrile, and carbalkoxy groups are considerably more reactive than monomers that show no possibility of conjugation. In Table XII-7 (after Mayo, Lewis, and Walling), if the reciprocals of a series of monomer reactivity ratios for various reference radicals at the top of each vertical column are $M_1 \cdot$ and the various monomers in the column are M_2, then the numbers in the column are $1/r_1 = k_{12}/k_{11}$. The numbers in each column can be considered to be the relative reactivities of the various monomers M_2 for the radical $M_1 \cdot$, the reactivity of M_1 for $M_1 \cdot$ being taken as unity (*i.e.*, k_{11} is taken as unity). It is clear that the values in any two vertical columns cannot be compared, but only the values within a column. Absolute comparisons could be made, however, if the absolute values for the specific reaction rates for growth were known.

The radicals at the top of Table XII-7 are listed in order of decreasing electron-donor tendencies. The monomers in the vertical column are arranged in order of decreasing over-all average activity, except for a few 1,2 disubstituted ethylenes arbitrarily arranged at the bottom of the table. If the activity of monomers were completely independent of the radical to which it was adding, then every column in Table XII-8 would show continually decreasing values for reactivity from the top of the table to the bottom. There is a sufficient uniformity in this decrease to conclude that an average reactivity of monomers toward radicals is a useful concept.

An attempt to describe the behavior of monomers in copolymerization on a quantitative basis was made by Alfrey and Price.[64] These authors assign a reactivity Q and a polarity e to every monomer. If the reactivities and polarities of monomers M_1 and M_2 are Q_1, e_1, Q_2, and e_2, respectively, then the monomer reactivity ratios are:

$$r_1 = \frac{Q_1}{Q_2} e^{-e_1(e_1 - e_2)} \qquad r_2 = \frac{Q_2}{Q_1} e^{-e_2(e_1 - e_2)}$$

Table XII-8 gives Q and e values for various monomers. Mayo, Lewis, and Walling have given the following estimate of the order of average reactivity of the monomer $H_2C{=}CHR$ toward free radicals (only R is written):

$C_6H_5-\ >\ H_2C{=}CH-\ >\ R-CO-\ >\ N{\equiv}C\ >\ RO-CO-\ >\ Br-\ >\ Cl-\ >$
$$RO-,\ RCH_2\ >\ H$$

The same substituents show the following order of ability to act as electron donors:

$RO-\ >\ H_2C{=}CH-\ >\ C_6H_5\ >\ RCH_2-\ >\ H-\ >\ Br-\ >\ Cl-\ >$
$$R-CO-,\ RO-CO-\ >\ N{=}C$$

One of the most important problems concerning the structure of vinyl polymers is whether they are formed completely in the "head to tail" structure:

$$\sim\!\!\!\sim CH_2CHXCH_2CHXCH_2CHX\!\!\sim\!\!\!\sim$$

or whether there also exists "head to head" sequences along the chain:

$$\sim\!\!\!\sim CH_2CHXCHXCH_2\!\!\sim\!\!\!\sim$$

This problem may be considered a problem in copolymerization, where the competing reactions are:

$$\sim\!\!\!\sim CH_2CHX\cdot + CH_2{=}CHX \xrightarrow{k_{11}} \sim\!\!\!\sim CH_2CHXCH_2CHX\cdot$$

$$\text{\textasciitilde wCH}_2\text{CHX} \cdot + \text{CHX}{=}\text{CH}_2 \xrightarrow{k_{12}} \text{\textasciitilde wCH}_2\text{CHXCHXCH}_2 \cdot$$

$$\text{\textasciitilde wCHXCH}_2 \cdot + \text{CHX}{=}\text{CH}_2 \xrightarrow{k_{21}} \text{\textasciitilde wCHXCH}_2\text{CHXCH}_2 \cdot$$

$$\text{\textasciitilde wCHXCH}_2 \cdot + \text{CH}_2{=}\text{CHX} \xrightarrow{k_{22}} \text{\textasciitilde wCHXCH}_2\text{CH}_2\text{CHX} \cdot$$

At present, it is believed that the initiating radical adds to the methylenic carbon atom of the vinyl monomer—the so-called anti-Markownikoff addition.[68] The growth reaction is then believed to occur almost exclusively by reaction k_{11} due to resonance stabilization and for steric reasons. This mechanism receives support from x-ray and infrared studies of polyvinyl polymers from which it appears that the head-to-tail structure is formed almost exclusively. It is conceivable that termination by combination would lead to a slight amount of head-to-head structure, in addition to the possibilities of an occasional head-to-head or tail-to-tail sequence due to the competing growth reactions k_{12}, k_{21}, and k_{22}.

Inasmuch as the head-to-tail structure would give rise to substitution on *alternate* carbon atoms whereas head-to-head structure involves substitution on *adjacent* carbon atoms, classical methods of organic chemistry can be used to distinguish these structures. In almost all cases, this evidence also favors the head-to-tail structure.[69]

G. INITIATION BY REDOX SYSTEMS

It has been demonstrated that radicals can induce the polymerization of vinyl and diene monomers in the gas phase, in the liquid phase, and in water solutions or emulsions. For gas phase polymerizations, radicals can be conveniently generated by photolysis of mercury dimethyl.

For the liquid phase (bulk polymerizations), radicals are produced by the decomposition of peroxides, hydroperoxides, azo compounds, etc. For aqueous polymerizations of water soluble monomers, or for emulsion polymerization of water soluble monomers, the use of so-called "redox" systems has provided a simple means of producing radicals that are available for initiating polymerization. A "redox" system is a combination of reducing agent plus a peroxide-type catalyst, the reducing agent acting as an activator. Although this effect was discovered around 1937, interpretation of

---

[68] M. S. Kharasch, M. C. McNab, and F. R. Mayo, *J. Am. Chem. Soc.*, **55**, 2521, 2531 (1933).

[69] C. S. Marvel in R. E. Burk and O. Grummitt, eds., *The Chemistry of Large Molecules*. Interscience, New York, 1943, pp. 219–241.

this effect was not forthcoming until 1945.[70-73] The particular advantage of redox initiation is that it makes possible rapid polymerization at low temperatures.

A typical example of redox initiation is the case of ferrous ion and hydrogen peroxide. In the absence of a polymerizable monomer, ferrous ions in excess of hydrogen peroxide catalyze the decomposition of hydrogen peroxide leading to the evolution of oxygen. Haber and Weiss[74] put forward the following reaction scheme, involving electron-transfer reactions, to account for this reaction:

$$H_2O_2 + Fe^{++} \longrightarrow HO^- + HO\cdot + Fe^{+++}$$
$$HO\cdot + Fe^{++} \longrightarrow HO^- + Fe^{+++}$$
$$HO\cdot + H_2O_2 \longrightarrow H_2O + HO_2\cdot$$
$$HO_2\cdot + H_2O_2 \longrightarrow HO\cdot + H_2O + O_2$$

In the presence of a polymerizable monomer, the evolution of oxygen can be repressed very considerably and polymerization of the monomer is induced. Evidently the monomer competes for the radicals produced in the above set of electron transfer reactions according to the following scheme:[75]

$$\text{(I)} \quad H_2O_2 + Fe^{++} \longrightarrow HO\cdot + HO^- + Fe^{+++}$$
$$\text{(II)} \quad HO\cdot + Fe^{++} \longrightarrow HO^- + Fe^{+++}$$
$$\text{(III)} \quad HO\cdot + CH_2{=}CHX \longrightarrow HOCH_2CHX\cdot \longrightarrow \text{polymerization}$$

The idea was tested by Evans, Baxendale, and co-workers[75] by study of the stoichiometry of the reaction in the absence and in the presence of monomers. When the molality of ferrous ions is equal to, or in excess of, that of the hydrogen peroxide, the reaction in the absence of monomer is limited to reactions (I) and (II) and the stoichiometry of the reaction corresponds to 1 mole of $H_2O_2 \equiv 2$ moles of ferrous ions. However, if reaction (III) occurs, then, since both ferrous ions and momomer compete for hydroxyl ion according to (II) and (III), it is to be expected that there will be a deviation in the stoichiometry toward that of 1 mole of hydrogen peroxide being equivalent to 1 mole of ferrous ions.

[70] R. O. R. Bacon, *Trans. Faraday Soc.*, **42**, 140 (1946).

[71] J. H. Baxendale, M. G. Evans, and G. S. Park, *Trans. Faraday Soc.*, **42**, 155 (1946).

[72] L. B. Morgan, *Trans. Faraday Soc.*, **42**, 169 (1946).

[73] D. Josefowitz and H. Mark, *Polymer Bull.*, **1**, 140 (1945).

[74] F. Haber and P. Weiss, *Proc. Roy. Soc.*, **A147**, 233 (1939).

[75] J. H. Baxendale, M. G. Evans, and G. S. Park, *Trans. Faraday Soc.*, **42**, 155 1946).

The exclusion of oxygen is very important in polymerizations of this type because oxygen can add to the free radicals and inhibit the reaction. As a matter of fact in the presence of oxygen, ferrous ion and hydrogen peroxide can be used as oxidation catalysts.

The rates of formation of ferric ion in the absence and presence of monomers were studied, colorimetric methods being used for determining the concentration of ferrous and ferric ions. It was found that at 25°C. the specific rate for the reaction:

$$Fe^{++} + H_2O_2 \xrightarrow{k_1} Fe^{+++} + HO\cdot + OH^-$$

is $k_1 = 1.78 \times 10^9 \exp(-10,000/RT)$ [moles/liter] $^{-1}$sec.$^{-1}$.

The kinetic scheme suggested for the polymerization of aqueous solutions of monomers is:

$$Fe^{++} + H_2O_2 \longrightarrow Fe^{+++} + OH^- + HO\cdot \quad k_1$$
$$HO\cdot + M \longrightarrow HOM_1\cdot \quad k_i$$
$$HOM_1\cdot + M \longrightarrow HO(M)_2\cdot$$
$$HO(M)_n\cdot + M \longrightarrow HO(M)_{n+1} \quad k_p$$
$$HO(M)_n\cdot + \cdot(M)_pOH \longrightarrow HO(M)_{n+p}OH \quad k_t$$

when integrated (using stationary-state conditions) the above equations give:

$$\log \frac{M}{M_0} = \frac{k_p}{\sqrt{k_1 k_t}} \log(1 + ak_1t) \qquad (XII.37)$$

where a is the initial molality of both ferrous ion and hydrogen peroxide, and M_0 is the initial concentration of monomer. This equation apparently fits the experimental results for polymerization of water soluble monomers.

Although the monomers (like acrylonitrile) are in aqueous solution, the polymers produced are insoluble, so it is not surprising that added emulsifying agents have a profound effect on the rate of polymerization.

It must be pointed out that the hydrogen peroxide–ferrous–ferric system may be more complicated than explained above, at least under conditions different from those of Evans, Baxendale, and Bywater. It is found in certain cases that the ferric ion also has a catalytic effect on polymerization in the presence of hydrogen peroxide.

In a series of studies on acrylonitrile in aqueous solution, Bacon[76] has found that polymerization initiated by persulfates is greatly accelerated by

[76] R. O. R. Bacon, *Trans. Faraday Soc.*, **42**, 140–155 (1946).

:he presence of reducing agents. The most effective activators were found :o be organic sulfides, hydrogen sulfide, hydroxy acids of sulfur that possess ·educing properties, and the salts of these acids. Silver nitrate showed great ıctivating efficiency, and metals such as copper, iron, and silver were also ≥ffective particularly if their surface area was large.

For use in low temperature emulsion polymerizations of GR-S it has ɔeen reported[77] that cumene hydroperoxide activated by a reducing agent ;uch as fructose and with a soluble iron salt such as ferrous or ferric pyro- phosphate gives a ten- to twenty-fold increase in the rate of polymerization. The use of redox systems such as this is the basis of the important develop- ments in the production of "cold rubber," whose properties as a tire rubber ıre reported to surpass those of natural rubber.

H. DIENE POLYMERIZATION

The polymerization of diene monomers such as isoprene and butadiene bears an over-all resemblance to the polymerization of vinyl monomers. The similarity of mechanism is strikingly borne out by the fact that dienes may be copolymerized with vinyl monomers and the theoretical treatment for vinyl copolymerization presented in section F applies to diene-vinyl copolymerization as well. Nevertheless, dienes show a versatility of be- havior which gives rise to structural isomerism not possible in vinyl mono- mers. Whereas a vinyl monomer is strictly bifunctional, and may be schematically represented as:

$$\cdot CH_2CHX \cdot$$

A diene monomer has the following possible schematic structures:

$$\cdot CH_2—CX=CH—CH_2 \cdot \qquad \cdot CH_2—\underset{\underset{CH_2}{\overset{\|}{\underset{|}{CH}}}}{\overset{X}{C}} \cdot \qquad \cdot \underset{\underset{CH_2}{\overset{\|}{\underset{|}{CX}}}}{CH—CH_2} \bullet \qquad \cdot CH_2\overset{\cdot\,\cdot}{C}XCHCH_2 \cdot$$

| 1,4 structure bifunctional | 1,2 structure bifunc- tional | 3,4 structure bifunc- tional | tetrafunctional |

In point of fact, dienes can polymerize as bifunctional monomers in either the 1,4, 1,2, or 3,4 configurations. The tendency to polymerize in the tetrafunctional form is very small, probably nonexistent. The cross linking that occurs during diene polymerizations is believed to occur by

---

[77] E. J. Vandenberg and G. E. Hulse, paper presented at the fall 1947 meeting of the American Chemical Society at New York.

activation of the double bonds left behind in the already built-up polymer chains (*e.g.*, by radical addition to these relatively inactive double bonds). Thus the tetrafunctionality of these monomers appears to be largely of a two-stage character.

As compared to natural rubber, which is believed to be linear polyisoprene with the isoprene residues in the 1,4 head-to-tail position, synthetic polyisoprene is not strictly linear, has 1,2 as well as 1,4 residues, and in the 1,4 residues is randomly *cis-trans* about the double bond whereas natural rubber is all *cis* about the double bond. The same irregularity is obtained when butadiene is polymerized or in copolymers of butadiene and vinyl monomers.

TABLE XII-9

STRUCTURAL FEATURES OF SOME DIENE POLYMERS

Polymer	1,4 addition, %	1,2 addition, %	3,4 addition, %	Total unsaturation, %
Natural rubber	96	0	0	96
Emulsion polyisoprene	88	10	0	98
Organometallic polyisoprene	80	17	0	97
Sodium polyisoprene	32	32	24	88
Emulsion polybutadiene	79 IR[a] 79 PBA[b]	—	—	95–97
Polybutadiene (organometallic catalyst)	70 IR 68 PBA	—	—	98
Polybutadiene (polymerized by potassium)	35–40 IR 50–58 PBA	—	—	89–94
Butadiene-styrene 75/25 (emulsion-polymerized GR-S)	81 IR 78–81 PBA	—	—	97
Butadiene-styrene 75/25 (organometallic catalyst)	68 PBA	—	—	95
Butadiene-styrene 75/25	20 IR 41–43 PBA	—	—	94

[a] IR refers to determination by infrared.
[b] PBA refers to determination by perbenzoic acid.

The structural sequences in natural and synthetic diene polymers have been studied by analysis of ozonolysis products.[78] The amount of 1,2 addition has been estimated by perbenzoic acid reaction, which reacts at different rates with internal and external double bonds.[79] Infrared[80] and x-rays[81]

[78] C. Harries, *Ann.*, **395**, 264 (1913). N. Rabjohn *et al.*, *J. Am. Chem. Soc.*, **69**, 314 (1947).

[79] E. R. Weidlein, *Chem. Eng. News*, **24**, 771 (1946).

[80] W. W. Coblentz and R. Stair, *J. Research Natl. Bur. Standards*, **15**, 295 (1935). D. Williams and B. Dale, *J. Applied Phys.*, **15**, 585 (1944). J. B. Field, D. E. Woodford, and S. D. Gehman, *J. Applied Phys.*, **17**, 386 (1946).

[81] S. D. Gehman, *Chem. Revs.*, **26**, 203 (1940).

ꜣave also been used to elucidate the structural features of diene polymers.
Citration with iodine chloride has been used to determine the percentage of
unsaturation based on the theoretical maximum.   D'Ianni[82] has summarized data on structural features of dienes and butadiene-styrene copolymers in Table XII-9.

The fact that in all cases the total unsaturation was less than 100% indicated that these polymers contained varying percentages of cyclized or
cross-linked structures.

Both branching and cross linking can occur in diene polymers according
to the following schemes:[83,84]

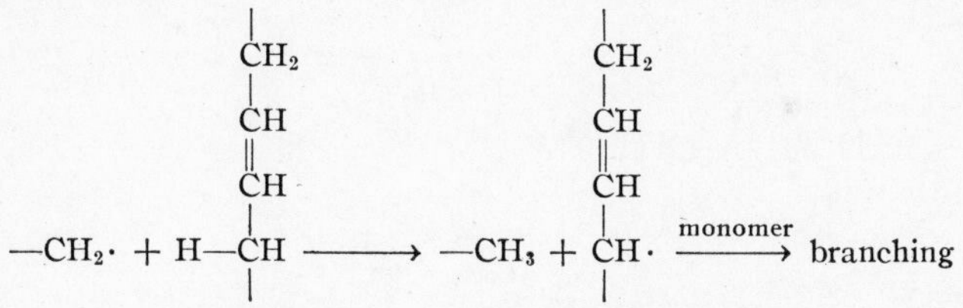

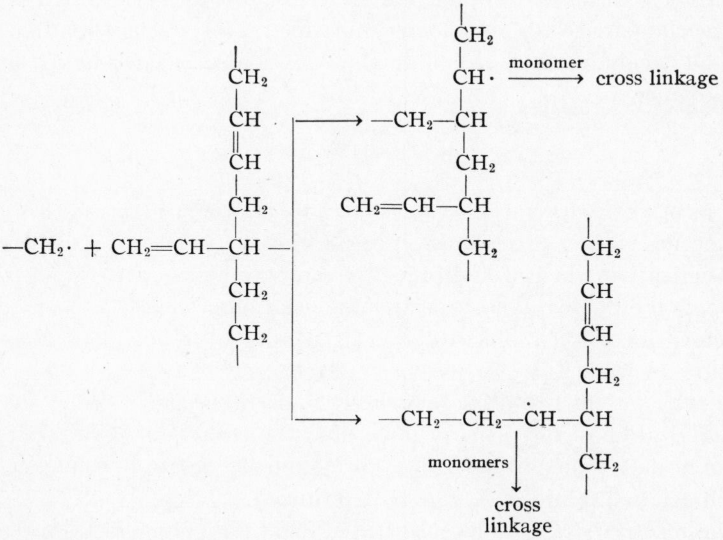

$$
\begin{array}{ccc}
& \overset{\displaystyle |}{CH_2} & \overset{\displaystyle |}{CH_2} \\
& \overset{\displaystyle |}{CH} & \overset{\displaystyle |}{CH} \\
& \overset{\displaystyle \|}{CH} & \overset{\displaystyle \|}{CH} \\
& \overset{\displaystyle |}{} & \overset{\displaystyle |}{} \\
—CH_2\cdot\ +\ H—CH & \longrightarrow\quad —CH_3\ +\ CH\cdot & \xrightarrow{\text{monomer}}\ \text{branching} \\
\overset{\displaystyle |}{} & \overset{\displaystyle |}{}
\end{array}
$$

$$
\begin{array}{l}
\qquad\qquad\qquad CH_2 \\
\qquad\qquad\qquad |\\
\qquad CH_2 \qquad\qquad CH\cdot \xrightarrow{\text{monomer}} \text{cross linkage} \\
\quad\ |\qquad\qquad\qquad | \\
\quad\ CH\ \longrightarrow —CH_2—CH \\
\quad\ \|\qquad\qquad\qquad | \\
\quad\ CH\qquad\qquad\quad CH_2 \\
\quad\ |\qquad\qquad\quad CH_2{=}CH—CH \\
\quad\ CH_2\qquad\qquad\qquad | \\
—CH_2\cdot\ +\ CH_2{=}CH—CH— \qquad\quad CH_2 \qquad\quad CH_2 \\
\quad\ |\qquad\qquad\qquad\qquad |\qquad\qquad | \\
\quad\ CH_2\qquad\qquad\qquad\qquad\ \ CH_2\qquad\quad CH \\
\quad\ |\qquad\qquad\qquad\qquad\qquad\qquad\quad \| \\
\quad\ CH_2\qquad\qquad\qquad\qquad\qquad\qquad CH \\
\qquad\qquad\qquad\qquad\qquad\qquad\qquad\quad | \\
\qquad\qquad\qquad\qquad\qquad\qquad\qquad\ CH_2 \\
\qquad\qquad\qquad \longrightarrow —CH_2—CH_2—CH—CH \\
\qquad\qquad\qquad\qquad\qquad\qquad\quad | \qquad\qquad | \\
\qquad\qquad\qquad\quad \text{monomers}\ \downarrow\qquad CH_2 \\
\qquad\qquad\qquad\qquad\qquad\qquad\qquad\quad | \\
\qquad\qquad\qquad\qquad\qquad\ \text{cross} \\
\qquad\qquad\qquad\qquad\qquad\ \text{linkage}
\end{array}
$$

Flory[84] has given a kinetic treatment of the dependence of the degree of
cross linking on conversion. If α is the degree of conversion, $[c^*]$ the absolute concentration of radicals, and k_2 the specific rate for growth, then:

[82] D'Ianni, *Ind. Eng. Chem.*, **40**, 253 (1948).
[83] H. S. Taylor and A. V. Tobolsky, *J. Am. Chem. Soc.*, **67**, 2063 (1945).
[84] P. J. Flory, *ibid.*, **69**, 2893 (1947).

$$d\alpha/dt = k_2[c^*][(1 - \alpha)] \qquad \text{(XII.38)}$$

The rate at which cross linkages are formed by addition of a growing radical to a double bond in a previously polymerized unit is $k_\nu[c^*]\alpha$. It is convenient to consider that a diolefin monomer which eventually becomes cross linked contributes two structural units, one to each of two "primary molecules." The term "primary molecules" is defined as being the molecules which would exist if cross linking additions had been omitted from the growth process.

If ν is taken to be the concentration of cross-linked units (expressed as moles of cross-linked units per mole of monomer initially present) then:

$$d\nu/dt = 2k_\nu[c^*]\alpha \qquad \text{(XII.39)}$$

or dividing (XII.39) by (XII.38):

$$d\nu/dt = 2K\alpha/(1 - \alpha) \qquad K = k_\nu/k_2 \qquad \text{(XII.40)}$$

K may be considered to be the reactivity ratio of an unsaturated polymer unit as compared with a monomer molecule. Integrating equation (XII.-40) and dividing ν by α to obtain the "density" ρ of cross-linked units in the polymer:

$$\rho = \nu/\alpha = -2K[1 + (1/\alpha)\ln(1 - \alpha)] \qquad \text{(XII.41)}$$

Graphs of ρ vs. α for various values of K are shown in Figure XII-6. Gelation occurs when ρ exceeds the reciprocal of the weight average degree of polymerization which would prevail if no cross linkages had been formed. The action of mercaptans in postponing gelation in diene polymerization is therefore due to their effect in lowering the degree of polymerization of the primary molecules.

Since $\rho = 1/\bar{P}_w$ at gelation, where $\bar{P}_w$ is the weight average degree of polymerization of the primary molecules, the cross-linking reactivity ratio K can be determined from (XII.41) if $\bar{P}_w$ and the degree of conversion α, at which gelation first occurs, can be determined.

The reactivity of various substituted dienes in polymerization reactions is a topic of great interest. Carothers[85] studied the rates of polymerization of various substituted dienes under standard conditions and found that those substituted in the 2nd and 3rd positions polymerize more rapidly than derivatives substituted in the 1st or 4th positions. It should be

[85] W. H. Carothers, *Trans. Faraday Soc.*, **32**, 39 (1936).

pointed out, however, that over-all rates of polymerization involve a combination of rate constants, and reactivity can be put on an absolute scale

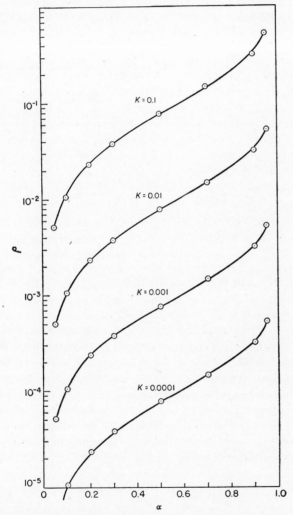

Fig. XII-6. Density of cross-linked units as a function of
monomer conversion for various values of K.

only after the absolute values of the rate constants are determined according to the methods of section E.

I. VULCANIZATION

In 1839, Charles Goodyear discovered the process of heating natural rubber with sulfur to convert the natural thermoplastic material into a thermoelastic product. The nature of this process naturally was the source of considerable speculation and research. The chief difficulties that lay in the path of the early investigators was a lack of adequate understanding of the structure of polymeric substances. Further, profound physical changes take place after only a slight extent of chemical reaction, and the insoluble nature of vulcanized rubber renders chemical analysis very difficult.

It is now almost universally accepted that the most important aspect of vulcanization (or "curing" as it is sometimes termed), is the introduction of chemical cross linkages between polymeric chains to give three-dimensional network structures. Vulcanization in this broader sense can be achieved without heat, as when natural rubber is cold vulcanized by S_2Cl_2 or by "active sulfur" from SO_2 and H_2S in the Peachey process. It can also be achieved by the use of nonsulfur-containing compounds as was discovered by Ostromislensky. Synthetically produced diene-vinyl copolymers such as GR-S (butadiene-styrene 75/25) can also be converted to synthetic rubbers by sulfur vulcanization or by nonsulfur-containing compounds. Finally, even saturated linear polymers such as polyesters or polyethyl acrylate can be vulcanized to thermoelastic rubbers by suitable cross-linking agents.

The exact nature of the reaction between sulfur and diene rubbers (natural and synthetic), which is still the basis for the most important vulcanization processes, is far from being elucidated. The situation is particularly complex, inasmuch as all "curing recipes" now contain, in addition to sulfur and rubber, accelerators such as tetramethylthiuram disulfide or mercaptobenzothiazole as well as zinc oxide. It is now generally conceded that a great variety of different reactions between rubber and sulfur probably take place during sulfur vulcanization. Amerongen and Houwink[86] have considered as possible the following combinations with sulfur proposed in the literature:

I   II   III   IV

[86] G. J. van Amerongen and R. Houwink, *Rev. gén. caoutchouc*, **19**, 303 (1942).

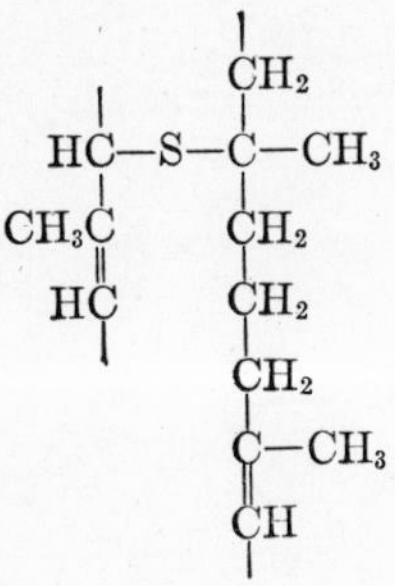

$$
\begin{array}{ccc}
\begin{matrix}
& | \\
& CH_2 \\
& | \\
HC-S-C-CH_3 \\
CH_3C \quad CH_2 \\
HC \quad CH_2 \\
\quad CH_2 \\
\quad C-CH_3 \\
\quad CH
\end{matrix}
&
\begin{matrix}
C-S-C \\
CH_3-C \quad C-CH_3
\end{matrix}
&
\begin{matrix}
H-C-S-S-CH \\
CH_3-CH \quad HC-CH_3
\end{matrix}
\\
\textbf{V} & \textbf{VI} & \textbf{VII}
\end{array}
$$

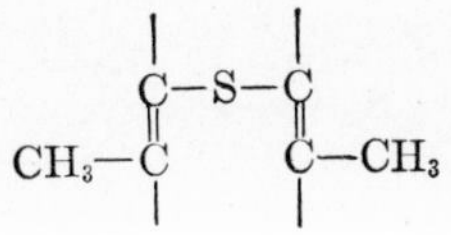

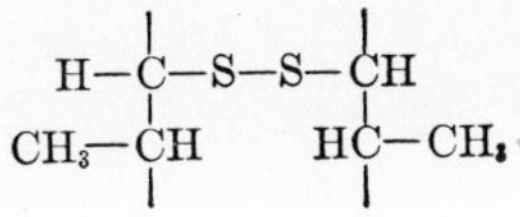

Structure I is believed to be largely present when ebonite is formed by treating rubber with the theoretical maximum amount of sulfur (32%). The structures (some of which are not very probable) include intramolecular and intermolecular combination with sulfur. In certain cases, combination with sulfur involves loss of unsaturation, but this is not always true. Furthermore, monosulfides, disulfides, and even higher polysulfides may be formed; in addition to which, sulfur may act as a catalyst for direct carbon-carbon linkage.

The most fruitful method of investigating the reaction between sulfur and rubber appears to be in the direction of studies of the reaction between sulfur and simple olefins such as cyclohexene. Farmer[87] states that the action of sulfur on simple monoolefins at about 140°C. appears to be that pairs of molecules become cross-linked by the sulfur, and that approximately one double bond is lost between each two interacting molecules. In the case of cyclohexene we have:

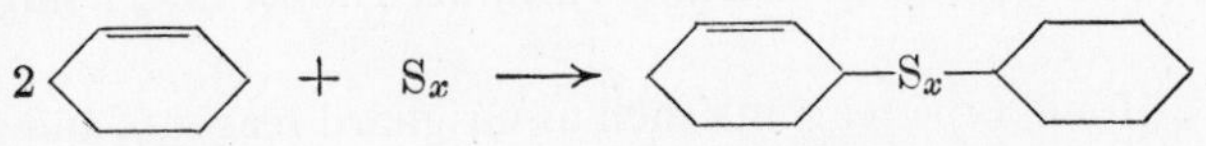

$$ 2\,\bigcirc + S_x \longrightarrow \bigcirc\!-\!S_x\!-\!\bigcirc $$

depending on conditions (and on the nature of the olefin) x may vary from 2 to 5. Farmer suggests the following chain mechanism for the reaction of cyclohexene and sulfur:

[87] E. H. Farmer, in H. Mark and G. S. Whitby, eds., *Advances in Colloid Science*, Vol. II. Interscience, New York, 1946, pages 299–361.

$$\text{(ring)} + S_x \longrightarrow \text{(ring)}\cdot \,+ HS_x\cdot$$

$$\text{(ring)}\cdot + S_x \longrightarrow \text{(ring)}S_x\cdot$$

$$\text{(ring)}S_x\cdot + \text{(ring)} \longrightarrow \text{(ring)}S_x\text{(ring)}\cdot$$

$$\text{(ring)}S_x\text{(ring)}\cdot + \text{(ring)} \longrightarrow \text{(ring)}S_x\text{(ring)} + \text{(ring)}\cdot$$

$$\text{(ring)} + HS_x\cdot \longrightarrow \text{(ring)}\cdot + HS_xH$$

The reaction of rubber with sulfur monochloride may well be simpler, e.g., the reaction of S_2Cl_2 with olefins is known to proceed as follows:

$$2CH_2{=}CH_2 + S_2Cl_2 \longrightarrow ClCH_2CH_2SCH_2CH_2Cl + S$$

The organic vulcanizing agents have been classified into several types.[88]

Type I. Compounds which decompose thermally at vulcanizing temperatures (20–170°C.) to yield free radicals. This includes benzoyl peroxide, the diazoaminobenzenes, dichloroazodicarbonamidine and the azodicarboxylates.

Type II. Suitable oxidants of appropriate reasonance structure, including quinones, quinonoximes and imines, and polynitrobenzenes.

Type III. Agents which yield free radicals on oxidation, such as aromatic amines and mercaptans, phenols and dihydric phenols, bring about vulcanization when used with a proper oxidizing agent. Two-dimensional phenol-formaldehyde resins will also vulcanize rubber under suitable conditions.

Type IV. Ionic type reagents such as Grignard reagents and zinc alkyls.

Type I organic vulcanizing agents will even vulcanize polymers containing no carbon-carbon double bonds. For example, Baker[89] found that benzoyl peroxide will vulcanize polyester rubbers presumably by first attacking the hydrogen atom on the carbon atom in the α position relative to the carbonyl group.

[88] T. Alfrey, J. G. Hendricks, R. M. Hershey, and H. Mark, *India Rubber World*, **12**, 577 (1945).

[89] W. O. Baker, *J. Am. Chem. Soc.*, **69**, 1125 (1947).

Using the reaction of cyclohexene with benzoyl peroxide as a model, Farmer[90] has outlined the vulcanization of rubber with benzoyl peroxide as follows.

(1) Benzoyl peroxide breaks down into benzoxy and phenyl radicals.

(2) The radicals attack the α-methylenic hydrogens to give radicals on the rubber chains. Benzoic acid is formed as by-product when benzoxy radicals are involved.

(3) A radical on one hydrocarbon chain adds to a double bond of another chain to form a carbon-to-carbon cross linkage. This entails a loss of unsaturation. A new radical is formed as follows:

$$
\begin{array}{ccc}
 & \overset{|}{C}H_2 & \\
H\overset{|}{C}\cdot & \overset{|}{C}H & \overset{|}{C}H_2 \\
CH_3\overset{|}{C} + \overset{||}{C}CH_3 \longrightarrow & & \overset{|}{C}\!-\!CH \\
H_2\overset{||}{C} & \overset{|}{C}H_2 & H_3C\overset{|}{C} \cdot CCH_3 \\
H_2\overset{|}{C} & \overset{|}{C}H_2 & H\overset{||}{C} \quad \overset{|}{C}H_2 \\
 & & H_2\overset{|}{C}
\end{array}
$$

(4) The radicals after a sequence of chain transfer reactions and additions to the double bonds finally terminate by mutual addition or disproportionation. In certain cases, addition of a radical from the catalyst occurs with a radical on the rubber chain, accounting for incorporation of catalyst fragments in the polymer chains.

J. EFFECT OF OXYGEN ON POLYMERIZATION

The presence of oxygen during polymerization has several apparently conflicting effects which have only recently been partially resolved. Small traces of oxygen often catalyze polymerization in the absence of other catalysts because the oxygen forms peroxides and hydroperoxides which initiate polymerization. However, it has recently been convincingly demonstrated that large quantities of oxygen will definitely inhibit polymerization.[91, 92]

Barnes[93] showed that photopolymerization of methyl methacrylate could be effectively inhibited by maintaining a constant pressure of oxygen above the methyl methacrylate. He postulated that light tends to form radicals,

[90] E. H. Farmer and S. Michael, *Rubber Chem. and Technol.*, 16, 465 (1943). See also T. Alfrey, J. G. Hendricks, R. M. Hershey, and H. Mark, *India Rubber World*, 112, 577 (1945).

[91] C. C. Price and C. E. Adams, *J. Am. Chem. Soc.*, 67, 1674 (1945).

[92] I. M. Kolthoff and W. S. Dale, *J. Am. Chem. Soc.*, 69, 441 (1947); 67, 672 (1945).

[93] C. E. Barnes, *J. Am. Chem. Soc.*, 67, 217 (1945).

but that oxygen immediately adds to the radical and thus effectively competes with polymerization.

$$M \xrightarrow{h\nu} M \cdot$$

$$M \cdot + M \longrightarrow M_2 \cdot, \text{ etc.}$$

$$M \cdot + O_2 \longrightarrow MO_2 \cdot$$

The same inhibitory effect of oxygen in the emulsion polymerization of tyrene was demonstrated by Price and Kolthoff.[91,92]

The fate of the $MO_2 \cdot$ radicals is of great interest. It is conceivable that hey might recombine to form peroxides:

$$MO_2 \cdot + MO_2 \cdot \longrightarrow MO_2M + O_2$$

The breakdown of the peroxides produces radicals that would catalyze polymerization if the oxygen were present initially in small amounts and was shortly used up. The effect of oxygen would then be to give a brief induction period followed by a peroxide-catalyzed polymerization.

However, if excess oxygen was maintained (for example, by attaching the system to a source of constant pressure oxygen or by leaving it open to the atmosphere), the induction period would be much greater, and side reactions would compete with polymerization. Medvedev and Zeitlin[94] showed that if styrene is polymerized in the presence of oxygen, there is a constant ratio between the rate of polymerization and the rate of oxidation (to form benzaldehyde and formaldehyde). They explain this in the following way:

Polymerization

$$\text{\tiny www}CH_2CH\varphi \cdot + CH_2{=}CH\varphi \longrightarrow \text{\tiny www}CH_2CH\varphi CH_2CH\varphi \cdot$$

Oxidation

$$\text{\tiny www}CH_2CH\varphi \cdot + O_2 \longrightarrow \text{\tiny www}CH_2CH\varphi OO \cdot$$

Peroxy link in polymer

$$\text{\tiny www}CH_2CH\varphi OO \cdot + CH_2{=}CH\varphi \longrightarrow \text{\tiny www}CH_2CH\varphi OOCH_2CH\varphi \cdot$$

Hydroperoxide formation

$$\text{\tiny www}CH_2CH\varphi OO \cdot + RH \longrightarrow \text{\tiny www}CH_2CH\varphi OOH + R \cdot$$

Dismutation of $RO_2 \cdot$ radical (questionable)

$$\text{\tiny www}CH_2CH\varphi CH_2CH\varphi OO \cdot \longrightarrow CH_2CH\varphi \cdot + CH_2O + CH\varphi O$$

[94] S. Medvedev and P. Zeitlin, *Acta Physicochim. U. R. S. S.*, **20**, 3 (1945).

Dismutation of peroxide

$$\text{\textasciitilde\textasciitilde CH}_2\text{CH}\varphi\text{OOCH}_2\text{CH}\varphi\text{\textasciitilde\textasciitilde} \longrightarrow \text{\textasciitilde\textasciitilde CH}_2\text{CH}\varphi\text{O}\cdot + \cdot\text{OCH}_2\text{CH}\varphi$$

Benzaldehyde formation

$$\text{\textasciitilde\textasciitilde CH}\varphi\text{CH}_2\text{CH}\varphi\text{O}\cdot \longrightarrow \text{\textasciitilde\textasciitilde CH}\varphi\text{CH}_2\cdot + \text{CH}\varphi\text{O}$$

Formaldehyde formation

$$\text{\textasciitilde\textasciitilde CH}_2\text{CH}\varphi\text{CH}_2\text{O}\cdot \longrightarrow \text{\textasciitilde\textasciitilde CH}_2\text{CH}\varphi\cdot + \text{CH}_2\text{O}$$

In other words, Medvedev and Zeitlin postulated that radicals of the type $RO_2\cdot$ are formed during polymerization (same assumption as that of Barnes), but that these radicals can add to monomer or can disproportionate to give aldehydes. Hydroperoxides may also be formed by chain transfer as discussed in Chapter XIII.

Staudinger[95] found that when diphenylethylene is polymerized in the presence of air a polyperoxide is formed:

$$\text{CH}_2\text{=}\text{C}\varphi_2 \xrightarrow{\text{O}_2} -[\text{CH}_2\text{C}\varphi_2\text{OOCH}_2\text{C}\varphi_2\text{OOCH}_2\text{C}\varphi_2]_n-$$

Kolthoff[96] found that, if styrene is emulsion polymerized in the presence of oxygen after an initial long induction period, a polymer is formed that appears to be a one-to-one copolymer of styrene and oxygen very similar to Staudinger's:

$$-\text{CH}_2\text{CH}\varphi\text{OOCH}_2\text{CH}\varphi\text{OOCH}_2\text{CH}\varphi\text{OOCH}_2\text{CH}\varphi-$$

The average degree of polymerization of this polyperoxide is about thirty. It decomposed on heating and Kolthoff claimed that the benzaldehyde and formaldehyde found by Medvedev and Zeitlin arose from the decomposition of the polyperoxide rather than from dismutation of the radical $RO_2\cdot$.

$$-\text{CH}_2\text{CH}\varphi\text{OOCH}_2\text{CH}\varphi\text{OOCH}_2\text{CH}\varphi\text{OOCH}_2\text{CH}\varphi$$

$$\longrightarrow \text{CH}_2\text{CH}\varphi\text{OOCH}_2\text{CH}\varphi\text{O}\cdot + \cdot\text{OCH}_2\text{CH}\varphi\text{OOCH}_2\text{CH}\varphi$$

$$\longrightarrow \text{CH}_2\text{CH}\varphi\text{OOCH}_2\cdot + \text{CH}\varphi\text{O} + \text{CH}_2\text{O} + -\text{CH}\varphi\text{OOCH}_2\text{CH}\varphi-$$

In addition to these effects, if the monomer is polymerized at high temperatures, oxidative degradation of the polymer of the type discussed in Chapter XIII can occur side by side with polymerization of the monomer, as shown by the work of Mesrobian.[97]

[95] H. Staudinger, *Ber.*, **58**, 1075 (1925); *Ann.*, **438**, 1 (1931).
[96] F. A. Bovey and I. M. Kolthoff, *J. Am. Chem. Soc.*, **69**, 2143 (1947).
[97] R. B. Mesrobian and A. V. Tobolsky, *J. Am. Chem. Soc.*, **67**, 785 (1945).

K. EMULSION POLYMERIZATION

The simplest type of vinyl or diene polymerization occurs in the pure liquid phase with radical-producing catalysts that are soluble in that phase. This is generally referred to as bulk polymerization. Sometimes, as in the case of vinyl acetate, the monomer is dissolved in solvent and polymerization is allowed to proceed in solution. This is usually described as solvent polymerization. Polymerizations may also be carried out by agitating the monomer by suitable stirring in water, so that oil droplets are formed that would coalesce if agitation ceased. In this case, polymerization is effected by use of monomer-soluble catalysts and is known as pearl polymerization or suspension polymerization. This is essentially a water-cooled bulk polymerization.[98] Polymerizations in the aqueous phase with water-soluble catalysts can be carried out with monomers that are highly water soluble as well as with monomers like styrene or butadiene whose solubility in water is extremely limited. Redox polymerizations in the absence of emulsifier are examples of this type or polymerization. Styrene or butadiene vapor, when passed into water containing potassium persulfate, will polymerize readily.

A very important method of polymerization, known as emulsion polymerization, is the type carried out with monomer, water, water-soluble catalyst and emulsifier (such as soap). A typical simple emulsion formula is:

Butadiene (comonomer)	75 g.
Styrene (comonomer)	25 g.
Water	180 g.
Potassium laurate (emulsifier)	5 g.
Potassium persulfate (catalyst)	0.3 g.
n-Lauryl mercaptan (regulator or modifier)	0.5 g.

This type of emulsion formula was used in the polymerization of GR-S and is known as the standard or mutual formula. The end product of an emulsion polymerization is a latex, very similar to the latices of natural rubber except that the emulsified latex particles are generally much smaller than those of natural rubber.

The unusual feature of emulsion polymerization as compared to the other type of polymerizations is that by this means one can generally obtain quite rapid rates of polymerization and still produce unusually high molecular weight polymers.

[98] W. P. Hohenstein and H. Mark, *J. Polymer Sci.*, **1**, 127, 549 (1946).

An interesting comparison of emulsion and bulk polymerization at 60°C. is given in Table XII-10 (after Ewart[99]).

TABLE XII-10

COMPARISON OF BULK AND EMULSION POLYMERIZATION OF STYRENE

	Bulk	Emulsion
Catalyst...............	0.0428 mole benzoyl per-oxide per liter	0.010 mole $K_2S_2O_8$ per liter
Soap..................	—	0.027 mole per liter
Rate..................	3.28% monomer converted to polymer per hour	60% conversion per hour
Free radical concn.......	2.7×10^{16} per liter	—
Polymer particles per liter styrene..............	—	1.35×10^{18}
DP...................	800	37,000
Diam. of sphere giving volumes per free radical...	4100 Å.	—
Diam. of latex particle....	—	1070 Å.

The mechanism and kinetics of emulsion polymerization have presented many difficulties and it is only recently that the problems seem to be nearing resolution. One of the first problems that had to be solved was the question of the locus of polymerization. Harkins[100] and co-workers have presented a fairly comprehensive interpretation of the conditions that prevail during emulsion polymerization (standard recipe). When first prepared, the emulsion consists mainly of large emulsified monomer droplets and soap micelles consisting of cylindrical double layers of soap molecules. The size of the emulsified monomer droplet (which is stabilized by a layer of soap molecules) depends on the rate of agitation, soap concentration, and viscosity of the oil. Under usual laboratory conditions the distribution of sizes of the oil droplets may have a peak in size distribution between 0.5 and 1.0 micron. The soap micelles are supposed to be double layers of soap (with a possible oil layer between them when oil is present). The total number of soap molecules per micelle depends, among other things, on the nature of the soap, and ranges from about 20 to 300.

The main locus for the initiation of polymerization is the monomer dissolved in the soap micelles. Free radicals probably produced in the aqueous phase diffuse into the soap micelles containing monomer and initiate the growth of polymer chains to produce a polymer particle that continues to absorb monomer. The emulsified monomer droplets act as reservoirs of

[99] High Polymer meeting of the Chemical Research Conferences A.A.A.S., July 1948.
[100] W. D. Harkins, *J. Am. Chem. Soc.*, **69**, 1428 (1947).

monomer; very little polymer is produced in the droplets, but monomer diffuses from these droplets through the aqueous phase to the soap micelles containing polymerizing monomer to build up polymer particles. As these polymer particles (with absorbed monomer) grow in size and number, they absorb more soap so that after polymerization has proceeded to the extent of 13–20% all micellar soap in the aqueous phase has disappeared. At this point no new polymer particles are formed from micelles. The original monomer droplets are being continually depleted until, at about 60% polymerization, all of the monomer droplets have disappeared. The emulsion now is composed largely of polymer particles (which had their origins in the soap micelles initially present). A secondary locus for initiation of polymer particles is the aqueous phase itself, the relative importance of this locus increasing with decreasing soap concentration. This locus remains partially effective until about 60% polymerization.

The locus in which nearly all of the polymer is formed is the polymer particles themselves. These take up monomer molecules from the aqueous phase, and the monomer in the polymer-monomer particles thus formed undergoes polymerization while simultaneously the particles take up more monomer. The polymer particles even toward the end of polymerization are small compared to the original emulsified monomer droplets. The distribution in size of polymer particles depends on conditions and increases with increasing yield, but under standard conditions (though without mercaptan) the distribution in size of polymer particles has a peak at around 600 Å. at 15% conversion and 850 Å. at 74% conversion.

Smith and Ewart[101] have treated the problem of the kinetics of emulsion polymerization, basing their treatment on the description of the loci of polymerization given by Harkins. Their treatment of the problem is divided into two parts: first, a consideration of the factors that determine the rate of polymerization in a single swollen polymer particle; and second, the question of how many polymer particles are formed.

The case is considered where the reaction takes place in N polymer particles suspended in the aqueous phase and where the free radicals originate in the aqueous phase and diffuse into the polymer particles. It is assumed that there is no ready mechanism by which free radicals once inside the polymer particles can diffuse out, and, in addition, the probability of mutual termination of two free radicals in the same particle is large enough so that the average time necessary for them to terminate is small compared to the average time interval between successive entrances of free radicals into

[101] W. V. Smith and R. H. Ewart, *J. Chem. Phys.*, **16**, 592 (1948).

a particle. Under these conditions the very interesting situation exists in which at the steady state approximately *one-half of the particles contain a single free radical and the other half contain none*. This case is the one that appears to apply to the emulsion polymerization of styrene under ordinary conditions.

The rate of polymerization per cubic centimeter of water under these conditions is:

$$\frac{-d[M]}{dt} = k_2 \, [\text{M}] \, \frac{N}{2} \qquad \text{(XII.42)}$$

where k_2 is the rate of chain propagation and N the number of polymer particles per cubic centimeter. If ρ is the rate of formation of free radicals per cubic centimeter of water phase (number of free radical per second per cubic centimeter) then the average polymerizing lifetime τ_p will be (assuming that all free radicals enter polymer particles):

$$\tau_p = N/2\rho \qquad \text{(XII.43)}$$

From these two equations the characteristic features of emulsion polymerization are clear.

It is possible to produce in emulsion polymerization a number of polymer particles per cubic centimeter that is large compared to the number of free radicals normally present per cubic centimeter in bulk phase polymerizations. For this reason the rate of emulsion polymerization can be made very high. Also it is clear from equation (XII.43) that the average lifetime of a particle increases with the number of particles; it is thus possible to have high rates and high degrees of polymerization in emulsion polymerization.

To obtain a rate expression for emulsion polymerization it is necessary to obtain an expression for N, the number of polymer particles. This depends mainly on the concentration of soap and on the rate, ρ, of formation of free radicals per cubic centimeter of water.   Smith and Ewart derive the expression:

$$N = k(\rho/\mu)^{2/5}(a_S S)^{3/5} \qquad \text{(XII.44)}$$

where k is a numerical constant:

$$0.37 < k < 0.53$$

μ is the rate of increase in volume of a particle, S is the amount of soap per cubic centimeter of the water phase, and a_S is the interfacial area of soap per unit of soap concentration, so that $a_S S$ is the total interfacial area of the soap.

The rate of emulsion polymerization under ordinary conditions is:

$$-d\mathrm{M}/dt = k_2 \, [\mathrm{M}] \, \frac{k}{2} \, (\rho/\mu)^{2/5} \, (a_S S)^{3/5} \qquad \text{(XII.45)}$$

L. CATIONIC, ANIONIC, AND SODIUM POLYMERIZATION

Friedel-Crafts catalysts, such as $TiCl_4$, $SnCl_4$, $AlCl_3$, and BF_3, can be used to catalyze the polymerization of vinyl monomers. Generally speaking, ionic polymerizations are very rapid, even at very low temperatures, and this has made exact studies of rates and kinetic interpretation of the polymerization mechanism quite difficult. Furthermore, in most cases, catalyst and monomer do not form a homogeneous system. Finally, traces of "impurities" such as water are often essential cocatalysts, or, as in the case of alcohols and ethers (under certain conditions), powerful inhibitors.

The polymerization of isobutylene to form polyisobutylene (Vistanex, Oppanol) and the copolymerization of isobutylene with approximately 1 mole per cent of isoprene to give Butyl polymer are important commercial processes. The polymerizations are carried out at temperatures as low as $-120°C.$ using ionic catalysts such as BF_3.[102] The temperature appears to have little effect on the reaction velocity provided the temperature is above the freezing point of isobutylene ($-140°C.$). On the other hand, increasing temperatures of polymerization produce lower molecular weight polymers.

Plesch, Polanyi, Evans, and Skinner[103] found that a trace amount of water was an essential cocatalyst for the $TiCl_4$ and BF_3 catalyzed polymerization of isobutylene. This was verified by Norrish and Russell[104] for the $SnCl_4$ catalyzed polymerization of isobutylene. In fact, these latter authors showed that the rate of polymerization at a fixed concentration of $SnCl_4$ was strictly proportional to the water concentration up to 0.5% at $-78.5°C.$ Even in the absence of added water, there is still a rate of polymerization corresponding to the presence of 0.015% water.

---

[102] R. M. Thomas, W. J. Sparks, P. K. Frolich, M. Otto, and M. Mueller-Cunradi, *J. Am. Chem. Soc.*, **62**, 276 (1940).

[103] H. Plesch, M. Polanyi, and H. A. Skinner, *J. Chem. Soc.*, **1947**, 257. A. G. Evans and M. Polanyi, *ibid.*, **1947**, 252.

[104] R. G. W. Norrish and K. E. Russell, *Nature*, **160**, 543 (1947).

In order to keep the $SnCl_4-$ isobutylene system homogeneous, the polar diluent, ethyl chloride, was used. The minimum concentration of metallic chloride below which no polymerization occurs is rather less than half the percentage of added water. Above this minimum value the rate is roughly proportional to the $SnCl_4$ concentration until at about 1% $SnCl_4$ the rate of polymerization starts becoming independent of catalyst concentration.

Ethyl alcohol, tertiary butyl alcohol, diethyl ether, acetone, and 1- and 2-butene all proved to be inhibitors of the reaction.

Norrish and Russell state tentatively that initiation occurs from both the positive and negative ions derived from the hydrated stannic chloride:

$$SnCl_4 \cdot O\!\!\begin{array}{c} H \\ \\ H \end{array} + 2\ \begin{array}{c} CH_3 \\ | \\ C\!=\!CH_2 \\ | \\ CH_3 \end{array} \longrightarrow\ \begin{array}{c} CH_3 \\ | \\ CH_3\!-\!C^+ \\ | \\ CH_3 \end{array} + SnCl_4 \cdot OH\ \begin{array}{c} CH_3 \\ | \\ C\!-\!CH_2^- \\ | \\ CH_3 \end{array}$$

Chain propagation is then presumed to proceed by successive addition of monomer units to the ionized complexes so that there are both positive and negative growing chains. Chain termination occurs by neutralization of oppositely charged chains. Polanyi and collaborators,[105] on the other hand, assumed the following mechanisms for the $TiCl_4$-catalyzed polymerization of isobutylene in which growth occurs only by monomer addition to the positive ions:

$$TiCl_4 + H_2O \longrightarrow TiCl_4 \cdot H_2O$$

Initiation

$$TiCl_4 \cdot H_2O + M \longrightarrow HM^+ + TiCl_4OH^-$$

$$HM^+ + M \longrightarrow HM_2^+$$

Propagation

$$HM_n^+ + M \longrightarrow HM_{n+1}^+$$

$$HM_{n+1}^+ + TiCl_4OH^- \longrightarrow M_{n+1} + TiCl_4 \cdot H_2O \qquad \text{Termination}$$

At $-78°C$. these authors[105] found that the activities of various catalysts in isobutylene polymerization varied widely, decreasing down the series BF_3, $AlBr_3$, $TiCl_4$, $TiBr_3$, and $SnCl_4$. The view that only positive ions grow in the Friedel-Crafts-catalyzed polymerization of isobutene has been more widely accepted than the idea that both positive and negative ions grow and terminate by mutual addition. Dainton and Sutherland,[106]

[105] A. G. Evans and M. Polanyi, *J. Chem. Soc.*, **1947**, 252.
[106] F. S. Dainton and G. B. B. M. Sutherland, *J. Polymer Sci.*, **4**, 37 (1949).

for example, confirm the presence of terminal double bonds in low molecular weight polyisobutylene, which can only arise by the ejection of a proton from the growing polymer ion.

The polymerization of styrene at 25°C. with $SbCl_5$, $SnCl_4$, and BF_3 as catalysts was investigated by Williams.[107] The catalysts were shown to have the following order of activity:

$$SbCl_5 > SnCl_4 > BF_3$$

Both styrene dimer and HCl were found to be poisons. The rate of monomer consumption was found to be proportional to the first power of catalyst and to the third power of monomer concentration. The polystyrenes prepared were of low molecular weight—between 2500 and 4000 at 25°C.

High molecular weight α-methylstyrene polymer can be made only by low temperature ionic polymerization. Pepper[108] has shown that the initial rate of polymerization of α-methylstyrene and also the molecular weight are both increased by increase of the dielectric constant of the solvent. This was explained in terms of the decreased rate of the termination reaction, since if the termination step involves the combining of unlike charges, the forces between them would be decreased by increasing the dielectric constant of the medium.

Vinyl ethers are also polymerized by ionic catalysts.[109] An interesting feature of vinyl ether polymerization is the fact that isobutyl vinyl ether under different conditions of polymerization will produce polymers of very different physical properties.[110]

One might say in review that there is general agreement concerning the cationic character of vinyl polymerization by catalysts such as BF_3, $SnCl_4$, $TiCl_4$, etc. Whether the presence of water is essential in all cases and the proton is always the initiating agent, or whether a reagent like BF_3 can itself add to the double bond to initiate cationic polymerization[111] is still not definitely settled:

$$F:\overset{\displaystyle F}{\underset{\displaystyle F}{B}} + CH_2::\overset{\displaystyle CH_3}{\underset{\displaystyle CH_3}{C}} \longrightarrow F:\overset{\displaystyle F}{\underset{\displaystyle F}{B}}:CH_2-\overset{\displaystyle CH_3}{\underset{\displaystyle CH_3}{C}}{}^+$$

[107] G. Williams, *J. Chem. Soc.*, **1940**, 775.

[108] D. C. Pepper, *Nature*, **158**, 789 (1946).

[109] D. D. Eley and D. C. Pepper, *Trans. Faraday Soc.*, **43**, 112 (1947).

[110] C. E. Schildknecht, S. T. Gross, and A. O. Zoss, *Ind. Eng. Chem.*, **41**, 1998 (1949).

[111] C. C. Price, *Ann. N. Y. Acad. Sci.*, **44**, 351 (1943).

Even less experimental work is available on another type of ionic polymerization, the theoretically possible base-catalyzed polymerization, which should proceed by an anionic chain mechanism.

Polymers of 2-nitropropene and other nitroolefins have been prepared using aqueous potassium bicarbonate as a catalyst.[112] These polymerizations probably proceed by an anionic mechanism yielding low molecular weight polymer. Methacrylonitrile, which contains the highly electronegative cyano group, and therefore is readily subject to nucleophilic attack, was shown by Beaman to polymerize with extreme rapidity at temperatures as low as $-75°C$. when treated with reagents such as RMgX, triphenyl methyl sodium, or sodium in liquid ammonia. The highly ionic nature of these reagents make it unlikely that they react by first cleaving to free radicals. The extreme speed of these reactions at low temperatures is another indication in favor of an ionic mechanism rather than a radical mechanism. Further, if the reaction were free radical in nature, one would expect that butadiene and styrene would be readily polymerized. In point of fact, no polymer is obtained with butadiene in this reaction, and styrene gives only low molecular weight polymers. This is understandable from the point of view of anionic chain polymerization because of the weak electronegative character of the vinyl and styrene side groups. Finally, typical radical chain inhibitors such as hydroquinone and its sodium salt did not affect these reactions. Beaman proposes that the base-induced polymerization proceeds as follows:

$$(1) \qquad A^-: + CH_2{=}\underset{R'}{\overset{R}{C}} \longrightarrow A{-}CH_2\underset{R'}{\overset{R}{C^-}}$$

$$(2) \qquad A{-}CH_2\underset{R'}{\overset{R}{C^-}} + nCH_2{=}\underset{R'}{\overset{R}{C}} \longrightarrow A{-}\left[CH_2{-}\underset{R'\cdot}{\overset{R}{C}}\right]_n CH_2\underset{R'}{\overset{R}{C{-}}}$$

$$(3) \qquad A{-}\left[CH_2{-}\underset{R'}{\overset{R}{C}}\right]{-}CH_2\underset{R'}{\overset{R}{C^-}} + H^+ \longrightarrow A\left[CH_2\underset{R'}{\overset{R}{C}}\right]_{n+1} H$$

The polymerization of butadiene by sodium was one of the first means of producing synthetic rubber.[113] The Russians were apparently producing large quantities of sodium-polymerized butadiene or "mass polymerized butadiene" during World War II. The present status of the theories of

[112] A. T. Blomquist, W. J. Tapp, and J. R. Johnson, *J. Am. Chem. Soc.*, **67**, 1519 (1945).
[113] C. Harries, *Ann.*, **383**, 213 (1911). R. E. Mathews and E. H. Strange, German Pat 249,868.

sodium polymerization is reviewed by Magat and Talalay.[114] Sodium-polymerized polybutadiene differs from the emulsion-prepared polymer in having a much higher percentage of 1,2 additions[115] and also a much sharper distribution of molecular weights.[116]

Rapid polymerization of dienes at low temperatures is also effected by the "Alfin catalysts," e.g., sodium isopropyl alcohol plus allyl sodium.[117]

It is perhaps possible that sodium- and potassium-catalyzed polymerizations proceed through the initial formation of sodium or potassium alkyls. These may then dissociate and produce an anionic-type polymerization of the type discussed by Beaman.

TABLE XII-11

POLYMER COMPOSITION FOR EQUIMOLAR STYRENE–
METHYL METHACRYLATE MIXTURES POLYMERIZED BY VARIOUS CATALYSTS

Catalyst	Temperature, °C.	Per cent styrene in initial polymer
None......................	60	51
Benzoyl peroxide.............	60	51
Light......................	60	51
MgClO₄......................	30	50
SnCl₄......................	30	>99
BF₃ etherate................	30	>99
Na......................	30	<1
K......................	30	<1

A very significant observation which emphasizes the difference between radical polymerization, cationic polymerization, and sodium polymerization is the fact that the copolymerization ratios r_1 and r_2 for styrene-methyl methacrylate have been shown to be extremely different for radical catalysis, Friedel-Crafts catalysis, and sodium catalysis.[118] In these experiments an equimolar mixture of styrene and methyl methacrylate was polymerized by various catalysts and the composition of the polymer formed initially was measured. Walling's data are summarized in Table XII-11.

[114] A. Talalay and M. Magat, *Synthetic Rubber from Alcohol*. Interscience, New York, 1945. Morton, *Chem. Revs.*, **35**, 1 (1944).

[115] B. L. Johnson, The Firestone Tire & Rubber Co., Research Laboratories, *private communication*. See Table XII-10.

[116] R. L. Scott, *Thesis*. Princeton University, 1945.

[117] A. A. Morton, E. E. Magat, and R. L. Letsinger, *J. Am. Chem. Soc.*, **69**, 950, 1675 (1947).

[118] C. Walling, *J. Am. Chem. Soc.*, in press.

XIII. DEGRADATION OF HIGH POLYMERS

The degradation of high polymer molecules is of interest from two different points of view. On the one hand, controlled degradation is often a necessity in our handling of polymeric materials, as in the milling of rubber, or degradation of polymers may be used as a synthetic method for the preparation of simpler molecules, as when we hydrolyze proteins to obtain amino acids. On the other hand, uncontrolled and unpreventable degradation occurs in all polymeric materials and is an important factor in limiting their practical use.

The processes of degradation bear an over-all relation to the processes of polymerization. Condensation polymers may be degraded by stepwise hydrolysis involving the rupture of the same bonds by which they have been formed. Vinyl polymers may often be depolymerized at high temperatures by a chain mechanism, which is essentially the reverse process by which they were polymerized. In addition, oxidative degradation is of fundamental importance in the aging and degradation of practically all polymers.

A. STATISTICS OF RANDOM DEGRADATION OF HIGH POLYMERS

The study by Meyer, Hopff, and Mark[1] of the random degradation of starch and the study by Kuhn and Freudenberg[2] of the random degradation of cellulose were among the first quantitative investigations in the field of polymer degradation. Starch and cellulose as shown at that time by a number of authors[3-8] are polymers of glucose residues connected by con-

---

[1] K. H. Meyer, H. Hop , and H. Mark, *Ber.*, **62**, 1103 (1922).

[2] W. Kuhn, *Ber.*, **63**, 1503 (1930); K. Freudenberg, W. Kuhn, *et al.*, *ibid.*, **63**, 1510 (1930).

[3] F. Klein, *Z. angew. Chem.*, **25**, 1409 (1912).

[4] W. N. Haworth and E. L. Hirst, *J. Chem. Soc.*, **119**, 193 (1921).

[5] K. Freudenberg, *Ber.*, **54**, 767 (1921).

[6] K. H. Meyer and H. Mark, *Ber.*, **61**, 593 (1928); see also *Z. physik. Chem.*, **2B**, 115 (1929).

[7] W. N. Haworth, *Helv. Chim. Acta*, **11**, 534 (1928).

[8] K. Freudenberg and E. Braun, *Ann.*, **460**, 288 (1928).

tinuous α-glucoside linkages in the case of starch and β-glucoside linkages in the case of cellulose. In the presence of strong acids they are completely hydrolyzed to glucose. In a quantitative study of the hydrolysis of cellulose, Kuhn and Freudenberg[2] first assumed that the initial size of the cellulose molecules was essentially infinite, and that the hydrolysis proceeded at random among the various glucosidic linkages. After a certain amount of hydrolysis has occurred, the probability of a bond being still unhydrolyzed is p, where p is the ratio of the unhydrolyzed glucosidic linkages to the total amount of glucosidic linkages initially present. The fraction $(1 - p)$ may therefore be considered the extent of hydrolysis. If we started with a very large molecule of $N_0 + 1$ segments (N_0 links) and after a certain time N cuts were achieved (producing N new molecules) the extent of hydrolysis would be defined as:

$$1 - p = N/N_0 = \text{extent of hydrolysis}$$

We now choose a glucose unit at random from the partially hydrolyzed mass, and ask what is the probability $W(n)$ that it belongs to an n-mer. The reasoning is now exactly similar to that discussed in the case of random linear condensation. In a linear molecule consisting of n glucose units, there must be $n - 1$ unhydrolyzed glucosidic linkages, and the two end groups must be hydrolyzed glucosidic linkages. The probability $W(n)$ is therefore:

$$W(n) = np^{n-1}(1 - p)^2 \qquad \text{(XIII.1)}$$

Using the same reasoning as in Chapter XII, section B, we arrive at the following formulas:

$$N_n = N_0 W(n)/n = N_0 p^{n-1}(1 - p)^2 \qquad \text{(XIII.2)}$$

$$N = \sum_{n=1}^{\infty} N_n = N_0(1 - p) \qquad \text{(XIII.3)}$$

$$\bar{P}_n = N_0/N = 1/(1 - p) \qquad \text{(XIII.4)}$$

$$\bar{P}_w = (1 + p)/(1 - p) \qquad \text{(XIII.5)}$$

where N_0 is the total number of glucose units present in the system (including free glucose or glucose incorporated in polymer), N_n is the number of n-mers, $\bar{P}_n$ is the number average degree of polymerization, and $\bar{P}_w$ the weight average degree of polymerization.

As the hydrolysis proceeds, there will be a certain degree of hydrolysis $(1 - p)$ at which n-mer is present in maximum amount. This value can be obtained by differentiating equation (XIII.1) with respect to $1 - p$ and setting the result equal to zero. The value of $(1 - p)_{max.}$ is related to n as follows:

$$(1 - p)_{max.} = 2/(n + 1) \qquad (XIII.6)$$

The weight fraction of n-mer at the value of $(1 - p)_{max.}$, which is the largest weight that this species has during the course of hydrolysis is:

$$W(n)_{max.} = n[2/(n + 1)]^2[(n - 1)/(n + 1)]^{n-1} \qquad (XIII.7)$$

Table XIII-1 shows data calculated by the aid of the above equations for the optimum extent of hydrolysis and the maximum weight fraction for a few values of n.

TABLE XIII-1

n	$(1 - p)_{max.}$	$W(n)_{max.}$
2	$2/3$	0.296
3	$1/2$	0.187
4	$2/5$	0.138
5	$1/3$	0.110
6	$2/7$	0.091
7	$1/4$	0.078
10	$2/11$	0.064

The above treatment is restricted to the random degradation of infinite linear polymers. In the case of cellulose it was found that this simple treatment was not quite adequate to explain all the facts of the hydrolysis. These will be presented after a discussion of the kinetic treatment of degradation.

Montroll and Simha[9] have given a statistical treatment for the size distribution arising from the degradation of a sharp fraction of polymer molecules of finite size n. At a degree of hydrolysis such that r links have been broken, the number of s-mers, N_s, arising from the hydrolysis of an n-mer is (where s-mer and n-mer refer to chains of s and n links, respectively):

$$N_s = p^{s-1}(1 - p)[2 + (n - s)(1 - p)] \qquad (XIII.8)$$

where $1 - p = r/n$.

[9] E. Montroll and R. Simha, *J. Chem. Phys.*, **8**, 721 (1940).

B. KINETICS OF RANDOM DEGRADATION

In a mass of linear polymer molecules containing in all N_0 segments, let us suppose that the number of polymer molecules present initially (at time $t = 0$) is equal to $N(0)$. The number of linkages $L(0)$ initially present is:

$$L(0) = N_0 - N(0) \tag{XIII.9}$$

This relationship is readily seen since the number of linkages in any linear polymer molecule is always one less than the number of segments in the molecule. If the mass of linear polymer molecules is subject to a random cleavage (hydrolysis) at the linkages, then, at time t, when the number of polymer molecules of all kinds is $N(t)$, the number of linkages $L(t)$ still remaining is given by:

$$L(t) = N_0 - N(t) \tag{XIII.10}$$

If the hydrolysis of the linkages obeys a first order kinetics, then

$$-\frac{1}{L(t)} \frac{dL(t)}{dt} = k_b \tag{XIII.11}$$

and upon integration:

$$L(t) = L(0)e^{-k_b t} \tag{XIII.12}$$

The rate constant k_b defined by equation (XIII.11) and used subsequently throughout this section is not necessarily to be regarded as a specific rate constant. It may include as a multiplicative factor the concentration of hydrolyzing agent assumed present in excess and which therefore remains constant during the course of the reaction. It may also include as a multiplicative factor the concentration of an hydrolysis catalyst.

Substituting equations (XIII.9) and (XIII.10) into equation (XIII.12) and dividing both sides of the equation by N_0, the total number of segments, one obtains:

$$1 - \frac{N(t)}{N_0} = \left(1 - \frac{N(0)}{N_0}\right) e^{-k_b t} \tag{XIII.13}$$

The number average degrees of polymerization, $\bar{P}_n(0)$ and $\bar{P}_n(t)$, at time $t = 0$ and at time t, respectively, are given by:

$$\bar{P}_n(0) = N_0/N(0) \tag{XIII.14}$$

$$\bar{P}_n(t) = N_0/N(t) \tag{XIII.15}$$

Substituting these values in equation (XIII.13), one obtains:

$$1 - \frac{1}{\bar{P}_n(t)} = \left(1 - \frac{1}{\bar{P}_n(0)}\right) e^{-k_b t} \qquad \text{(XIII.16)}$$

or, by taking logarithms:

$$\ln\left(1 - \frac{1}{\bar{P}_n(t)}\right) = \ln\left(1 - \frac{1}{\bar{P}_n(0)}\right) - k_b t \qquad \text{(XIII.17)}$$

Formulas (XIII.16) and (XIII.17) were first derived by af Ekenstam[10] and are valid no matter what the initial distribution in sizes may be. These equations become particularly simple if the degradations are not carried out to very low degrees of polymerization. In this case we can expand the logarithms in equation (XIII.17) to obtain:

$$\frac{1}{\bar{P}_n(t)} \cong \frac{1}{\bar{P}_n(0)} + k_b t \qquad \text{(XIII.18)}$$

or:

$$\frac{N(t)}{N_0} \cong \frac{N(0)}{N_0} + k_b t \qquad \text{(XIII.19)}$$

In other words, in cases where we are dealing with a first order random hydrolysis, a plot of the reciprocal number average degree of polymerization against time should give a straight line until we reach very low degrees of polymerization. Equation (XIII.19) shows that the number of titratable end groups (assuming one end group per molecule) should increase linearly with time during random hydrolysis until very low degrees of polymerization are reached.

If we have some means of determining the number average molecular weight $\bar{M}_n$ as a function of time during degradation, the following general relationship holds, since a new molecule is formed with each cut:

$$\frac{1}{\bar{M}_n(t)} = \text{number of moles originally present per gram}$$
$$+ \text{ number of moles of bonds cut per gram}$$

The number average degree of polymerization may be obtained by end-group titration or by freezing-point depression in the range of low molecular weights. In the range of high molecular weights it is very convenient to follow the change in degree of polymerization by viscosity measurements.

[10] A. af Ekenstam, *Ber.*, **69**, 540, 553 (1936).

In this case, however, one measures a viscosity average degree of polymerization rather than the number average degree of polymerization. In case Staudinger's law applies, the viscosity average degree of polymerization is a weight average value.

In order to obtain size distribution during random degradation, we must obtain more general equations.[11] If we consider the random degradation of a polymeric mass containing, in total, N_0 segments, the following kinetic equations are obeyed:

$$dN_x/dt = -k_b(x - 1)N_x + 2k_b \sum_{y=x+1}^{\infty} N_y \qquad (XIII.20)$$

where N_x is equal to the number of x-mers present at time t, and k_b is the rate constant for the first order splitting of the bonds.

The first term in the equation arises from the disappearance of x-mer due to a splitting reaction at any of its $x - 1$ bonds; the second term arises from the fact that any molecule larger than x-mer can be split into an x-mer by an appropriate cut at either end of the molecule.

If the initial condition of the polymer which is subsequently degraded is such that the polymer has a random distribution of sizes, we can set the boundary condition at $t = 0$ as:

$$N_x(0) = N_0 p_0^{x-1}(1 - p_0)^2 \qquad x = 1,2,3,4\ldots \qquad (XIII.21)$$

where p_0 is a parameter which defines the initial distribution. The solution of equations (XIII.20) subject to the boundary condition (XIII.21) is:

$$N_x(t) = N_0 p^{x-1}(1 - p)^2 \qquad x = 1,2,3\ldots$$

$$\bar{P}_n(t) = 1/(1 - p)$$

$$\bar{P}_w(t) = (1 + p)/(1 - p) = \coth \frac{k_b}{2}(t + t') \qquad (XIII.22)$$

$$p = p_0 \exp(-k_b t) = \exp[-k_b(t + t')]$$

$$t' = -(1/k_b) \ln p_0$$

For all but the very lowest range of degrees of polymerization, the following approximate equations hold very precisely:

$$1/\bar{P}_n(t) = 1/\bar{P}_n(0) + k_b t \qquad (XIII.23)$$

$$1/\bar{P}_w(t) = 1/\bar{P}_w(0) + k_b t/2 \qquad (XIII.24)$$

[11] R. Simha, *J. Applied Phys.*, **12**, 569 (1941).

If we start with a sharp fraction of polymeric material such that the initial degree of polymerization is n, and the total number of segments is N_0, then the initial condition is:

$$N_n(0) = N_0/n$$
$$N_x(0) = 0 \qquad x \neq n \tag{XIII.25}$$

If this material is subject to a random first order degradation of its linkages, the size distribution at time t is:[11]

$$N_n(t) = \frac{N_0}{n} p^{n-1}$$

$$N_x(t) = \frac{N_0}{n} p^{x-1}(1 - p)[2 + (n - x - 1)(1 - p)] \tag{XIII.26}$$

$$\bar{P}_n(t) = \frac{1}{1 - [1 - (1/n)]p}$$

$$p = \exp(-k_b t)$$

The results for the uniform fraction can be generalized easily to obtain the size distribution during random hydrolysis of any arbitrary initial size distribution by a process of simple summation.

It is also of interest to consider a system in which a stepwise bimolecular condensation of the type considered in Chapter XI, section E, is competing with a first order random degradation such as considered in this section. Such a system may well be encountered when dibasic acids are condensed with diamine in the presence of extra water. If we have such a competition between condensation and hydrolysis, then starting with the monomer, the reaction never goes to completion, and the degree of polymerization approaches a finite value. The solution of this problem has been worked out[12] in terms of the ratio of k_b to k_f, where k_b is the first order reaction rate constant for the hydrolysis reaction and k_f the bimolecular rate constant for the type I condensation reaction. Graphs of the extent of reaction and the number average degree of polymerization as a function of time for various values of k_b/k_f are given in Figures XIII-1 and XIII-2.

C. DEGRADATION OF CELLULOSE

Freudenberg, Kuhn, and co-workers[13] studied the rate of hydrolysis of cellulose (and of some lower polysaccharides) in 51% ($d = 1.415$) sulfuric

[12] P. J. Blatz and A. V. Tobolsky, *J. Phys. Chem.*, **49**, 77 (1945).

[13] K. Freudenberg, W. Kuhn, W. Durr, F. Bolz, and G. Steinbrunn, *Ber.*, **63**, 1510 (1930).

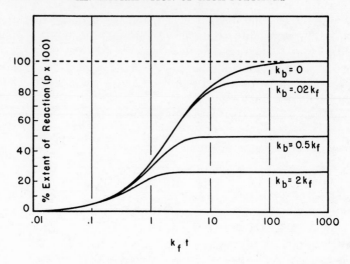

Fig. XIII-1. Extent of reaction as function of time during condensation in the presence of a competing hydrolysis reaction (k_f has been defined as being $1/2$ the value adopted in ref. 12 to make the notation correspond to Sect. E of Chap. XI).

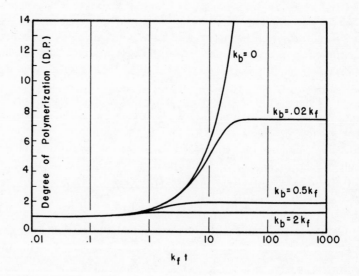

Fig. XIII-2. Polymerization degree as function of time during condensation in presence of a competing hydrolysis reaction (for k_f see Fig. XIII-1).

acid solution at 18° and 30°C. The hydrolysis was followed by optical rotation and by hypoiodite titrations of the aldose end group. Attempts to fit this data by first order random hydrolysis showed that the rate constant increased as degradation continued. In order to explain the observed results it was necessary to assume two first order rate constants. One of these constants is for the linkage adjacent to the reducing end group (which is taken to be the same as that found for the hydrolysis of cellobiose): $k_1 = 1.07 \times 10^{-4}$ min.$^{-1}$ at 18°C. and 6.94×10^{-4} at 30°C. The other constant, common to all other linkages is $k_i (k_i = 0.305 \times 10^{-4}$ at 18°C. and 2.34×10^{-4} at 30°C.). A mathematical formula that expressed the degree of hydrolysis $(1 - p)$ in terms of k_1, k_i, and t was worked out by Kuhn[14] and close agreement between observed and calculated values of the degree of hydrolysis as a function of time was obtained. This work leaves little doubt about the general uniformity of the glucosidic bonds in cellulose dissolved in strong mineral acids.

The maximum amount of cellobiose, cellotriose, cellotetrose, and cellopentose formed during the degradation of cellulose in strongly acid media were compared with the theoretical maxima obtained during random degradation as given by equation (XIII.7). The fact that much more cellobiose is obtained than predicted by the theory of random degradation is more evidence in favor of preferred splitting at the ends of the chain.

The kinetics of degradation of methylated cellulose in fuming hydrochloric acid was studied by Wolfrom, Sowden, and Lassettre,[15] using continuous mercaptylation of the aldose groups formed on bond rupture to follow the course of the reaction. The range of these measurements was from a degree of polymerization 150 to 50, and number of titratable end groups was found to increase linearly with time in this range as in eq. (XIII.19). The degree of polymerization is apparently sufficiently high in this case so that the enhanced reactivity of the terminal linkages does not affect the experimental results and the kinetics follows the law of random first-order degradation.

When strong mineral acids, such as those used in the experiments described above are employed, the process of getting cellulose into solution causes considerable breakdown before the first measurements can be made. In the event that milder acid hydrolysis is used, so that the initial molecular weight of the cellulose is high, the changes in degree of polymerization

[14] W. Kuhn, *Z. physik. Chem.*, **159**, 368 (1932). K. Freudenberg and W. Kuhn, *Ber.*, **65**, 484 (1932).
[15] M. L. Wolfrom, J. C. Sowden, and E. N. Lassettre, *J. Am. Chem. Soc.*, **61**, 1072 (1939).

are best observed viscometrically. In most cases of mild acid hydrolysis, such as in dilute HCl, the cellulose remains undissolved and the degradation proceeds *heterogeneously*. In these experiments, portions of the undissolved cellulose are removed from time to time, and a molecular weight determination is made by dissolving in cuprammonium.

Sisson, Coppick, and Battista[16] observed the hydrolysis of cellulose in $5N$ HCl at 18°C. starting with a material whose initial degree of polymerization was 835. They find that the rate constant decreases from a value of $k = 3.3 \times 10^{-4}$ min.$^{-1}$ for the first 120 hours to a value of $k = 1.3 \times 10^{-5}$ for the subsequent 360 hours. Similar results were obtained by Philipp, Nelson, and Ziifle[17] with $6N$ HCl at 100°C. and by Pacsu[18] with 10% lactic acid at 95°C.

Philipp[17] and Roseveare[19] have argued that the slowing down of the rate of hydrolysis during heterogeneous degradation is due to the different rates of penetrability of acid into the crystalline and amorphous regions in cellulose, whereas Pacsu[18] has advocated the existence of occasional acid-sensitive linkages regularly spaced in the cellulose structure.

Degradation experiments in concentrated (about 85%) phosphoric acid provide a means by which the possible existence of a relatively few acid-sensitive linkages in the cellulose structure can be tested. Cellulose will dissolve relatively rapidly in this reagent, and the rate of hydrolysis is sufficiently slow so that the first viscosity determinations on the dissolved cellulose can be completed while the degree of polymerization is of the order of magnitude of 1000. This means that studies of the subsequent hydrolysis should be capable of revealing the existence of weak linkages if they are present to an extent larger than one per thousand, and, because the cellulose is dissolved, all the linkages are equally accessible to the reagent.

Schulz[20] has claimed evidence for the existence of weak linkages on the basis of fractionation experiments which gave much sharper distributions of molecular weight than would be predicted on the basis of random hydrolysis.

On the other hand, the kinetic data in phosphoric acid obtained to date by several workers give no positive evidence of the existence of two linkages.

[16] W. A. Sisson, Coppick, and Battista, *private communication* to E. Pacsu (footnote 18).

[17] H. J. Philipp, M. L. Nelson, and H. M. Ziifle, *Textile Research J.*, **17**, 585 (1947).

[18] E. Pacsu, *J. Polymer Sci.*, **2**, 565 (1947).

[19] W. E. Roseveare, R. C. Waller, and J. N. Wilson, *Textile Research J.*, **18**, 114 (1948).

[20] G. V. Schulz and H. J. Löhmann, *J. prakt. Chem.*, **157**, 238 (1941). G. V. Schulz and E. Husemann, *Z. naturforsch.*, **1**, 15, 268 (1946).

In Figure XIII-3 are plotted the data of various workers in the form suggested by equation (XIII.18), namely, reciprocal degree of polymeriza-

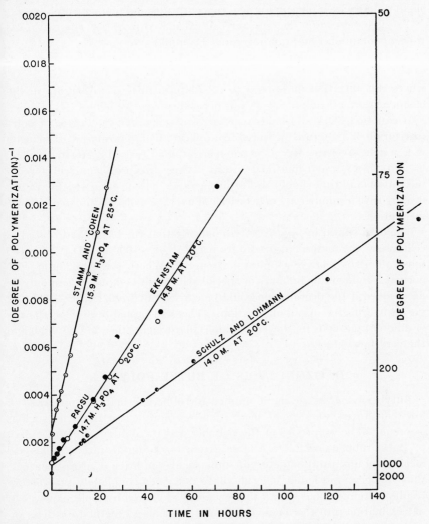

Fig. XIII-3. Reciprocal degree of polymerization vs. time during hydrolysis of cellulose in phosphoric acid.[21]

[21] A. J. Stamm and W. E. Cohen, *J. Phys. Chem.*. **42**, 921 (1928). L. A. Hiller and E. Pacsu, *Textile Researh J.*, **16**, 564 (1946). A. af Ekenstam, *Ber.*, **69**, 549,553 (1936). G. V. Schulz and H. J. Löhmann, *J. prakt. Chem.*, **157**, 238 (1941). H. Staudinger and G. Daumiller, *Ber.*, **70**, 2508 (1937).

tion versus time. Plotted in this way, all the data seem to fit straight lines, the difference in rate constants being easily understandable in view of the slight differences in phosphoric acid concentration and temperature.

The polymerization degrees were all calculated from the viscosity relationship adapted from Staudinger and Daumiller:

$$\text{D.P.} = 55.5[\eta] \qquad\qquad \text{(XIII.27)}$$

where concentration units used to calculate intrinsic viscosity are in the customary American units of grams per 100 cubic centimeters.

If equation (XIII.27) holds for sharp fractions then the degree of polymerization of a mixture measured by application of viscosity measurements is a weight average degree of polymerization. According to eqs. (XIII. 23 and 24) a straight line relationship between reciprocal degree of polymerization and time should obtain during random hydrolysis whether we are dealing with a number average or weight average molecular degree of polymerization.

The data shown in Figure XIII-3 indicate that the bonds hydrolyzed in cellulose as the material degrades from a D.P. of $\sim$1000 to a D.P. of $\sim$100 must all be of relatively uniform strength. Whether the bonds are the normal 1,4-glucosidic linkages or special acid-sensitive linkages can only be determined if the degradation could be carried out from D.P. $\sim$1000 to a very small degree of polymerization. This will probably involve the use of different methods for measuring molecular weights for the very high and the very low values.

D. OZONOLYSIS OF BUTYL POLYMER

Butyl polymer is the name applied to rubberlike material prepared by low temperature ionic copolymerization of isobutylene with dienes such as isoprene. The properties of the polymer and its ability to be vulcanized to Butyl rubber depend to a large extent on its unsaturation. Classical methods of unsaturation determination, such as addition of nitrosobenzene, thiocyanogen, and iodine chloride, have not given completely satisfactory results. Rehner[22] has shown that ozonolysis followed by molecular weight determination provides a convenient and satisfactory method for determination of the double bonds in Butyl polymer. His method provides an excellent illustration of the utilization of the principles of random degradation.

[22] J. Rehner, *Ind. Eng. Chem.*, **36**, 118 (1944); *Ind. Eng. Chem., Anal. Ed.*, **17**, 367 (1945).

It is very difficult to get more than one or two percent of isoprene into the copolymer structure. Most of the isoprene apparently enters the copolymer in the 1,4 position[23]; the location of the isoprene residues in the copolymer structure is most certainly nearly random, since it was shown that no sequences of isoprene could be found in the Butyl polymer chain.

The method of Rehner consists in passing ozonized air containing about 0.25 volume per cent of ozone through a solution prepared by dissolving 10–15 grams of Butyl polymer in 100–200 ml. of highly purified carbon tetrachloride at 0°C. The intrinsic viscosity of the solution measured either in tetrachloride or in diisobutylene decreases rapidly, reaching a minimum value in two hours, and remains constant for at least an additional five hours. The same results are achieved (after slightly longer times to reach the viscosity minimum) with lower concentrations of ozone. Air itself passed through the solution *at this temperature* under these conditions does not appreciably alter the viscosity.

It seems clear that the polymer chains are cleaved by the ozone at the double bonds, and the limiting viscosity that is reached is a measure of the molecular weight of the portions of the chain between double bonds.

To convert this to a quantitative method it is necessary to convert the viscosity average molecular weight to a number average molecular weight. Flory[24] has shown that the intrinsic viscosity–molecular weight relationship for polyisobutylene (as for Butyl polymer) dissolved in diisobutylene is:

$$\log \bar{M}_v = 5.378 + 1.56 \log [\eta] \qquad (\text{XIII.28})$$

where $\bar{M}_v$ is the viscosity average molecular weight, and $[\eta]$ is the intrinsic viscosity. This corresponds to a relationship of the form:

$$[\eta] = KM^a \qquad (\text{where } a = 0.64) \qquad (\text{XIII.29})$$

According to Flory[24] the viscosity average molecular weight for a system which obeys equation (XIII.29) is:

$$\bar{M}_v = (\Sigma_x N_x M_x{}^{a+1} / \Sigma N_x M_x)^{1/a} \qquad (\text{XIII.30})$$

where N_x is the number of x-mers and M_x is the molecular weight of the x-mer.

[23] J. Rehner, *Ind. Eng. Chem.*, **36**, 46 (1944).
[24] P. J. Flory, *J. Am. Chem. Soc.*, **65**, 372 (1943).

The distribution of molecular weights of the Butyl polymer after ozonolysis presumably follows the law of random degradation:

$$N_x = N_0 p^{x-1}(1 - p)^2 \qquad\qquad \text{(XIII.31)}$$

where N_0 is the total number of segments and $1 - p$ is the probability of cleavage. Substituting equation (XIII.31) into equation (XIII.30), it can be shown that:

$$\bar{M}_v/\bar{M}_n = [\Gamma(2 + a)]^{1/a} \qquad\qquad \text{(XIII.32)}$$

where Γ refers to the tabulated gamma function. Since, for polyisobutylene or Butyl polymer, $a = 0.64$:

$$\bar{M}_v/\bar{M}_n = 1.832 \qquad\qquad \text{(XIII.33)}$$

Equations (XIII.32) and (XIII.33) provide the necessary formulas whereby the measured viscosity average molecular weight can be converted to the theoretically important number average molecular weight.

The number average molecular weight of the ozone-degraded polymer can be used to determine directly the mole percent of isoprene in the original polymer by means of the formula

$$U = 5610/\bar{M}_n \qquad\qquad \text{(XIII.34)}$$

where U is the unsaturation of the original polymer expressed as moles of isoprene per 100 moles of isobutylene units (the molecular weight of 100 moles of isobutylene units is 5610).

The cleavage of the double bond by ozone under these conditions produces one carbonyl group and one carboxyl (or aldehyde group) per double bond. Since the molecular weights of the ozonized polymers are sufficiently low for fairly accurate end group analysis, Rehner was able to confirm his results in this way.

For polymers like natural rubber and Buna S, which contain many double bonds, the degradation by atmospheric ozone is an important practical problem. Such attack is much more serious when the rubber is maintained in a stretched condition. The problem of ozone degradation is not yet completely understood, particularly with regard to the massive cleavage of the rubber by ozone that takes place under certain conditions.[25] Ozone attack is not to be confused with photoactivated oxidation, and can be shown to occur as readily during the night as during the day.

[25] R. G. Newton, *Rubber Chem. Technol.*, **18**, 504 (1945).

E. CHAIN REACTION DEPOLYMERIZATIONS

Just as the hydrolysis of condensation polymers bears a close similarity to the process of condensation in that both reactions are stepwise processes often catalyzed by identical agents, so too is there an over-all similarity between addition polymerization and the depolymerization of addition polymers. Chalmers[26] stated that "the decomposition of high polymers has many features which suggests the existence of a chain mechanism of an inverse character to that involved in their generation."

The pyrolysis of hydrocarbons at high temperatures has indeed been admirably interpreted in terms of radical chain reactions.[27] If a radical is formed somewhere along a hydrocarbon molecule, this radical may dismute at high temperature as follows:

$$CH_3-CH_2-CH_2-CH_2-\overset{\cdot}{C}-CH_3 \longrightarrow CH_3-CH_2-CH_2\cdot + CH_2=\overset{|}{C}-CH_3$$
$$\underset{CH_3}{|} \qquad\qquad\qquad\qquad\qquad\qquad CH_3$$

$$\longrightarrow CH_3\cdot + CH_2=CH_2 + CH_2=\overset{|}{C}-CH_3$$
$$\underset{CH_3}{|}$$

The first step (*i.e.*, the initial formation of the radical) is the difficult step. Although the appearance of a radical in a given molecule may result from an easily accomplished chain transfer reaction, the production of new radicals must come from a relatively difficult process such as the fission of a carbon-carbon link. In many cases the formation of radicals probably comes from traces of oxygen, peroxides, or other impurities. The process of dismutation exemplified above indicates that chain cleavage occurs in the carbon-carbon bond once removed from the odd electron.

The rules of hydrocarbon pyrolysis can be applied to the depolymerization of vinyl and diene polymers at elevated temperatures in the absence of oxygen.[28] The first cleavage may occur by the spontaneous fission of a covalent bond. (This is most likely at a weak bond in the polymer structure such as a carbon-carbon bond where carbon atoms are heavily loaded as would occur in an occasional head-to-head addition, or perhaps at a peroxy link somewhere along the polymer chain; or finally, the radical end group, whose addition to the double bond started the process of addition polymerization, might spontaneously dissociate at sufficiently elevated

[26] W. Chalmers, *J. Am. Chem. Soc.*, **56**, 912 (1934).
[27] F. O. Rice and K. K. Rice, *The Aliphatic Free Radicals.* Johns Hopkins Press, Baltimore, 1935.
[28] H. S. Taylor and A. V. Tobolsky, *J. Am. Chem. Soc.*, **67**, 2063 (1945).

temperatures.) Furthermore, if by radical chain transfer a radical were formed somewhere along the polymeric chain, the dismutation would proceed as follows:

$$CH_2CHXCH_2CHXCH_2CHXCH_2\dot{C}XCH_2CHXCH_2CHX— \longrightarrow$$

$$—CH_2CHXCH_2CHXCH_2CHX\cdot + CH_2{=}CXCH_2CHXCH_2CHX—$$

The next steps would involve the continuous peeling off of monomer units:

$$—CH_2CHXCH_2CHX\cdot + CH_2{=}CHX, \quad etc.$$

Once a radical is formed at the end of a chain by any of the methods discussed above, it is probable that the entire chain disappears by a continued peeling off of monomer units unless the radical activity is lost by mutual addition or disproportionation of two radicals, or (more likely) by a transfer of radical activity to another chain.

Relatively few detailed kinetic studies of depolymerization appear in the literature. Grassie and Melville[29] have recently discussed the thermal degradation of polymethyl methacrylate. They used a molecular still in which the pressure of the monomer never exceeded 10^{-2} mm. These conditions ensured, first, that no oxidative fission took place and, second, that repolymerization or secondary reactions of the monomer were excluded. The rate of production of monomer was measured and molecular weight of the residue determined. Degradation was detectable at 160° and 220°C., and there was a suitable working rate of production of monomer. The rate of monomer production is very dependent on the nature of the end groups on the polymer, but not on the molecular weight of the original polymer. The molecular weight of the polymer left behind shows no decrease in the initial stages of the production of monomer. Toward the end of the reaction there is a definite decrease in molecular weight, but the lower the molecular weight the greater the degree of degradation before this takes place. With a polymethyl methacrylate of molecular weight 36,000, Melville and Grassie claim that 65% of the polymer degrades to monomer before the molecular weight of the product left behind begins to fall.

All these results are in accord with the idea that the initiation of the degradation begins at the end of the polymer chain and then once the initial break occurs, the entire polymer chain unravels to monomer units. The rate of production of monomer would be independent of molecular weight because, although the rate of initiation will be proportional to the number

[29] N. Grassie and H. W. Melville, *Discussions of The Faraday Society*, **2**, 378 (1947).

of vulnerable ends (and therefore inversely proportional to the number average molecular weight), the number of monomer units obtainable from a given polymer molecule will be directly proportional to the molecular weight.

Monomer production is, however, dependent on the nature of the end groups on the polymer chain. Photopolymer degrades most easily, benzoyl peroxide catalyzed polymer with phenyl or benzyl groups at one end of each molecule degrades less easily, and polymer with diphenylcyanomethyl groups at each end degrades very slowly.

If the reaction is indeed a radical chain reaction, substances which will give up hydrogen atoms readily to active radicals to give stable compounds or otherwise act to stabilize free radicals should inhibit the reaction. Most inhibitors and retarders are not suitable for use at 220°C. However, Melville and Grassie found that the dyestuff 1,4-diaminoanthraquinone and its leuco compound were both very effective in stopping degradation at 220°C.

There are apparently quite definite differences in the thermal degradation of polystyrene as reported by Jellinek and by Hall[30] and the above results for polymethyl methacrylate.

In the case of polystyrene the first effect of degradation at elevated temperatures (250–350°C.) is an initial rapid decrease in intrinsic viscosity followed by a slow fall in intrinsic viscosity that is linear with time. After the initial chain scission there is a steady zero order production of monomer. The size distribution of degraded polymer is considerably sharper and the amount of monomer produced is 10^3 or 10^4 times higher than would be predicted from the theory of random scission. Also, the degradation stops at a certain chain length, which is different for different temperatures and different initial chain lengths. The results, according to Jellinek, are in accord with the following mechanism:

(1) Initiation..............Chain scission at weak links (possibly oxygenated or peroxy links) producing active chain ends.

(2) Propagation............Production of monomer by peeling off from active chain ends.

(3) Termination............Loss of activity of chain ends (perhaps by mutual addition or disproportionation).

The suggested mechanism for production of monomer during depolymerization is clearly the microscopic inverse of the propagation step during

[30] H. H. G. Jellinek, *Discussions of the Faraday Society,* **2**, 397 (1947); *J. Polymer Sci.,* **3**, 600 (1948); **4**, 1, 13 (1949). See also R. W. Hall, *Discussions of the Faraday Society,* **2**, 396 (1947).

polymerization, and may perhaps be termed a depropagation reaction. The energy of activation for the depropagation step is in fact equal to the energy of activation for propagation plus the heat of polymerization.[28] Because of the close similarity in mechanism for polymerization and depolymerization, it was suggested that, under suitable kinetic conditions, (*i.e.*, high temperatures and in the presence of a source of radicals), it might be possible to obtain equilibrium between polymerization and depolymerization in vinyl systems.[31] Attempts were made to achieve this experimentally by starting with various mixtures of styrene and polystyrene in toluene and exposing them to light and air, or to other sources of radicals, at 100°C. It was found that under suitable conditions the monomer solutions showed a rise in viscosity to a constant value, and the monomer-polymer mixtures showed a fall in viscosity to the same constant value as for the monomer. The concurrence of polymerization and degradation under these conditions was therefore established. It is doubtful, however, that the degradation reaction in most of these cases was a straightforward depolymerization and that reversibility between polymerization and depolymerization was obtained. The catalysts such as oxygen plus light, or benzoyl peroxide, which were used to supply radicals were very probably directly involved in the degradation reactions under these conditions. A true thermal equilibrium for styrene–polystyrene systems could probably be attained in finite times only at much higher temperatures, and at these higher temperatures side reactions would be difficult to exclude.

An alternative and promising approach to the study of the reversibility of the propagation step in vinyl polymerizations is provided by examination of the effect of depropagation on the polymerization reaction itself—particularly the phenomenon of the ceiling temperature. This phenomenon has been most thoroughly studied for copolymers of olefins and sulfur dioxide, which polymerize rapidly under suitable conditions (*e.g.*, ultraviolet light) at low temperatures, but which show practically no polymerization above a certain fairly sharply defined temperature called the ceiling temperature. For isobutene–sulfur dioxide copolymers the ceiling temperature is below room temperature. Dainton and Ivin[32] have attributed this phenomenon to the fact that, at the ceiling temperature, the rates of propagation and depropagation become equal. According to these authors, every vinyl polymerization should have a ceiling temperature T_x, the temperature at which the free energy of formation of the polymer from the

[31] R. B. Mesrobian and A. V. Tobolsky, *J. Am. Chem. Soc.*, **67**, 785 (1945).
[32] F. S. Dainton and K. J. Ivin, *Nature*, **162**, 705 (1948).

reactants, under the given conditions specified by the subscript x, is zero. Hence:

$$T_x = \Delta H_x / \Delta S_x$$

where ΔH_x and ΔS_x are the increments at T_x of the heat content and entropy per mole of monomer polymerized. These increments also apply to the changes in heat content and entropy associated with the propagation reaction, provided that the polymer chains are long. Monomers like polyisobutylene and α-methylstyrene, with low heats of polymerization and high negative entropies of polymerization, should have relatively low ceiling temperatures.

Figure XIII-4 shows how the rate of polymerization of 1-butene in sulfur dioxide appears to approach zero at a certain critical temperature.[32]

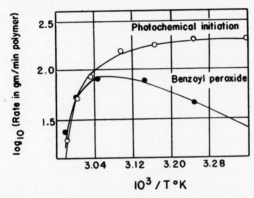

Fig. XIII-4. Temperature dependence of the rate of polysulfone formation in mixtures containing 1 mole of 1-butene in 10 moles sulfur dioxide.[32]

F. OXIDATION OF POLYMERS: FORMATION AND BREAKDOWN OF HYDROPEROXIDES

At sufficiently high temperatures, degradation of polymers will occur in the absence of oxygen. Molecular oxygen, such as present in air, will cause degradation of polymeric materials at relatively low temperatures, even at room temperature after a sufficiently long time. Inasmuch as it was recognized very early that the aging of rubbers and other high polymers was in large part due to oxidation processes, a great deal of effort was directed to the elucidation of this reaction.* It was recognized, for example, that the

* Early work on the oxidative degradation of rubber is reviewed in C. C. Davis and J. T. Blake, *Chemistry and Technology of Rubber*, Reinhold, New York, 1937.

relatively low temperature oxidation of rubber and other polymers is autocatalytic chain reactions, and the formation of hydroxy, carbonyl, carboxy, and peroxy groups was noted. The existence of long-lived intermediates that catalyze further oxidation was inferred from the fact that rubber, cellulose, or other polymers exposed to light and air will later undergo rapid deterioration even in the absence of light or oxygen. It was also observed that oxidative degradation in certain cases brought about a lowering of molecular weight, which could only be due to chain cleavage, and in other cases oxidative degradation apparently caused gelation and oxido-vulcanization due to cross linking. The catalytic effect of light and oxygen made it appear probable that these reactions were radical reactions. Furthermore, it was realized that whereas the chemical nature of the oxidative degradation of polymers must be analogous to the degradation of short-chain hydrocarbon analogs, the physical properties of polymers are particularly sensitive to oxidative degradation. This is because relatively few oxidative cuts along the molecular chain will produce a marked lowering of molecular weight and thereby decrease tensile strength; or, a relatively few cross linkages induced by oxygen will produce a gel structure with resultant embrittlement of the polymer. For example, a single cut in a chain of molecular weight 500,000 may lower the molecular weight to 250,000; yet, such a cleavage would be undetectable by standard analytical methods for functional groups.

The recognition of the importance of oxidative aging led to the introduction of antioxidants in the rubber industry during the 1930's. This resulted in a two- or three-fold increase in the useful life of rubber tires. Similar developments were made in other industries using high polymers.

A very important advance in the understanding of the oxidation processes in hydrocarbon polymers was Farmer's emphasis of the important role of hydroperoxide formation in olefinic systems.

Farmer and Sundralingham[33] first verified the discovery of Criegee, Pilz, and Flygare[34] that the product obtained by exposing cyclohexene to oxygen in the presence of light was a hydroperoxide of the following structure:

[33] E. H. Farmer and A. Sundralingham, *J. Chem. Soc.*, **1943**, 125.
[34] R. Criegee, H. Pilz, and H. Flygare, *Ber.*, **72**, 1799 (1939).

This hydroperoxide decomposes to give secondary oxidation products.

In a series of papers, Farmer and co-workers showed that during the oxidation of natural rubber and low molecular polyisoprenes all of the oxygen absorbed in the initial stages enters the structure in peroxidic form without loss of unsaturation in the substrate. They concluded that the primary products of oxidation are peroxides—most probably hydroperoxides formed at the carbon atoms not involved in a double bond. Secondary autoxidative changes occur side by side with further peroxidation. These secondary reactions include chain scission, cross linking of chain molecules and formation of hydroxyl and carbonyl groups. The secondary reactions were attributed to reactions of the hydroperoxide and the double bond. The exact nature of these reactions, particularly the scission reaction, was very difficult to determine with certainty in these relatively complex systems.

The importance of hydroperoxides in the oxidation of saturated hydrocarbons was indicated by Vaughan and Rust[35] and by George and Walsh[36] in their interpretation of Chavanne's results[37] on the oxidation of 1,3-dimethylcyclopentane. These authors state that the first product of oxidation of this hydrocarbon is the hydroperoxide, and they introduce a mechanism of decomposition which accounts for the observed products and provides a satisfactory basis for an understanding of chain cleavage.

The radical (IV) can either abstract a hydrogen atom from another hydrocarbon molecule, or it can dimerize. Both the resulting ketone and diketone have been observed by Chavannes:

[35] F. F. Rust and W. E. Vaughan, U. S. Pats. 2,396,206 and 2,396,217.

[36] P. George and A. D. Walsh, *Trans. Faraday Soc.*, **42**, 94 (1946).

[37] G. Chavanne and O. Miller, *Bull. soc. chim. Belg.*, **40**, 611 (1931).

It is also possible (although this was not mentioned by George and Walsh) that the radical formed in step (III) can abstract a hydrogen from a neighboring hydrocarbon to give the tertiary alcohol (also found by Chavanne).

The credibility of the mechanism of George and Walsh is greatly enhanced by studies of the decomposition of di-*tert*-alkyl peroxides by Raley, Rust, and Vaughan.[38] These authors show that the decomposition of di-*tert*-butyl peroxide in the gas phase and in various solvents follows a first-order rate law, the rate-determining step being the scission of the O—O bond. The products (methane, acetone, and *tert*-butyl alcohol) are in accord with the following mechanism:

(1) $(CH_3)_3C-O-O-C(CH_3)_3 \longrightarrow 2(CH_3)_3CO\cdot$

(2) $(CH_3)_3CO\cdot + R'H \longrightarrow (CH_3)_3COH + R'\cdot$

(3a) $(CH_3)_3CO\cdot \longrightarrow (CH_3)_2CO + CH_3\cdot$

(3b) $CH_3\cdot + R'H \longrightarrow CH_4 + R'\cdot$

In the gas phase (where step 2 is of much less importance) the first-order rate constant for decomposition of di-*tert*-butyl peroxide is $k' = 3.2 \times 10^{16} e^{-39,100/RT}$. This rate constant for decomposition is not very markedly changed when the peroxide is dissolved in various solvents (cumene, *tert*-butylbenzene, tri-*n*-butylamine). The relative amounts of acetone and *tert*-butyl alcohol formed at different temperatures during the decomposition of the peroxide in these various solvents enables one to calculate the

[38] J. H. Raley, F. F. Rust, and W. E. Vaughan, *J. Am. Chem. Soc.*, **70**, 88, 1336 (1948). J. H. Raley, F. H. Seubold, Jr., and W. E. Vaughan, *J. Am. Chem. Soc.*, **70**, 95 (1948).

difference in activation energies for steps *3a* and *2*. It turns out that:

$$E_{3(a)} - E_2 \sim 16 \text{ kcal.}$$

The decomposition of other peroxides and hydroperoxides are not all so straightforward as is the case for di-*tert*-butyl peroxide. The decomposition of benzoyl peroxide in various solvents, which has been studied by numerous authors, has recently been shown by Nozaki and Bartlett[39] to vary profoundly with the solvent. In this case there exists, in addition to a first-order spontaneous cleavage of the peroxy bond, a radical-induced decomposition of the benzoyl peroxide which is three-halves order with respect to the peroxide concentration. The decomposition of many secondary hydroperoxides occurs by a splitting-off of water. Thus the decomposition of tetralin hydroperoxide proceeds by a first-order splitting-off of water to form tetralone.[40]

G. KINETICS OF OXYGEN ABSORPTION

The rate at which rubber and other polymers absorb oxygen has long been used as a criterion for oxidizability. Comparative studies of the rate of oxygen absorption of a wide variety of polymers at elevated temperatures have shown that, although all polymers are subject to oxidative degradation, the presence of double bonds and methyl groups along the chain appear to enhance the rate of oxidation, whereas certain other groups such as phenyl appear to have a retarding effect.[41] Comparison of the effects of antioxidants, vulcanization agents, etc. have also been made, using rate of oxygen absorption at elevated temperatures as a criterion for oxidizability.

Recent detailed interpretations of the kinetics of oxygen absorption have greatly increased our knowledge of the oxidation process. Bolland and Gee[42] have studied the kinetics of the oxidation of ethyl linoleate by measuring the hydroperoxide concentration and the rate of oxygen absorption at constant oxygen pressure over a range of pressures. In separate experiments they also studied the rate of decomposition of the ethyl linoleate hydroperoxide and found it to be second order.

To explain their observed data, these authors were led to postulate the following chain reaction. At the very beginning of the reaction, when no appreciable quantity of hydroperoxide is present:

[39] K. Nozaki and P. D. Bartlett, *J. Am. Chem. Soc.*, **68**, 1686 (1946); **69**, 2299 (1947).
[40] R. Robertson and W. A. Waters, *J. Chem. Soc.*, **1948**, 1578.
[41] R. B. Mesrobian and A. V. Tobolsky, *J. Polymer Sci.*, **2**, 463 (1947).
[42] J. L. Bolland and G. Gee, *Trans. Faraday Soc.*, **42**, 236 (1946).

Initiation:

$$RH + O_2 \xrightarrow{k_1'} R\cdot + \cdot OOH$$

Growth:

$$R\cdot + O_2 \xrightarrow{k_2} RO_2\cdot$$

$$RO_2\cdot + RH \xrightarrow{k_3} ROOH + R\cdot$$

Termination:

$$R\cdot + R\cdot \xrightarrow{k_4} RR$$

$$RO_2\cdot + R\cdot \xrightarrow{k_5} RO_2R$$

$$RO_2\cdot + RO_2\cdot \xrightarrow{k_6} RO_2R + O_2$$

Where RH represents the ethyl linoleate molecule:

$$CH_3(CH_2)_4CH{=}CH{-}CH_2{-}CH{=}CH{-}(CH_2)_7COOEt$$

and $R\cdot$ represents the radical:

$$CH_3(CH_2)_4CH{=}CH{-}\overset{\cdot}{C}H{-}CH{=}CH{-}(CH_2)_7COOEt$$

As soon as an appreciable quantity of hydroperoxide is built up, the decomposition of hydroperoxide to give radicals becomes rate-controlling.

The mechanism of oxidation now becomes:

$$2\ ROOH \xrightarrow{k_1} \text{radicals}$$

$$R\cdot + O_2 \xrightarrow{k_2} RO_2\cdot$$

$$RO_2\cdot + RH \xrightarrow{k_3} ROOH + R\cdot \qquad\qquad\text{(A)}$$

$$R\cdot + R\cdot \xrightarrow{k_4} RR$$

$$RO_2\cdot + R\cdot \xrightarrow{k_5} RO_2R$$

$$RO_2\cdot + RO_2\cdot \xrightarrow{k_6} RO_2R + O_2$$

At high oxygen pressures, where $RO_2\cdot$ is present in excess of $R\cdot$, the termination step k_6 is predominant. At low oxygen pressures, where $R\cdot$ is present in excess of $RO_2\cdot$, the termination step k_4 is the most important. Under conditions such that the decomposition of hydroperoxide is the important chain initiation step, but if this decomposition is still sufficiently slow so that the chain length of the oxidation process is large, equations A can be integrated to obtain the rate of oxygen absorption $d[O_2]/dt$ for both low and high oxygen pressures:

$$(low) \qquad d[O_2]/dt = k_2(k_1/k_4)^{1/2}[ROOH][O_2] \qquad (XIII.35)$$

$$(high) \qquad d[O_2]/dt = k_3(k_1/k_6)^{1/2}[ROOH][RH] \qquad (XIII.36)$$

In their studies of the autoxidation of ethyl linoleate, Bolland and Gee found that under their experimental conditions every molecule of oxygen absorbed could be identified as forming a hydroperoxide group in the substrate. The experimental results for rate of oxygen uptake and the rate of hydroperoxide formation were in agreement with equations (XIII.35) and (XIII.36). Also, the rate of decomposition of the ethyl linoleate hydroperoxide was studied separately and found to be second order with respect to hydroperoxide concentration.

As the hydroperoxide concentration builds up, the rate of decomposition of hydroperoxide can become comparable with the rate of the propagation steps. In these circumstances the chain length of the oxidation reaction becomes small, and the rate of breakdown of the hydroperoxide is no longer negligible as compared to its formation in the propagation step k_3. In fact, as the autoxidation proceeds a steady-state concentration of hydroperoxide will be reached at which the rates of formation and decomposition of hydroperoxide are equal. At this point the rate of oxygen absorption will approach a constant maximum value; however, the oxygen absorbed by the system is now no longer causing an increase in the hydroperoxide concentration but is instead to be found in the products of decomposition of the hydroperoxide and in the termination products.

The approach to the steady-state concentration of hydroperoxide and the maximum rate of oxygen absorption can be accelerated by use of high temperatures or of light, or by activators, all of which will facilitate the breakdown of hydroperoxide. Bolland and Gee did not observe the maximum rate effect in their studies of ethyl linoleate oxidation because their oxidations were carried out under relatively mild conditions.

Equations A (for high oxygen pressures) can nevertheless be integrated over the entire autocatalytic region including the region in which the chain lengths of the oxidation are small.[43] Graphs of total oxygen absorption and total hydroperoxide concentration as functions of time are shown in Figure XIII-5. The maximum rate of oxygen absorption and the steady-state concentration of hydroperoxide are:

$$d[O_2]/dt_{max.} = k_3^2[RH]^2/k_6 \qquad (XIII.37)$$

$$[ROOH]_{max.} = k_3[RH]/(k_1k_6)^{1/2} \qquad (XIII.38)$$

Equations (XIII.37) and (XIII.38) were derived with the assumption that the concentration [RH] remains essentially constant during the autox-

[43] A. V. Tobolsky, D. Metz and R. B. Mesrobian, *J. Am. Chem. Soc.*, **72**, 1942 (1950).

idation, and neglecting the possibility that the products of oxidation might enter into the oxidation mechanism in a very direct fashion, as by activating the decomposition of hydroperoxide.

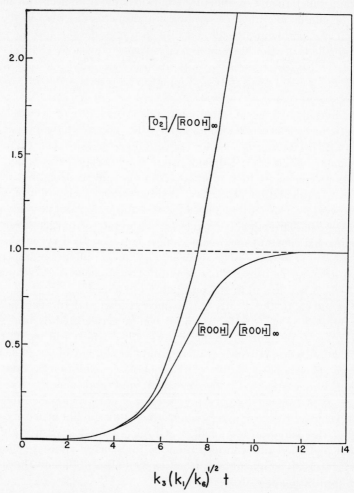

Fig. XIII-5. Hydroperoxide formation and oxygen absorption vs. time in autoxidations proceeding according to mechanism A. The ratio of initial to final concentration of hydroperoxide is taken to be 0.001.[43]

Bolland and Gee also discuss the benzoyl peroxide catalyzed oxidation of ethyl linoleate, showing that it fits into the scheme A by merely considering that the initiation step is the first-order decomposition of benzoyl peroxide to radicals rather than the decomposition of the hydroperoxide. Bolland and Ten Have[44] also considered the mechanism of the inhibition of oxidation in the light of the kinetic scheme developed above. The action of the inhibitor is presumed to be the destruction of the chain carrier $RO_2 \cdot$:

$$RO_2 \cdot + \text{inhibitor} \longrightarrow \text{inactive products}$$

H. SCISSION AND CROSS LINKING

Many of the important changes in physical properties that occur in high polymers during degradation and oxidation are the result of simultaneous reactions that we may term aggregative and disaggregative reactions.[41,45,46] Aggregative reactions are reactions such as further polymerization, branching, and cross linking, which tend to increase the molecular weight. Disaggregation reactions are reactions such as scission or depolymerization, which tend to decrease molecular weight. Cyclization also occurs and, in general, the effect on physical properties produced by cyclization is very similar to the effect produced by aggregative reactions.

These processes, which for simplicity we shall term scission and cross linking, result from the reactions such as dismutation, coupling, addition to double bonds, etc., which the active species $R \cdot$, $RO \cdot$, $RO_2 \cdot$ and $ROOH$ discussed in the previous sections undergo. The relative rates of scission and cross linking depend on the concentration of the various active species and on the comparative ease with which they undergo the various reactions listed below.

Aggregative Reactions:

$$R \cdot + R \cdot \longrightarrow RR$$
$$RO_2 \cdot + R \cdot \longrightarrow RO_2R$$
$$RO_2 \cdot + RO_2 \cdot \longrightarrow RO_2R + O_2$$
$$R \cdot + C{=}C \longrightarrow R{-}C{-}\dot{C}$$
$$RO_2 \cdot + C{=}C \longrightarrow RO_2C{-}\dot{C}$$

Disaggregative Reactions:

$$\text{$\sim$}CH_2CHXCH_2\dot{C}XCH_2CHX\text{$\sim$} \longrightarrow \text{$\sim$}CH_2CHX \cdot + CH_2{=}CXCH_2CHX$$
$$\text{$\sim$}CH_2CHXCH_2CHXCH_2CHX \cdot \longrightarrow \text{$\sim$}CH_2CHXCH_2CHX \cdot + CH_2{=}CHX$$

[44] J. L. Bolland and P. Ten Have, *Discussions of the Faraday Society*, **2**, 252 (1947).
[45] D. Spence and J. D. Ferry, *J. Am. Chem. Soc.*, **59**, 1648 (1937).
[46] H. Stevens, *J. Soc. Chem. Ind.*, **64**, 135 (1945).

$\text{CH}_2\text{CHXCH}_2\text{CHXOOCH}_2\text{CHX} \longrightarrow \text{CH}_2\text{CHXCH}_2\text{CHXO}\cdot + \cdot\text{OCH}_2\text{CHX}$

$\text{CH}_2\text{CHXCH}_2\text{CHXO}\cdot \longrightarrow \text{CH}_2\text{CHXCH}_2\cdot + \text{CHXO}$

$\text{CH}_2\text{CHXCH}_2\text{CX(OOH)CH}_2\text{CHX} \longrightarrow \text{CH}_2\text{CHXCH}_2\text{CXO} + \cdot\text{OH} +$
$\cdot\text{CH}_2\text{CHX}$

$\text{CH}_2\text{CHXCH}_2\text{CHXCH}_2\text{CHX} \longrightarrow \text{CH}_2\text{CHXCH}_2\text{CHX}\cdot + \cdot\text{CH}_2\text{CHX}$

Low oxygen pressures favor a predominance of R· over RO₂·. At high temperatures and in the absence of oxygen, continued dismutation of the radical R· leads to large-scale depolymerizations in many cases (e.g., polystyrene and polymethyl methacrylate).

Although scission and cross linking occur side by side during the degradation in air of almost all polymeric materials the separate rates may be isolated and measured by certain devices. Degradation in dilute solution in inert solvents isolates the scission reactions because the molecules are kept sufficiently far apart to suppress cross linking. In addition, measurements of continuous and intermittent relaxation of stress and permanent set have been used to study these reactions in vulcanized rubbers.[47,48] If the scission reaction predominates, the polymers will tend to soften during degradation, whereas if the cross-linking reactions predominate, the polymers will tend to harden.

From studies of a number of synthetic rubbers it appears that carbon-carbon double bonds along the chain and pendant vinyl side groups enhance the rate of both cross linking and scission, favoring the former. Methyl side groups enhance the rate of scission very markedly. Many side groups seem to retard both scission and cross linking. For example, cross-linked polystyrene, polyethylacrylate rubbers, and polyester rubbers are very resistant to scission and cross linking at high temperatures as measured by continuous and intermittent stress relaxation.

I. SPLITTING OFF OF HYDROGEN CHLORIDE, HYDROGEN CYANIDE, ETC. DURING DEGRADATION

When certain polymers, such as polyvinyl chloride, polyvinylidene chloride, polyvinyl acetate, polyacrylonitrile, etc., are subject to the degrading influences of heat, light, air, etc., in addition to the reactions discussed in the previous sections, there also are evolved such products as hydrochloric acid, leaving behind unsaturated carbon-carbon bonds along the polymer chains.

[47] A. V. Tobolsky, I. B. Prettyman, and J. H. Dillon, *J. Applied Phys.*, **15**, 380 (1944).
[48] R. D. Andrews, A. V. Tobolsky, and E. E. Hanson, *J. Applied Phys.*, **17**, 352 (1946).

Boyer[49] has recently discussed the color changes that occur during the degradation of polyvinyl and polyvinylidene chloride. He considers that the splitting of HCl from the polymer chains is nearly random, leaving behind sequences of double bonds. In particular, Boyer calculates from the total amount of HCl split off, the number of conjugated double bond sequences of various lengths. From the known optical absorptive properties of conjugated double bond systems, one can calculate the light absorption coefficient of the degraded polyvinyl chloride films as a function of wave length. Reasonably satisfactory agreement with experiment is obtained.

[49] R. F. Boyer, *J. Phys. & Colloid Chem.*, **51,** 80 (1947).

AUTHOR INDEX

A

Abderhalden, E., 391
Adam, N. K., 142, 165, 207
Adams, C. E., 418, 447, 448 (ref. 91)
Albrecht, G., 34
Alcock, T. C., 79
Alekseeva, W., 413
Alfrey, T., Jr., 99, 148, 258, 287, 290, 331, 335, 362, 425, 427, 429, 434 (ref. 64), 435, 446, 447
Alyea, H. N., 418
Ambrose, E. J., 80
Amerongen, G. J. van, 276, 444
Andrade, E. N. da C., 281, 282
Andrews, R. D., 335, 341, 343, 344, 352, 355, 356, 486
Arrhenius, S., 301
Astbury, W. T., 33, 244, 245 (ref. 59), 357
Auer, E. E., 423

B

Bacon, R. O. R., 437, 438
Badger, R. M., 58
Baker, W. O., 33, 51, 133, 147, 242, 376, 446
Bamford, C. H., 423, 424
Bancelin, 284
Bangham, E. C., 15
Bardeen, J., 164
Barnes, C. E., 447
Barr, G., 279
Barrer, R., 281
Barry, A. J., 290, 339
Bartlett, P. D., 403, 419, 422, 423, 424, 433, 481
Bartovics, A., 287, 290
Bath, J., 83
Batschinski, A., 281
Battista, 468
Bauer, N., 40

Baxendale, J. H., 290, 437, 438
Beach, J. Y., 16, 91
Beaman, R. G., 457, 458
Beamer, W. H., 15
Beams, J. W., 313
Becker, R., 334
Bekkedahl, N., 147, 359
Bengen, M. F., 137
Benoit, H., 102
Berchet, G. J., 389
Bergmann, E., 49, 50
Bergmann, M., 133
Berkeley, E. E., 244
Berl, E., 279
Bernal, J. D., 36, 163, 169, 170, 185, 203, 210, 211
Bernal, J. J., 224, 225, 226
Bernstein, H. J., 88
Bertram, A., 67
Bethe, H., 119
Bevilacqua, E. B., 423
Bickel, A. F., 423
Biltz, W., 279
Bingham, E. C., 279, 304, 305
Biscoe, J., 313
Bjerrum, N., 70
Blake, J. T., 477
Blaker, R. H., 58
Blatz, P. J., 350, 465
Blomquist, A. T., 457
Bloomfield, 273
Boeder, P., 319, 320
Boehm, G., 320
Boehm, J., 196, 197
Boelhouwer, J. W. M., 289, 295
Boer, J. H. de, 134, 135, 197
Boissonnas, C. G., 253
Bolland, J. L., 481, 483, 484, 485
Bolz, F., 465
Booys, J. de, 301

SUBJECT INDEX

A

Absolute velocity constants for vinyl polymerization, 419–424
  data, 423
Absorption spectra, infrared, of polymers, 79–83
Acid-catalyzed polycondensations, 376–377
α-Amino acids, condensation of, 391
Aggregation, between molecules, 127–146
  formation by dispersion forces, 134–136
Ammonium chloride, electron diffraction diagrams, 12
Anionic polymerization of vinyl monomers, 457–458
Anomalous flow of liquids, 304–306
Association, by dipole forces, 128–134
  in water, hydrogen fluoride, alcohols, 128–134
  molecular, involving conjugated and aromatic systems, 137–141
  of carboxylic acids, 141–143
Association energy(ies), between nitroaromatics and condensed ring systems (table), 140
  of carboxylic acids (table), 142
Asterisms, in Laue diagrams, 5
Atomic distances, from moments of inertia (table), 68
  in liquid alkali metals, 223
Atomic lattices, 162
Average molecular weights, 274–275
Axial ratio, from diffusion measurements, 309–311
  of molecules, effect on viscosity, 284–285

B

Band spectra, 65
Base-molar, 287

Benzene, resonating structures and molar refraction, 43
Birefringence, and viscoelastic behavior in crystalline polymers, 361
  at glass transition in polymers, 348
  of fibers, 44
  of stretched rubber, 331
  streaming, in liquids and solutions, 318–320
Boltzmann equation, 250, 323
Bond constants of molecules, 70
Bonds, covalent, normal, table, 15
  single, normal, table, 15
Branch points in polycondensation polymers, 387
Brownian movement, 307–308
Bulk modulus, 323
Butane, configurations, 89
Butyl polymer, ozonolysis, 470–472

C

Cage model for peroxide-initiated vinyl polymerizations, 409–410
Capillary flow of Newtonian and non-Newtonian liquids, 304
Capillary viscometer, 250
Caprolactam polymerization, 382
Carbon-carbon double bond, 395–400
N-Carboxy amino acid anhydrides, 391–393
Carboxylic acids, association, 141–143
Carothers equation, 368–369
Catalysts for vinyl polymerization, table, 402
Cationic polymerization of vinyl monomers, 454–458
Ceiling temperatures in polymerization, 476–477
Cellulose, degradation of, 465–470
  micelle dimensions in, 235
  unit cell of, 37

502   SUBJECT INDEX